EVERYMAN, I will go with thee,

and be thy guide,

In thy most need to go by thy side

ROBERT BURTON

Born in 1577. Entered Brasenose College, Oxford, 1593. Student of Christ Church, 1599; B.D., 1614. Vicar of St Thomas's, Oxford, 1616, and rector of Seagrave from 1630 until his death in 1640.

ROBERT BURTON

The Anatomy
of Melancholy

IN THREE VOLUMES · VOLUME ONE

INTRODUCTION BY
HOLBROOK JACKSON

DENT: LONDON
EVERYMAN'S LIBRARY
DUTTON: NEW YORK

All rights reserved
Made in Great Britain
at the
Aldine Press · Letchworth · Herts
for
J. M. DENT & SONS LTD
Aldine House · Bedford Street · London
First included in Everyman's Library 1932
Last reprinted 1964

NO. *886*

INTRODUCTION

It is ironical that a treatise of melancholy should have become one of the great entertainments among English writings; but the irony is accidental, for if the author of the *Anatomy of Melancholy* was not precisely of the breed of Mark Tapley he was no hypochondriac, and had no intention of compiling a doleful work. Robert Burton was a good-humoured pessimist, and unless he himself had told us we should not have guessed that he was addicted to a melancholy, lamentable enough for him, but most fortunate for us because it was the first cause of a delightful book. For proof of his fundamental amiability we must recall Bishop Kennett's story which tells how Burton, when the melancholy weighed upon him, would leave his study in Christ Church, Oxford, stroll down to Folly Bridge and recreate himself by listening to the vigorous back-chat of the bargees. He confesses, however, that he wrote the *Anatomy* to relieve his own melancholy. We do not know whether the disease yielded to the treatment, but we do know that, for over three centuries, his work has been a prophylactic against the megrims, and his kindly if irascible soul still goes marching on in successive editions of his masterpiece, blazing new trails of pleasure among the generations succeeding that which was enriched by his presence.

There are few details of his life, and few are necessary, for if ever author were embodied in a book or if ever book were the presentment of an author, that author was Robert Burton and that book the *Anatomy of Melancholy*. The biographical facts are that he was born at Lindley Hall in Leicestershire on 8th February, 1577, the fourth of a family of nine; that he went to the Free School at Sutton Coldfield and later to Nuneaton Grammar School; that he entered Brasenose College in 1593, was elected a student of Christ Church in 1599, took his B.D. in 1614, became Vicar of St. Thomas, Oxford, two years later, and was presented with the living of Seagrave in Leicestershire, by his patron George, Lord Berkeley, in 1630. He was a ready versifier in both Latin and English, contributed to several academic anthologies, and in his thirty-first year wrote *Philosophaster*, a satirical comedy in Latin verse. This, his first sustained work, was rewritten in 1615 and performed by the students in the Hall of Christ Church in 1617.[1] The *Anatomy of Melancholy* was published in 1621, and went through five editions during the author's life. The last edition which he saw through the press was that of 1638, for in the following year he died at the age of sixty-three and was buried in the Cathedral of the University where his brother William, author of the *Description of Leicestershire* (1622), erected a monument to his memory in the form of a portrait bust, tinted to the life, after the manner of those times.

His life was uneventful. "I have lived," he says, "a silent, sedentary, solitary, private life, *mihi & musis* in the University as long almost as *Xenocrates* in *Athens, ad senectam fere*, to learn wisdom as he did, penned up most part in my study." This we may accept literally, although he was a parson, and for some years a pluralist parson, with the duties of his incumbencies, which he probably reduced by delegation or neglect. Yet it would be unsafe to conclude that even·so large and complicated a work as the *Anatomy* was necessarily a whole-time job. Diligence and an enjoyment of drudgery can accomplish miracles in the spare time of a busy life. Burton may have been reclusive, but he was no hermit. Apart from his position as a clerk in Holy Orders, there is evidence of other activities: he was librarian of his college, and for a year at least, a Clerk of Oxford Market. Primarily, however, he was a scholar and a bookman agreeably cloistered in his own rooms, with plenty of books,[2] or in the admirable library of "the most flourishing College in Europe," or the Bodleian, endeavouring by his researches into the causes and cure of melancholy to be more than "a drone" or "an unprofitable and unworthy member of so learned and noble a society," and to avoid writing "that which should be in any way dishonourable to such a royal and ample foundation."

Such a man might have lapsed into pedantry; but although he uses a pedantic method his outlook is far from it, and he

---

[1] *Philosophaster* remained in MS. until 1862, when it was edited by William Edward Buckley and published by the Roxburghe Club. The first translation was made by Paul Jordan-Smith and published by Stanford University, California, in 1931.

[2] He owned about 2,000 volumes, which he bequeathed to the library of his College and the Bodleian.

himself has few of the vices of the schoolman. Nor is his solemn vocation reflected in his style. The *Anatomy*, indeed, is often unparsonic; even his admonitions are tolerant and urbane, whilst his conversation was said to be lively, although, as Thomas Hearne is careful to record, "very innocent." But of such details we know little, for it is a curious fact that, although a familiar figure in the university life of his day and a popular author, he shared with Shakespeare an almost complete immunity from contemporary gossip. Beyond the documentary evidence of his offices and the few autobiographical details dotted about his book, no contemporary references of any importance have come to light, and Burton had been dead over fifty years before Anthony à Wood's character of him appeared in the *Athenæ Oxonienses*. Wood never met him, but talked with those who had. But even then the Oxford historian is not essential, for as likely a character could be drawn from the hints and admissions in Burton's own book.

"He was," says Anthony Wood, "an exact Mathematician, a curious calculator of Nativities, a general read Scholar, a thro'-pac'd Philologist, and one that understood the surveying of Lands well. As he was by many accounted a severe student, a devourer of Authors, a melancholy and humorous Person; so by others, who knew him well, a Person of great honesty, plain dealing and Charity. I have heard some of the Ancients of Christ Church often say that his Company was very merry, facete and juvenile, and no man did surpass him for his ready and dextrous interlarding his common discourses among them with Verses from the Poets or Sentences from classical Authors, which being then the fashion in the University, made his Company more acceptable."

We know how he looked from his portraits, of which there are three: a painting in oils at Brasenose, the engraved miniature by Le Blon in the emblematic frontispiece of the *Anatomy*, and the painted bust in the Cathedral at Oxford. From these sources we may compose a portrait of our English Democritus among his books in the agreeable setting of a famous and already venerable college: a thick-set, plumpish man, with dark brown beard of formal cut; there is a satiric glint in the large eyes, and intelligence and memory are revealed in the monumental forehead; his nose is enterprising and he has the snap mouth of the well-opinioned, corrected by an indulgent nether lip. It is the face of a character such as

England often produced in those days and sometimes even now: a competent, thoughtful, self-sufficient face, with a hint of shyness which might indicate a preference for a sheltered life rather than a life of adventure, unless it were adventures among books. And from this composite present-ment we may safely infer a genial yet reclusive, diffident yet self-opinionated man, who might be friendly but not demon-strative, tolerant yet irascible, and who would suffer fools sadly rather than gladly.

Yet when we have said all and listened attentively to Anthony Wood we have not probed very far into the soul of Robert Burton. We have not yet divined that entity which is he and none other. The Anatomist is, indeed, somewhat of a paradox. Like most interesting men, he is not quite consistent. He preaches the happy mean and does not practise it. His book is always excessive. He overloads every statement. It is the most sententious book ever written, yet it reads trippingly as a novel. It is packed with common sense and uncommon nonsense. He is never tired of apologizing for his long-windedness, and immediately starts expatiating again. He fears that he will go too far in his exposition of love-melancholy, and does. He was never married, but marriage has no mysteries for him. He laughs at humanity and weeps over the sorrows and stupidities of men. He is scientifical and superstitious at one and the same time. He is as frank as a pornographer and as mincing as a prude. He mixes facetiæ with theology. He is not a deliberate humorist, yet he is often funnier than the pro-fessional wag. He is most frivolous when he is most earnest; and when he is frank and colloquial he is most profound. Like Whitman, he is large and multitudinous. He spills himself and the whole of ancient learning into his book and adroitly turns the medley into an ordered theme which, because of its great size, may weary his reader but never bore him.

Robert Burton was a bookman first and last. He lived among books and upon them, and devoted the greater part of his life to the writing of an epitome or quintessence of the books of all times. His treatise is the legitimate offspring of a bookish mind, and although it is largely a distillation of authors it is an original work. The *Anatomy* looks like a crude assembly of quotations and it is indeed a vast mobiliza-tion of the notions and expressions of others, yet it is not they but the rifler who is revealed on every page, it is he, not they, who peeps from behind every quotation. The reason is clear. He is an artist in literary mosaic, using the shreds and patches he has torn from the work of others to make a picture emphatically his own. Books are his raw material. Other artists fashion images out of clay, contrive fabrics and forms of stone, symphonies of words, sounds, or pigments. Burton makes a cosmos out of quotations. He raids the writings of the past, which he often finds neglected or in ruins, and reassembles them in a structure of his own, much as the ruins of Rome were pillaged by the builders of the Renaissance and worked into the temples and palaces of a new civilization.

His apologies for this fascinating literary structure seem superfluous, but they are due neither to mock modesty nor to a sense of inferiority. Burton never lacked proper conceit. He was convinced of his ability to accomplish his task and he believed in his own sagacity. Authors rarely compile works running into half a million words without being encouraged by the conviction that they are doing something worth doing. His apologetics were, of course, a convention; no seventeenth-century work was complete without a prefatory vindication. He not only excuses himself for his subject and his manner of presenting it, he apologizes even for his title. He wrote about melancholy not solely, it would seem, to relieve himself of that distemper, as he asserts in one place, but because he thought it "a subject most necessary and commodious, less common and controversial than Divinity, which I do acknowledge to be the queen of professions." His title to-day seems explicit enough. It is unnecessary for him to cite precedents, for anatomies were almost as common then as anthologies are now. But if it is a little odd, he will let it stand, since ' it is a kind of policy in these days to prefix a phantastical title to a book which is to be sold—for as larks come down to a day-net, many vain readers will tarry and stand gazing, like silly passengers, at an antic picture in a painter's shop, that will not look at a judicious piece." For the same reason he commits his treatise, in the main, to the English language. " It was not mine intent," he says, "to prostitute my muse in English," but if he had composed his work in Latin he could not have got it printed: "Any scurrile pamphlet is welcome to our mercenary stationers in English," he complains, "but in Latin they will not deal." But we do not join him in reviling those mercenary publishers, for if they had not thought of their profits they would have robbed us of ours and Burton, like so many flourishing wits, would lie smothered in oblivion.

His style is peculiar only as it is linked with a method which demands lavish quotation and citation. He is a master of both these arts. The quantity, audacity, and aptness of his quotations have always astounded and refreshed his readers; and he is easily the greatest collector and co-ordinator of apophthegms in an age which had many notable specialists in that craft. Stripped, however, of these characteristic and entertaining encumbrances, Burton's prose is direct and normal. It has a brisk, staccato style, which guarantees the fluency of his long and leisurely book. He is often charged with eccentricity; but if we allow for the inevitable quaintness created by time such a charge cannot be upheld. Burton is a self-conscious quoter and a deviser of processions of glittering words and epithets, but he is no mere phrase-maker. He does not invent a phrase for its own sake, and then stand back to admire it as one feels Browne doing and Donne doing. His style is too colloquial for that. It is like good talk. You can hear the cadence of a disputatious yet friendly voice tirelessly advising and expounding, but always redeemed from monotony by an apt twist or a whimsical turn, and when these fail, he brings up his reserves of curious tales which he marshals with ingenuity and gusto.

The *Anatomy* is great in size and scope. It ranges over all times and places, diving into the past, dipping into the future, and even glancing ironically at the present. Although his theme is melancholy, he contrives by a method of inter-mission and digression to glance at almost every human interest or endeavour. The work is thus a commentary upon the life and habits of the human race. It is a bridge between medieval and modern thought: the swan song of authoritarian scholasticism (all that Glanvill condemned in his *Scepsis Scientifica*), and an anticipation of the method of deduction from observed facts. He adopts the traditional form of the conspectus of his time. The work is arranged in three "partitions" and numerous "sections," "members," and "subsections," the titles and sub-titles being set out synoptic-ally at the beginning of each part. In addition to the parts and chapters proper there are several admitted "digressions," often the size of a treatise, and "a satirical Preface conducing to the . . . Discourse" which fills seventy-eight pages, folio, in the definitive edition.

Sir William Osler described the *Anatomy* as "the greatest medical treatise written by a layman." But apart from the main theme there are sections which, although organically related to it, are complete essays in themselves. Some of these do pioneer work. The long and fascinating chapter called "A Digression of Air" is the first essay in climatology, and the section on "Religious Melancholy" is the first study of that subject. His psychological study of sex anticipates Havelock Ellis, and his repudiation of romantic love, Bernard Shaw; his chapters on "Jealousy" contain all the ingredients of the post-war problem-novel; whilst buried in the famous preface is a Utopia which suggests Wells. Burton is revealed as a sound political economist, a little-Englander, a protectionist, an opponent of monopolies, an enemy of war, an advocate of better highways, the extension of inland waterways, the reclamation of marshlands, the building of garden villages, and the granting of old age pensions.

The *Anatomy of Melancholy* is one of those books which possess something like human character and behaviour, the kind of book which seems to have grown. Few books are more definitely or more curiously imbued with their authorship. The *Anatomy* is Burton, and Burton the *Anatomy*. To read it is to read him: to read him is to talk with him, to know him as we know the great persons of fiction, or those few writers who have so projected themselves into their works as to have achieved for their own personalities what the great novelists and dramatists have achieved for the characters of their stories and plays. Burton, like Montaigne, Pepys, and Lamb, has made a fiction of himself, stranger and more interesting than fact.

It was born in 1621, when Burton was forty-five: a small quarto, of nearly nine hundred pages, exceedingly plump for its size. During the following seventeen years it continued to grow and improve through four editions, 1624, 1628, 1632, and 1638, each in small folio, but, after the author's death in 1639–40, decline began. Inferior printing and paper set in with the edition of 1651, the first reprint after Burton's death and the last to contain his corrections. In 1660 another edition appears, still more degenerate in character, and the seventeenth-century editions end with the lanky folio of 1676, from which all charm and character have gone. There were no further editions for a hundred and twenty-four years. No book of the century exhibits more clearly the personal influence of author upon printer. The hand of Burton is revealed in all the editions up to 1638. There are innumerable changes, often small and even whimsical, sometimes considerable, which bear evidence of a taste and fancy other than what at that time spontaneously issued even from the Oxford printing office. The author, true bookman as he was, must have had many an exciting wrangle with his publishers, Henry Cripps and Leonard Lichfield, "Printer to the famous University," coming out, as I gather, victoriously, for he has contrived also to leave his own mark upon the typography of the book into which he had put so much of himself.

The appreciation of Burton is a test of bookishness, and although he has never lacked readers, even during the dark age, 1677–1799, when no edition of the *Anatomy* appeared, there have not been lacking those who have belittled and misrepresented him. I am not concerned at the moment with his defence, even if it were necessary, which it is not, for there is no reason why any one should read him unless he wishes to do so. Burton is for the Burtonian. But it is necessary to refer to the misrepresenters, both ancient and modern, because many of them have sinned ignorantly. Critics and commentators have not always taken the trouble to read, still less understand the book, hence much popular nonsense, of which Hallam's description of the *Anatomy* as "a sweeping of the miscellaneous literature from the Bodleian Library," and Lowell's

> A mire ankle-deep of deliberate confusion,
> Made up of old jumbles of classic allusion,

are typical specimens.

Burton has been oftener damned with faint praise than scoffed at by the ignorantly learned. I know of only one downright depreciator, the Manx poet, T. E. Brown. In a vigorous and humourless essay, contributed to the *New Review* in 1895, this minor poet and major schoolmaster can find no good word for our good Burton. His learning is but a "parade," the "product of omnivorous folio-bolting and quarto-gulping, urged on and sustained by inordinate vanity"; his method naught but a "pseudo-method," a mere "affectation of method and order." Brown concedes, however, that Burton has "slanging power . . . a wondrous hurly-burly of

INTRODUCTION XV

priggish regard. Like Charles Lamb, he is opposed to reprints
of the *Anatomy*. "I do not know a more heartless sight than
the reprint of the *Anatomy of Melancholy*," says Lamb.
"What need was there of unearthing the bones of that fantastic old great man, to expose them in a winding-sheet of the
newest fashion to modern censure? What hapless stationer
could dream of Burton ever becoming popular?" Brown is
not so generous or so romantic. An old Burton has a charm,
he admits, but only "in an old library; old dust embalms it,
old memories haunt it. It is worth seeking there": and he
thinks it ought to be read there *in situ*. "Neglect, decay,"
he admonishes, "must be the fate of all such ponderous
eccentricities. And to smarten them up, and turn them out
spick-and-span, radiant and raw, into the forum of literature,
is a doubtful sort of proceeding. They belong to the cave,
and scholars are their natural friends and custodians. Leave
them to the scholars." Brown was wrong, but there is
evidence that he had at least read his Burton.

His appreciators extend from his own day to ours. He
received honourable mention from Anthony Wood, and he
gets a good word even from malicious Thomas Hearne, who
incidentally gives a hint of the fallen prestige of the *Anatomy*
during the first half of the eighteenth century. "No book
sold better formerly," he writes in his diary (1734), "than
Burton's *Anatomy of Melancholy*, in which there is a great
variety of learning, so that it hath been a common-place for
filchers. It hath a great many impressions, and the book-
seller got an estate by it; but now 'tis disregarded, and a good
fair copy (although of the seventh impression) may be
purshased for one shilling, well bound. . . ." Twenty years
later, Dr. Thomas Herring, Archbishop of Canterbury, told a
friend to "look into" the *Anatomy*, as Burton was "one of the
pleasantest, the most learned and the most full of sterling
sense. . . . the wits of Queen Anne's reign, and the beginning
of George the first's were not a little beholden to him."

The legend of Burton as a crib for the lazy and a mine for
the creative is well established. The *Anatomy* is a lucky-bag,
whether you are a plagiarist, legitimately predatory, or an
adventurous reader, like Dr. Johnson, whom it "took out of bed
two hours sooner than he wanted to rise." Many authors of
genius have rifled Burton to the advantage of our literature.
John Ferriar, in his *Illustrations of Sterne*, reproves Laurence

Sterne for incorporating into *Tristram Shandy* so much of the *Anatomy*, "once the favourite of the learned and the witty, and a source of surreptitious learning to many others." Wharton's discovery that Milton was not above taking hints from Burton, when composing *Il Penseroso*, is the occasion for a neat appreciation of the *Anatomy*: "The writer's variety of learning, his quotations from scarce and curious books, his pedantry sparkling with rude wit and shapeless elegance, miscellaneous matter, intermixture of agreeable tales and illustrations, and perhaps, above all, the singularities of his feelings cloathed in an uncommon quaintness of style, have contributed to render it, even to modern readers, a valuable repository of amusement and information."

These references indicate continuous interest over a period which knew not Burton in person or in a new edition. With the turn of the century the *Anatomy* comes once more into favour. Byron tells Moore that it is the most useful book "to a man who wishes to acquire a reputation of being well read, with the least trouble." But Lamb was probably its rediscoverer. It was well within his zone of research and appreciation. He composes an amusing pastiche of its style, and it is doubtless through him that Keats and his friends hear of it. Charles Brown gives the poet a copy of the 1813 edition in 1819. Keats reads the volume through "carefully, with pen in hand, scoring the margins constantly," annotating, and indexing special passages on the last fly-leaf. In the very year of the gift he writes "Lamia," which is based upon a well-known passage in the *Anatomy*. From then until now interest in the book grows. Dibdin possesses "the cubical quarto of 1621, the tapering folio of 1678 [sic], and all the intermediate editions," and "these copies were all bound in picked russia by Faulkner; for then, Charles Lewis 'was not.'" "What an extraordinary book it is," he exclaims, "and what an extraordinary portion of it is the chapter on 'Love Melancholy'! I was grateful for the octavo reprint of it, which has gone through two editions: but Burton has not yet been clothed in the editorial garb which ought to encircle his shoulders." A hundred years have passed away, and although over forty editions of the *Anatomy* have appeared, Dibdin's wish has not yet been carried out. But Burton is not without honour even in our hurried days, for he has perhaps more readers now than ever he had, and in the last decade Mr. Francis Meynell has admitted him into the distinguished company of the Nonesuch Press. An American edition with "an all-English text" has been published under the editorship of Mr. Floyd Dell and Mr. Paul Jordan-Smith, and now the *Anatomy* achieves apotheosis as a popular classic in the honoured ranks of Everyman's Library.

HOLBROOK JACKSON.

1932.

SELECT BIBLIOGRAPHY

The Anatomy of Melancholy. 1621. Revised editions, 1624, 1628, 1632, 1638, 1651. Reprinted, 1660, 1676. No further reprints appeared until 1800, when a two-volume edition was published. Since then many editions have been issued in one, two, or three volumes.

An edition in two volumes, folio, illustrated by E. McKnight Kauffer, was published by the Nonesuch Press, in 1925.

The first American edition was published in Philadelphia, 1836.

Philosophaster. A satirical comedy, written in Latin, 1606–17. First edition, 1862. Edited by William Edward Buckley, and published by the Roxburghe Club. First edition in English, translated and edited by Paul Jordan-Smith, Stanford University, California, 1931. This edition includes for the first time Burton's minor writings in prose and verse.

For information about Burton and his books see:

(a) *Oxford Bibliographical Proceedings and Papers.* Vol. I, pt. 3. "'Robert Burton and the Anatomy of Melancholy,' Papers by Sir William Osler, Professor Edward Bensly, and others. Edited by F. Madan, M.A." 1926.

(b) *Bibliographia Burtoniana:* A Study of Robert Burton's "The Anatomy of Melancholy," with a Bibliography. By Paul Jordan-Smith. 1931.

EDITORIAL NOTE

THE fact that no manuscript exists of *The Anatomy of Melancholy* has placed Burton, like Shakespeare, at the mercy of editors and printers. Burton himself was confessedly careless in the revision of the printed sheets, and preferred in each successive edition to add new matter rather than correct the old. The work thus swelled; and even the first posthumous edition, the sixth, includes a number of additions and corrections which Burton intended to have incorporated himself, had he lived. The present text follows the sixth edition, collated with the fifth, which is superior in point of typography. Many egregious misprints, some of which were perpetuated even into the nineteenth century, have been cleared away; but it has been taken into account that numerous errors, especially of quotation, were Burton's own, and these it would be presumptuous and anachronistic to remove. Considerable use has been made of the edition of the nineteenth century, which commands the most attention: that of the Rev. A. R. Shilleto in 1893. Several emendations to this edition have been made by Professor Edward Bensly in the Ninth and Tenth Series of *Notes and Queries*, and to his understanding of Burton the present editor wishes to make acknowledgment. As in later reprints of *The Anatomy* since the edition of 1800, the choice of type, punctuation, and spelling in this edition has been in the interest of clarity and agreeableness to a present-day reader. Where it does not interfere with Burton's own paraphrase, translations have been added to the quotations from Latin and Greek, and a glossary of archaic words is contained in the third volume. Burton's annotations, printed originally in the margin, have for clearance of the text been printed at the end of each volume, together with a few notes by the present editor [in square brackets].

CONTENTS

	PAGE
INTRODUCTION by Holbrook Jackson	vii
EDITORIAL NOTE	xviii
DEMOCRITUS JUNIOR TO HIS BOOK	3
THE ARGUMENT OF THE FRONTISPIECE	7
THE AUTHOR'S ABSTRACT OF MELANCHOLY	11
DEMOCRITUS JUNIOR TO THE READER	15
TO THE READER WHO EMPLOYS HIS LEISURE ILL	124
THE SYNOPSIS OF THE FIRST PARTITION	126

THE FIRST PARTITION:

Section 1. Of Diseases in General, and of Melancholy; with a Digression of Anatomy	130
Section 2. Causes of Melancholy; with a Digression of Spirits	177
Section 3. Symptoms of Melancholy	382
Section 4. Prognostics of Melancholy	429
NOTES	441

DEMOCRITUS JUNIOR AD LIBRUM SUUM

VADE liber, qualis, non ausim dicere, felix,
  Te nisi felicem fecerit Alma dies.
Vade tamen quocunque lubet, quascunque per oras,
  Et Genium Domini fac imitere tui.
I blandas inter Charites, mystamque saluta
  Musarum quemvis, si tibi lector erit.
Rura colas, urbem, subeasve palatia regum,
  Submisse, placide, te sine dente geras.
Nobilis, aut si quis te forte inspexerit heros,
  Da te morigerum, perlegat usque lubet.
Est quod Nobilitas, est quod desideret heros,
  Gratior hæc forsan charta placere potest.
Si quis morosus Cato, tetricusque Senator,
  Hunc etiam librum forte videre velit,
Sive magistratus, tum te reverenter habeto;
  Sed nullus; muscas non capiunt aquilæ.
Non vacat his tempus fugitivum impendere nugis,
  Nec tales cupio; par mihi lector erit.
Si matrona gravis casu diverterit istuc,
  Illustris domina, aut te Comitissa legat:
Est quod displiceat, placeat, quod forsitan illis,
  Ingerere his noli te modo, pande tamen.
At si virgo tuas dignabitur inclyta chartas
  Tangere, sive schedis hæreat illa tuis:
Da modo te facilem, et quædam folia esse memento
  Conveniant oculis quæ magis apta suis.
Si generosa ancilla tuos aut alma puella
  Visura est ludos, annue, pande lubens.
Dic utinam nunc ipse meus (nam diligit istas)
  In præsens esset conspiciendus herus.[1]
Ignotus notusve mihi de gente togata
  Sive aget in ludis, pulpita sive colet,
Sive in Lycæo, et nugas evolverit istas,
  Si quasdam mendas viderit inspiciens,
Da veniam Authori, dices; nam plurima vellet
  Expungi, quæ jam displicuisse sciat.
Sive Melancholicus quisquam, seu blandus Amator,
  Aulicus aut Civis, seu bene comptus Eques
Huc appellat, age et tuto te crede legenti,
  Multa istic forsan non male nata leget.
Quod fugiat, caveat, quodque amplexabitur, ista
  Pagina fortassis promere multa potest.

3

At si quis Medicus coram te sistet, amice
  Fac circumspecte, et te sine labe geras:
Inveniet namque ipse meis quoque plurima scriptis,
  Non leve subsidium quæ sibi forsan erunt.
Si quis Causidicus chartas impingat in istas,
  Nil mihi vobiscum, pessima turba vale;
Sit nisi vir bonus, et juris sine fraude peritus,
  Tum legat, et forsan doctior inde siet.
Si quis cordatus, facilis, lectorque benignus
  Huc oculos vertat, quæ velit ipse legat;
Candidus ignoscet, metuas nil, pande libenter,
  Offensus mendis non erit ille tuis,
Laudabit nonnulla. Venit si Rhetor ineptus,
  Limata et tersa, et qui bene cocta petit,
Claude citus librum; nulla hic nisi ferrea verba,
  Offendent stomachum quæ minus apta suum.
At si quis non eximius de plebe poeta,
  Annue; namque istic plurima ficta leget.
Nos sumus e numero, nullus mihi spirat Apollo,
  Grandiloquus Vates quilibet esse nequit.
Si criticus Lector, tumidus Censorque molestus,
  Zoilus et Momus, si rabiosa cohors:
Ringe, freme, et noli tum pandere, turba malignis
  Si occurrat sannis invidiosa suis:
Fac fugias; si nulla tibi sit copia eundi
  Contemnes, tacite scommata quæque feres.
Frendeat, allatret, vacuas gannitibus auras
  Impleat, haud cures; his placuisse nefas.
Verum age si forsan divertat purior hospes,
  Cuique sales, ludi, displiceantque joci,
Objiciatque tibi sordes, lascivaque: dices,
  Lasciva est Domino et Musa jocosa tuo,
Nec lasciva tamen, si pensitet omne; sed esto;
  Sit lasciva licet pagina, vita proba est.
Barbarus, indoctusque rudis spectator in istam
  Si messem intrudat, fuste fugabis eum,
Fungum pelle procul (jubeo), nam quid mihi fungo?
  Conveniunt stomacho non minus ista suo.
Sed nec pelle tamen; læto omnes accipe vultu,
  Quos, quas, vel quales, inde vel unde viros.
Gratus erit quicunque venit, gratissimus hospes
  Quisquis erit, facilis difficilisque mihi.
Nam si culparit, quædam culpasse juvabit,
  Culpando faciet me meliora sequi.
Sed si laudarit, neque laudibus efferar ullis,
  Sit satis hisce malis opposuisse bonum.
Hæc sunt quæ nostro placuit mandare libello,
  Et quæ dimittens dicere jussit Herus.

DEMOCRITUS JUNIOR TO HIS BOOK

PARAPHRASTIC METRICAL TRANSLATION

Go forth, my book, into the open day;
    Happy, if made so by its garish eye.
O'er earth's wide surface take thy vagrant way,
    To imitate thy master's genius try.
The Graces three, the Muses nine salute,
    Should those who love them try to con thy lore.
The country, city seek, grand thrones to boot,
    With gentle courtesy humbly bow before.
Should nobles gallant, soldiers frank and brave
    Seek thy acquaintance, hail their first advance:
From twitch of care thy pleasant vein may save,
    May laughter cause or wisdom give perchance.
Some surly Cato, senator austere,
    Haply may wish to peep into thy book:
Seem very nothing—tremble and revere:
    No forceful eagles, butterflies e'er look.
They love not thee: of them then little seek,
    And wish for readers triflers like thyself.
Of ludeful matron watchful catch the beck,
    Or gorgeous countess full of pride and pelf.
They may say "Pish!" and frown, and yet read on:
    Cry odd, and silly, coarse, and yet amusing.
Should dainty damsels seek thy page to con,
    Spread thy best stores: to them be ne'er refusing:
Say, "Fair one, master loves thee dear as life;
    Would he were here to gaze on thy sweet look."
Should known or unknown student, free'd from strife
    Of logic and the schools, explore my book:
Cry, "Mercy, critic, and thy book withhold:
    Be some few errors pardon'd though observ'd:
An humble author to implore makes bold,
    Thy kind indulgence, even undeserv'd."
Should melancholy wight or pensive lover,
    Courtier, snug cit, or carpet knight so trim
Our blossoms cull, he 'll find himself in clover,
    Gain sense from precept, laughter from our whim.
Should learned leech with solemn air unfold
    Thy leaves, beware, be civil, and be wise:
Thy volume many precepts sage may hold,
    His well-fraught head may find no trifling prize.
Should crafty lawyer trespass on our ground,
    Caitiffs avaunt! disturbing tribe away!

Unless (white crow) an honest one be found;
    He 'll better, wiser go for what we say.
Should some ripe scholar, gentle and benign,
    With candour, care, and judgment thee peruse:
Thy faults to kind oblivion he 'll consign;
    Nor to thy merit will his praise refuse.
Thou may'st be searched for polish'd words and verse
    By flippant spouter, emptiest of praters:
Tell him to seek them in some mawkish verse:
    My periods are all rough as nutmeg graters.
The dogg'rel poet, wishing thee to read,
    Reject not; let him glean thy jests and stories.
His brother I, of lowly sembling breed:
    Apollo grants to few Parnassian glories.
Menac'd by critic with sour furrowed brow,
    Momus or Zoilus or Scotch reviewer:
Ruffle your heckle, grin and growl and vow:
    Ill-natured foes you thus will find the fewer.
When foul-mouth'd senseless railers cry thee down,
    Reply not; fly, and show the rogues thy stern:
They are not worthy even of a frown:
    Good taste or breeding they can never learn;
Or let them clamour, turn a callous ear,
    As though in dread of some harsh donkey's bray.
If chid by censor, friendly though severe,
    To such explain and turn thee not away.
Thy vein, says he perchance, is all too free;
    Thy smutty language suits not learned pen:
Reply, "Good Sir, throughout, the context see;
    Thought chastens thought; so prithee judge again.
Besides, although my master's pen may wander
    Through devious paths, by which it ought not stray,
His life is pure, beyond the breath of slander:
    So pardon grant; 'tis merely but his way."
Some rugged ruffian makes a hideous rout—
    Brandish thy cudgel, threaten him to baste;
The filthy fungus far from thee cast out;
    Such noxious banquets never suit my taste.
Yet, calm and cautious, moderate thy ire,
    Be ever courteous should the case allow—
Sweet malt is ever made by gentle fire:
    Warm to thy friends, give all a civil bow.
Even censure sometimes teaches to improve,
    Slight frosts have often cured too rank a crop;
So, candid blame my spleen shall never move,
    For skilful gard'ners wayward branches lop.
Go then, my book, and bear my words in mind;
Guides safe at once, and pleasant them you 'll find.]

THE ARGUMENT OF THE FRONTISPIECE [1]

TEN distinct squares here seen apart,
Are joined in one by cutter's art.

I

Old Democritus under a tree,
Sits on a stone with book on knee;
About him hang there many features,
Of cats, dogs, and such-like creatures,
Of which he makes anatomy,
The seat of black choler to see.
Over his head appears the sky,
And Saturn, Lord of melancholy.

II

To the left a landscape of Jealousy,
Presents itself unto thine eye.
A kingfisher, a swan, an hern,
Two fighting-cocks you may discern,
Two roaring bulls each other hie,
To assault concerning venery.
Symbols are these; I say no more,
Conceive the rest by that 's afore.

III

The next of Solitariness,
A portraiture doth well express,
By sleeping dog, cat: buck and doe,
Hares, conies in the desert go:
Bats, owls the shady bowers over,
In melancholy darkness hover.
Mark well: if 't be not as 't should be,
Blame the bad cutter, and not me.

IV

I' th' under column there doth stand
Inamorato with folded hand;
Down hangs his head, terse and polite,
Some ditty sure he doth indite.

His lute and books about him lie,
As symptoms of his vanity.
If this do not enough disclose,
To paint him, take thyself by th' nose.

V

Hypocondriacus leans on his arm,
Wind in his side doth him much harm,
And troubles him full sore, God knows,
Much pain he hath and many woes.
About him pots and glasses lie,
Newly brought from 's apothecary.
This Saturn's aspects signify,
You see them portray'd in the sky.

VI

Beneath them kneeling on his knee,
A Superstitious man you see:
He fasts, prays, on his idol fixt,
Tormented hope and fear betwixt:
For hell perhaps he takes more pain,
Than thou dost heaven itself to gain.
Alas poor soul, I pity thee,
What stars incline thee so to be?

VII

But see the Madman rage downright
With furious looks, a ghastly sight.
Naked in chains bound doth he lie,
And roars amain, he knows not why.
Observe him; for as in a glass,
Thine angry portraiture it was.
His picture keep still in thy presence;
'Twixt him and thee there 's no difference.

VIII, IX

Borage and Hellebore fill two scenes,
Sovereign plants to purge the veins
Of melancholy, and cheer the heart,
Of those black fumes which make it smart;
To clear the brain of misty fogs,
Which dull our senses, and soul clogs.
The best medicine that e'er God made
For this malady, if well assay'd.

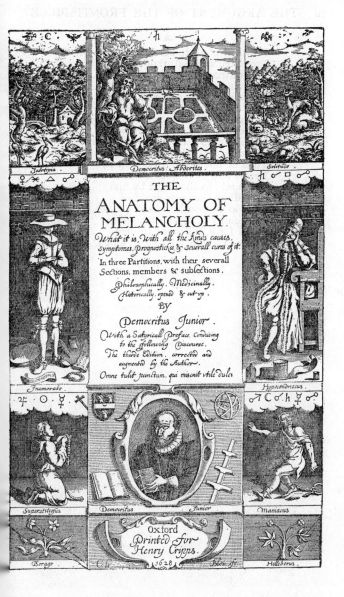

Zelotipia .   *Democritus Abderites .*   *Solitudo .*

THE
ANATOMY OF
MELANCHOLY.
What it is. With all the kinds, causes,
Symptomes, Prognostickes, & severall cures of it.
In three Partitions, with their severall
Sections, members & subsections.
Philosophically, Medicinally,
Historically, opened & cut up .
BY
Democritus Junior.
With a Satyricall Preface, Conducing
to the following Discourse.
The third Edition, corrected and
augmented by the Author .
Omne tulit punctum, qui miscuit vtile dulci

Inamorato .   *Hypocondriacus .*

Superstitiosus   *Democritus   Junior*   *Maniacus*

Oxford
Printed for
Henry Cripps.

Borago   1628   *Helleborus .*

X

Now last of all to fill a place,
Presented is the Author's face;
And in that habit which he wears,
His image to the world appears.
His mind no art can well express,
That by his writings you may guess.
It was not pride, nor yet vainglory
(Though others do it commonly),
Made him do this: if you must know,
The printer would needs have it so.
Then do not frown or scoff at it,
Deride not, or detract a whit,
For surely as thou dost by him,
He will do the same again.
Then look upon 't, behold and see,
As thou lik'st it, so it likes thee.
And I for it will stand in view,
Thine to command, reader, adieu.

THE AUTHOR'S ABSTRACT OF MELANCHOLY,

Διαλογικῶς

WHEN I go musing all alone,
Thinking of divers things fore-known
When I build castles in the air,
Void of sorrow and void of fear,
Pleasing myself with phantasms sweet,
Methinks the time runs very fleet.
    All my joys to this are folly,
     Naught so sweet as melancholy.
When I lie waking all alone,
Recounting what I have ill done,
My thoughts on me then tyrannize,
Fear and sorrow me surprise,
Whether I tarry still or go,
Methinks the time moves very slow.
    All my griefs to this are jolly,
     Naught so sad as melancholy.
When to myself I act and smile,
With pleasing thoughts the time beguile,
By a brook side or wood so green,
Unheard, unsought for, or unseen,
A thousand pleasures do me bless,
And crown my soul with happiness.
    All my joys besides are folly,
     None so sweet as melancholy.
When I lie, sit, or walk alone,
I sigh, I grieve, making great moan,
In a dark grove, or irksome den,
With discontents and Furies then,
A thousand miseries at once
Mine heavy heart and soul ensconce,
    All my griefs to this are jolly,
     None so sour as melancholy.
Methinks I hear, methinks I see,
Sweet music, wondrous melody,
Towns, palaces, and cities fine;
Here now, then there; the world is mine,
Rare beauties, gallant ladies shine,
Whate'er is lovely or divine.
    All other joys to this are folly,
     None so sweet as melancholy.

Methinks I hear, methinks I see,
Ghosts, goblins, fiends; my phantasy
Presents a thousand ugly shapes,
Headless bears, black men, and apes,
Doleful outcries, and fearful sights,
My sad and dismal soul affrights.
    All my griefs to this are jolly,
      None so damn'd as melancholy.

Methinks I court, methinks I kiss,
Methinks I now embrace my miss.
O blessed days, O sweet content,
In Paradise my time is spent.
Such thoughts may still my fancy move,
So may I ever be in love.
    All my joys to this are folly,
      Naught so sweet as melancholy.

When I recount love's many frights,
My sighs and tears, my waking nights,
My jealous fits; O mine hard fate
I now repent, but 'tis too late.
No torment is so bad as love,
So bitter to my soul can prove.
    All my griefs to this are jolly,
      Naught so harsh as melancholy.

Friends and companions get you gone,
'Tis my desire to be alone;
Ne'er well but when my thoughts and I
Do domineer in privacy.
No gem, no treasure like to this,
'Tis my delight, my crown, my bliss.
    All my joys to this are folly,
      Naught so sweet as melancholy.

'Tis my sole plague to be alone,
I am a beast, a monster grown,
I will no light nor company,
I find it now my misery.
The scene is turn'd, my joys are gone,
Fear, discontent, and sorrows come.
    All my griefs to this are folly,
      Naught so fierce as melancholy.

I 'll not change life with any king,
I ravisht am: can the world bring
More joy, than still to laugh and smile,
In pleasant toys time to beguile?
Do not, O do not trouble me,
So sweet content I feel and see.
    All my joys to this are folly,
      None so divine as melancholy.

I 'll change my state with any wretch,
Thou canst from gaol or dunghill fetch;
My pain 's past cure, another hell,
I may not in this torment dwell!
Now desperate I hate my life,
Lend me a halter or a knife;
   All my griefs to this are jolly,
   Naught so damn'd as melancholy.

DEMOCRITUS JUNIOR TO THE READER

GENTLE READER, I presume thou wilt be very inquisitive to know what antic or personate actor this is, that so insolently intrudes upon this common theatre to the world's view, arrogating another man's name; whence he is, why he doth it, and what he hath to say. Although, as he said,[1] *Primum si noluero, non respondebo, quis coacturus est?* I am a free man born, and may choose whether I will tell; who can compel me? if I be urged, I will as readily reply as that Egyptian in Plutarch,[2] when a curious fellow would needs know what he had in his basket, *Quum vides velatam, quid inquiris in rem absconditam?* It was therefore covered, because he should not know what was in it. Seek not after that which is hid ; if the contents please thee, " and be for thy use, suppose the Man in the Moon, or whom thou wilt, to be the author";[3] I would not willingly be known. Yet in some sort to give thee satisfaction, which is more than I need, I will show a reason, both of this usurped name, title, and subject. And first of the name of Democritus ; lest any man by reason of it should be deceived, expecting a pasquil, a satire, some ridiculous treatise (as I myself should have done), some prodigious tenent, or paradox of the earth's motion, of infinite worlds, *in infinito vacuo, ex fortuita atomorum collisione*, in an infinite waste, so caused by an accidental collision of motes in the sun, all which Democritus held, Epicurus and their master Leucippus of old maintained, and are lately revived by Copernicus, Brunus, and some others. Besides, it hath been always an ordinary custom, as Gellius observes,[4] " for later writers and impostors to broach many absurd and insolent fictions under the name of so noble a philosopher as Democritus, to get themselves credit, and by that means the more to be respected," as artificers usually do, *Novo qui marmori ascribunt Praxitelen suo* [who sign the name of Praxiteles on a new statue of their own]. 'Tis not so with me.

> *Non hic Centauros, non Gorgonas, Harpyasque*
> *Invenies, hominem pagina nostra sapit.*[5]

No Centaurs here, or Gorgons look to find,
My subject is of man and humankind.

15

Thou thyself art the subject of my discourse.

Quicquid agunt homines, votum, timor, ira, voluptas,
Gaudia, discursus, nostri farrago libelli.[1]

Whate'er men do, vows, fears, in ire, in sport,
Joys, wand'rings, are the sum of my report.

My intent is no otherwise to use his name, than Mercurius Gallobelgicus, Mercurius Britannicus, use the name of Mercury, Democritus Christianus,[2] etc.; although there be some other circumstances for which I have masked myself under this vizard, and some peculiar respects which I cannot so well express, until I have set down a brief character of this our Democritus, what he was, with an epitome of his life.

Democritus, as he is described by Hippocrates[3] and Laertius,[4] was a little wearish old man, very melancholy by nature, averse from company in his latter days, and much given to solitariness,[5] a famous philosopher in his age, *coævus* with Socrates,[6] wholly addicted to his studies at the last, and to a private life: writ many excellent works, a great divine, according to the divinity of those times, an expert physician, a politician, an excellent mathematician, as *Diacosmus*[7] and the rest of his works do witness. He was much delighted with the studies of husbandry, saith Columella,[8] and often I find him cited by Constantinus[9] and others treating of that subject. He knew the natures, differences of all beasts, plants, fishes, birds; and, as some say, could understand the tunes and voices of them.[10] In a word, he was *omnifariam doctus*, a general scholar, a great student; and to the intent he might better contemplate, I find it related by some,[11] that he put out his eyes, and was in his old age voluntarily blind, yet saw more than all Greece besides, and writ of every subject,[12] *Nihil in toto opificio naturæ, de quo non scripsit* [there was nothing in the whole range of nature about which he did not write]. A man of an excellent wit, profound conceit; and to attain knowledge the better in his younger years he travelled to Egypt and Athens,[13] to confer with learned men, "admired of some, despised of others."[14] After a wandering life, he settled at Abdera, a town in Thrace, and was sent for thither to be their law-maker, recorder, or town clerk as some will; or as others, he was there bred and born. Howsoever it was, there he lived at last in a garden in the suburbs, wholly betaking himself to his studies and a private life, "saving that sometimes he would walk down to the haven,[15] and laugh heartily at such variety of ridiculous objects, which there he saw."[16] Such a one was Democritus.

But in the meantime, how doth this concern me, or upon what reference do I usurp his habit? I confess, indeed, that to compare myself unto him for aught I have yet said, were both impudency and arrogancy. I do not presume to make any parallel, *antistat mihi millibus trecentis* [he is immeasurably ahead of me], *parvus sum, nullus sum, altum nec spiro, nec spero* [1] [I am insignificant, a nobody, with little ambition and small prospects]. Yet thus much I will say of myself, and that I hope without all suspicion of pride, or self-conceit, I have lived a silent, sedentary, solitary, private life, *mihi et musis* [for myself and my studies] in the university, as long almost as Xenocrates in Athens, *ad senectam fere* [practically to old age] to learn wisdom as he did, penned up most part in my study. For I have been brought up a student in the most flourishing college of Europe, *augustissimo collegio*,[2] and can brag with Jovius,[3] almost, *in ea luce domicilii Vaticani, totius orbis celeberrimi, per 37 annos multa opportunaque didici* [for 37 years I have made good use of my opportunities for study in the world-renowned library of the Vatican] ; for thirty years I have continued (having the use of as good libraries as ever he had [4]) a scholar, and would be therefore loath, either by living as a drone to be an unprofitable or unworthy member of so learned and noble a society, or to write that which should be anyway dishonourable to such a royal and ample foundation. Something I have done, though by my profession a divine, yet *turbine raptus ingenii*, as he [5] said, out of a running wit, an unconstant, unsettled mind, I had a great desire (not able to attain to a superficial skill in any) to have some smattering in all, to be *aliquis in omnibus, nullus in singulis* [a somebody in general knowledge, a nobody in any one subject], which Plato commends,[6] out of him Lipsius approves and furthers,[7] " as fit to be imprinted in all curious wits, not to be a slave of one science, or dwell altogether in one subject, as most do, but to rove abroad, *centum puer artium* [one who can turn his hand to anything], to have an oar in every man's boat, to taste of every dish, and sip of every cup," [8] which, saith Montaigne,[9] was well performed by Aristotle and his learned countryman Adrian Turnebus. This roving humour (though not with like success) I have ever had, and like a ranging spaniel, that barks at every bird he sees, leaving his game, I have followed all, saving that which I should, and may justly complain, and truly, *qui ubique est, nusquam est* [he who is everywhere is nowhere], which Gesner did in modesty,[10] that I have read

many books, but to little purpose, for want of good method ;
I have confusedly tumbled over divers authors in our libraries,
with small profit for want of art, order, memory, judgment.
I never travelled but in map or card, in which my unconfined
thoughts have freely expatiated, as having ever been especially
delighted with the study of cosmography. Saturn was lord of
my geniture, culminating, etc., and Mars principal significator
of manners, in partile conjunction with mine ascendant ; both
fortunate in their houses, etc.[1] I am not poor, I am not rich ;
nihil est, nihil deest, I have little, I want nothing : all my
treasure is in Minerva's tower. Greater preferment as I could
never get, so am I not in debt for it, I have a competency (*laus
Deo*) from my noble and munificent patrons, though I live still
a collegiate student, as Democritus in his garden, and lead a
monastic life, *ipse mihi theatrum* [sufficient entertainment to
myself], sequestered from those tumults and troubles of the
world, *et tanquam in specula positus* (as he said[2]), in some
high place above you all, like *Stoicus sapiens, omnia sæcula,
præterita præsentiaque videns, uno velut intuitu* [the Stoic philosopher, surveying with one sweep all ages down to the present],
I hear and see what is done abroad, how others run, ride,
turmoil, and macerate themselves in court and country,[3] far
from those wrangling lawsuits, *aulæ vanitatem, fori ambitionem,
ridere mecum soleo* [I laugh to myself at the vanities of the
court, the intrigues of public life], I laugh at all; "only secure
lest my suit go amiss, my ships perish," corn and cattle miscarry,
trade decay, "I have no wife nor children good or bad to provide
for."[4]   A mere spectator of other men's fortunes and adventures,
and how they act their parts, which methinks are diversely
presented unto me, as from a common theatre or scene. I hear
new news every day, and those ordinary rumours of war, plagues,
fires, inundations, thefts, murders, massacres, meteors, comets,
spectrums, prodigies, apparitions, of towns taken, cities besieged
in France, Germany, Turkey, Persia, Poland, etc., daily musters
and preparations, and such-like, which these tempestuous times
afford, battles fought, so many men slain, monomachies, ship
wrecks, piracies, and sea-fights, peace, leagues, stratagems, and
fresh alarums. A vast confusion of vows, wishes, actions, edicts,
petitions, lawsuits, pleas, laws, proclamations, complaints,
grievances are daily brought to our ears. New books every day,
pamphlets, currantoes, stories, whole catalogues of volumes of
all sorts, new paradoxes, opinions, schisms, heresies, controversies in philosophy, religion, etc. Now come tidings of weddings

maskings, mummeries, entertainments, jubilees, embassies, tilts and tournaments, trophies, triumphs, revels, sports, plays : then again, as in a new shifted scene, treasons, cheating tricks, robberies, enormous villainies in all kinds, funerals, burials, deaths of princes, new discoveries, expeditions; now comical, then tragical matters. To-day we hear of new lords and officers created, to-morrow of some great men deposed, and then again of fresh honours conferred ; one is let loose, another imprisoned ; one purchaseth, another breaketh ; he thrives, his neighbour turns bankrupt ; now plenty, then again dearth and famine ; one runs, another rides, wrangles, laughs, weeps, etc. Thus I daily hear, and such-like, both private and public news; amidst the gallantry and misery of the world—jollity, pride, perplexities and cares, simplicity and villainy ; subtlety, knavery, candour and integrity, mutually mixed and offering themselves—I rub on *privus privatus* [in complete privacy] ; as I have still lived, so I now continue, *statu quo prius*, left to a solitary life and mine own domestic discontents : saving that sometimes, *ne quid mentiar* [not to conceal anything], as Diogenes went into the city and Democritus to the haven to see fashions, I did for my recreation now and then walk abroad, look into the world, and could not choose but make some little observation, *non tam sagax observator, ac simplex recitator* [less by way of shrewd remark than of simple statement of fact], not as they did, to scoff or laugh at all, but with a mixed passion.

Bilem sæpe, jocum vestri movere tumultus.[1]

[Your fond heats have been,
How oft ! the objects of my mirth and spleen.]

did sometime laugh and scoff with Lucian, and satirically tax with Menippus, lament with Heraclitus, sometimes again was *petulanti splene cachinno*[2] [with mocking temper moved to laughter loud], and then again, *urere bilis jecur*[3] [my liver was aflame with gall], I was much moved to see that abuse which I could not mend. In which passion howsoever I may sympathize with him or them, 'tis for no such respect I shroud myself under his name ; but either in an unknown habit to assume a little more liberty and freedom of speech, or if you will needs know, for that reason and only respect which Hippocrates relates at large in his Epistle to Damagetus, wherein he both express, how coming to visit him one day, he found Democritus in his garden at Abdera, in the suburbs, under a shady bower,[4] with a book on his knees, busy at his study,[5]

sometimes writing, sometimes walking. The subject of his
book was melancholy and madness ; about him lay the carcasses
of many several beasts, newly by him cut up and anatomized;
not that he did contemn God's creatures, as he told Hippocrates,
but to find out the seat of this *atra bilis*, or melancholy, whence
it proceeds, and how it was engendered in men's bodies, to the
intent he might better cure it in himself, and by his writings
and observations teach others how to prevent and avoid it.[1]
Which good intent of his, Hippocrates highly commended :
Democritus Junior is therefore bold to imitate, and because he
left it unperfect, and it is now lost, *quasi succenturiator Democriti*
[as a substitute for Democritus], to revive again, prosecute,
and finish in this treatise.

You have had a reason of the name. If the title and inscription
offend your gravity, were it a sufficient justification to accuse
others, I could produce many sober treatises, even sermons
themselves, which in their fronts carry more phantastical names.
Howsoever, it is a kind of policy in these days, to prefix a
phantastical title to a book which is to be sold ; for, as larks come
down to a day-net, many vain readers will tarry and stand gazing
like silly passengers at an antic picture in a painter's shop, that
will not look at a judicious piece. And, indeed, as Scaliger
observes,[2] " nothing more invites a reader than an argument
unlooked for, unthought of, and sells better than a scurrile
pamphlet," *tum maxime cum novitas excitat palatum* [most
of all when it has the spice of novelty]. "Many men," saith
Gellius,[3] " are very conceited in their inscriptions," " and able"
(as Pliny quotes out of Seneca [4]) "to make him loiter by the way
that went in haste to fetch a midwife for his daughter, now ready
to lie down." For my part, I have honourable precedents for
this which I have done:[5] I will cite one for all, Anthony Zara
Pap. Episc., his Anatomy of Wit, in four sections, members,
subsections, etc., to be read in our libraries.

If any man except against the matter or manner of treating
of this my subject, and will demand a reason of it, I can allege
more than one. I write of melancholy, by being busy to avoid
melancholy. There is no greater cause of melancholy than
idleness, " no better cure than business," as Rhasis holds :
and howbeit *stultus labor est ineptiarum*, to be busy in toys is to
small purpose, yet hear that divine Seneca, better *aliud agere quam
nihil*, better do to no end than nothing. I writ therefore, and
busied myself in this playing labour, *otiosaque diligentia ut vitarem
torporem feriandi* [to escape the ennui of idleness by a leisurely

kind of employment], with Vectius in Macrobius, *atque otium in utile verterem negotium* [and so turn leisure to good account].

> *Simul et jucunda et idonea dicere vitæ,*
> *Lectorem delectando simul atque monendo.*[1]

[At once to profit and delight mankind,
And with the pleasing have th' instructive joined.]

To this end I write, like them, saith Lucian, that "recite to trees, and declaim to pillars for want of auditors": as Paulus Ægineta ingenuously confesseth, "not that anything was unknown or omitted, but to exercise myself," [2] which course if some took, I think it would be good for their bodies, and much better for their souls; or peradventure as others do, for fame, to show myself (*Scire tuum nihil est, nisi te scire hoc sciat alter* [your own knowledge is nothing unless another also knows that you know]). I might be of Thucydides' opinion, "To know a thing and not to express it, is all one as if he knew it not." [3] When I first took this task in hand, *et quod ait ille,*[4] *impellente genio negotium suscepi* [and, as he saith, I undertook the work from some inner impulse], this I aimed at, *vel ut lenirem animum scribendo,*[5] [or] to ease my mind by writing; for I had *gravidum cor, fœdum caput,* a kind of imposthume in my head, which I was very desirous to be unladen of, and could imagine no fitter evacuation than this. Besides, I might not well refrain, for *ubi dolor, ibi digitus,* one must needs scratch where it itches. I was not a little offended with this malady, shall I say my mistress Melancholy, my Egeria, or my *malus genius* [evil genius]? and for that cause, as he that is stung with a scorpion, I would expel *clavum clavo* [a nail with a nail], comfort one sorrow with another, idleness with idleness,[6] *ut ex vipera theriacum* [as an antidote out of a serpent's venom], make an antidote out of that which was the prime cause of my disease. Or as he did, of whom Felix Plater speaks,[7] that thought he had some of Aristophanes' frogs in his belly, still crying *Brececcex, coax, coax, oop, oop,* and for that cause studied physic seven years, and travelled over most part of Europe to ease himself; to do myself good I turned over such physicians as our libraries would afford, or my private friends impart,[8] and have taken this pains. And why not? Cardan professeth he wrote his book *de Consolatione* after his son's death, to comfort himself; so did Tully write of the same subject with like intent after his daughter's departure, if it be his at least, or some impostor's put out in his name, which Lipsius probably suspects. Concerning myself, I can peradventure affirm with Marius in Sallust, "That which others hear or read of, I felt and practised myself; they get their knowledge by books, I mine by melancholizing." [1] *Experto crede Roberto.* Something I can speak out of experience, *ærumnabilis experientia me docuit* [sorrowful experience has taught me]; and with her in the poet, *Haud ignara mali miseris succurrere disco,*[2] I would help others out of a fellow-feeling; and, as that virtuous lady did of old, " being a leper herself, bestow all her portion to build an hospital for lepers," [3] I will spend my time and knowledge, which are my greatest fortunes, for the common good of all.

Yea, but you will infer that this is *actum agere,*[4] an unnecessary work, *cramben bis coctam apponere,*[5] the same again and again in other words. To what purpose? "Nothing is omitted that may well be said," [6] so thought Lucian in the like theme. How many excellent physicians have written just volumes and elaborate tracts of this subject! No news here; that which I have is stolen from others, *Dicitque mihi mea pagina, fur es* [7] [my page cries out to me, You are a thief]. If that severe doom of Synesius be true, "It is a greater offence to steal dead men's labours than their clothes," [8] what shall become of most writers? I hold up my hand at the bar among others, and am guilty of felony in this kind, *habes confitentem reum* [the defendant pleads guilty], I am content to be pressed with the rest. 'Tis most true, *tenet insanabile multos scribendi cacoethes,*[9] and "there is no end of writing of books," [10] as the wise man found of old, in this scribbling age [11] especially, wherein "the number of books is without number" (as a worthy man saith [12]), "presses be oppressed," and out of an itching humour that every man hath to show himself, desirous of fame and honour [13] (*scribimus indocti doctique* [we all write, learned and ignorant alike]), he will write no matter what, and scrape together it boots not whence. "Bewitched with this desire of fame,[14] *etiam mediis in morbis* [even in the midst of illness]," to the disparagement of their health, and scarce able to hold a pen, they must say something, "and get themselves a name," saith Scaliger, "though it be to the downfall and ruin of many others." [15] To be counted writers, *scriptores ut salutentur* [to be addressed as authors], to be thought and held polymaths and polyhistors, *apud imperitum vulgus* [among the ignorant crowd], *ob ventosæ nomen artis* [to get a name for a worthless talent], to get a paper-kingdom:

nulla spe quæstus sed ampla famæ [with no hope of gain but great hope of fame], in this precipitate, ambitious age, *nunc ut est sæculum, inter immaturam eruditionem, ambitiosum et præceps* ('tis Scaliger's censure [1]); and they that are scarce auditors, *vix auditores*, must be masters and teachers, before they be capable and fit hearers. They will rush into all learning, *togatam, armatam* [civil or military], divine, human authors, rake over all indexes and pamphlets for notes, as our merchants do strange havens for traffic, write great tomes, *cum non sint re vera doctiores, sed loquaciores*, whenas they are not thereby better scholars, but greater praters. They commonly pretend public good, but as Gesner observes,[2] 'tis pride and vanity that eggs them on; no news or aught worthy of note, but the same in other terms. *Ne feriarentur fortasse typographi, vel ideo scribendum est aliquid ut se vixisse testentur* [they have to write to keep the printers occupied, or even to show that they are alive]. As apothecaries we make new mixtures every day, pour out of one vessel into another; and as those old Romans robbed all the cities of the world to set out their bad-sited Rome, we skim off the cream of other men's wits, pick the choice flowers of their tilled gardens to set out our own sterile plots. *Castrant alios ut libros suos per se graciles alieno adipe suffarciant* (so Jovius inveighs[3]): they lard their lean books with the fat of others' works. *Ineruditi fures* [unlettered thieves], etc. A fault that every writer finds, as I do now, and yet faulty themselves, *trium literarum homines,*[4] all thieves; they pilfer out of old writers to stuff up their new comments, scrape Ennius' dung-hills, and out of Democritus' pit,[5] as I have done. By which means it comes to pass, "that not only libraries and shops are full of our putid papers, but every close-stool and jakes," [6] *Scribunt carmina quæ legunt cacantes*; they serve to put under pies, to lap spice in,[7] and keep roast-meat from burning. "With us in France," saith Scaliger,[8] "every man hath liberty to write, but few ability. Heretofore learning was graced by judicious scholars, but now noble sciences are vilified by base and illiterate scribblers,"[9] that either write from vainglory, need, to get money, or as parasites to flatter and collogue with some great men, they put out *burras, quisquiliasque ineptiasque* [10] [trifles, trash, nonsense]. "Amongst so many thousand authors you shall scarce find one, by reading of whom you shall be any whit better, but rather much worse," [11] *quibus inficitur potius, quam perficitur*, by which he is rather infected than anyway perfected.

Qui talia legit,
Quid didicit tandem, quid scit nisi somnia, nugas? [1]

[Who reads such stuff, what does he learn to know
Save idle dreams and vain frivolities?]

So that oftentimes it falls out (which Callimachus taxed of
old) a great book is a great mischief. Cardan finds fault with
Frenchmen and Germans,[2] for their scribbling to no purpose; *Non,
inquit, ab edendo deterreo, modo novum aliquid inveniant,* he doth
not bar them to write, so that it be some new invention of their
own; but we weave the same web still, twist the same rope
again and again; or if it be a new invention, 'tis but some bauble
or toy which idle fellows write, for as idle fellows to read, and
who so cannot invent? "He must have a barren wit, that in
this scribbling age can forge nothing."[3] "Princes show their
armies, rich men vaunt their buildings, soldiers their manhood,
and scholars vent their toys";[4] they must read, they must
hear whether they will or no.

Et quodcunque semel chartis illeverit, omnes
Gestiet a furno redeuntes scire lacuque,
Et pueros et anus. [5]

What once is said and writ, all men must know,
Old wives and children as they come and go.

"What a company of poets hath this year brought out!" as
Pliny complains to Sossius Senecio; "this April every day some
or other have recited."[6] What a catalogue of new books all this
year, all this age (I say), have our Frankfort marts, our domestic
marts brought out! Twice a year, *proferunt se nova ingenia
et ostentant,*[7] we stretch our wits out, and set them to sale, *magno
conatu nihil agimus* [we do nothing with a great expenditure
of energy]. So that, which Gesner much desires,[8] if a speedy
reformation be not had, by some prince's edicts and grave
supervisors, to restrain this liberty, it will run on *in infinitum.
Quis tam avidus librorum helluo?* [Where can we find such a
glutton of books?], who can read them? As already, we shall
have a vast chaos and confusion of books, we are oppressed
with them,[9] our eyes ache with reading, our fingers with
turning.[10] For my part I am one of the number, *nos
numerus sumus*: I do not deny it, I have only this of Macrobius
to say for myself, *Omne meum, nihil meum,* 'tis all mine, and
none mine. As a good housewife out of divers fleeces weaves
one piece of cloth, a bee gathers wax and honey out of many
flowers, and makes a new bundle of all, *Floriferis ut apes in*

saltibus omnia libant [as bees in flowery glades sip from each cup], I have laboriously collected this cento out of divers writers,[1] and that *sine injuria*, I have wronged no authors, but given every man his own; which Hierome so much commends in Nepotian,[2] he stole not whole verses, pages, tracts, as some do nowadays, concealing their authors' names, but still said this was Cyprian's, that Lactantius', that Hilarius', so said Minucius Felix, so Victorinus, thus far Arnobius: I cite and quote mine authors (which, howsoever some illiterate scribblers account pedantical, as a cloak of ignorance, and opposite to their affected fine style, I must and will use), *sumpsi, non surripui* [I have taken, not filched]; and what Varro, *lib. 3 de re rust.*, speaks of bees, *minime maleficæ nullius opus vellicantes faciunt deterius* [they do little harm, and damage no one in extracting honey], I can say of myself, Whom have I injured? The matter is theirs most part, and yet mine, *apparet unde sumptum sit* [it is plain whence it was taken] (which Seneca approves), *aliud tamen quam unde sumptum sit apparet,* [yet it becomes something different in its new setting]; which nature doth with the aliment of our bodies incorporate, digest, assimilate, I do *concoquere quod hausi* [assimilate what I have swallowed], dispose of what I take. I make them pay tribute to set out this my *Macaronicon,* the method only is mine own; I must usurp that of Wecker *e Ter., nihil dictum quod non dictum prius, methodus sola artificem ostendit,*[3] we can say nothing but what hath been said, the composition and method is ours only, and shows a scholar. Oribasius, Aetius, Avicenna, have all out of Galen, but to their own method, *diverso stilo, non diversa fide.* Our poets steal from Homer; he spews, saith Ælian, they lick it up. Divines use Austin's words *verbatim* still, and our story-dressers do as much; he that comes last is commonly best,

> *donec quid grandius ætas*
> *Postera sorsque ferat melior.*

> [Till a later age,
> More favoured, shall produce a nobler page.]

Though there were many giants of old in physic and philosophy, yet I say with Didacus Stella,[4] "A dwarf standing on the shoulders of a giant may see farther than a giant himself"; I may likely add, alter, and see farther than my predecessors; and it is no greater prejudice for me to indite after others, than for Ælianus Montaltus, that famous physician, to write *de morbis capitis* [about diseases of the head] after Jason Pratensis,

Heurnius, Hildesheim, etc., many horses to run in a race, one logician, one rhetorician, after another. Oppose then what thou wilt,

> *Allatres licet usque nos et usque,*
> *Et gannitibus improbis lacessas,*

> [Though you bark at me as much as you please, and growl threateningly,]

I solve it thus. And for those other faults of barbarism, Doric dialect, extemporanean style, tautologies, apish imitation, a rhapsody of rags gathered together from several dung-hills,[1] excrements of authors, toys and fopperies confusedly tumbled out, without art, invention, judgment, wit, learning, harsh, raw, rude, phantastical, absurd, insolent, indiscreet, ill-composed, indigested, vain, scurrile, idle, dull, and dry; I confess all ('tis partly affected), thou canst not think worse of me than I do of myself. 'Tis not worth the reading, I yield it, I desire thee not to lose time in perusing so vain a subject, I should be peradventure loath myself to read him or thee so writing; 'tis not *operæ pretium* [worth while]. All I say is this, that I have precedents for it,[2] which Isocrates calls *perfugium iis qui peccant* [a refuge for sinners], others as absurd, vain, idle, illiterate, etc. *Nonnulli alii idem fecerunt*, others have done as much, it may be more, and perhaps thou thyself, *Novimus et qui te, etc.* [we know someone who has seen you also]. We have all our faults; *scimus, et hanc veniam, etc.* [we know and beg pardon], thou censurest me, so have I done others, and may do thee,[3] *Cædimus, inque vicem, etc.* [we smite, and in turn, etc.], 'tis *lex talionis, quid pro quo*. Go now, censure, criticize, scoff, and rail.

> *Nasutus sis usque licet, sis denique nasus:*
> *Non potes in nugas dicere plura meas,*
> *Ipse ego quam dixi,* etc.[4]

Wert thou all scoffs and flouts, a very Momus,
Than we ourselves, thou canst not say worse of us.

Thus, as when women scold, have I cried whore first, and in some men's censures I am afraid I have overshot myself; *Laudare se vani, vituperare stulti* [self-praise is boastful, self-depreciation foolish], as I do not arrogate, I will not derogate. *Primus vestrum non sum, nec imus*, I am none of the best, I am none of the meanest of you. As I am an inch, or so many feet, so many parasangs, after him or him, I may be peradventure an ace before thee. Be it therefore as it is, well or ill, I have assayed, put myself upon the stage; I must abide the censure, I may not escape it. It is most true, *stilus virum arguit*, our style bewrays us, and as hunters find their game by the trace, so is a man's genius descried by his works;[1] *multo melius ex sermone quam lineamentis de moribus hominum judicamus* [we can judge a man's character much better from his conversation than his physiognomy]; 'twas old Cato's rule. I have laid myself open (I know it) in this treatise, turned mine inside outward: I shall be censured, I doubt not; for, to say truth with Erasmus, *nihil morosius hominum judiciis*, there 's naught so peevish as men's judgments; yet this is some comfort, *ut palata, sic judicia*, our censures are as various as our palates.

> *Tres mihi convivæ prope dissentire videntur,*
> *Poscentes vario multum diversa palato*, etc.[2]

> [Three guests I have, dissenting at my feast,
> Requiring each to gratify his taste
> With different food.]

Our writings are as so many dishes, our readers guests, our books like beauty, that which one admires another rejects; so are we approved as men's fancies are inclined. *Pro captu lectoris habent sua fata libelli* [the fate of books depends on the fancy of the reader]. That which is most pleasing to one is *amaracum sui*, most harsh to another. *Quot homines, tot sententiæ*, so many men, so many minds: that which thou condemnest he commends. *Quod petis, id sane est invisum acidumque duobus* [3] [what attracts you, others find sour and repulsive]. He respects matter, thou art wholly for words; he loves a loose and free style, thou art all for neat composition, strong lines, hyperboles, allegories; he desires a fine frontispiece, enticing pictures, such as Hieron. Natali the Jesuit hath cut to the Dominicals,[4] to draw on the reader's attention, which thou rejectest; that which one admires, another explodes as most absurd and ridiculous. If it be not point-blank to his humour, his method, his conceit, *si quid forsan omissum, quod is animo conceperit, si quæ dictio*,[5] etc., if aught be omitted, or added, which he likes, or dislikes, thou art *mancipium paucæ lectionis*, an idiot, an ass, *nullus es*, or *plagiarius*, a trifler, a trivant, thou art an idle fellow; or else it is a thing of mere industry, a collection without wit or invention, a very toy. *Facilia sic putant omnes quæ jam facta, nec de salebris cogitant, ubi via strata* [6] [when a thing has once been done, people think it easy; when the road is made, they forget how rough the way used to be]; so men are valued, their labours vilified by fellows of no worth them-selves, as things of naught, who could not have done as much. *Unusquisque abundat sensu suo*, every man abounds in his own sense; and whilst each particular party is so affected, how should one please all?

> *Quid dem? quid non dem?   Renuis tu quod jubet ille.*[1]
>
> [What courses must I choose?
> What not?   What he would order you refuse.]

How shall I hope to express myself to each man's humour and conceit, or to give satisfaction to all?[2]   Some understand too little, some too much, *qui similiter in legendos libros, atque in salutandos homines irruunt, non cogitantes quales, sed quibus vestibus induti sint* [they pay their respects to books on the same principle as to people, judging not by the character but by the outer garb], as Austin observes,[3] not regarding what, but who write, *orexin habet auctoris celebritas*[4] [the author's name creates a demand], not valuing the metal, but the stamp that is upon it, *cantharum aspiciunt, non quid in eo* [they look only at the jar, not at its contents].   If he be not rich, in great place, polite and brave, a great doctor, or full-fraught with grand titles, though never so well qualified, he is a dunce; but, as Baronius hath it of Cardinal Caraffa's works,[5] he is a mere hog that rejects any man for his poverty.   Some are too partial, as friends to overween, others come with a prejudice to carp, vilify, detract, and scoff (*qui de me forsan, quicquid est, omni contemptu contemptius judicant* [who perhaps regard anything I produce as utterly beneath contempt]); some as bees for honey, some as spiders to gather poison.   What shall I do in this case?   As a Dutch host, if you come to an inn in Germany and dislike your fare, diet, lodging, etc., replies in a surly tone, *Aliud tibi quæras diversorium,*[6] If you like not this, get you to another inn: I resolve, if you like not my writing, go read something else.   I do not much esteem thy censure, take thy course, 'tis not as thou wilt, not as I will, but when we have both done, that of Plinius Secundus to Trajan[7] will prove true, "Every man's witty labour takes not, except the matter, subject, occasion, and some commending favourite happen to it."   If I be taxed, exploded by thee and some such, I shall haply be approved and commended by others, and so have been (*Expertus loquor*), and may truly say with Jovius in like case[8] (*absit verbo jactantia* [without boasting]), *heroum quorundam, pontificum, et virorum nobilium familiaritatem et amicitiam*

*gratasque gratias, et multorum bene laudatorum laudes sum inde
promeritus* [1] [I have on this account been honoured with the
intimate friendship of prominent military men, clergymen, and
nobles, and have earned their favour along with the praises of
many persons of repute]; as I have been honoured by some
worthy men, so have I been vilified by others, and shall be.
At the first publishing of this book, which Probus of Persius'
Satires, [2] *editum librum continuo mirari homines, atque avide
deripere cœperunt* [when the book first appeared, people opened
their eyes, and began eagerly to pick holes in it], I may in
some sort apply to this my work; the first, second, and third
edition were suddenly gone, eagerly read, and, as I have said,
not so much approved by some as scornfully rejected by others.
But it was Democritus his fortune, *Idem admirationi et irrisioni
habitus* [3] [he was the object both of admiration and scorn].
'Twas Seneca's fate, that superintendent of wit, learning, judgment, *ad stuporem doctus* [4] [amazingly learned], the best of
Greek and Latin writers in Plutarch's opinion; "that renowned
corrector of vice," as Fabius terms him, [5] "and painful omniscious philosopher, that writ so excellently and admirably well,"
could not please all parties, or escape censure. How is he
vilified by Caligula, [6] A. Gellius, Fabius, and Lipsius himself, his
chief propugner! *In eo pleraque perniciosa,* saith the same
Fabius, many childish tracts and sentences he hath, *sermo
illaboratus,* too negligent often and remiss, as A. Gellius observes,
*oratio vulgaris et protrita, dicaces et ineptæ sententiæ, eruditio
plebeia* [a homely and commonplace style, far-fetched and
foolish ideas, mediocre learning], an homely shallow writer as
he is. *In partibus spinas et fastidia habet* [he is very involved
and stilted in parts], saith Lipsius; [7] and, as in all his other
works, so especially in his epistles, *aliæ in argutiis et ineptiis
occupantur, intricatus alicubi, et parum compositus, sine copia
rerum hoc fecit* [some are full of idle subtleties; sometimes he is
involved and ill arranged, and this without any great wealth
of matter], he jumbles up many things together immethodically,
after the Stoics' fashion, *parum ordinavit, multa accumulavit,*
etc. If Seneca be thus lashed, and many famous men that
I could name, what shall I expect? How shall I, that am *vix
umbra tanti philosophi* [scarce the shadow of so great a philo-
sopher], hope to please? "No man so absolute," Erasmus
holds, [8] "to satisfy all, except antiquity, prescription, etc., set
a bar." But as I have proved in Seneca, this will not always
take place, how shall I evade? 'Tis the common doom of all

writers, I must (I say) abide it; I seek not applause; *Non ego ventosæ venor suffragia plebis* [1] [I court not the favour of the fickle crowd]; again, *non sum adeo informis* [I am not so ugly], I would not be vilified. [2]

> *Laudatus abunde,*
> *Non fastiditus si tibi, lector, ero.* [3]

[Sufficient praise for me if thou disdainest me not, O worthy reader.]

I fear good men's censures, and to their favourable acceptance I submit my labours,

> *et linguas mancipiorum*
> *Contemno.* [4]

[I scorn the talk of slaves.]

As the barking of a dog, I securely contemn those malicious and scurrile obloquies, flouts, calumnies of railers and detractors; I scorn the rest. What therefore I have said, *pro tenuitate mea* [to the best of my poor ability], I have said.

One or two things yet I was desirous to have amended if I could, concerning the manner of handling this my subject, for which I must apologize, *deprecari*, and upon better advice give the friendly reader notice. It was not mine intent to prostitute my muse in English, or to divulge *secreta Minervæ*, but to have exposed this more contract in Latin, if I could have got it printed. Any scurrile pamphlet is welcome to our mercenary stationers in English; they print all,

> *cuduntque libellos*
> *In quorum foliis vix simia nuda cacaret;*

but in Latin they will not deal; which is one of the reasons Nicholas Car, in his oration of the paucity of English writers, gives, that so many flourishing wits are smothered in oblivion, lie dead and buried in this our nation. [5] Another main fault is, that I have not revised the copy, and amended the style, which now flows remissly, as it was first conceived; but my leisure would not permit; *Feci nec quod potui, nec quod volui*, I confess it is neither as I would, nor as it should be.

> *Cum relego scripsisse pudet, quia plurima cerno*
> *Me quoque quæ fuerant judice digna lini.* [6]

> When I peruse this tract which I have writ,
> I am abash'd, and much I hold unfit.

Et quod gravissimum [and what is most serious], in the matter itself, many things I disallow at this present, which when I writ,

Non eadem est ætas, non mens [1] [I was younger and more foolish]; I would willingly retract much, etc., but 'tis too late, I can only crave pardon now for what is amiss.

I might indeed (had I wisely done), observed that precept of the poet, *Nonumque prematur in annum* [keep back your work for nine years before printing], and have taken more care: or, as Alexander the physician would have done by lapis lazuli, fifty times washed before it be used, I should have revised, corrected, and amended this tract; but I had not (as I said) that happy leisure, no amanuenses or assistants. Pancrates in Lucian,[2] wanting a servant as he went from Memphis to Coptus in Egypt, took a door-bar, and after some superstitious words pronounced (Eucrates the relater was then present) made it stand up like a serving-man, fetch him water, turn the spit, serve in supper, and what work he would besides; and when he had done that service he desired, turned his man to a stick again. I have no such skill to make new men at my pleasure, or means to hire them; no whistle to call like the master of a ship, and bid them run, etc. I have no such authority, no such benefactors, as that noble Ambrosius was to Origen,[3] allowing him six or seven amanuenses to write out his dictates; I must for that cause do my business myself, and was therefore enforced, as a bear doth her whelps, to bring forth this confused lump; I had not time to lick it into form, as she doth her young ones, but even so to publish it as it was first written, *quicquid in buccam venit* [whatever came uppermost], in an extemporean style, as I do commonly all other exercises,[4] *effudi quicquid dictavit genius meus* [I poured out whatever came into my mind], out of a confused company of notes, and writ with as small deliberation as I do ordinarily speak, without all affectation of big words, fustian phrases, jingling terms, tropes, strong lines, that like Acestes' arrows caught fire as they flew,[5] strains of wit, brave heats, elogies, hyperbolical exornations, elegancies, etc., which many so much affect. I am *aquæ potor* [6] [a water-drinker], drink no wine at all, which so much improves our modern wits, a loose, plain, rude writer, *ficum voco ficum et ligonem ligonem* [I call a fig a fig and a spade a spade], and as free, as loose, *idem calamo quod in mente* [what my mind thinks my pen writes], I call a spade a spade,[7] *animis hæc scribo, non auribus* [I write for the mind, not the ear], I respect matter, not words; remembering that of Cardan, *verba propter res, non res propter verba* [words should minister to matter, not vice versa], and seeking with Seneca, *quid scribam, non quemadmodum,* rather what than how to write: for as Philo thinks, "He that is conversant about matter neglects words, and those that excel in this art of speaking have no profound learning."[1]

> *Verba nitent phaleris, at nullas verba medullas*
> *Intus habent.*[2]

[Their words well tricked, but void of pith within.]

Besides, it was the observation of that wise Seneca, "When you see a fellow careful about his words, and neat in his speech, know this for a certainty, that man's mind is busied about toys, there's no solidity in him."[3] *Non est ornamentum virile concinnitas* [prettiness is not a masculine adornment]: as he said of a nightingale, *Vox es, præterea nihil* [you are a voice and nothing more], etc. I am therefore in this point a professed disciple of Apollonius, a scholar of Socrates,[4] I neglect phrases, and labour wholly to inform my reader's understanding, not to please his ear; 'tis not my study or intent to compose neatly, which an orator requires, but to express myself readily and plainly as it happens. So that as a river runs sometimes precipitate and swift, then dull and slow; now direct, then *per ambages* [winding]; now deep, then shallow; now muddy, then clear; now broad, then narrow; doth my style flow: now serious, then light; now comical, then satirical; now more elaborate, then remiss, as the present subject required, or as at that time I was affected. And if thou vouchsafe to read this treatise, it shall seem no otherwise to thee than the way to an ordinary traveller, sometimes fair, sometimes foul; here champaign, there enclosed; barren in one place, better soil in another: by woods, groves, hills, dales, plains, etc. I shall lead thee *per ardua montium, et lubrica vallium, et roscida cespitum, et glebosa camporum*[5] [over steep mountains, slippery glades, wet grass, and sticky fields], through variety of objects, that which thou shalt like and surely dislike.

For the matter itself or method, if it be faulty, consider I pray you that of Columella, *Nihil perfectum, aut a singulari consummatum industria* [nothing can be perfected or completed by the efforts of a single individual], no man can observe all, much is defective no doubt, may be justly taxed, altered, and avoided in Galen, Aristotle, those great masters. *Boni venatoris* (one holds[6]) *plures feras capere, non omnes,* he is a good huntsman can catch some, not all: I have done my endeavour. Besides, I dwell not in this study, *Non hic sulcos ducimus, non hoc pulvere desudamus* [I am not driving a furrow here, this is not my field of labour], I am but a smatterer, I confess, a stranger, here and there I pull a flower;[1] I do easily grant, if a rigid censurer should criticize on this which I have writ, he should not find three sole faults, as Scaliger in Terence, but three hundred. So many as he hath done in Cardan's Subtleties, as many notable errors as Gul. Laurembergius, a late professor of Rostock, discovers in that Anatomy of Laurentius,[2] or Barocius the Venetian in Sacroboscus. And although this be a sixth edition, in which I should have been more accurate, corrected all those former escapes, yet it was *magni laboris opus*, so difficult and tedious, that, as carpenters do find out of experience, 'tis much better build a new sometimes, than repair an old house; I could as soon write as much more as alter that which is written. If aught therefore be amiss (as I grant there is), I require a friendly admonition, no bitter invective, *Sint Musis socii Charites, Furia omnis abesto*[3] [let the Graces come with the Muses, but let the Furies keep away], otherwise, as in ordinary controversies, *funem contentionis nectamus, sed cui bono?* We may contend, and likely misuse each other, but to what purpose? We are both scholars, say,

Arcades ambo,
Et cantare pares, et respondere parati.[4]

[Both young Arcadians, both alike inspir'd
To sing and answer as the song requir'd.]

If we do wrangle, what shall we get by it? Trouble and wrong ourselves, make sport to others. If I be convict of an error, I will yield, I will amend. *Si quid bonis moribus, si quid veritati dissentaneum, in sacris vel humanis literis a me dictum sit, id nec dictum esto* [if I have said anything contrary to good morals or to truth as expressed either in sacred or profane letters, let it be regarded as unsaid]. In the meantime I require a favourable censure of all faults omitted, harsh compositions, pleonasms of words, tautological repetitions (though Seneca bear me out, *nunquam nimis dicitur, quod nunquam satis dicitur* [that is never said too often, which cannot be said often enough]), perturbations of tenses, numbers, printers' faults, etc. My translations are sometimes rather paraphrases than interpretations, *non ad verbum* [not literal], but, as an author, I use more liberty, and that's only taken which was to my purpose. Quotations are often inserted in the text, which makes the style more harsh, or in the margin as it happened. Greek authors, Plato, Plutarch,

Athenæus, etc., I have cited out of their interpreters, because the original was not so ready. I have mingled *sacra profanis* [sacred with profane], but I hope not profaned, and in repetition of authors' names, ranked them *per accidens* [as they occurred], not according to chronology; sometimes neoterics before ancients, as my memory suggested. Some things are here altered, expunged in this sixth edition, others amended, much added, because many good authors in all kinds are come to my hands since,[1] and 'tis no prejudice, no such indecorum or oversight.

> *Nunquam ita quicquam bene subducta ratione ad vitam fuit,*
> *Quin res, ætas, usus, semper aliquid apportent novi,*
> *Aliquid moneant, ut illa quæ scire te credas, nescias,*
> *Et quæ tibi putaris prima, in exercendo ut repudias.*[2]

> Ne'er was aught yet at first contriv'd so fit,
> But use, age, or something would alter it;
> Advise thee better, and, upon peruse,
> Make thee not say, and what thou tak'st refuse.

But I am now resolved never to put this treatise out again; *Ne quid nimis* [not too much of anything], I will not hereafter add, alter, or retract; I have done. The last and greatest exception is, that I, being a divine, have meddled with physic.

> *Tantumne est ab re tua otii tibi,*
> *Aliena ut cures, eaque nihil quæ ad te attinent ?*[3]

which Menedemus objected to Chremes; have I so much leisure, or little business of mine own, as to look after other men's matters which concern me not? What have I to do with physic? *Quod medicorum est promittant medici* [let doctors look after their own job]. The Lacedæmonians were once in counsel about state matters,[4] a debauched fellow spake excellent well, and to the purpose, his speech was generally approved: a grave senator steps up, and by all means would have it repealed, though good, because *dehonestabatur pessimo auctore*, it had no better an author; let some good man relate the same, and then it should pass. This counsel was embraced, *factum est*, and it was registered forthwith, *Et sic bona sententia mansit, malus auctor mutatus est* [and so the good plan was retained, the bad counsellor was dismissed]. Thou sayest as much of me, *stomachosus* [peevish] as thou art, and grantest peradventure this which I have written in physic, not to be amiss, had another done it, a professed physician, or so; but why should I meddle with this tract? Hear me speak. There be many other subjects,

I do easily grant, both in humanity and divinity, fit to be treated of, of which had I written *ad ostentationem* only, to show myself, I should have rather chosen, and in which I have been more conversant, I could have more willingly luxuriated, and better satisfied myself and others; but that at this time I was fatally driven upon this rock of melancholy, and carried away by this by-stream, which, as a rillet, is deducted from the main channel of my studies, in which I have pleased and busied myself at idle hours, as a subject most necessary and commodious. Not that I prefer it before divinity, which I do acknowledge to be the queen of professions, and to which all the rest are as handmaids, but that in divinity I saw no such great need. For had I written positively, there be so many books in that kind, so many commentators, treatises, pamphlets, expositions, sermons, that whole teams of oxen cannot draw them; and had I been as forward and ambitious as some others, I might have haply printed a sermon at Paul's Cross, a sermon in St. Mary's Oxon, a sermon in Christ Church, or a sermon before the right honourable, right reverend, a sermon before the right worshipful, a sermon in Latin, in English, a sermon with a name, a sermon without, a sermon, a sermon, etc. But I have been ever as desirous to suppress my labours in this kind, as others have been to press and publish theirs. To have written in controversy had been to cut off an hydra's head, *lis litem generat*,[1] one [dispute] begets another, so many duplications, triplications, and swarms of questions *in sacro bello hoc quod stili mucrone agitur* [in this sacred war which is waged with the pen], that having once begun, I should never make an end. One had much better, as Alexander the Sixth, Pope, long since observed, provoke a great prince than a begging friar,[2] a Jesuit, or a seminary priest, I will add, for *inexpugnabile genus hoc hominum*, they are an irrefragable society, they must and will have the last word; and that with such eagerness, impudence, abominable lying, falsifying, and bitterness in their questions they proceed, that as he said, *Furorne cæcus, an rapit vis acrior, an culpa? responsum date.*[3] Blind fury, or error, or rashness, or what it is that eggs them, I know not; I am sure many times, which Austin perceived long since,[4] *tempestate contentionis, serenitas caritatis obnubilatur*, with this tempest of contention the serenity of charity is overclouded, and there be too many spirits conjured up already in this kind in all sciences, and more than we can tell how to lay, which do so furiously rage, and keep such a racket, that as Fabius said,[5] "It had been much better for some of them to have been born dumb, and altogether illiterate, than so far to dote to their own destruction."

> *At melius fuerat non scribere, namque tacere*
> *Tutum semper erit.*
>
> [Better it had been not to write at all:
> From saying naught no mischief can befall.]

'Tis a general fault, as Severinus the Dane complains in physic, "Unhappy men as we are, we spend our days in unprofitable questions and disputations," intricate subtleties, *de lana caprina* [about a goat's fleece], about moonshine in the water, "leaving in the meantime those chiefest treasures of nature untouched, wherein the best medicines for all manner of diseases are to be found, and do not only neglect them ourselves, but hinder, condemn, forbid, and scoff at others, that are willing to inquire after them." [1] These motives at this present have induced me to make choice of this medicinal subject.

If any physician in the meantime shall infer, *Ne sutor ultra crepidam*,[2] and find himself grieved that I have intruded into his profession, I will tell him in brief, I do not otherwise by them than they do by us, if it be for their advantage. I know many of their sect which have taken orders in hope of a benefice, 'tis a common transition, and why may not a melancholy divine, that can get nothing but by simony, profess physic? Drusianus, an Italian (Crusianus, but corruptly, Trithemius calls him), "because he was not fortunate in his practice, forsook his profession, and writ afterwards in divinity." [3] Marsilius Ficinus was *semel et simul*, a priest and a physician at once, and T. Linacre in his old age took orders.[4] The Jesuits profess both at this time, divers of them *permissu superiorum* [by the permission of the superiors], chirurgeons, panders, bawds, and midwives, etc. Many poor country vicars, for want of other means, are driven to their shifts, to turn mountebanks, quacksalvers, empirics, and if our greedy patrons hold us to such hard conditions as commonly they do, they will make most of us work at some trade, as Paul did, at last turn taskers, maltsters, costermongers, graziers, sell ale as some have done, or worse. Howsoever, in undertaking this task, I hope I shall commit no great error or indecorum; if all be considered aright, I can vindicate myself with Georgius Braunus and Hieronymus Hemingius, those two learned divines; who (to borrow a line or two of mine elder brother [5]), drawn by a "natural love, the one of pictures and maps, prospectives and chorographical delights, writ that ample Theatre of Cities; the other to the study of genealogies, penned *Theatrum Genealogicum*." Or else I can excuse my studies with Lessius the Jesuit in like case.[1] It is a disease of the soul on which I am to treat, and as much appertaining to a divine as to a physician, and who knows not what an agreement there is betwixt these two professions? A good divine either is or ought to be a good physician, a spiritual physician at least, as our Saviour calls Himself, and was indeed (Matt. iv, 23; Luke v, 18; Luke vii, 21). They differ but in object, the one of the body, the other of the soul, and use divers medicines to cure: one amends *animam per corpus* [the soul through the body], the other *corpus per animam* [the body through the soul] as our Regius Professor of Physic well informed us in a learned lecture of his not long since.[2] One helps the vices and passions of the soul, anger, lust, desperation, pride, presumption, etc., by applying that spiritual physic; as the other uses proper remedies in bodily diseases. Now this being a common infirmity of body and soul, and such a one that hath as much need of a spiritual as a corporal cure, I could not find a fitter task to busy myself about, a more apposite theme, so necessary, so commodious, and generally concerning all sorts of men, that should so equally participate of both, and require a whole physician. A divine in this compound mixed malady can do little alone, a physician in some kinds of melancholy much less, both make an absolute cure.

Alterius sic altera poscit opem.[3]

[When in friendship joined,
A mutual succour in each other find.]

And 'tis proper to them both, and I hope not unbeseeming me, who am by my profession a divine, and by mine inclination a physician. I had Jupiter in my sixth house; I say with Beroaldus, *non sum medicus, nec medicinæ prorsus expers* [I am not a doctor, yet have some knowledge of medicine], in the theoric of physic I have taken some pains, not with an intent to practise, but to satisfy myself, which was a cause likewise of the first undertaking of this subject.

If these reasons do not satisfy thee, good reader, as Alexander Munificus, that bountiful prelate, sometime Bishop of Lincoln, when he had built six castles, *ad invidiam operis eluendam*, saith Mr. Camden,[4] to take away the envy of his work (which very words Nubrigensis hath of Roger the rich Bishop of Salisbury, who in King Stephen's time built Sherborne Castle. and that of Devizes), to divert the scandal or imputation which might be thence inferred, built so many religious houses; if this my discourse be over-medicinal, or savour too much of humanity, I promise thee that I will hereafter make thee amends in some treatise of divinity. But this I hope shall suffice, when you have more fully considered of the matter of this my subject, *rem substratam*, melancholy, madness, and of the reasons following, which were my chief motives: the generality of the disease, the necessity of the cure, and the commodity or common good that will arise to all men by the knowledge of it, as shall at large appear in the ensuing preface. And I doubt not but that in the end you will say with me, that to anatomize this humour aright, through all the members of this our *microcosmos*, is as great a task as to reconcile those chronological errors in the Assyrian monarchy, find out the quadrature of a circle, the creeks and sounds of the north-east or north-west passages, and all out as good a discovery as that hungry Spaniard's [1] of *Terra Australis Incognita*, as great a trouble as to perfect the motion of Mars and Mercury, which so crucifies our astronomers, or to rectify the Gregorian calendar. I am so affected for my part, and hope as Theophrastus did by his Characters, "that our posterity, O friend Polycles, shall be the better for this which we have written, by correcting and rectifying what is amiss in themselves by our examples, and applying our precepts and cautions to their own use." [2] And as that great captain Zisca would have a drum made of his skin when he was dead, because he thought the very noise of it would put his enemies to flight, I doubt not but that these following lines, when they shall be recited, or hereafter read, will drive away melancholy (though I be gone) as much as Zisca's drum could terrify his foes. Yet one caution let me give by the way to my present or future reader, who is actually melancholy, that he read not the symptoms or prognostics in this following tract,[3] lest by applying that which he reads to himself, aggravating, appropriating things generally spoken to his own person (as melancholy men for the most part do), he trouble or hurt himself, and get in conclusion more harm than good. I advise them therefore warily to peruse that tract; *Lapides loquitur* (so said Agrippa, *de occ. Phil.*[4]), *et caveant lectores ne cerebrum iis excutiat* [he discourses stones, and the readers must beware lest he break their heads]. The rest I doubt not they may securely read, and to their benefit. But I am over-tedious, I proceed.

Of the necessity and generality of this which I have said, if any man doubt, I shall desire him to make a brief survey of the world, as Cyprian adviseth Donat; "supposing himself to be transported to the top of some high mountain, and thence to behold the tumults and chances of this wavering world, he cannot choose but either laugh at, or pity it." [1] St. Hierome, out of a strong imagination, being in the wilderness, conceived with himself that he then saw them dancing in Rome; and if thou shalt either conceive, or climb to see, thou shalt soon perceive that all the world is mad, that it is melancholy, dotes; that it is (which Epichthonius Cosmopolites expressed not many years since in a map) made like a fool's head (with that motto, *Caput helleboro dignum* [a head requiring hellebore]); a crazed head, *cavea stultorum*, a fools' paradise, or as Apollonius, a common prison of gulls, cheaters, flatterers, etc., and needs to be reformed. Strabo, in the ninth book of his Geography, compares Greece to the picture of a man, which comparison of his Nic. Gerbelius, in his exposition of Sophianus' map, approves; the breast lies open from those Acroceraunian hills in Epirus to the Sunian promontory in Attica; Pagæ and Megara are the two shoulders; that Isthmus of Corinth the neck; and Peloponnesus the head. If this allusion hold, 'tis sure a mad head; Morea may be Moria [Folly]; and to speak what I think, the inhabitants of modern Greece swerve as much from reason and true religion at this day, as that Morea doth from the picture of a man. Examine the rest in like sort, and you shall find that kingdoms and provinces are melancholy, cities and families, all creatures, vegetal, sensible, and rational, that all sorts, sects, ages, conditions, are out of tune, as in Cebes' Table, *omnes errorem bibunt*, before they come into the world, they are intoxicated by error's cup, from the highest to the lowest have need of physic, and those particular actions in Seneca,[2] where father and son prove one another mad, may be general; Porcius Latro shall plead against us all. For indeed who is not a fool, melancholy, mad? *Qui nil molitur inepte*,[3] who is not brain-sick? Folly, melancholy, madness, are but one disease, delirium is a common name to all. Alexander Gordonius, Jason Pratensis, Savonarola, Guianerius, Montaltus, confound them as differing *secundum magis et minus*; so doth David (Ps. lxxv, 4), "I said unto the fools, deal not so madly," and 'twas an old Stoical paradox, *omnes stultos insanire*,[4] all fools are mad, though some madder than others. And who is not a fool, who is free from melancholy? Who is not touched more or less in habit or disposition? If in disposition, "ill dispositions beget habits, if they persevere," saith Plutarch,[1] habits either are or turn to diseases. 'Tis the same which Tully maintains in the second of his Tusculans, *omnium insipientum animi in morbo sunt, et perturbatorum,* fools are sick, and all that are troubled in mind: for what is sickness, but as Gregory Tholosanus defines it, "a dissolution or perturbation of the bodily league, which health combines": [2] and who is not sick, or ill disposed? In whom doth not passion, anger, envy, discontent, fear, and sorrow reign? Who labours not of this disease? Give me but a little leave, and you shall see by what testimonies, confessions, arguments I will evince it, that most men are mad, that they had as much need to go a pilgrimage to the Anticyræ (as in Strabo's time they did [3]) as in our days they run to Compostella, our Lady of Sichem, or Loretto to seek for help; that it is like to be as prosperous a voyage as that of Guiana, and that there is much more need of hellebore than of tobacco.

That men are so misaffected, melancholy, mad, giddy-headed, hear the testimony of Solomon (Eccles. ii, 12): "And I turned to behold wisdom, madness and folly," etc.; and v. 23: "All his days are sorrow, his travail grief, and his heart taketh no rest in the night." So that, take melancholy in what sense you will, properly or improperly, in disposition or habit, for pleasure or for pain, dotage, discontent, fear, sorrow, madness, for part or all, truly or metaphorically, 'tis all one. Laughter itself is madness according to Solomon, and as St. Paul hath it, "Worldly sorrow brings death." "The hearts of the sons of men are evil, and madness is in their hearts while they live " (Eccles. ix, 3). Wise men themselves are no better (Eccles. i, 18): "In the multitude of wisdom is much grief, and he that increaseth wisdom increaseth sorrow." He hated life itself, nothing pleased him, he hated his labour (chap. ii, 17); all, as he concludes, is "sorrow, grief, vanity, vexation of spirit." [4] And though he were the wisest man in the world, *sanctuarium sapientiæ* [a shrine of wisdom], and had wisdom in abundance, he will not vindicate himself, or justify his own actions. "Surely I am more foolish than any man, and have not the understanding of a man in me" (Prov. xxx, 2). Be they Solomon's words, or the words of Agur, the son of Jakeh, they are canonical. David, a man after God's own heart, confesseth as much of himself (Ps. lxxiii, 21, 22): "So foolish was I and ignorant, I was even as a beast before thee"; and condemns all for fools (Ps. liii; xxxii, 9; xlix, 20). He compares them to "beasts, horses, and mules, in which there is no understanding." The Apostle Paul accuseth himself in like sort (2 Cor. xi, 21): "I would you would suffer a little my foolishness, I speak foolishly." "The whole head is sick," saith Esay,[1] "and the heart is heavy" (chap. i, 5); and makes lighter of them than of oxen and asses, "the ox knows his owner," etc. Read Deut. xxxii, 6; Jer. iv; Amos iii, 1; Ephes. v, 6. "Be not mad, be not deceived; foolish Galatians, who hath bewitched you?" How often are they branded with this epithet of madness and folly! No word so frequent amongst the Fathers of the Church and divines; you may see what an opinion they had of the world, and how they valued men's actions.

I know that we think far otherwise, and hold them most part wise men that are in authority, princes, magistrates, rich men, they are wise men born, all politicians and statesmen must needs be so, for who dare speak against them?[2] And on the other, so corrupt is our judgment, we esteem wise and honest men fools. Which Democritus well signified in an epistle of his to Hippocrates: the Abderites "account virtue madness,"[3] and so do most men living. Shall I tell you the reason of it? Fortune and Virtue, Wisdom and Folly, their seconds, upon a time contended in the Olympics; every man thought that Fortune and Folly would have the worst, and pitied their cases; but it fell out otherwise.[4] Fortune was blind and cared not where she stroke, nor whom, without laws, *andabatorum instar* [like blind gladiators], etc. Folly, rash and inconsiderate, esteemed as little what she said or did. Virtue and Wisdom gave place, were hissed out and exploded by the common people, Folly and Fortune admired, and so are all their followers ever since:[5] knaves and fools commonly fare and deserve best in worldlings' eyes and opinions. Many good men have no better fate in their ages: Achish (1 Sam. xxi, 14) held David for a madman. Elisha[6] and the rest were no otherwise esteemed. David was derided of the common people (Ps. lxxi, 6): "I am become a monster to many." And generally we are accounted fools for Christ (1 Cor. iv, 10). "We fools thought his life madness, and his end without honour" (Wisd. v, 4). Christ and His Apostles were censured in like sort (John x; Mark iii; Acts xxvi). And so were all Christians in Pliny's time, *fuerunt et alii similis dementiæ*[7] [there were others similarly crazed], etc., and called not long after, *vesaniæ sectatores, eversores hominum, polluti novatores, fanatici, canes, malefici, venefici, Galilæi homunciones*[8] [devotees of madness, destroyers of society, blasphemous innovators, fanatics, dogs, criminals, poisoners,

Galilean manikins], etc. 'Tis an ordinary thing with us to account honest, devout, orthodox, divine, religious, plain-dealing men idiots, asses, that cannot or will not lie and dissemble, shift, flatter, *accommodare se ad eum locum ubi nati sunt* [adapt themselves to the station in which they were born],make good bargains, supplant, thrive, *patronis inservire, solennes ascendendi modos apprehendere, leges, mores, consuetudines recte observare, candide laudare, fortiter defendere, sententias amplecti, dubitare de nullis, credere omnia, accipere omnia, nihil reprehendere, cæteraque quæ promotionem ferunt et securitatem, quæ sine ambage felicem reddunt hominem, et vere sapientem apud nos* [fawn upon their patrons, learn the usual methods of getting on, be scrupulous in the observance of laws, manners, customs, praise in glowing terms, defend with vigour, adopt others' opinions, doubt nothing, believe everything, endure everything, resent nothing, and do all the other things which lead to promotion and safe position, which make a man fortunate beyond all question, and truly wise, according to our notions]; that cannot temporize as other men do, hand and take bribes, etc.,[1] but fear God, and make a conscience of their doings. But the Holy Ghost, that knows better how to judge, He calls them fools. "The fool hath said in his heart" (Ps. liii, 1). "And their ways utter their folly" (Ps. xlix, 13). "For what can be more mad, than for a little worldly pleasure to procure unto themselves eternal punishment?" [2] as Gregory and others inculcate unto us.

Yea, even all those great philosophers the world hath ever had in admiration, whose works we do so much esteem, that gave precepts of wisdom to others, inventors of arts and sciences, Socrates the wisest man of his time by the Oracle of Apollo, whom his two scholars, Plato [3] and Xenophon,[4] so much extol and magnify with those honourable titles, "best and wisest of all mortal men, the happiest, and most just"; and as Alcibiades incomparably commends him;[5] Achilles was a worthy man, but Brasidas and others were as worthy as himself; Antenor and Nestor were as good as Pericles, and so of the rest; but none present, before or after Socrates, *nemo veterum neque eorum qui nunc sunt* [none of the ancients nor of those of our own day], were ever such, will match, or come near him. Those seven wise men of Greece, those British Druids, Indian Brachmanni, Ethiopian Gymnosophists, Magi of the Persians, Apollonius (of whom Philostratus, *non doctus, sed natus sapiens*, wise from his cradle), Epicurus, so much admired by his scholar Lucretius:

Qui genus humanum ingenio superavit, et omnes
Perstrinxit stellas exortus ut ætherius sol.

Whose wit excell'd the wits of men as far,
As the sun rising doth obscure a star.

Or that so much renowned Empedocles:

Ut vix humana videatur stirpe creatus.[1]

[So that he scarce seems sprung from human stock.]

All those of whom we read such hyperbolical elogiums,[2] as
of Aristotle, that he was wisdom itself in the abstract, a miracle
of nature,[3] breathing libraries, as Eunapius of Longinus, lights
of nature, giants for wit, quintessence of wit, divine spirits,
eagles in the clouds, fallen from heaven, gods, spirits, lamps of
the world, dictators, *Nulla ferant talem secla futura virum* [No
future age shall such a man produce], monarchs, miracles,
superintendents of wit and learning, *Oceanus, Phænix, Atlas,
monstrum, portentum hominis, orbis universi musæum, ultimus
humanæ naturæ conatus, naturæ maritus* [Oceanus, Phœnix,
Atlas, a prodigy, a marvel of a man, a museum of the whole
world, the supreme product of humanity, the spouse of Nature],

merito cui doctior orbis
Submissis defert fascibus imperium.

[To whom the learned world,
As to its rightful monarch, homage pays.]

As Ælian writ of Protagoras and Gorgias, we may say of them
all, *tantum a sapientibus abfuerunt, quantum a viris pueri* [they
could no more be called wise than boys men], they were children
in respect, infants, not eagles, but kites; novices, illiterate,
eunuchi sapientiæ. And although they were the wisest, and
most admired in their age, as he censured Alexander, I do them,
there were 10,000 in his army as worthy captains (had they
been in place of command), as valiant as himself; there were
myriads of men wiser in those days, and yet all short of what
they ought to be. Lactantius, in his book of Wisdom,[4] proves
them to be dizzards, fools, asses, madmen, so full of absurd and
ridiculous tenents and brain-sick positions, that to his thinking
never any old woman or sick person doted worse. Democritus
took all from Leucippus, and left, saith he, "the inheritance of
his folly to Epicurus," [5] *insanienti dum sapientiæ*, etc.[6] The
like he holds of Plato, Aristippus, and the rest, making
no difference "betwixt them and beasts, saving that they
could speak." [7] Theodoret, in his tract *de cur. Græc. affect.*,[8]

manifestly evinces as much of Socrates, whom though that oracle
of Apollo confirmed to be the wisest man then living, and
saved him from the plague, whom 2000 years have admired, of
whom some will as soon speak evil as of Christ, yet *re vera* [in
reality], he was an illiterate idiot, as Aristophanes calls him,[1]
irrisor et ambitiosus [a scoffer and fond of praise], as his
master Aristotle terms him, *scurra Atticus* [an Attic buffoon],
as Zeno, an enemy to all arts and sciences,[2] as Athenæus, to
philosophers and travellers, an opinative ass, a caviller, a kind
of pedant; for his manners, as Theod. Cyrensis describes him,
a sodomite,[3] an atheist (so convict by Anytus), *iracundus et
ebrius, dicax* [hot-tempered, a heavy drinker, quarrelsome],
etc., a pot-companion, by Plato's own confession, a sturdy
drinker; and that of all others he was most sottish, a very
madman in his actions and opinions. Pythagoras was part
philosopher, part magician, or part witch. If you desire to
hear more of Apollonius, a great wise man, sometime paralleled
by Julian the Apostate to Christ, I refer you to that learned
tract of Eusebius against Hierocles, and for them all to Lucian's
Piscator, Icaromenippus, Necyomantia: their actions, opinions
in general were so prodigious, absurd, ridiculous, which they
broached and maintained, their books and elaborate treatises
were full of dotage, which Tully *ad Atticum* long since observed,
delirant plerumque scriptores in libris suis [writers mostly rave
in their books], their lives being opposite to their words, they
commended poverty to others, and were most covetous themselves, extolled love and peace, and yet persecuted one another
with virulent hate and malice. They could give precepts for
verse and prose, but not a man of them (as Seneca tells them
home[4]) could moderate his affections. Their music did show
us *flebiles modos* [sad airs], etc., how to rise and fall, but they
could not so contain themselves as in adversity not to make
a lamentable tone. They will measure ground by geometry,
set down limits, divide and subdivide, but cannot yet prescribe
quantum homini satis [how much is enough for a man], or keep
within compass of reason and discretion. They can square
circles, but understand not the state of their own souls, describe
right lines and crooked, etc., but know not what is right in
this life, *quid in vita rectum sit ignorant*; so that as he said
Nescio an Anticyram ratio illis destinet omnem, I think all the
Anticyræ will not restore them to their wits. If these men
now,[5] that held Zenodotus' heart, Crates' liver,[6] Epictetus' lanthorn, were so sottish, and had no more brains than so many

beetles, what shall we think of the commonalty? what of the rest?

Yea, but will you infer, that is true of heathens, if they be conferred with Christians (1 Cor. iii, 19): "The wisdom of this world is foolishness with God," "earthly and devilish," as James calls it (iii, 15). "They were vain in their imaginations, and their foolish heart was full of darkness" (Rom. i, 21). "When they professed themselves wise, became fools" (v. 22). Their witty works are admired here on earth, whilst their souls are tormented in hell-fire. In some sense, *Christiani Crassiani*, Christians are Crassians, and if compared to that wisdom, no better than fools. *Quis est sapiens? Solus Deus*, Pythagoras replies.[1] "God is only wise" (Rom. xvi), Paul determines, "only good," as Austin well contends, "and no man living can be justified in His sight." "God looked down from heaven upon the children of men, to see if any did understand" (Ps. liii, 2, 3), but all are corrupt, err. "None doth good, no, not one" (Rom. iii, 12). Job aggravates this (iv, 18): "Behold, he found no steadfastness in his servants, and laid folly upon his angels"; (v. 19,) "How much more on them that dwell in houses of clay!" In this sense we are all fools, and the Scripture alone is *arx Minervæ*[2] [the citadel of Minerva], we and our writings are shallow and unperfect. But I do not so mean; even in our ordinary dealings we are no better than fools. "All our actions," as Pliny told Trajan,[3] "upbraid us of folly," our whole course of life is but matter of laughter: we are not soberly wise; and the world itself, which ought at least to be wise by reason of his antiquity, as Hugo de Prato Florido will have it,[4] *semper stultizat*, "is every day more foolish than other; the more it is whipped, the worse it is, and as a child will still be crowned with roses and flowers." We are apish in it, *asini bipedes* [two-legged asses], and every place is full *inversorum Apuleiorum*, of metamorphosed and two-legged asses,[5] *inversorum Silenorum* [of metamorphosed Silenuses], childish, *pueri instar bimuli, tremula patris dormientis in ulna* [like a two-year-old child, sleeping on its father's arm]. Jovianus Pontanus, *Antonio Dial.*, brings in some laughing at an old man, that by reason of his age was a little fond, but as he admonisheth there, *Ne mireris, mi hospes, de hoc sene*, marvel not at him only, for *tota hæc civitas delirat*, all our town dotes in like sort, we are a company of fools.[6] Ask not with him in the poet, *Larvæ hunc intemperiæ insaniæque agitant senem?*[7] What madness ghosts this old man? but, What madness ghosts

us all? For we are *ad unum omnes,* all mad, *semel insanivimus
omnes,* not once, but always so, *et semel, et simul, et semper,* ever
and altogether as bad as he; and not *senex bis puer, delira anus*
[an old man is in his second boyhood, an old woman dotes],
but say it of us all, *semper pueri,* young and old, all dote, as
Lactantius proves out of Seneca; and no difference betwixt
us and children, saving that *majora ludimus, et grandioribus
pupis,* they play with babies of clouts and such toys, we sport
with greater baubles. We cannot accuse or condemn one
another, being faulty ourselves, *deliramenta loqueris,* you talk
idly, or as Mitio upbraided Demea, *insanis, aufer te* [1] [you are
mad, away with you], for we are as mad our own selves, and it
is hard to say which is the worst. Nay, 'tis universally so;
Vitam regit fortuna, non sapientia [2] [life is governed by chance,
not wisdom].

When Socrates had taken great pains to find out a wise man, [3]
and to that purpose had consulted with philosophers, poets,
artificers, he concludes all men were fools; and though it procured him both anger and much envy, yet in all companies he
would openly profess it. When Supputius in Pontanus [4] had
travelled all over Europe to confer with a wise man, he returned
at last without his errand, and could find none. Cardan
concurs with him: "Few there are (for aught I can perceive)
well in their wits." [5] So doth Tully: "I see everything to be
done foolishly and unadvisedly." [6]

> *Ille sinistrorsum, hic dextrorsum, unus utrique
> Error, sed variis illudit partibus omnes.*

> One reels to this, another to that wall ;
> 'Tis the same error that deludes them all.

They dote all, but not alike, Μανία γὰρ οὐ πᾶσιν ὁμοία, not in the
same kind. "One is covetous, a second lascivious, a third
ambitious, a fourth envious, etc.," [7] as Damasippus the Stoic
hath well illustrated in the poet:

> *Desipiunt omnes æque ac tu.* [8]

> [And they who call you fool, with equal claim
> May plead an ample title to the name.]

'Tis an inbred malady in every one of us, there is *seminarium
stultitiæ,* a seminary of folly, "which, if it be stirred up, or get
ahead, will run *in infinitum,* and infinitely varies, as we ourselves
are severally addicted," saith Balthasar Castilio: [9] and cannot
so easily be rooted out, it takes such fast hold, as Tully holds

altæ radices stultitiæ [deep are the roots of folly], so we are bred, and so we continue.[1] Some say there be two main defects of wit, error and ignorance, to which all others are reduced; by ignorance we know not things necessary, by error we know them falsely. Ignorance is a privation, error a positive act. From ignorance comes vice, from error heresy, etc. But make how many kinds you will, divide and subdivide, few men are free, or that do not impinge on some one kind or other. *Sic plerumque agitat stultos inscitia* [2] [so are the foolish commonly a prey to ignorance], as he that examines his own and other men's actions shall find.

Charon in Lucian,[3] as he wittily feigns, was conducted by Mercury to such a place, where he might see all the world at once; after he had sufficiently viewed, and looked about, Mercury would needs know of him what he had observed. He told him that he saw a vast multitude and a promiscuous, their habitations like molehills, the men as emmets, "he could discern cities like so many hives of bees, wherein every bee had a sting, and they did naught else but sting one another, some domineering like hornets bigger than the rest, some like filching wasps, others as drones." Over their heads were hovering a confused company of perturbations, hope, fear, anger, avarice, ignorance, etc., and a multitude of diseases hanging, which they still pulled on their pates. Some were brawling, some fighting, riding, running, *sollicite ambientes, callide litigantes* [earnestly suing or cunningly disputing], for toys and trifles, and such momentany things; their towns and provinces mere factions, rich against poor, poor against rich, nobles against artificers, they against nobles, and so the rest. In conclusion, he condemned them all for madmen, fools, idiots, asses, *O stulti, quænam hæc est amentia?* O fools, O madmen! he exclaims, *insana studia, insani labores*, etc., mad endeavours, mad actions, mad, mad, mad, *O seclum insipiens et infacetum,*[4] a giddy-headed age. Heraclitus the philosopher, out of a serious meditation of men's lives, fell a-weeping, and with continual tears bewailed their misery, madness, and folly. Democritus, on the other side, burst out a-laughing, their whole life seemed to him so ridiculous, and he was so far carried with this ironical passion, that the citizens of Abdera took him to be mad, and sent therefore ambassadors to Hippocrates the physician, that he would exercise his skill upon him. But the story is set down at large by Hippocrates, in his Epistle to Damagetus, which, because it is not impertinent to this discourse, I will insert verbatim almost as it is delivered by Hippocrates himself, with all the circumstances belonging unto it.

When Hippocrates was now come to Abdera, the people of the city came flocking about him, some weeping, some entreating of him that he would do his best. After some little repast, he went to see Democritus, the people following him, whom he found (as before) in his garden in the suburbs all alone, "sitting upon a stone under a plane tree, without hose or shoes, with a book on his knees, cutting up several beasts, and busy at his study." [1] The multitude stood gazing round about to see the congress. Hippocrates, after a little pause, saluted him by his name, whom he resaluted, ashamed almost that he could not call him likewise by his, or that he had forgot it. Hippocrates demanded of him what he was doing: he told him that he was "busy in cutting up several beasts, to find out the cause of madness and melancholy." [2] Hippocrates commended his work, admiring his happiness and leisure. "And why," quoth Democritus, "have not you that leisure?" "Because," replied Hippocrates, "domestical affairs hinder, necessary to be done for ourselves, neighbours, friends; expenses, diseases, frailties and mortalities which happen; wife, children, servants, and such businesses which deprive us of our time." At this speech Democritus profusely laughed (his friends and the people standing by, weeping in the meantime, and lamenting his madness). Hippocrates asked the reason why he laughed. He told him, "At the vanities and the fopperies of the time, to see men so empty of all virtuous actions, to hunt so far after gold, having no end of ambition; to take such infinite pains for a little glory, and to be favoured of men; to make such deep mines into the earth for gold, and many times to find nothing, with loss of their lives and fortunes. Some to love dogs, others horses, some to desire to be obeyed in many provinces, and yet themselves will know no obedience.[3] Some to love their wives dearly at first, and after a while to forsake and hate them; [4] begetting children, with much care and cost for their education, yet when they grow to man's estate, to despise, neglect, and leave them naked to the world's mercy.[5] Do not these behaviours express their intolerable folly? [6] When men live in peace, they covet war, detesting quietness, deposing kings, and advancing others in their stead,[7] murdering some men to beget children of their wives. How many strange humours are in men! When they are poor and needy, they seek riches, and when they have them, they do not enjoy them, but hide them underground, or else wastefully spend them. O wise Hippocrates, I laugh at such things being done, but much more when no good comes of them, and when they are done to so ill purpose. There is no truth or justice found amongst them, for they daily plead one against another, the son against the father and the mother, brother against brother, kindred and friends of the same quality; [1] and all this for riches, whereof after death they cannot be possessors. And yet, notwithstanding, they will defame and kill one another, commit all unlawful actions, contemning God and men, friends and country. They make great account of many senseless things, esteeming them as a great part of their treasure, statues, pictures, and such-like movables, dear-bought, and so cunningly wrought, as nothing but speech wanteth in them,[2] and yet they hate living persons speaking to them.[3] Others affect difficult things; if they dwell on firm land they will remove to an island, and thence to land again, being no way constant to their desires. They commend courage and strength in wars, and let themselves be conquered by lust and avarice; they are, in brief, as disordered in their minds as Thersites was in his body. And now, methinks, O most worthy Hippocrates, you should not reprehend my laughing, perceiving so many fooleries in men; for no man will mock his own folly, but that which he seeth in a second, and so they justly mock one another.[4] The drunkard calls him a glutton whom he knows to be sober. Many men love the sea, others husbandry; briefly, they cannot agree in their own trades and professions, much less in their lives and actions."

When Hippocrates heard these words so readily uttered, without premeditation, to declare the world's vanity, full of ridiculous contrariety, he made answer, "That necessity compelled men to many such actions, and divers wills ensuing from divine permission, that we might not be idle, being nothing is so odious to them as sloth and negligence. Besides, men cannot foresee future events, in this uncertainty of human affairs; they would not so marry, if they could foretell the causes of their dislike and separation; or parents, if they knew the hour of their children's death, so tenderly provide for them; or an husband-man sow, if he thought there would be no increase; or a merchant adventure to sea, if he foresaw shipwreck; or be a magistrate, if presently to be deposed. Alas, worthy Democritus, every man hopes the best, and to that end he doth it, and therefore no such cause, or ridiculous occasion, of laughter."

Democritus, hearing this poor excuse, laughed again aloud,

perceiving he wholly mistook him, and did not well understand what he had said concerning perturbations and tranquillity of the mind. "Insomuch that, if men would govern their actions by discretion and providence, they would not declare themselves fools as now they do, and he should have no cause of laughter; but" (quoth he) "they swell in this life as if they were immortal, and demi-gods, for want of understanding. It were enough to make them wise, if they would but consider the mutability of this world, and how it wheels about, nothing being firm and sure. He that is now above, to-morrow is beneath; he that sate on this side to-day, to-morrow is hurled on the other; and not considering these matters, they fall into many inconveniences and troubles, coveting things of no profit and thirsting after them, tumbling headlong into many calamities. So that if men would attempt no more than what they can bear, they should lead contented lives and, learning to know themselves, would limit their ambition;[1] they would perceive then that nature hath enough without seeking such superfluities and unprofitable things, which bring nothing with them but grief and molestation. As a fat body is more subject to diseases, so are rich men to absurdities and fooleries, to many casualties and cross inconveniences. There are many that take no heed what happeneth to others by bad conversation, and therefore overthrow themselves in the same manner through their own fault, not foreseeing dangers manifest. These are things (O more than mad," quoth he) "that give me matter of laughter, by suffering the pains of your impieties, as your avarice, envy, malice, enormous villainies, mutinies, unsatiable desires, conspiracies, and other incurable vices; besides your dissimulation and hypocrisy,[2] bearing deadly hatred one to the other, and yet shadowing it with a good face, flying out into all filthy lusts, and transgressions of all laws, both of nature and civility. Many things which they have left off, after a while they fall to again, husbandry, navigation; and leave again, fickle and unconstant as they are. When they are young, they would be old; and old, young. Princes commend a private life,[3] private men itch after honour; a magistrate commends a quiet life, a quiet man would be in his office, and obeyed as he is: and what is the cause of all this, but that they know not themselves? Some delight to destroy, one to build, another to spoil one country to enrich another and himself.[4] In all these things they are like children,[5] in whom is no judgment or counsel, and resemble beasts, saving that beasts are better than they, as being contented with nature. When shall you see a lion hide gold in the ground, or a bull contend for better pasture?[1] When a boar is thirsty, he drinks what will serve him, and no more; and when his belly is full, ceaseth to eat: but men are immoderate in both; as in lust, they covet carnal copulation at set times, men always, ruinating thereby the health of their bodies. And doth it not deserve laughter to see an amorous fool torment himself for a wench; weep, howl for a misshapen slut, a dowdy sometimes, that might have his choice of the finest beauties? Is there any remedy for this in physic? I do anatomize and cut up these poor beasts,[2] to see these distempers, vanities, and follies, yet such proof were better made on man's body, if my kind nature would endure it: who from the hour of his birth is most miserable, weak, and sickly;[3] when he sucks he is guided by others, when he is grown great practiseth unhappiness and is sturdy, and when old, a child again, and repenteth him of his life past."[4] And here being interrupted by one that brought books, he fell to it again, that all were mad, careless, stupid. "To prove my former speeches, look into courts, or private houses. Judges give judgment according to their own advantage, doing manifest wrong to poor innocents to please others.[5] Notaries alter sentences, and for money lose their deeds. Some make false moneys; others counterfeit false weights. Some abuse their parents, yea, corrupt their own sisters; others make long libels and pasquils, defaming men of good life, and extol such as are lewd and vicious. Some rob one, some another; magistrates make laws against thieves, and are the veriest thieves themselves.[6] Some kill themselves, others despair, not obtaining their desires. Some dance, sing, laugh, feast and banquet, whilst others sigh, languish, mourn and lament, having neither meat, drink, nor clothes. Some prank up their bodies, and have their minds full of execrable vices.[7] Some trot about to bear false witness, and say anything for money;[8] and though judges know of it, yet for a bribe they wink at it, and suffer false contracts to prevail against equity. Women are all day a-dressing, to pleasure other men abroad, and go like sluts at home, not caring to please their own husbands whom they should. Seeing men are so fickle, so sottish, so intemperate, why should not I laugh at those to whom folly seems wisdom, will not be cured, and perceive it not?"[9]

It grew late: Hippocrates left him; and no sooner was he come away, but all the citizens came about flocking, to know how he liked him. He told them in brief, that notwithstanding those small neglects of his attire, body, diet, the world had not a wiser, a more learned, a more honest man, and they were much deceived to say that he was mad.[1]

Thus Democritus esteemed of the world in his time, and this was the cause of his laughter: and good cause he had.

> *Olim jure quidem, nunc plus, Democrite, ride;*
> *Quin rides ? vita hæc nunc mage ridicula est.*[2]

> Democritus did well to laugh of old,
> Good cause he had, but now much more ;
> This life of ours is more ridiculous
> Than that of his, or long before.

Never so much cause of laughter as now, never so many fools and madmen. 'Tis not one Democritus will serve turn to laugh in these days; we have now need of a "Democritus to laugh at Democritus";[3] one jester to flout at another, one fool to fleer at another: a great stentorian Democritus, as big as that Rhodian Colossus. For now, as Sarisburiensis said in his time,[4] *totus mundus histrionem agit*, the whole world plays the fool; we have a new theatre, a new scene, a new Comedy of Errors, a new company of personate actors; *Volupiæ sacra* [the rites of the goddess of pleasure] (as Calcaginus willingly feigns in his Apologues) are celebrated all the world over, where all the actors were madmen and fools, and every hour changed habits, or took that which came next.[5] He that was a mariner to-day, is an apothecary to-morrow; a smith one while, a philosopher another, *in his Volupiæ ludis* [in these fêtes of the goddess of pleasure]; a king now with his crown, robes, sceptre, attendants, by and by drove a loaded ass before him like a carter, etc. If Democritus were alive now, he should see strange alterations, a new company of counterfeit vizards, whifflers, Cuman asses, maskers, mummers, painted puppets, outsides, fantastic shadows, gulls, monsters, giddy-heads, butterflies. And so many of them are indeed (if all be true that I have read[6]). For when Jupiter and Juno's wedding was solemnized of old, the gods were all invited to the feast, and many noble men besides. Amongst the rest came Chrysalus, a Persian prince, bravely attended, rich in golden attires, in gay robes, with a majestical presence, but otherwise an ass. The gods, seeing him come in such pomp and state, rose up to give him place, *ex habitu hominem metientes* [measuring the man by his garb]; but Jupiter, perceiving what he was, a light, fantastic, idle fellow, turned him and his proud followers into butterflies: [1] and so they continue still (for aught I know to the contrary) roving about in pied coats, and are called chrysalides by the wiser sort of men: that is, golden outsides, drones, flies, and things of no worth. Multitudes of such, etc.

Ubique invenies
Stultos avaros, sycophantas prodigos.

[You will find everywhere miserly fools and spendthrift sycophants.]

Many additions, much increase of madness, folly, vanity, should Democritus observe, were he now to travel, or could get leave of Pluto to come see fashions, as Charon did in Lucian, to visit our cities of Moronia Pia and Moronia Felix: [2] sure I think he would break the rim of his belly with laughing. *Si foret in terris rideret Democritus* [were Democritus alive, how would he laugh!], *seu*,[3] etc.

A satirical Roman in his time thought all vice, folly, and madness were all at full sea, *Omne in præcipiti vitium stetit*[4] [every vice was in headlong career].

Josephus the historian taxeth his countrymen Jews for bragging of their vices, publishing their follies, and that they did contend amongst themselves who should be most notorious in villainies; [5] but we flow higher in madness, far beyond them,

Mox daturi progeniem vitiosiorem,[6]

[And yet with crimes to us unknown,
Our sons shall mark the coming age their own,]

and the latter end (you know whose oracle it is) is like to be worst. 'Tis not to be denied, the world alters every day; *Ruunt urbes, regna transferuntur* [cities fall, kingdoms are transferred], etc., *variantur habitus, leges innovantur* [fashions change, laws are altered], as Petrarch observes,[7] we change language, habits, laws, customs, manners, but not vices, not diseases, not the symptoms of folly and madness, they are still the same. And as a river, we see, keeps the like name and place, but not water, and yet ever runs, *Labitur et labetur in omne volubilis ævum*;[8] our times and persons alter, vices are the same, and ever will be; look how nightingales sang of old, cocks crowed, kine lowed, sheep bleated, sparrows chirped, dogs barked, so they do still; we keep our madness still, play the fools still, *nec dum finitus Orestes* [and the play is not yet finished]; we are of the same humours and inclinations as our predecessors were; you shall find us all alike, much at one, we and our sons, *Et nati natorum, et qui nascuntur ab illis*, and so shall our posterity continue to the last. But to speak of times present.

If Democritus were alive now, and should but see the superstition of our age, our religious madness,[1] as Meteran calls it, *religiosam insaniam*,[2] so many professed Christians, yet so few imitators of Christ; so much talk of religion, so much science, so little conscience; so much knowledge, so many preachers, so little practice; such variety of sects, such have and hold of all sides, *obvia signis Signa*[3] [standards ranged against standards], etc., such absurd and ridiculous traditions and ceremonies; if he should meet a Capuchin,[4] a Franciscan, a pharisaical Jesuit, a man-serpent, a shave-crowned monk in his robes, a begging friar, or see their three-crowned Sovereign Lord the Pope, poor Peter's successor, *servus servorum Dei* [the servant of the servants of God], to depose kings with his foot, to tread on emperors' necks, make them stand barefoot and bare-legged at his gates, hold his bridle and stirrup, etc. (O that Peter and Paul were alive to see this!); if he should observe a prince creep so devoutly to kiss his toe,[5] and those red-cap cardinals, poor parish priests of old, now princes' companions; what would he say? *Cælum ipsum petitur stultitia* [folly seeks entrance to heaven itself]. Had he met some of our devout pilgrims going barefoot to Jerusalem, our Lady of Loretto, Rome, St. Iago, St. Thomas' Shrine, to creep to those counterfeit and maggot-eaten relics; had he been present at a Mass, and seen such kissing of paxes, crucifixes, cringes, duckings, their several attires and ceremonies, pictures of saints, indulgences, pardons, vigils, fasting, feasts, crossing, knocking, kneeling at Ave-Maries, bells, with many such,[6] *jucunda rudi spectacula plebi* [fine spectacles to please the mob], praying in gibberish, and mumbling of beads. Had he heard an old woman say her prayers in Latin, their sprinkling of holy water, and going a procession:

Incedunt monachorum agmina mille;
Quid memorem vexilla, cruces, idolaque culta, etc.;[7]

[Monks in thousands marching along, with banners, crosses, images, and so forth;]

their breviaries, bulls, hallowed beans, exorcisms, pictures, curious crosses, fables and bables; had he read the Golden Legend, the Turks' Alcoran, or Jews' Talmud, the Rabbins' Comments, what would he have thought? How dost thou think he might have been affected? Had he more particularly examined a Jesuit's life amongst the rest, he should have seen an hypocrite profess poverty, and yet possess more goods and lands than many princes, to have infinite treasures and revenues;[1] teach others to fast, and play the gluttons themselves; like watermen, that row one way and look another. Vow virginity, talk of holiness, and yet indeed a notorious bawd, and famous fornicator, *lascivum pecus* [a wanton creature], a very goat.[2] Monks by profession,[3] such as give over the world, and the vanities of it, and yet a Machiavellian rout interested in all matters of state:[4] holy men, peace-makers, and yet composed of envy, lust, ambition, hatred, and malice; firebrands, *adulta patriæ pestis* [a full-grown scourge of their country], traitors, assassinates, *hac itur ad astra* [in this way heaven is won], and this is to supererogate, and merit heaven for themselves and others. Had he seen, on the adverse side, some of our nice and curious schismatics in another extreme abhor all ceremonies, and rather lose their lives and livings than do or admit anything papists have formerly used, though in things indifferent (they alone are the true Church, *sal terræ*, *cum sint omnium insulsissimi* [the salt of the earth, though they are of all people the most insipid]); formalists, out of fear and base flattery, like so many weather-cocks turn round, a rout of temporizers, ready to embrace and maintain all that is or shall be proposed in hope of preferment; another Epicurean company, lying at lurch as so many vultures, watching for a prey of Church goods, and ready to rise by the downfall of any: as Lucian said in like case, what dost thou think Democritus would have done, had he been spectator of these things?[5]

Or had he but observed the common people follow like so many sheep one of their fellows drawn by the horns over a gap, some for zeal, some for fear, *quo se cunque rapit tempestas* [wherever they are whirled along], to credit all, examine nothing, and yet ready to die before they will abjure any of those ceremonies to which they have been accustomed; others out of hypocrisy frequent sermons, knock their breasts, turn up their eyes, pretend zeal, desire reformation, and yet professed usurers, gripers, monsters of men, harpies, devils in their lives, to express nothing less.

What would he have said to see, hear, and read so many bloody battles, so many thousands slain at once, such streams of blood able to turn mills, *unius ob noxam furiasque* [through the mad guilt of one person], or to make sport for princes, without any just cause, "for vain titles" (saith Austin), "precedency, some wench, or such-like toy, or out of desire of domineering, vainglory, malice, revenge, folly, madness," [1] (goodly causes all, *ob quas universus orbis bellis et cædibus misceatur* [for plunging the whole world into an orgy of war and slaughter]), whilst statesmen themselves in the meantime are secure at home, pampered with all delights and pleasures, take their ease, and follow their lusts, not considering what intolerable misery poor soldiers endure, their often wounds, hunger, thirst, etc., the lamentable cares, torments, calamities, and oppressions that accompany such proceedings, they feel not, take no notice of it. "So wars are begun, by the persuasion of a few deboshed, hair-brain, poor, dissolute, hungry captains, parasitical fawners, unquiet Hotspurs, restless innovators, green heads, to satisfy one man's private spleen, lust, ambition, avarice, etc."; *tales rapiunt scelerata in prælia causæ* [such causes bring on war with all its crimes]. *Flos hominum* [the flower of mankind], proper men, well proportioned, carefully brought up, able both in body and mind, sound, led like so many beasts to the slaughter in the flower of their years, pride, and full strength, without all remorse and pity, sacrificed to Pluto, killed up as so many sheep, for devils' food, 40,000 at once.[2] At once, said I, that were tolerable, but these wars last always, and for ages; nothing so familiar as this hacking and hewing, massacres, murders, desolations; *ignoto cœlum clangore remugit* [the skies re-echo the unwonted noise], they care not what mischief they procure, so that they may enrich themselves for the present; they will so long blow the coals of contention, till all the world be consumed with fire. The siege of Troy lasted ten years, eight months; there died 870,000 Grecians, 670,000 Trojans at the taking of the city, and after were slain 276,000 men, women, and children of all sorts.[3] Cæsar killed a million, Mahomet the second Turk 300,000 persons;[4] Sicinius Dentatus fought in an hundred battles, eight times in single combat he overcame, had forty wounds before, was rewarded with 140 crowns, triumphed nine times for his good service. M. Sergius had 32 wounds; Scæva, the centurion, I know not how many; every nation had their Hectors, Scipios, Cæsars, and Alexanders. Our Edward the Fourth was in 26 battles afoot:[5] and as they do all, he glories in it, 'tis related to his honour. At the siege of Hierusalem, 1,100,000 died with sword and famine. At the battle of Cannæ, 70,000 men were slain, as Polybius records,[6] and as many at Battle Abbey with us; and 'tis no news to fight from sun to sun, as they did, as Constantine and Licinius, etc. At the siege of Ostend (the devil's academy), a poor town in respect, a small fort, but a great grave, 120,000 men lost their lives, besides whole towns, dorps, and hospitals, full of maimed soldiers; there were engines, fireworks, and what-soever the devil could invent to do mischief with 2,500,000 iron bullets shot of 40 pound weight, three or four millions of gold consumed. "Who" (saith mine author) "can be sufficiently amazed at their flinty hearts, obstinacy, fury, blindness, who, without any likelihood of good success, hazard poor soldiers, and lead them without pity to the slaughter, which may justly be called the rage of furious beasts, that run without reason upon their own deaths?" [1] *quis malus genius, quæ furia, quæ pestis,* etc., [2] what plague, what fury brought so devilish, so brutish a thing as war first into men's minds? Who made so soft and peaceable a creature, born to love, mercy, meekness, so to rave, rage like beasts, and run on to their own destruction? How may Nature expostulate with mankind, *Ego te divinum animal finxi,* etc., I made thee an harmless, quiet, a divine creature! how may God expostulate, and all good men! yet, *horum facta* (as one condoles [3]) *tantum admirantur, et heroum numero habent* [these alone are admired for their deeds and counted as heroes]: these are the brave spirits, the gallants of the world, these admired alone, triumph alone, have statues, crowns, pyramids, obelisks to their eternal fame, that immortal genius attends on them, *hac itur ad astra.* When Rhodes was besieged, *fossæ urbis cadaveribus repletæ sunt,* [4] the ditches were full of dead carcasses: and as when the said Solyman, Great Turk, beleaguered Vienna, they lay level with the top of the walls. This they make a sport of, and will do it to their friends and confederates, against oaths, vows, promises, by treachery or otherwise; *dolus an virtus? quis in hoste requirat?* [5] [guile or valour? against an enemy, 'tis all one], leagues and laws of arms (*silent leges inter arma* [6] [amid the clash of arms the law is mute]), for their advantage, *omnia jura, divina, humana, proculcata plerumque sunt,* God's and men's laws are trampled underfoot, the sword alone determines all; to satisfy their lust and spleen, they care not what they attempt, say, or do, *Rara fides probitasque viris qui castra sequuntur* [7] ['tis rare to find faith or honour among those who go to war]. Nothing so common as to have "father fight against the son, brother against brother, kinsman against kinsman, kingdom against kingdom, province against province, Christians against Christians": [8] *a quibus nec unquam cogitatione fuerunt læsi,* of whom they never had offence in thought, word, or deed. Infinite treasures consumed, towns burned, flourishing cities sacked and ruinated, *quodque animus meminisse horret* [and what the mind shudders to remember], goodly countries depopulated and left desolate, old inhabitants expelled, trade and traffic decayed, maids deflowered, *Virgines nondum thalamis jugatæ, Et comis nondum positis ephebi* [maidens not yet married and youths not yet come to man's estate]; chaste matrons cry out with Andromache, *Concubitum mox cogar pati ejus, qui interemit Hectorem*,[1] they shall be compelled peradventure to lie with them that erst killed their husbands: to see rich, poor, sick, sound, lords, servants, *eodem omnes incommodo macti*, consumed all or maimed, etc., *et quicquid gaudens scelere animus audet, et perversa mens* [and whatever a criminal mind and perverted disposition can prompt], saith Cyprian, and whatsoever torment, misery, mischief, hell itself, the devil, fury and rage can invent to their own ruin and destruction;[2] so abominable a thing is war, as Gerbelius concludes, *adeo fœda et abominanda res est bellum, ex quo hominum cædes, vastationes*,[3] etc., the scourge of God, cause, effect, fruit, and punishment of sin, and not *tonsura humani generis* [the mere pruning of the human race], as Tertullian calls it, but *ruina* [its destruction]. Had Democritus been present at the late civil wars in France, those abominable wars— *bellaque matribus detestata* [wars, of mothers loathed]—"where, in less than ten years, ten thousand men were consumed," saith Collignius, twenty thousand churches overthrown;[4] nay, the whole kingdom subverted (as Richard Dinoth adds[5]): so many myriads of the commons were butchered up, with sword, famine, war, *tanto odio utrinque ut barbari ad abhorrendam lanienam obstupescerent*, with such feral hatred, the world was amazed at it: or at our late Pharsalian fields, in the time of Henry the Sixth, between the Houses of Lancaster and York, an hundred thousand men slain, one writes;[6] another, ten thousand families were rooted out,[7] "that no man can but marvel," saith Comineus,"at that barbarous immanity,feral madness,committed betwixt men of the same nation, language, and religion." *Quis furor, O cives?*[8] "Why do the Gentiles so furiously rage?" saith the Prophet David (Ps. ii, 1). But we may ask, why do the Christians so furiously rage? *Arma volunt, quare poscunt, rapiuntque juventus?*[9] [Why do the youth call for war and rush to arms?] Unfit for Gentiles, much less for us so to tyrannize, as the Spaniards in the West Indies, that killed up in forty-two years (if we may believe Bartholomæus à Casa,[10] their own bishop) twelve millions of men, with stupend and exquisite torments; neither should I lie (said he) if I said fifty millions. I omit those French massacres, Sicilian Evensongs, the Duke of Alva's tyrannies,[1] our gunpowder machinations, and that fourth fury, as one calls it,[2] the Spanish Inquisition, which quite obscures those ten persecutions; *sævit toto Mars impius orbe*[3] [the ruthless rage of war spreads o'er the world]. Is not this *mundus furiosus*, a mad world, as he terms it,[4] *insanum bellum*? are not these madmen, as Scaliger concludes, *qui in prælio acerba morte, insaniæ suæ memoriam pro perpetuo teste relinquunt posteritati*,[5] which leave so frequent battles as perpetual memorials of their madness to all succeeding ages? Would this, think you, have enforced our Democritus to laughter, or rather made him turn his tune, alter his tone, and weep with Heraclitus,[6] or rather howl, roar, and tear his hair in commiseration, stand amazed;[7] or as the poets feign, that Niobe was for grief quite stupefied, and turned to a stone? I have not yet said the worst, that which is more absurd and mad, in their tumults, seditions, civil and unjust wars,[8] *quod stulte suscipitur, impie geritur, misere finitur*[9] [begun in folly, continued in crime, and ended in misery]. Such wars I mean; for all are not to be condemned, as those phantastical anabaptists vainly conceive. Our Christian tactics are all out as necessary as the Roman *acies*, or Grecian phalanx; to be a soldier is a most noble and honourable profession (as the world is), not to be spared, they are our best walls and bulwarks, and I do therefore acknowledge that of Tully to be most true,[10] "All our civil affairs, all our studies, all our pleading, industry, and commendation, lies under the protection of warlike virtues, and whensoever there is any suspicion of tumult, all our arts cease." Wars are most behoveful, and *bellatores agricolis civitati sunt utiliores* [fighting men are more useful to the State than husbandmen] as Tyrius defends:[11] and valour is much to be commended in a wise man; but they mistake most part, *auferre, trucidare, rapere, falsis nominibus virtutem vocant*, etc. ('twas Galgacus' observation in Tacitus), they term theft, murder, and rapine, virtue, by a wrong name; rapes, slaughters, massacres, etc., *jocus et ludus*, are pretty pastimes, as Ludovicus Vives notes. "They commonly call the most hair-brain bloodsuckers, strongest thieves, the most desperate villains, treacherous rogues, inhuman murderers, rash, cruel and dissolute caitiffs, courageous and generous spirits, heroical and worthy captains, brave men-at-arms,[12] valiant and renowned soldiers, possessed with a brute persuasion of false honour," [1] as Pontus Heuter in his Burgundian History complains. By means of which it comes to pass that daily so many voluntaries offer themselves, leaving their sweet wives, children, friends, for sixpence (if they can get it) a day, prostitute their lives and limbs, desire to enter upon breaches, lie sentinel, perdu, give the first onset, stand in the fore-front of the battle, marching bravely on, with a cheerful noise of drums and trumpets, such vigour and alacrity, so many banners streaming in the air, glittering armours, motions of plumes, woods of pikes and swords, variety of colours, cost and magnificence, as if they went in triumph, now victors to the Capitol, and with such pomp as when Darius' army marched to meet Alexander at Issus. Void of all fear, they run into imminent dangers, cannon's mouth, etc., *ut vulneribus suis ferrum hostium hebetent* [to blunt the enemy's sword on their own flesh], saith Barletius,[2] to get a name of valour, honour and applause, which lasts not neither, for it is but a mere flash this fame, and like a rose, *intra diem unum extinguitur*, 'tis gone in an instant. Of fifteen thousand proletaries slain in a battle, scarce fifteen are recorded in history, or one alone, the general perhaps, and after a while his and their names are likewise blotted out, the whole battle itself is forgotten. Those Grecian orators, *summa vi ingenii et eloquentiæ* [with great genius and eloquence], set out the renowned overthrows at Thermopylæ, Salamis, Marathon, Mycale, Mantinea, Chæronæa, Platæa. The Romans record their battle at Cannæ, and Pharsalian Fields, but they do but record, and we scarce hear of them. And yet this supposed honour, popular applause, desire of immortality by this means, pride and vainglory spurs them on many times rashly and unadvisedly, to make away themselves and multitudes of others. Alexander was sorry because there were no more worlds for him to conquer; he is admired by some for it, *animosa vox videtur, et regia*, 'twas spoken like a prince; but as wise Seneca censures him,[3] 'twas *vox inquissima et stultissima*, 'twas spoken like a bedlam fool; and that sentence which the same Seneca appropriates to his father Philip and him, I apply to them all, *non minores fuere pestes mortalium quam inundatio, quam conflagratio, quibus*,[4] etc., they did as much mischief to mortal men as fire and water, those merciless elements, when they rage. Which is yet more to be lamented, they persuade them this hellish course of life is holy, they promise heaven to such as venture their lives *bello sacro* [in a sacred war], and that by these bloody wars, as Persians,[5] Greeks, and Romans of old, as modern Turks do now their commons, to encourage them to fight, *ut cadant infeliciter* [1] [to die miserably (? *feliciter*, "happily")], "if they die in the field, they go directly to heaven, and shall be canonized for saints" (O diabolical invention!), put in the chronicles, *in perpetuam rei memoriam*, to their eternal memory: whenas in truth, as some hold, it were much better (since wars are the scourge of God for sin, by which he punisheth mortal men's peevishness and folly) such brutish stories were suppressed, because *ad morum institutionem nihil habent*, they conduce not at all to manners, or good life.[2] But they will have it thus nevertheless, and so they "put a note of divinity upon the most cruel and pernicious plague of humankind,"[3] adore such men with grand titles, degrees, statues, images, honour, applaud, and highly reward them for their good service, no greater glory than to die in the field.[4] So Africanus is extolled by Ennius; Mars, and Hercules,[5] and I know not how many besides of old, were deified, went this way to heaven, that were indeed bloody butchers, wicked destroyers, and troublers of the world, prodigious monsters, hell-hounds, feral plagues, devourers, common executioners of humankind, as Lactantius truly proves, and Cyprian to Donatus, such as were desperate in wars, and precipitately made away themselves (like those Celts in Damascene, with ridiculous valour, *ut dedecorosum putarent muro ruenti se subducere*, [so that they thought it] a disgrace to run away for a rotten wall, now ready to fall on their heads), such as will not rush on a sword's point, or seek to shun a cannon's shot, are base cowards, and no valiant men. By which means, *madet orbis mutuo sanguine*, the earth wallows in her own blood, *sævit amor ferri et scelerati insania belli* [6] [a mad lust for war with all its horrors is rampant], and for that which, if it be done in private, a man shall be rigorously executed, "and which is no less than murder itself; if the same fact be done in public in wars, it is called manhood, and the party is honoured for it."[7] *Prosperum et felix scelus virtus vocatur* [8] [vice, when successful, is called virtue]. We measure all as Turks do, by the event, and most part, as Cyprian notes, in all ages, countries, places, *sævitiæ magnitudo impunitatem sceleris acquirit*, the foulness of the fact vindicates the offender. One is crowned for that for which another is tormented: *Ille crucem sceleris pretium tulit, hic diadema;* [9] made a knight, a lord, an earl, a great duke (as Agrippa notes [10]) for which another should have hung in gibbets, as a terror to the rest:

et tamen alter,
Si fecisset idem, caderet sub judice morum.[1]

[Had another done the same, he would have been brought up
before the censor.]

A poor sheep-stealer is hanged for stealing of victuals, compelled
peradventure by necessity of that intolerable cold, hunger, and
thirst, to save himself from starving: but a great man in office
may securely rob whole provinces,[2] undo thousands, pill and
poll, oppress *ad libitum,* flay, grind, tyrannize, enrich himself by
spoils of the commons, be uncontrollable in his actions, and
after all, be recompensed with turgent titles, honoured for his
good service, and no man dare find fault, or mutter at it.[3]

How would our Democritus have been affected to see a wicked
caitiff, or "fool, a very idiot, a funge, a golden ass, a monster of
men, to have many good men, wise men, learned men to attend
upon him with all submission, as an appendix to his riches,
for that respect alone, because he hath more wealth and money,
and to honour him with divine titles and bombast epithets,"
to smother him with fumes and eulogies, whom they know to be a
dizzard, a fool, a covetous wretch, a beast, etc., "because he is
rich"![5]   To see *sub exuviis leonis onagrum* [an ass in a lion's skin]
a filthy loathsome carcass, a Gorgon's head puffed up by parasites, assume this unto himself, glorious titles, in worth an
infant, a Cuman ass, a painted sepulchre, an Egyptian temple.
To see a withered face, a diseased, deformed, cankered complexion, a rotten carcass, a viperous mind and Epicurean soul
set out with orient pearls, jewels, diadems, perfumes, curious
elaborate works, as proud of his clothes as a child of his new
coats; and a goodly person, of an angelic divine countenance,
a saint, an humble mind, a meek spirit, clothed in rags, beg, and
now ready to be starved!   To see a silly contemptible slovem
in apparel, ragged in his coat, polite in speech, of a divine
spirit, wise; another neat in clothes, spruce, full of courtesy,
empty of grace, wit, talk nonsense!

To see so many lawyers, advocates, so many tribunals, so
little justice; so many magistrates, so little care of common
good; so many laws, yet never more disorders; *tribunal litium
segetem* [the court a crop of lawsuits], the tribunal a labyrinth, so many thousand suits in one court sometimes, so
violently followed!   To see *injustissimum sæpe juri præsiden-
tem, impium religioni, imperitissimum eruditioni, otiosissimum
labori, monstrosum humanitati* [the greatest wrongdoer often
administering justice, the most impious in charge of religion,

the most ignorant presiding over learning, the most idle over
employment, and the most heartless over the distribution of
charity]! To see a lamb executed, a wolf pronounce sentence,[1]
latro [a robber] arraigned, and *fur* [a thief] sit on the bench,
the judge severely punish others, and do worse himself, *eundem
furtum facere et punire,*[2] *rapinam plectere, quum sit ipse raptor*[3]
[the same man commit the theft and punish it, punish robbery
and be himself a robber]! Laws altered, misconstrued, inter-
preted pro and con, as the judge is made by friends, bribed, or
otherwise affected as a nose of wax, good to-day, none to-
to-morrow;[4] or firm in his opinion, cast in his! Sentence prolonged, changed, *ad arbitrium judicis* [at the pleasure of the
judge], still the same case, "one thrust out of his inheritance,
another falsely put in by favour, false deeds or wills."[5] *Incisæ
leges negliguntur*, laws are made and not kept; or if put in execution, they be some silly ones that are punished.[6] As put case
it be fornication, the father will disinherit or abdicate his child,
quite cashier him (Out, villain, begone, come no more in my
sight); a poor man is miserably tormented with loss of his
estate perhaps, goods, fortunes, good name, for ever disgraced,
forsaken, and must do penance to the utmost; a mortal sin, and
yet, make the worst of it, *Numquid aliud fecit*, saith Tranio in the
poet,[7] *nisi quod faciunt summis nati generibus ?* he hath done
no more than what gentlemen usually do. *Neque novum, neque
mirum, neque secus quam alii solent*[8] ['tis neither new nor
strange nor different from what others do]. For in a great
person, right worshipful sir, a right honourable grandee, 'tis
not a venial sin, no, not a peccadillo, 'tis no offence at all, a
common and ordinary thing, no man takes notice of it; he
justifies it in public, and peradventure brags of it,

> *Nam quod turpe bonis, Titio, Seioque, decebat
> Crispinum.*[9]

[For what would be base in good men, Titius, and Seius,
became Crispinus.]

Many poor men, younger brothers, etc., by reason of bad policy
and idle education (for they are likely brought up in no calling),
are compelled to beg or steal, and then hanged for theft;[10]
than which what can be more ignominious? *non minus enim
turpe principi multa supplicia, quam medico multa funera* [a
prince is no less discredited by frequent sentences on his subjects than a doctor by frequent deaths among his patients],
'tis the governor's fault; *libentius verberant quam docent*, as

schoolmasters do, rather correct their pupils than teach them when they do amiss. "They had more need provide there should be no more thieves and beggars, as they ought with good policy, and take away the occasions, than let them run on as they do to their own destruction":[1] root out likewise those causes of wrangling, a multitude of lawyers, and compose controversies, *lites lustrales et seculares* [age-long lawsuits], by some more compendious means. Whereas now for every toy and trifle they go to law, *mugit litibus insanum forum, et sævit invicem discordantium rabies*[2] [the courts are a bedlam, and the fury of litigants knows no bounds], they are ready to pull out one another's throats; and for commodity "to squeeze blood," saith Hierome, "out of their brother's heart,"[3] defame, lie, disgrace, backbite, rail, bear false witness, swear, forswear, fight and wrangle, spend their goods, lives, fortunes, friends, undo one another, to enrich an harpy advocate, that preys upon them both, and cries *Eia Socrates! eia Xanthippe!*[4] or some corrupt judge, that like the kite in Æsop, while the mouse and frog fought, carried both away.[5] Generally they prey one upon another as so many ravenous birds, brute beasts, devouring fishes, no medium, *omnes hic aut captantur aut captant; aut cadavera quæ lacerantur, aut corvi qui lacerant,*[6] either deceive or be deceived; tear others or be torn in pieces themselves; like so many buckets in a well, as one riseth another falleth, one's empty, another's full; his ruin is a ladder to the third; such are our ordinary proceedings. What's the market? A place, according to Anacharsis, wherein they cozen one another, a trap; nay, what's the world itself? A vast chaos, a confusion of manners, as fickle as the air, *domicilium insanorum* [a madhouse], a turbulent troop full of impurities, a mart of walking spirits, goblins, the theatre of hypocrisy, a shop of knavery, flattery, a nursery of villainy, the scene of babbling, the school of giddiness, the academy of vice;[8] a warfare, *ubi velis noli. pugnandum, aut vincas aut succumbas* [where you have to fight whether you will or no, and either conquer or go under], in which kill or be killed; wherein every man is for himself, his private ends, and stands upon his own guard. No charity, love, friendship, fear of God, alliance, affinity, consanguinity, Christianity, can contain them, but if they be anyway offended, or that string of commodity be touched, they fall foul.[9] Old friends become bitter enemies on a sudden for toys and small offences, and they that erst were willing to do all mutual offices of love and kindness, now revile and persecute one another to death, with more than Vatinian hatred, and will not be reconciled. So long as they are behoveful, they love, or may bestead each other, but when there is no more good to be expected, as they do by an old dog, hang him up or cashier him: which Cato[1] counts a great indecorum, to use men like old shoes or broken glasses, which are flung to the dunghill; he could not find in his heart to sell an old ox, much less to turn away an old servant: but they, instead of recompense, revile him, and when they have made him an instrument of their villainy, as Bajazet the Second, Emperor of the Turks, did by Acomethes Bassa,[2] make him away, or instead of reward, hate him to death, as Silius was served by Tiberius.[3] In a word, every man for his own ends. Our *summum bonum* is commodity, and the goddess we adore *Dea Moneta*, Queen Money, to whom we daily offer sacrifice, which steers our hearts, hands, affections, all:[4] that most powerful goddess, by whom we are reared, depressed, elevated, esteemed the sole commandress of our actions,[5] for which we pray, run, ride, go, come, labour, and contend as fishes do for a crumb that falleth into the water. It is not worth, virtue (that's *bonum theatrale* [a theatrical good]), wisdom, valour, learning, honesty, religion, or any sufficiency for which we are respected, but money, greatness, office, honour, authority;[6] honesty is accounted folly; knavery, policy; men admired out of opinion,[7] not as they are, but as they seem to be: such shifting, lying, cogging, plotting, counterplotting, temporizing, flattering, cozening, dissembling, "that of necessity one must highly offend God if he be conformable to the world," *Cretizare cum Crete* [to do at Crete as the Cretans do], "or else live in contempt, disgrace, and misery."[8] One takes upon him temperance, holiness, another austerity, a third an affected kind of simplicity, whenas indeed he, and he, and he, and the rest are hypocrites, ambidexters,[9] outsides, so many turning pictures, a lion on the one side, a lamb on the other.[10] How would Democritus have been affected to see these things!

To see a man turn himself into all shapes like a chameleon, or as Proteus, *omnia transformans sese in miracula rerum* [who transformed himself into every possible shape], to act twenty parts and persons at once for his advantage, to temporize and vary like Mercury the planet, good with good, bad with bad; having a several face, garb, and character for every one he meets; of all religions, humours, inclinations; to fawn like a spaniel, *mentitis et mimicis obsequiis* [with feigned and hypocritical observance], rage like a lion, bark like a cur, fight like a dragon, sting like a serpent, as meek as a lamb, and yet again grin like a tiger, weep like a crocodile, insult over some, and yet others domineer over him, here command, there crouch, tyrannize in one place, be baffled in another, a wise man at home, a fool abroad to make others merry.

To see so much difference betwixt words and deeds, so many parasangs betwixt tongue and heart, men like stage-players act variety of parts, give good precepts to others, [to] soar aloft, whilst they themselves grovel on the ground.[1]

To see a man protest friendship, kiss his hand, *quem mallet truncatum videre* [2] [whom he would like to see decapitated], smile with an intent to do mischief, or cozen him whom he salutes,[3] magnify his friend unworthy with hyperbolical elogiums; his enemy, albeit a good man, to vilify and disgrace him, yea, all his actions, with the utmost livor and malice can invent.[4]

To see a servant able to buy out his master, him that carries the mace more worth than the magistrate,[5] which Plato, *lib.* ii *de leg.*, absolutely forbids, Epictetus abhors. An horse that tills the land fed with chaff, an idle jade have provender in abundance;[6] him that makes shoes go barefoot himself, him that sells meat almost pined; a toiling drudge starve, a drone flourish.

To see men buy smoke for wares, castles built with fools' heads, men like apes follow the fashions in tires, gestures, actions: if the king laugh, all laugh:

> *Rides? majore cachinno*
> *Concutitur, flet si lacrimas conspexit amici.*[7]

[Should you smile, a heartier laughter shakes his sides;
he sees you weep, and tears drop from his eyes.]

Alexander stooped, so did his courtiers;[8] Alphonsus turned his head, and so did his parasites. Sabina Poppæa, Nero's wife wore amber-coloured hair, so did all the Roman ladies in an instant, her fashion was theirs.[9]

To see men wholly led by affection, admired and censured out of opinion without judgment: an inconsiderate multitude, like so many dogs in a village, if one bark, all bark without a cause as fortune's fan turns, if a man be in favour, or commended by some great one, all the world applauds him; if in disgrace in an instant all hate him,[10] and as at the sun when he is eclipsed that erst took no notice, now gaze and stare upon him.

To see a man wear his brains in his belly,[1] his guts in his head, an hundred oaks on his back, to devour an hundred oxen at a meal, nay more, to devour houses and towns, or as those Anthropophagi, to eat one another.[2]

To see a man roll himself up like a snowball, from base beggary to right worshipful and right honourable titles, unjustly to screw himself into honours and offices; another to starve his genius, damn his soul to gather wealth, which he shall not enjoy, which his prodigal son melts and consumes in an instant.[3]

To see the κακοζηλίαν [unhappy rivalry] of our times, a man spend all his forces, means, time, fortunes, to be a favourite's favourite's favourite, etc., a parasite's parasite's parasite, that may scorn the servile world as having enough already.

To see an hirsute beggar's brat, that lately fed on scraps, crept and whined, crying to all, and for an old jerkin ran of errands, now ruffle in silk and satin, bravely mounted, jovial and polite, now scorn his old friends and familiars, neglect his kindred, insult over his betters, domineer over all.

To see a scholar crouch and creep to an illiterate peasant for a meal's meat; a scrivener better paid for an obligation, a falconer receive greater wages than a student: a lawyer get more in a day than a philosopher in a year, better reward for an hour than a scholar for a twelvemonth's study; him that can paint Thais, play on a fiddle, curl hair,[4] etc., sooner get preferment than a philologer or a poet.

To see a fond mother, like Æsop's ape, hug her child to death; a wittol wink at his wife's honesty, and too perspicuous in all other affairs;[5] one stumble at a straw, and leap over a block; rob Peter, and pay Paul; scrape unjust sums with one hand, purchase great manors by corruption, fraud and cozenage, and liberally to distribute to the poor with the other, give a remnant to pious uses, etc.; penny wise, pound foolish; blind men judge of colours; wise men silent, fools talk; find fault with others, and do worse themselves;[6] denounce that in public which he doth in secret;[7] and which Aurelius Victor gives out of Augustus, severely censure that in a third, of which he is most guilty himself.

To see a poor fellow, or an hired servant, venture his life for his new master that will scarce give him his wages at year's end; a country colone toil and moil, till and drudge for a prodigal idle drone, that devours all the gain, or lasciviously consumes with phantastical expenses; a nobleman in a bravado to encounter death, and for a small flash of honour to cast away himself; a worldling tremble at an executor, and yet not fear hell-fire; to wish and hope for immortality, desire to be happy, and yet by all means avoid death, a necessary passage to bring him to it.

To see a foolhardy fellow, like those old Danes *qui decollari malunt quam verberari*, [who would] die rather than be punished, in a sottish humour embrace death with alacrity, yet scorn to lament his own sins and miseries, or his dearest friends' departures.[1]

To see wise men degraded, fools preferred; one govern towns and cities, and yet a silly woman overrules him at home; command a province, and yet his own servants or children prescribe laws to him,[2] as Themistocles' son did in Greece; "What I will" (said he) "my mother wills, and what my mother wills, my father doth."[3] To see horses ride in a coach, men draw it; dogs devour their masters; towers build masons; children rule; old men go to school; women wear the breeches; sheep demolish towns, devour men,[4] etc.; and in a word, the world turned upside downward! *O viveret Democritus!* [would Democritus were alive again!]

To insist in every particular were one of Hercules' labours, there's so many ridiculous instances as motes in the sun.[5] *Quantum est in rebus inane!* [How much vanity there is in things!] And who can speak of all? *Crimine ab uno disce omnes* [from one charge learn all], take this for a taste.

But these are obvious to sense, trivial and well known, easy to be discerned. How would Democritus have been moved, had he seen the secrets of their hearts![6] If every man had a window in his breast, which Momus would have had in Vulcan's man, or, that which Tully so much wished, it were written in every man's forehead, *quid quisque de republica sentiret*, what he thought; or that it could be effected in an instant, which Mercury did by Charon in Lucian, by touching of his eyes, to make him discern *semel et simul rumores et susurros* [forthwith rumours and whispers],

> *Spes hominum cæcas, morbos, votumque labores,*
> *Et passim toto volitantes æthere curas:*
>
> Blind hopes and wishes, their thoughts and affairs,
> Whispers and rumours, and those flying cares;

that he could *cubiculorum obductas foras recludere et secreta cordium penetrare* [unlock the doors of bedchambers and read inmost thoughts], which Cyprian desired,[7] open doors and locks

shoot bolts, as Lucian's Gallus did with a feather of his tail: or
Gyges' invisible ring, or some rare perspective glass, or otacousti-
con, which would so multiply *species* [appearances] that a man
might hear and see all at once (as Martianus Capella's Jupiter
did in a spear which he held in his hand, which did present
unto him all that was daily done upon the face of the earth),[1]
observe cuckolds' horns, forgeries of alchemists, the philosopher's
stone, new projectors, etc., and all those works of darkness,
foolish vows, hopes, fears, and wishes, what a deal of laughter
would it have afforded! He should have seen windmills in one
man's head, an hornet's nest in another. Or had he been
present with Icaromenippus in Lucian at Jupiter's whispering
place, and heard one pray for rain, another for fair weather;
one for his wife's, another for his father's death, etc., "to ask
that at God's hand which they are abashed any man should
hear," [2] how would he have been confounded! Would he,
think you, or any man else, say that these men were well in
their wits? *Hæc sani esse hominis quis sanus juret Orestes?*
Can all the hellebore in the Anticyræ cure these men? No,
sure, "an acre of hellebore will not do it." [3]

That which is more to be lamented, they are mad like Seneca's
blind woman, and will not acknowledge, or seek for any cure of
it,[4] for *pauci vident morbum suum, omnes amant* [few see their
own diseases, and all are attached to them]. If our leg or arm
offend us, we covet by all means possible to redress it; and if we
labour of a bodily disease, we send for a physician;[5] but for
the diseases of the mind, we take no notice of them.[6] Lust
harrows us on the one side; envy, anger, ambition on the other.
We are torn in pieces by our passions, as so many wild horses,
one in disposition, another in habit; one is melancholy, another
mad; and which of us all seeks for help, doth acknowledge his
error, or knows he is sick? [7] As that stupid fellow put out
the candle because the biting fleas should not find him, he
shrouds himself in an unknown habit, borrowed titles, because
nobody should discern him. Every man thinks with himself,
Egomet videor mihi sanus [I regard myself as sane], I am well,
I am wise, and laughs at others. And 'tis a general fault
amongst them all, that which our forefathers have approved,
diet, apparel, opinions, humours, customs, manners, we deride
and reject in our time as absurd. Old men account juniors
all fools,[8] when they are mere dizzards; and as to sailors
erræque urbesque recedunt, they move, the land stands still;
the world hath much more wit, they dote themselves. Turks

deride us, we them; Italians Frenchmen, accounting them light-headed fellows; the French scoff again at Italians, and at their several customs; Greeks have condemned all the world but themselves of barbarism, the world as much vilifies them now; we account Germans heavy, dull fellows, explode many of their fashions; they as contemptibly think of us; Spaniards laugh at all, and all again at them. So are we fools and ridiculous, absurd in our actions, carriages, diet, apparel, customs, and consultations; we scoff and point one at another,[1] whenas in conclusion all are fools, "and they the veriest asses that hide their ears most."[2] A private man, if he be resolved with himself, or set on an opinion, accounts all idiots and asses that are not affected as he is, *nil rectum, nisi quod placuit sibi, ducit*,[3] that are not so minded (*quodque volunt homines se bene velle putant* [4] [men ever count their own desires as right]), all fools that think not as he doth; he will not say with Atticus, *Suam cuique sponsam, mihi meam*, let every man enjoy his own spouse; but his alone is fair, *suus amor*, etc., and scorns all in respect of himself, will imitate none, hear none but himself,[5] as Pliny said, a law and example to himself.[6] And that which Hippocrates, in his Epistle to Dionysius, reprehended of old, is verified in our times, *Quisque in alio superfluum esse censet, ipse quod non habet nec curat*, that which he hath not himself or doth not esteem, he accounts superfluity, an idle quality, a mere foppery in another: like Æsop's fox, when he had lost his tail, would have all his fellow foxes cut off theirs. The Chinese say that we Europeans have one eye, they themselves two, all the world else is blind (though Scaliger accounts them brutes too, *merum pecus* [mere cattle]);[7] so thou and thy sectaries are only wise, others indifferent, the rest beside themselves, mere idiots and asses. Thus, not acknowledging our own errors and imperfections, we securely deride others, as if we alone were free, and spectators of the rest, accounting it an excellent thing, as indeed it is, *aliena optimum frui insania* to make ourselves merry with other men's obliquities, whenas he himself is more faulty than the rest, *mutato nomine, de te fabula narratur* [change but the name, the tale applies to you] he may take himself by the nose for a fool; and which one calls *maximum stultitiæ specimen* [a gross exhibition of folly], to be ridiculous to others, and not to perceive or take notice of it, as Marsyas was when he contended with Apollo, *non intelligens se deridiculo haberi* [not perceiving that he was being made a laughing-stock], saith Apuleius;[8] 'tis his own cause, he is a convict madman, as Austin well infers, "In the eyes of wise men and angels he seems like one that to our thinking walks with his heels upward." [1] So thou laughest at me, and I at thee, both at a third; and he returns that of the poet upon us again, *Hei mihi, insanire me aiunt, quum ipsi ultro insaniant.*[2] We accuse others of madness, of folly, and are the veriest dizzards ourselves. For it is a great sign and property of a fool (which Eccles. x, 3, points at) out of pride and self-conceit to insult, vilify, condemn, censure, and call other men fools (*Non videmus manticæ quod a tergo est* [we do not see what we have on our backs]), to tax that in others of which we are most faulty; teach that which we follow not ourselves: for an inconstant man to write of constancy, a profane liver prescribe rules of sanctity and piety, a dizzard himself make a treatise of wisdom, or with Sallust to rail downright at spoilers of countries, and yet in office to be a most grievous poller himself.[3] This argues weakness, and is an evident sign of such parties' indiscretion. *Peccat uter nostrum cruce dignius?*[4] [Which of us deserves more to be crucified?] "Who is the fool now?" Or else peradventure in some places we are all mad for company, and so 'tis not seen; *Societas erroris et dementiæ pariter absurditatem et admirationem tollit* [folly and madness, when widely diffused, cease to be either ridiculous or strange]. 'Tis with us, as it was of old (in Tully's censure at least[5]) with C. Fimbria in Rome, a bold, hair-brain, mad fellow, and so esteemed of all, such only excepted that were as mad as himself: now in such a case there is no notice taken of it.[6]

> *Nimirum insanus paucis videatur ; eo quod*
> *Maxima pars hominum morbo jactatur eodem.*

> When all are mad, where all are like opprest,
> Who can discern one madman from the rest?

But put case they do perceive it, and someone be manifestly convicted of madness, he now takes notice of his folly, be it in action, gesture, speech,[7] a vain humour he hath in building, bragging, jangling, spending, gaming, courting, scribbling, prating, for which he is ridiculous to others, on which he dotes, he doth acknowledge as much:[8] yet with all the rhetoric thou hast, thou canst not so recall him, but to the contrary notwithstanding, he will persevere in his dotage. 'Tis *amabilis insania, et mentis gratissimus error* [a lovable madness, a most pleasing aberration], so pleasing, so delicious, that he cannot leave it.[9] He knows his error, but will not seek to decline it; tell him what the event will be, beggary, sorrow, sickness, disgrace, shame, loss, madness, yet "an angry man will prefer vengeance, a lascivious his whore, a thief his booty, a glutton his belly, before his welfare." [1] Tell an epicure, a covetous man, an ambitious man of his irregular course, wean him from it a little, *Pol me occidistis amici*, he cries anon, you have undone him, and as "a dog to his vomit," [2] he returns to it again; no persuasion will take place, no counsel, say what thou canst,

> *Clames licet et mare cœlo*
> *Confundas,*
>
> [Though you shout enough to make the welkin ring,]

surdo narras [your words fall on deaf ears]; demonstrate as Ulysses did to Elpenor and Gryllus, and the rest of his companions, "those swinish men," [3] he is irrefragable in his humour, he will be a hog still; bray him in a mortar, he will be the same. If he be in an heresy, or some perverse opinion, settled as some of our ignorant papists are, convince his understanding, show him the several follies and absurd fopperies of that sect, force him to say, *veris vincor* [I bow to facts], make it as clear as the sun, he will err still, peevish and obstinate as he is; [4] and as he said, *si in hoc erro, libenter erro, nec hunc errorem auferri mihi volo* [5] [if I am wrong in this, I am glad to be wrong, I do not wish to be weaned from this error]; I will do as I have done, as my predecessors have done, and as my friends now do: [6] I will dote for company. Say now, are these men mad or no? *Heus age, responde* [8] [answer, I say], are they ridiculous? *cede quemvis arbitrum* [take any judge you please], are they *sana mentis*, sober, wise, and discreet? have they common sense? *uter est insanior horum?* [9] [which of these two is the madder?] I am of Democritus' opinion for my part, I hold them worthy to be laughed at; a company of brain-sick dizzards, as mad as Orestes and Athamas, [10] that they may go "ride the ass," and all sail along to the Anticyræ in the "ship of fools" for company together. I need not much labour to prove this which I say otherwise than thus, make any solemn protestation, or swear, I think you will believe me without an oath; say at a word, are they fools? refer it to you, though you be likewise fools and madmen yourselves, and I as mad to ask the question; for what said our comical Mercury?

> *Justum ab injustis petere insipientia est.* [11]
>
> ['Tis folly to expect justice from the unjust.]

I 'll stand to your censure yet, what think you?

But forasmuch as I undertook at first, that kingdoms, provinces, families, were melancholy as well as private men, I will examine them in particular, and that which I have hitherto dilated at random, in more general terms, I will particularly insist in, prove with more special and evident arguments, testimonies, illustrations, and that in brief. *Nunc accipe quare desipiant omnes æque ac tu*[1] [now hear why all are as mad as you]. My first argument is borrowed from Solomon, an arrow drawn out of his sententious quiver (Prov. iii, 7), "Be not wise in thine own eyes." And xxvi, 12, "Seest thou a man wise in his own conceit? more hope is of a fool than of him." Isaiah pronounceth a woe against such men (chap. v, 21), "that are wise in their own eyes, and prudent in their own sight." For hence we may gather that it is a great offence, and men are much deceived that think too well of themselves, an especial argument to convince them of folly. "Many men" (saith Seneca) "had been without question wise, had they not had an opinion that they had attained to perfection of knowledge already, even before they had gone half-way,"[2] too forward, too ripe, *præproperi*, too quick and ready, *cito prudentes, cito pii, cito mariti, cito patres, cito sacerdotes, cito omnis officii capaces et curiosi*[3] [in a trice they are wise, they are pious, they are husbands, fathers, priests, qualified and ambitious for every station], they had too good a conceit of themselves, and that marred all; of their worth, valour, skill, art, learning, judgment, eloquence, their good parts; all their geese are swans, and that manifestly proves them to be no better than fools. In former times they had but even wise men, now you can scarce find so many fools. Thales sent the golden tripos, which the fishermen found and the oracle commanded to be "given to the wisest,"[4] to Bias, Bias to Solon, etc. If such a thing were now found, we should all fight for it, as the three goddesses did for the golden apple, we are so wise: we have women politicians, children metaphysicians; every silly fellow can square a circle, make perpetual motions, find the philosopher's stone, interpret *Apocalypsis*, make new theorics, a new system of the world, new logic, new philosophy, etc. *Nostra utique regio*, saith Petronius, "our country is so full of deified spirits, divine souls, that you may sooner find a god than a man amongst us,"[5] we think so well of ourselves; and that is an ample testimony of much folly.

My second argument is grounded upon the like place of scripture, which though before mentioned in effect, yet for some reasons is to be repeated (and by Plato's good leave, I may do it, δὶς τὸ καλὸν ῥηθὲν οὐδὲν βλάπτει[1] [there is no harm in saying a good thing twice]). "Fools" (saith David) "by reason of their transgressions," etc. (Ps. cvii, 17). Hence Musculus infers all transgressors must needs be fools. So we read (Rom. ii) "Tribulation and anguish on the soul of every man that doeth evil"; but all do evil. And Isaiah lxv, 14, "My servants shall sing for joy, and ye[2] shall cry for sorrow of heart, and vexation of mind." 'Tis ratified by the common consent of all philosophers. "Dishonesty" (saith Cardan) "is nothing else but folly and madness." *Probus quis nobiscum vivit?*[3] Show me an honest man. *Nemo malus qui non stultus* [there is no criminal who is not also a fool], 'tis Fabius' aphorism to the same end. If none honest, none wise, then all fools. And well may they be so accounted for who will account him otherwise, *qui iter adornat in occidentem quum properaret in orientem*, that goes backward all his life westward, when he is bound to the east? or hold him a wise man (saith Musculus[4]) "that prefers momentany pleasures to eternity, that spends his master's goods in his absence, forthwith to be condemned for it?" *Nequicquam sapit qui sibi non sapit* [in vain is he wise who is not wise for himself]. Who will say that a sick man is wise, that eats and drinks to overthrow the temperature of his body? Can you account him wise or discreet that would willingly have his health, and yet will do nothing that should procure or continue it? Theodoret, out of Plotinus the Platonist, "holds it a ridiculous thing for a man to live after his own laws, to do that which is offensive to God, and yet to hope that He should save him: and when he voluntarily neglects his own safety, and contemns the means, to think to be delivered by another."[5] Who will say these men are wise?

A third argument may be derived from the precedent. All men are carried away with passion, discontent, lust, pleasures, etc. they generally hate those virtues they should love, and love such vices they should hate. Therefore more than melancholy, quite mad, brute beasts, and void of reason, so Chrysostom contends; or rather dead and buried alive, as Philo Judæus concludes it for a certainty,[7] of all such that are carried away with passions, or labour of any disease of the mind. "Where is fear and sorrow," there, Lactantius stiffly maintains, "wisdom cannot dwell."[8]

Qui cupiet, metuet quoque porro,
Qui metuens vivit, liber mihi non erit unquam.

[Who hath desires must ever fearful be;
Who lives in fear cannot be counted free.]

Seneca and the rest of the Stoics are of opinion that, where is any the least perturbation, wisdom may not be found. "What more ridiculous," as Lactantius urges, "than to hear how Xerxes whipped the Hellespont, threatened the mountain Athos, and the like?" [1] To speak *ad rem*, who is free from passion? [2] *Mortalis nemo est quem non attingat dolor, morbusve* as Tully [3] determines out of an old poem, no mortal men can avoid sorrow and sickness, and sorrow is an inseparable companion from melancholy. Chrysostom pleads farther yet, that they are more than mad, very beasts, stupefied and void of common sense: "For how" (saith he) "shall I know thee to be a man, when thou kickest like an ass, neighest like a horse after women, ravest in lust like a bull, ravenest like a bear, stingest like a scorpion, rapest like a wolf, as subtle as a fox, as impudent as a dog? Shall I say thou art a man, that hast all the symptoms of a beast? How shall I know thee to be a man? By thy shape? That affrights me more, when I see a beast in likeness of a man." [4]

Seneca [5] calls that of Epicurus *magnificam vocem*, an heroical speech, "A fool still begins to live," and accounts it a filthy lightness in men, every day to lay new foundations of their life, but who doth otherwise? One travels, another builds; one for this, another for that business, and old folks are as far out as the rest; *O dementem senectutem!* [alas for the madness of old age!], Tully exclaims. Therefore young, old, middle age, all are stupid, and dote.

Æneas Sylvius,[6] amongst many other, sets down three special ways to find a fool by. He is a fool that seeks that he cannot find: he is a fool that seeks that which being found will do him more harm than good: he is a fool that, having variety of ways to bring him to his journey's end, takes that which is worst. If so, methinks most men are fools; examine their courses, and you shall soon perceive what dizzards and madmen the major part are.

Beroaldus will have drunkards, afternoon-men, and such as more than ordinarily delight in drink, to be mad. The first pot quencheth thirst, so Panyasis the poet determines in Athenæus; *secunda Gratiis, Horis et Dionyso*, the second makes merry; the third for pleasure; *quarta ad insaniam*, the fourth makes them mad. If this position be true, what a catalogue of madmen shall we have! what shall they be that drink four times four? *Nonne supra omnem furorem, supra omnem insaniam reddunt insanissimos?* [Does not drink render them insane beyond all fury and madness?] I am of his opinion, they are more than mad, much worse than mad.

The Abderites condemned Democritus for a madman, because he was sometimes sad, and sometimes again profusely merry.[1] *Hac patria* (saith Hippocrates) *ob risum furere et insanire dicunt*, his countrymen hold him mad because he laughs; and therefore "he desires him to advise all his friends at Rhodes, that they do not laugh too much, or be over-sad." [2] Had those Abderites been conversant with us, and but seen what fleering and grinning there is in this age, they would certainly have concluded, we had been all out of our wits.[3]

Aristotle in his Ethics holds *felix idemque sapiens*, to be wise and happy are reciprocal terms, *bonus idemque sapiens honestus* [the honourable man is both good and wise]. 'Tis Tully's paradox, "wise men are free, but fools are slaves," [4] liberty is a power to live according to his own laws, as we will ourselves. Who hath this liberty? who is free?

> *Sapiens sibique imperiosus,*
> *Quem neque pauperies, neque mors, neque vincula terrent,*
> *Responsare cupidinibus, contemnere honores*
> *Fortis, et in seipso totus teres atque rotundus.*[5]

> He is wise that can command his own will,
> Valiant and constant to himself still,
> Whom poverty nor death, nor bands can fright,
> Checks his desires, scorns honours, just and right.

But where shall such a man be found? If nowhere, then *e diametro*, we are all slaves, senseless, or worse. *Nemo malus felix* [no wicked man is happy]. But no man is happy in this life, none good, therefore no man wise. *Rari quippe boni*[6] [good men are few and far between]. For one virtue you shall find ten vices in the same party; *pauci Promethei, multi Epimethei* [there are few Prometheuses, many Epimetheuses]. We may peradventure usurp the name, or attribute it to others for favour, as Carolus Sapiens, Philippus Bonus, Lodovicus Pius,[7] etc., and describe the properties of a wise man, as Tully doth an orator, Xenophon Cyrus, Castilio a courtier, Galen temperament, an aristocracy is described by politicians. But where shall such a man be found?

> *Vir bonus et sapiens, qualem vix repperit unum*
> *Millibus e multis hominum consultus Apollo.*

> A wise, a good man in a million,
> Apollo consulted could scarce find one.

A man is a miracle of himself, but Trismegistus adds, *Maximum miraculum homo sapiens*, a wise man is a wonder: *multi thyrsigeri pauci Bacchi* [many carry the thyrsus, but there are few Bacchuses].

Alexander when he was presented with that rich and costly casket of King Darius, and every man advised him what to put in it, he reserved it to keep Homer's works, as the most precious jewel of human wit, and yet Scaliger[1] upbraids Homer's Muse, *nutricem insanæ sapientiæ*, a nursery of madness, impudent as a court lady, that blushes at nothing.[2]   Jacobus Mycillus, Gilbertus Cognatus, Erasmus, and almost all posterity admire Lucian's luxuriant wit, yet Scaliger rejects him in his censure, and calls him the Cerberus of the Muses.   Socrates, whom all the world so much magnified, is by Lactantius and Theodoret condemned for a fool.   Plutarch extols Seneca's wit beyond all the Greeks, *nulli secundus*, yet Seneca saith of himself, "When I would solace myself with a fool, I reflect upon myself, and there I have him."[3]   Cardan, in his sixteenth book of Subtleties, reckons up twelve supereminent, acute philosophers, for worth, subtlety, and wisdom: Archimedes, Galen, Vitruvius, Archytas Tarentinus, Euclid, Geber, that first inventor of algebra, Alkindus the mathematician, both Arabians, with others.   But his *triumviri terrarum* [great triumvirate] far beyond the rest, are Ptolemæus, Plotinus, Hippocrates.   Scaliger, *Exercitat.* 224, scoffs at this censure of his, calls some of them carpenters and mechanicians, he makes Galen *fimbriam Hippocratis*, a skirt of Hippocrates; and the said Cardan[4] himself elsewhere condemns both Galen and Hippocrates for tediousness, obscurity, confusion.   Paracelsus will have them both mere idiots, infants in physic and philosophy.   Scaliger and Cardan admire Suisset the calculator, *qui pene modum excessit humani ingenii* [whose talents were almost superhuman], and yet Lod. Vives[5] calls them *nugas Suisseticas*: and Cardan, opposite to himself in another place, contemns those ancients in respect of times present, *majoresque nostros ad præsentes collatos juste pueros appellari*[6] [and says our forbears compared with the present generation might fairly be called boys].   In conclusion, the said Cardan[7] and Saint Bernard will admit none into this catalogue of wise men, but only prophets and apostles;[8] how they esteem themselves, you have heard before.   We are worldly-wise, admire ourselves, and seek for applause: but hear Saint Bernard, *Quanto magis foras es sapiens, tanto magis intus stultus efficeris, etc., in omnibus es prudens, circa teipsum insipiens:*[9] the more wise thou art to others, the more fool to thyself.   I may not deny but that there is some folly approved, a divine fury, a holy madness, even a spiritual drunkenness in the saints of God themselves; *sanctam insaniam* Bernard calls it (though not as blaspheming Vorstius,[1] would infer it as a passion incident to God Himself, but) familiar to good men, as that of Paul (2 Cor.), "he was a fool," etc., and (Rom. ix) he wisheth himself "to be anathematized for them." Such is that drunkenness which Ficinus speaks of, when the soul is elevated and ravished with a divine taste of that heavenly nectar, which poets deciphered by the sacrifice of Dionysus; and in this sense, with the poet, *insanire lubet*, as Austin exhorts us, *ad ebrietatem se quisque paret*,[2] let's all be mad and drunk.[3] But we commonly mistake, and go beyond our commission, we reel to the opposite part, we are not capable [4] of it, and as he said [5] of the Greeks, *Vos Græci semper pueri* [you Greeks are all boys], *vos Britanni, Galli, Germani, Itali* [you British, French, Germans, Italians], etc., you are a company of fools.

Proceed now *a partibus ad totum*, or from the whole to parts, and you shall find no other issue; the parts shall be sufficiently dilated in this following Preface. The whole must needs follow by a sorites or induction. Every multitude is mad,[6] *bellua multorum capitum* [a many-headed beast], precipitate and rash without judgment, *stultum animal*, a roaring rout. Roger Bacon proves it out of Aristotle,[7] *Vulgus dividi in oppositum contra sapientes, quod vulgo videtur verum, falsum est:* that which the commonalty accounts true, is most part false, they are still opposite to wise men, but all the world is of this humour (*vulgus*), and thou thyself art *de vulgo*, one of the commonalty, and he, and he, and so are all the rest; and therefore, as Phocion concludes, to be approved in naught you say or do, mere idiots and asses. Begin then where you will, go backward or forward, choose out of the whole pack, wink and choose, you shall find them all alike, "never a barrel better herring." [8]

Copernicus, Atlas his successor, is of opinion the earth is a planet, moves and shines to others, as the moon doth to us. Digges, Gilbert, Keplerus, Origanus, and others, defend this hypothesis of his in sober sadness, and that the moon is inhabited: if it be so that the earth is a moon, then are we also giddy, vertiginous and lunatic within this sublunary maze.

I could produce such arguments till dark night: if you should hear the rest,

Ante diem clauso component vesper Olympo:

[The day would sooner than the tale be done:]

but, according to my promise, I will descend to particulars. This melancholy extends itself not to men only, but even to vegetals and sensibles. I speak not of those creatures which are saturnine, melancholy by nature, as lead and such-like minerals, or those plants, rue, cypress, etc., and hellebore itself, of which Agrippa treats,[1] fishes, birds, and beasts, hares, conies, dormice, etc., owls, bats, nightbirds, but that artificial, which is perceived in them all. Remove a plant, it will pine away, which is especially perceived in date trees, as you may read at large in Constantine's Husbandry, that antipathy betwixt the vine and the cabbage, wine and oil. Put a bird in a cage, he will die for sullenness, or a beast in a pen, or take his young ones or companions from him, and see what effect it will cause. But who perceives not these common passions of sensible creatures, fear, sorrow, etc.? Of all other, dogs are most subject to this malady, insomuch some hold they dream as men do, and through violence of melancholy run mad; I could relate many stories of dogs that have died for grief, and pined away for loss of their masters, but they are common in every author.[2]

Kingdoms, provinces, and politic bodies are likewise sensible and subject to this disease, as Boterus in his Politics hath proved at large.[3] "As in human bodies" (saith he) "there be divers alterations proceeding from humours, so there be many diseases in a commonwealth, which do as diversely happen from several distempers," as you may easily perceive by their particular symptoms. For where you shall see the people civil, obedient to God and princes, judicious, peaceable and quiet, rich, fortunate, and flourish,[4] to live in peace, in unity and concord, a country well tilled, many fair-built and populous cities, *ubi incolæ nitent*, [where,] as old Cato said,[5] the people are neat, polite and terse, *ubi bene beateque vivunt* [where they live well and happily], which our politicians make the chief end of a commonwealth; and which Aristotle, *Polit. lib. 3, cap. 4*, calls *commune bonum* [6] [the common weal], Polybius, *lib. 6, optabilem et selectum statum* [an enviable and ideal condition], that country is free from melancholy; as it was in Italy in the time of Augustus, now in China, now in many other flourishing kingdoms of Europe. But whereas you shall see many discontents, common grievances, complaints, poverty, barbarism, beggary, plagues, wars, rebellions, seditions, mutinies, contentions, idleness, riot, epicurism, the land lie untilled, waste, full of bogs, fens, deserts, etc., cities decayed, base and poor towns, villages depopulated, the people squalid, ugly, uncivil; that kingdom, that country, must needs be discontent, melancholy, hath a sick body, and had need to be reformed.

Now that cannot well be effected, till the causes of these maladies be first removed, which commonly proceed from their own default, or some accidental inconvenience: as to be sited in a bad clime, too far north, sterile, in a barren place, as the desert of Libya, deserts of Arabia, places void of waters, as those of Lop and Belgian in Asia, or in a bad air, as at Alexandretta, Bantam, Pisa, Durazzo, St. John de Ulloa, etc., or in danger of the sea's continual inundations, as in many places of the Low Countries and elsewhere, or near some bad neighbours, as Hungarians to Turks, Podolians to Tartars, or almost any bordering countries, they live in fear still, and by reason of hostile incursions are oftentimes left desolate. So are cities by reason of wars,[1] fires, plagues, inundations, wild beasts,[2] decay of trades, barred havens, the sea's violence, as Antwerp may witness of late, Syracuse of old, Brundusium in Italy, Rye and Dover with us, and many that at this day suspect the sea's fury and rage, and labour against it as the Venetians to their inestimable charge. But the most frequent maladies are such as proceed from themselves, as first when religion and God's service is neglected, innovated or altered, where they do not fear God, obey their prince, where atheism, Epicurism, sacrilege, simony, etc., and all such impieties are freely committed, that country cannot prosper. When Abraham came to Gerar, and saw a bad land, he said, sure the fear of God was not in that place. Cyprian Echovius,[3] a Spanish chorographer, above all other cities of Spain, commends Barcino,[4] "in which there was no beggar, no man poor, etc., but all rich, and in good estate," and he gives the reason, "because they were more religious than their neighbours." Why was Israel so often spoiled by their enemies, led into captivity, etc., but for their idolatry, neglect of God's word, for sacrilege, even for one Achan's fault? And what shall we expect that have such multitudes of Achans, church robbers, simoniacal patrons, etc.? how can they hope to flourish that neglect divine duties, that live most part like epicures?

Other common grievances are generally noxious to a body politic; alteration of laws and customs, breaking privileges, general oppressions, seditions, etc., observed by Aristotle, Bodine, Boterus, Junius, Arnisæus, etc. I will only point at some of the chiefest. *Impotentia gubernandi, ataxia,* confusion, ill government, which proceeds from unskilful, slothful, griping, covetous, unjust, rash, or tyrannizing magistrates, when they are fools, idiots, children, proud, wilful, partial, indiscreet, oppressors, giddy heads, tyrants, not able or unfit to manage such offices:[1] many noble cities and flourishing kingdoms by that means are desolate, the whole body groans under such heads,[2] and all the members must needs be disaffected, as at this day those goodly provinces in Asia Minor, etc., groan under the burden of a Turkish government; and those vast kingdoms of Muscovia, Russia, under a tyrannizing duke.[3] Who ever heard of more civil and rich populous countries than those of Greece, Asia Minor, "abounding with all wealth, multitudes of inhabitants, force, power, splendour, and magnificence?"[4] and that miracle of countries, the Holy Land, that in so small a compass of ground[5] could maintain so many towns, cities, produce so many fighting men? Egypt, another paradise, now barbarous and desert, and almost waste, by the despotical government of an imperious Turk, *intolerabili servitutis jugo premitur* [is subjected to an intolerable servitude] (one saith[6]); not only fire and water, goods or lands, *sed ipse spiritus ab insolentissimi victoris pendet nutu,* [but] such is their slavery, their lives and souls depend upon his insolent will and command: a tyrant that spoils all wheresoever he comes, insomuch that an historian complains, "If an old inhabitant should now see them, he would not know them, if a traveller, or stranger, it would grieve his heart to behold them."[7] Whereas Aristotle notes, *Novæ exactiones, nova onera imposita,*[8] new burdens and exactions daily come upon them, like those of which Zosimus, *lib.* 2, so grievous, *ut viri uxores, patres filios prostituerent ut exactoribus e quæstu,* etc., they must needs be discontent, *hinc civitatum gemitus et ploratus,* as Tully holds,[9] hence come those complaints and tears of cities, "poor, miserable, rebellious, and desperate subjects," as Hippolytus adds;[10] and as a judicious countryman of ours observed not long since, in a survey of that great Duchy of Tuscany,[11] the people lived much grieved and discontent, as appeared by their manifold and manifest complainings in that kind: "That the state was like a sick body which had lately taken physic, whose humours are not yet well settled, and weakened so much by purging, that nothing was left but melancholy."

Whereas the princes and potentates are immoderate in lust, hypocrites, epicures, of no religion, but in show: *Quid hypocrisi fragilius?* what so brittle and unsure? what sooner subverts their estates than wandering and raging lusts on their subjects' wives, daughters? to say no worse. That they should *facem præferre,* lead the way to all virtuous actions, are the ringleaders oftentimes of all mischief and dissolute courses, and by that means their countries are plagued, "and they themselves often ruined, banished, or murdered by conspiracy of their subjects,"[1] as Sardanapalus was, Dionysius Junior, Heliogabalus, Periander, Pisistratus, Tarquinius, Timocrates, Childericus, Appius Claudius, Andronicus, Galeacius Sforsia,[2] Alexander Medices, etc.

Whereas the princes or great men are malicious, envious, factious, ambitious, emulators, they tear a commonwealth asunder, as so many Guelfs and Ghibellines disturb the quietness of it, and with mutual murders let it bleed to death;[3] our histories are too full of such barbarous inhumanities, and the miseries that issue from them.

Whereas they be like so many horse-leeches, hungry, griping, corrupt, covetous,[4] *avaritiæ mancipia* [slaves of avarice], ravenous as wolves (for as Tully writes, *Qui præest prodest, et qui pecudibus præest, debet eorum utilitati inservire* [to rule is to serve; he who rules sheep must devote himself to their interests]), or such as prefer their private before the public good (for as he said [5] long since, *Res privatæ publicis semper officere* [private interest always interferes with public service]); or whereas they be illiterate, ignorant, empirics in policy, *ubi deest facultas virtus* (Aristot. *Pol.* 5, *cap.* 8), *et scientia* [6] [deficient in talents character, and knowledge], wise only by inheritance, and in authority by birthright, favour, or for their wealth and titles there must needs be a fault, a great defect:[7] because, as an old philosopher affirms,[8] such men are not always fit: "Of an infinite number, few alone are senators, and of those few, fewer good, and of that small number of honest, good, and noble men few that are learned, wise, discreet and sufficient, able to discharge such places"; it must needs turn to the confusion of a state.

For as the princes are, so are the people;[9] *Qualis rex, tali grex*: and which Antigonus right well said of old, *qui Macedoniæ regem erudit, omnes etiam subditos erudit*,[10] he that teacheth the King of Macedon, teacheth all his subjects, is a true saying still.

> For princes are the glass, the school, the book,
> Where subjects' eyes do learn, do read, do look.

> *Velocius et citius nos*
> *Corrumpunt vitiorum exempla domestica, magnis*
> *Cum subeant animos auctoribus.*

> [Domestic examples of vice corrupt us more swiftly
> and sooner, when in stirring our passions they
> are backed by the example of the great]

Their examples are soonest followed, vices entertained; if they be profane, irreligious, lascivious, riotous, epicures, factious, covetous, ambitious, illiterate, so will the commons most part be idle, unthrifts, prone to lust, drunkards, and therefore poor and needy (ἡ πενία στάσιν ἐμποιεῖ καὶ κακουργίαν, for poverty begets sedition and villainy), upon all occasions ready to mutiny and rebel, discontent still, complaining, murmuring, grudging, apt to all outrages, thefts, treasons, murders, innovations, in debt, shifters, cozeners, outlaws, *profligatæ famæ ac vitæ* [of bad repute and dissolute life]. It was an old politician's aphorism, "They that are poor and bad envy rich, hate good men, abhor the present government, wish for a new, and would have all turned topsy-turvy." [1] When Catiline rebelled in Rome, he got a company of such debauched rogues together, they were his familiars and coadjutors, and such have been your rebels most part in all ages, Jack Cade, Tom Straw, Kett and his companions.

Where they be generally riotous and contentious, where there be many discords, many laws, many lawsuits, many lawyers, and many physicians, it is a manifest sign of a distempered, melancholy state, as Plato long since maintained: [2] for where such kind of men swarm, they will make more work for themselves, and that body politic diseased, which was otherwise sound. A general mischief in these our times, an insensible plague, and never so many of them: "which are now multiplied" (saith Mat. Geraldus, a lawyer himself) "as so many locusts, not the parents, but the plagues of the country, and for the most part a supercilious, bad, covetous, litigious generation of men, [3] *rumenimulga natio*, etc., a purse-milking nation, a clamorous company, gowned vultures, [4] *qui ex injuria vivunt et sanguine civium* [5] [who live by robbing and killing their fellow-citizens], thieves and seminaries of discord; worse than any pollers by the highway side, *auri accipitres, auri exterebronides, pecuniarum amiolæ, quadruplatores, curiæ harpagones, fori tintinnabula, monstra hominum, mangones*, etc., that take upon them to make peace, but are indeed the very disturbers of our peace, a company of irreligious harpies, scraping, griping catchpoles (I mean our common hungry pettifoggers, *rabulas forenses*, love and honour in the meantime all good laws, and worthy lawyers, that are so many oracles and pilots of a well-governed commonwealth [6]), without art, without judgment, that do more harm, as Livy said, [7] *quam bella externa, fames, morbive*, than sickness, wars, hunger, diseases; "and cause a most incredible destruction of a commonwealth," saith Sesellius, [8] a famous civilian sometime in Paris. As ivy doth by an oak, embrace it so long, until it hath got the heart out of it, so do they by such places they inhabit; no counsel at all, no justice, no speech to be had, *nisi eum premulseris* [unless you grease his palm], he must be fee'd still, or else he is as mute as a fish, better open an oyster without a knife. *Experto crede* (saith Sarisburiensis[1]), *in manus eorum millies incidi, et Charon immitis qui nulli pepercit unquam, his longe clementior est:* "I speak out of experience, I have been a thousand times amongst them, and Charon himself is more gentle than they; he is contented with his single pay, but they multiply still, they are never satisfied";[2] besides, they have *damnificas linguas*, as he terms it, *nisi funibus argenteis vincias* [ruinous tongues, unless you bind them with silver chains], they must be fee'd to say nothing, and get more to hold their peace than we can to say our best.[3] They will speak their clients fair, and invite them to their tables, but, as he follows it, "of all injustice there is none so pernicious as that of theirs, which, when they deceive most, will seem to be honest men."[4] They take upon them to be peacemakers, *et fovere causas humilium* [to espouse the cause of the lowly], to help them to their right, *patrocinantur afflictis* [they champion the oppressed], but all is for their own good, *ut loculos pleniorum exhauriant*[5] [to drain the purses of the wealthy], they plead for poor men gratis, but they are but as a stale to catch others. If there be no jar, they can make a jar,[6] out of the law itself find still some quirk or other, to set them at odds, and continue causes so long, *lustra aliquot* [for decades], I know not how many years before the cause is heard, and when 'tis judged and determined, by reason of some tricks and error, it is as fresh to begin, after twice seven years sometimes, as it was at first; and so they prolong time, delay suits, till they have enriched themselves and beggared their clients. And, as Cato inveighed against Isocrates' scholars,[7] we may justly tax our wrangling lawyers, they do *consenescere in litibus* [grow old over a lawsuit], are so litigious and busy here on earth, that I think they will plead their clients' causes hereafter, some of them in hell. Simlerus complains amongst the Switzers th' advocates in his time, that when they should make an end they began controversies, and "protract their causes man years, persuading them their title is good, till their patrimonie be consumed, and that they have spent more in seeking tha the thing is worth, or they shall get by the recovery."[8] S that he that goes to law, as the proverb is, holds a wolf by th'

ears,[1] or as a sheep in a storm runs for shelter to a briar, if he
prosecute his cause he is consumed, if he surcease his suit he
loseth all;[2] what difference? They had wont heretofore, saith
Austin, to end matters *per communes arbitros* [by arbitration];
and so in Switzerland (we are informed by Simlerus), "they
had some common arbitrators or daysmen in every town, that
made a friendly composition betwixt man and man, and he much
wonders at their honest simplicity, that could keep peace so
well, and end such great causes by that means."[3]   At Fez in
Africa, they have neither lawyers nor advocates; but if there
be any controversies amongst them, both parties, plaintiff and
defendant, come to their Alfakins or chief judge, "and at once,
without any further appeals or pitiful delays, the cause is heard
and ended."[4]   Our forefathers, as a worthy chorographer of ours
observes,[5] had wont *pauculis cruculis aureis*, with a few golden
crosses, and lines in verse, [to] make all conveyances, assurances.
And such was the candour and integrity of succeeding ages,
that a deed (as I have oft seen) to convey a whole manor was
implicite contained in some twenty lines or thereabouts; like
that schede or *scytala Laconica*,[6] so much renowned of old in all
contracts, which Tully so earnestly commends to Atticus,[7]
Plutarch in his *Lysander*, Aristotle, *Polit.*, Thucydides, *lib.* 1,
Diodorus[8] and Suidas approve and magnify for that laconic
brevity in this kind; and well they might, for, according to
Tertullian,[9] *certa sunt paucis*, there is much more certainty in
fewer words.   And so was it of old throughout: but now many
skins of parchment will scarce serve turn; he that buys and
sells a house must have a house full of writings, there be so
many circumstances, so many words, such tautological repetitions of all particulars (to avoid cavillation, they say); but we
find, by our woeful experience, that to subtle wits it is a cause
of much more contention and variance, and scarce any con-
veyance so accurately penned by one, which another will not
find a crack in, or cavil at; if any one word be misplaced, any
little error, all is disannulled.   That which is law to-day is
none to-morrow; that which is sound in one man's opinion is
most faulty to another; that, in conclusion, here is nothing
amongst us but contention and confusion, we bandy one against
another.   And that which long since Plutarch complained of
them in Asia,[10] may be verified in our times.   "These men here
assembled, come not to sacrifice to their gods, to offer Jupiter
their first-fruits, or merriments to Bacchus; but a yearly
disease exasperating Asia hath brought them hither, to make

an end of their controversies and lawsuits." 'Tis *multitudo perdentium et pereuntium*, a destructive rout that seek one another's ruin. Such most part are our ordinary suitors, termers, clients; new stirs every day, mistakes, errors, cavils, and at this present, as I have heard, in some one court I know not how many thousand causes: no person free, no title almost good, with such bitterness in following, so many slights, procrastinations, delays, forgery, such cost (for infinite sums are inconsiderately spent), violence and malice, I know not by whose fault, lawyers, clients, laws, both or all: but as Paul reprehended the Corinthians long since,[1] I may more positively infer now: "There is a fault amongst you, and I speak it to your shame; Is there not a wise man amongst you, to judge between his brethren?[2] but that a brother goes to law with a brother." And Christ's counsel concerning lawsuits was never so fit to be inculcated as in this age: "Agree with thine adversary quickly,"[3] etc. (Matt. v, 25).

I could repeat many such particular grievances, which must disturb a body politic. To shut up all in brief, where good government is, prudent and wise princes, there all things thrive and prosper, peace and happiness is in that land: where it is otherwise, all things are ugly to behold, incult, barbarous, uncivil, a paradise is turned to a wilderness. This island amongst the rest, our next neighbours the French and Germans, may be a sufficient witness, that in a short time, by that prudent policy of the Romans, was brought from barbarism; see but what Cæsar reports of us, and Tacitus of those old Germans; they were once as uncivil as they in Virginia, yet by planting of colonies and good laws, they became, from barbarous outlaws, to be full of rich and populous cities, as now they are, and most flourishing kingdoms.[4] Even so might Virginia, and those wild Irish, have been civilized long since, if that order had been heretofore taken, which now begins, of planting colonies, etc. I have read a discourse,[5] printed *anno* 1612, "discovering the true causes why Ireland was never entirely subdued, or brought under obedience to the Crown of England, until the beginning of his Majesty's happy reign." Yet if his reason were thoroughly scanned by a judicious politician, I am afraid he would not altogether be approved, but that it would turn to the dishonour of our nation, to suffer it to lie so long waste. Yea, and if some travellers should see (to come nearer home) those rich United Provinces of Holland, Zealand, etc., over against us; those neat cities and populous towns, full of most industrious artificers, so much land recovered from the sea,[1] and so painfully preserved by those artificial inventions, so wonderfully approved, as that of Bemster in Holland, *ut nihil huic par aut simile invenias in toto orbe*, saith Bertius the geographer, all the world cannot match it, so many navigable channels from place to place, made by men's hands, etc.,[2] and on the other side so many thousand acres of our fens lie drowned, our cities thin, and those vile, poor, and ugly to behold in respect of theirs, our trades decayed, our still running rivers stopped, and that beneficial use of transportation wholly neglected, so many havens void of ships and towns, so many parks and forests for pleasure, barren heaths, so many villages depopulated, etc., I think sure he would find some fault.

I may not deny but that this nation of ours doth *bene audire apud exteros* [is highly reputed abroad], is a most noble, a most flourishing kingdom, by common consent of all geographers,[3] historians, politicians, 'tis *unica velut arx* [a peerless stronghold], and which Quintius in Livy said of the inhabitants of Peloponnesus may be well applied to us, we are *testudines testa sua inclusi*, like so many tortoises in our shells, safely defended by an angry sea, as a wall on all sides. Our island hath many such honourable elogiums; and as a learned countryman of ours right well hath it, "Ever since the Normans' first coming into England, this country, both for military matters and all other of civility, hath been paralleled with the most flourishing kingdoms of Europe and our Christian world,"[4] a blessed, a rich country, and one of the Fortunate Isles: and for some things preferred before other countries,[5] for expert seamen, our laborious discoveries, art of navigation, true merchants, they carry the bell away from all other nations, even the Portugals and Hollanders themselves; "without all fear," saith Boterus, "furrowing the ocean winter and summer, and two of their captains, with no less valour than fortune, have sailed round about the world."[6] We have besides many particular blessings,[7] which our neighbours want, the Gospel truly preached, church discipline established, long peace and quietness, free from exactions, foreign fears, invasions, domestical seditions, well manured, fortified by art and nature, and now most happy in that fortunate union of England and Scotland,[8] which our forefathers have laboured to effect, and desired to see. But in which we excel all others, a wise, learned, religious king, another Numa, a second Augustus, a true Josiah; most worthy senators, a learned clergy, an obedient commonalty, etc. Yet amongst many roses some

thistles grow, some bad weeds and enormities, which much
disturb the peace of this body politic, eclipse the honour and
glory of it, fit to be rooted out, and with all speed to be reformed.

The first is idleness, by reason of which we have many swarms
of rogues and beggars, thieves, drunkards, and discontented
persons (whom Lycurgus in Plutarch calls *morbos reipublicæ*,
the boils of the commonwealth), many poor people in all our
towns, *civitates ignobiles*, as Polydore [1] calls them, base-built
cities, inglorious, poor, small, rare in sight, ruinous, and thin
of inhabitants. Our land is fertile, we may not deny, full of all
good things, and why doth it not then abound with cities, as
well as Italy, France, Germany, the Low Countries? Because
their policy hath been otherwise, and we are not so thrifty,
circumspect, industrious. Idleness is the *malus genius* [evil
genius] of our nation. For as Boterus [2] justly argues, fertility
of a country is not enough, except art and industry be joined
unto it. According to Aristotle, riches are either natural or
artificial; natural are good land, fair mines, etc., artificial are
manufactures, coins, etc. Many kingdoms are fertile, but thin
of inhabitants, as that Duchy of Piedmont in Italy, which
Leander Albertus so much magnifies for corn, wine, fruits, etc.,
yet nothing near so populous as those which are more barren.
"England," saith he, "London only excepted, hath never a
populous city, and yet a fruitful country." [3] I find 46 cities
and walled towns in Alsatia, a small province in Germany, 50
castles, an infinite number of villages, no ground idle, no, no
rocky places or tops of hills are untilled, as Munster informeth
us.[4] In Greichgea, a small territory on the Necker, 24 Italian
miles over, I read of 20 walled towns, innumerable villages
each one containing 150 houses most part, besides castles and
noblemen's palaces.[5] I observe in Turinge [6] in Dutchland
(twelve miles over by their scale) 12 counties, and in them 14
cities, 2000 villages 144 towns, 250 castles.[7] In Bavaria 34
cities, 46 towns, etc.[8] *Portugallia interamnis*,[9] a small plot of
ground, hath 1460 parishes,[10] 130 monasteries, 200 bridges.
Malta, a barren island, yields 20,000 inhabitants. But of all
the rest, I admire Lues Guicciardine's relations of the Low
Countries. Holland hath 26 cities, 400 great villages; Zealand
10 cities, 102 parishes; Brabant, 26 cities, 102 parishes;
Flanders, 28 cities, 90 towns, 1154 villages, besides abbeys
castles, etc. The Low Countries generally have three cities at
least for one of ours, and those far more populous and rich: and
what is the cause, but their industry and excellency in all

manner of trades; their commerce, which is maintained by
a multitude of tradesmen, so many excellent channels made by
art, and opportune havens, to which they build their cities? all
which we have in like measure, or at least may have.   But
their chiefest loadstone, which draws all manner of commerce
and merchandise, which maintains their present estate, is not
fertility of soil, but industry that enricheth them, the gold
mines of Peru or Nova Hispania may not compare with them.
They have neither gold nor silver of their own, wine nor oil, or
scarce any corn growing in those United Provinces, little or no
wood, tin, lead, iron, silk, wool, any stuff almost, or metal; and
yet Hungary, Transylvania, that brag of their mines, fertile
England, cannot compare with them.   I dare boldly say, that
neither France, Tarentum, Apulia, Lombardy, or any part of
Italy, Valence in Spain, or that pleasant Andalusia, with their
excellent fruits, wine and oil, two harvests, no, not any part of
Europe, is so flourishing, so rich, so populous, so full of good
ships, of well-built cities, so abounding with all things necessary
for the use of man.   'Tis our Indies, an epitome of China, and
all by reason of their industry, good policy, and commerce.
Industry is a loadstone to draw all good things; that alone
makes countries flourish, cities populous, and will enforce by
reason of much manure, which necessarily follows, a barren
soil to be fertile and good,[1] as sheep, saith Dion, mend a bad
pasture.[2]

Tell me, politicians, why is that fruitful Palestina, noble
Greece, Egypt, Asia Minor, so much decayed, and (mere carcasses now) fallen from that they were?   The ground is the same,
but the government is altered, the people are grown slothful,
idle, their good husbandry, policy, and industry is decayed.
Non fatigata aut effeta humus, as Columella well informs Sylvinus,
sed nostra fit inertia, etc.[3]   [the soil is not worked out or
exhausted, but is barren only through our sloth].   May a
man believe that which Aristotle in his Politics, Pausanias,
Stephanus, Sophianus, Gerbelius relate of old Greece?   I find
heretofore seventy cities in Epirus overthrown by Paulus
Æmilius, a goodly province in times past, now left desolate of
good towns and almost inhabitants.[4]   Sixty-two cities in
Macedonia in Strabo's time.   I find thirty in Laconia, but now
scarce so many villages, saith Gerbelius.   If any man from
Mount Taygetus should view the country round about, and see
tot delicias, tot urbes per Peloponnesum dispersas, so many delicate
and brave-built cities, with such cost and exquisite cunning, so

neatly set out in Peloponnesus, he should perceive them now ruinous and overthrown, burnt, waste, desolate, and laid level with the ground.[1]   *Incredibile dictu* ['tis not to be believed], etc.   And as he laments, *Quis talia fando Temperet a lacrimis? Quis tam durus aut ferreus* [Who, telling such a tale, can refrain from tears?   Who is so stony-hearted, etc.], (so he prosecutes it).   Who is he that can sufficiently condole and commiserate these ruins?   Where are those 4000 cities of Egypt, those 100 cities in Crete?   Are they now come to two?   What saith Pliny and Ælian of old Italy?   There were in former ages 1166 cities: Blondus and Machiaval both grant them now nothing near so populous and full of good towns as in the time of Augustus (for now Leander Albertus can find but 300 at most), and if we may give credit to Livy, not then so strong and puissant as of old: "They mustered seventy legions in former times, which now the known world will scarce yield."[2]   Alexander built seventy cities in a short space for his part, our Sultans and Turks demolish twice as many, and leave all desolate.   Many will not believe but that our island of Great Britain is now more populous than ever it was; yet let them read Bede, Leland, and others, they shall find it most flourished in the Saxon Heptarchy, and in the Conqueror's time was far better inhabited than at this present.   See that Domesday Book, and show me those thousands of parishes which are now decayed, cities ruined, villages depopulated, etc.   The lesser the territory is, commonly the richer it is.   *Parvus sed bene cultus ager* [a small farm, but well tilled].   As those Athenian, Lacedæmonian, Arcadian, Elean, Sicyonian, Messenian, etc., commonwealths of Greece make ample proof, as those imperial cities and free states of Germany may witness, those cantons of Switzers, Rheti, Grisons, Walloons, territories of Tuscany, Luke and Senes[3] of old, Piedmont, Mantua, Venice in Italy, Ragusa, etc.

That prince, therefore, as Boterus adviseth,[4] that will have a rich country and fair cities, let him get good trades, privileges painful inhabitants, artificers, and suffer no rude matter unwrought, as tin, iron, wool, lead, etc., to be transported out of his country—a thing in part seriously attempted amongst us but not effected.[5]   And because industry of men, and multitude of trade, so much avails to the ornament and enriching of a kingdom, those ancient Massilians would admit no man into their city that had not some trade.[6]   Selim, the first Turkish emperor,[7] procured a thousand good artificers to be brought from Tauris to Constantinople. The Polanders indented with Henry, Duke of Anjou, their new-chosen king, to bring with him an hundred families of artificers into Poland. James the First in Scotland (as Buchanan writes[1]) sent for the best artificers he could get in Europe, and gave them great rewards to teach his subjects their several trades. Edward the Third, our most renowned king, to his eternal memory brought clothing first into this island, transporting some families of artificers from Gaunt hither. How many goodly cities could I reckon up, that thrive wholly by trade, where thousands of inhabitants live singular well by their fingers' ends! As Florence in Italy by making cloth of gold; great Milan by silk and all curious works; Arras in Artois by those fair hangings; many cities in Spain, many in France, Germany, have none other maintenance, especially those within the land. Mecca, in Arabia Petræa, stands in a most unfruitful country, that wants water, amongst the rocks (as Vertomannus describes it), and yet it is a most elegant and pleasant city, by reason of the traffic of the east and west.[2] Ormus in Persia is a most famous mart-town, hath naught else but the opportunity of the haven to make it flourish. Corinth, a noble city (*lumen Græciæ*, Tully calls it, the eye of Greece), by reason of Cenchreæ and Lechæum, those excellent ports, drew all that traffic of the Ionian and Ægean Seas to it; and yet the country about it was *curva et superciliosa*, as Strabo terms it,[3] rugged and harsh. We may say the same of Athens, Actium, Thebes, Sparta, and most of those towns in Greece. Nuremberg in Germany is sited in a most barren soil, yet a noble imperial city, by the sole industry of artificers and cunning trades; they draw the riches of most countries to them, so expert in manufactures, that, as Sallust long since gave out of the like, *sedem animæ in extremis digitis habent*, their soul, or *intellectus agens*, was placed in their fingers' ends; and so we may say of Basil, Spires, Cambrai, Frankfort, etc. It is almost incredible to speak what some write of Mexico and the cities adjoining to it, no place in the world at their first discovery more populous; [what] Mat. Riccius, the Jesuit,[4] and some others, relate of the industry of the Chinese, most populous countries, not a beggar or an idle person to be seen, and how by that means they prosper and flourish. We have the same means, able bodies, pliant wits, matter of all sorts, wool, flax, iron, tin, lead, wood, etc., many excellent subjects to work upon, only industry is wanting. We send our best commodities beyond the seas, which they make good use of to their

necessities, set themselves a-work about, and severally improve
sending the same to us back at dear rates, or else make toy
and baubles of the tails of them, which they sell to us again
at as great a reckoning as the whole. In most of our cities
some few excepted, like Spanish loiterers,[1] we live wholly by
tippling-inns and ale-houses; malting are their best ploughs,
their greatest traffic to sell ale. Meteran and some other
object to us that we are no whit so industrious as the Hollanders: "Manual trades" (saith he) "which are more curious o
troublesome, are wholly exercised by strangers: they dwell i
a sea full of fish, but they are so idle, they will not catch s
much as shall serve their own turns, but buy it of their neighbours." [2] Tush! *Mare liberum* [3] [the sea is free], they fis
under our noses, and sell it to us when they have done, at thei
own prices.

> *Pudet hæc opprobria nobis*
> *Et dici potuisse, et non potuisse refelli.*

I am ashamed to hear this objected by strangers, and know
not how to answer it.

Amongst our towns, there is only London that bears th
face of a city,[4] *Epitome Britanniæ,*[5] a famous emporium, secon
to none beyond seas, a noble mart: but *sola crescit decrescer
tibus aliis* [it grows only at the expense of the rest]; and ye
in my slender judgment, defective in many things. The res
(some few excepted [6]) are in mean estate, ruinous most par
poor, and full of beggars, by reason of their decayed trade
neglected or bad policy, idleness of their inhabitants, rio
which had rather beg or loiter, and be ready to starve, than worl

I cannot deny but that something may be said in defence o
our cities, that they are not so fair built (for the sole magn
ficence of this kingdom (concerning buildings) hath been of ol
in those Norman castles and religious houses), so rich, thick
sited, populous, as in some other countries;[7] besides the reason
Cardan gives, *Subtil. lib.* 9, we want wine and oil, their tw
harvests, we dwell in a colder air, and for that cause must
little more liberally feed of flesh,[8] as all northern countries dc
our provisions will not therefore extend to the maintenance o
so many; yet notwithstanding we have matter of all sorts, a
open sea for traffic, as well as the rest, goodly havens. An
how can we excuse our negligence, our riot, drunkenness, etc
and such enormities that follow it? We have excellent law
enacted, you will say, severe statutes, houses of correctio
etc., to small purpose it seems; it is not houses will serve, bu

cities of correction; our trades generally ought to be reformed, wants supplied.[1] In other countries they have the same grievances, I confess, but that doth not excuse us, wants,[2] defects, enormities, idle drones, tumults, discords, contention, lawsuits, many laws made against them to repress those innumerable brawls and lawsuits, excess in apparel, diet, decay of tillage, depopulations, especially against rogues, beggars,[3] Egyptian vagabonds (so termed at least), which have swarmed all over Germany, France, Italy, Poland,[4] as you may read in Munster,[5] Cranzius, and Aventinus; as those Tartars and Arabians at this day do in the eastern countries: yet such has been the iniquity of all ages, as it seems to small purpose. *Nemo in nostra civitate mendicus esto* [let there be no beggars in our state], saith Plato: he will have them purged from a commonwealth,[6] "as a bad humour from the body," [7] that are like so many ulcers and boils, and must be cured before the melancholy body can be eased.

What Carolus Magnus, the Chinese, the Spaniards, the Duke of Saxony, and many other states, have decreed in this case, read Arnisæus, *cap.* 19; Boterus, *lib.* 8, *cap.* 2; Osorius, *De rebus gest. Eman. lib.* 11. When a country is overstocked with people, as a pasture is oft overlaid with cattle, they had wont in former times to disburden themselves by sending out colonies, or by wars, as those old Romans; or by employing them at home about some public buildings, as bridges, roadways, for which those Romans were famous in this island; as Augustus Cæsar did in Rome, the Spaniards in their Indian mines, as at Potosi in Peru, where some thirty thousand men are still at work, six thousand furnaces ever boiling, etc., aqueducts, bridges, havens, those stupend works of Trajan,[8] Claudius at Ostia,[9] Dioclesiani Thermæ,[10] Fucinus Lacus,[11] that Piræus in Athens, made by Themistocles, ampitheatrums of curious marble, as at Verona, Civitas Philippi and Heraclea in Thrace, those Appian and Flaminian Ways, prodigious works all may witness; and rather than they should be idle,[12] as those Egyptian Pharaohs, Mœris, and Sesostris did,[13] to task their subjects to build unnecessary pyramids, obelisks, labyrinths, channels, lakes, gigantic works all, to divert them from rebellion, riot, drunkenness, *quo scilicet alantur et ne vagando laborare desuescant* [14] [that they might support themselves and not become vagrants and idlers].

Another eyesore is that want of conduct and navigable rivers, a great blemish, as Boterus,[15] Hippolytus à Collibus,[16] and other politicians hold, if it be neglected in a commonwealth. Admirable cost and charge is bestowed in the Low Countries on this behalf, in the duchy of Milan, territory of Padua, in France,[1] Italy, China, and so likewise about corrivations of water to moisten and refresh barren grounds, to drain fens, bogs, and moors. Masinissa made many inward parts of Barbary and Numidia in Africa, before his time incult and horrid, fruitful and bartable by this means. Great industry is generally used all over the eastern countries in this kind, especially in Egypt, about Babylon and Damascus, as Vertomannus and Gotardus Arthus [2] relate; about Barcelona, Segovia, Murcia, and many other places of Spain, Milan in Italy; by reason of which their soil is much improved, and infinite commodities arise to the inhabitants.

The Turks of late attempted to cut that isthmus betwixt Africa and Asia, which Sesostris and Darius,[3] and some Pharaohs of Egypt, had formerly undertaken, but with ill success, as Diodorus Siculus records,[4] and Pliny, for that the Red Sea, being three cubits higher than Egypt,[5] would have drowned all the country, *cœpto destiterant*, they left off; yet as the same Diodorus writes,[6] Ptolemy renewed the work many years after, and absolved in it a more opportune place.

That Isthmus of Corinth was likewise undertaken to be made navigable by Demetrius, by Julius Cæsar, Nero, Domitian, Herodes Atticus, to make a speedy passage, and less dangerous, from the Ionian and Ægean Seas; [7] but because it could not be so well effected, the Peloponnesians built a wall like our Picts' Wall about Schœnus, where Neptune's temple stood, and in the shortest cut over the Isthmus, of which Diodorus, *lib.* 11, Herodotus, *lib.* 8, *Uran.* Our latter writers call it Hexamilium, which Amurath the Turk demolished, the Venetians, *anno* 1453, repaired in fifteen days with thirty thousand men. Some, saith Acosta, would have a passage cut from Panama to Nombre de Dios in America. Thuanus and Serres, the French historians, speak of a famous aqueduct in France, intended in Henry the Fourth's time, from the Loire to the Seine, and from Rhodanus to Loire. The like to which was formerly assayed by Domitian the emperor, from Arar to Moselle, which Cornelius Tacitus speaks of in the thirteenth of his Annals, after by Charles the Great and others.[8] Much cost hath in former times been bestowed in either new making or mending channels of rivers, and their passages (as Aurelianus did by Tiber to make it navigable to Rome, to convey corn from

Egypt to the city, *vadum alvei tumentis effodit*, saith Vopiscus, *et Tiberis ripas extruxit* [he deepened the bed of the river, and banked up the sides], he cut fords, made banks, etc.), decayed havens, which Claudius the emperor, with infinite pains and charges, attempted at Ostia, as I have said, the Venetians at this day to preserve their city. Many excellent means to enrich their territories have been fostered, invented in most provinces of Europe, as planting some Indian plants amongst us, silkworms; the very mulberry leaves in the plains of Granada yield thirty thousand crowns per annum to the King of Spain's coffers, besides those many trades and artificers that are busied about them in the kingdom of Granada, Murcia, and all over Spain.[1] In France a great benefit is raised by salt, etc. Whether these things might not be as happily attempted with us, and with like success, it may be controverted, silkworms (I mean), vines, fir-trees, etc. Cardan exhorts Edward the Sixth to plant olives, and is fully persuaded they would prosper in this island. With us, navigable rivers are most part neglected; our streams are not great, I confess, by reason of the narrowness of the island, yet they run smoothly and even, not headlong, swift, or amongst rocks and shelves, as foaming Rhodanus and Loire in France, Tigris in Mesopotamia, violent Durius[2] in Spain, with cataracts and whirlpools, as the Rhine and Danubius, about Schaffhausen, Laufenburg, Linz, and Krems, to endanger navigators; or broad, shallow, as Neckar in the Palatinate, Tibris in Italy; but calm and fair as Arar in France, Hebrus in Macedonia, Eurotas in Laconia, they gently glide along, and might as well be repaired, many of them (I mean Wye, Trent, Ouse, Thamesis at Oxford, the defect of which we feel in the meantime) as the river of Lea from Ware to London. B[ishop] Atwater of old, or, as some will, Henry I, made a channel from Trent to Lincoln, navigable, which now, saith Mr. Camden, is decayed,[3] and much mention is made of anchors, and such-like monuments found about old Verulamium;[4] good ships have formerly come to Exeter, and many such places, whose channels, havens, ports, are now barred and rejected. We contemn this benefit of carriage by waters, and are therefore compelled in the inner parts of this island, because portage is so dear, to eat up our commodities ourselves, and live like so many boars in a sty, for want of vent and utterance.

We have many excellent havens, royal havens, Falmouth, Portsmouth, Milford, etc., equivalent, if not to be preferred, to that Indian Havana, old Brundusium in Italy, Aulis in Greece,

Ambracia in Acarnania, Suda in Crete, which have few ships in them, little or no traffic or trade, which have scarce a village on them, able to bear great cities, *sed viderint politici* [but this is a matter for our statesmen]. I could here justly tax many other neglects, abuses, errors, defects among us and in other countries, depopulations, riot, drunkenness, etc., and many such, *quæ nunc in aurem susurrare non libet* [which I would not now so much as whisper]. But I must take heed, *ne quid gravius dicam*, that I do not overshoot myself. *Sus Minervam* [the sow would teach Minerva], I am forth of my element, as you peradventure suppose; and sometimes *veritas odium parit* [truth makes enemies], as he said, "verjuice and oatmeal is good for a parrot." For as Lucian said of an historian, I say of a politician: he that will freely speak and write must be for ever no subject, under no prince or law, but lay out the matter truly as it is, not caring what any can, will, like or dislike.

We have good laws, I deny not, to rectify such enormities, and so in all other countries, but it seems not always to good purpose. We had need of some general visitor in our age, that should reform what is amiss; a just army of Rosy-cross men,[1] for they will amend all matters (they say), religion, policy, manners, with arts, sciences, etc.; another Attila, Tamerlane, Hercules, to strive with Achelous, *Augeæ stabulum purgare* [to cleanse the Augean stables], to subdue tyrants, as he did Diomedes and Busiris:[2] to expel thieves, as he did Cacus and Lacinius: to vindicate poor captives, as he did Hesione: to pass the torrid zone, the deserts of Libya, and purge the world of monsters and Centaurs: or another Theban Crates to reform our manners, to compose quarrels and controversies, as in his time he did, and was therefore adored for a god in Athens. "As Hercules purged the world of monsters, and subdued them, so did he fight against envy, lust, anger, avarice, etc., and all those feral vices and monsters of the mind."[3] It were to be wished we had some such visitor, or, if wishing would serve, one had such a ring or rings as Timolaus desired in Lucian,[4] by virtue of which he should be as strong as ten thousand men, or an army of giants, go invisible, open gates and castle doors, have what treasure he would, transport himself in an instant to what place he desired, alter affections, cure all manner of diseases, that he might range over the world, and reform all distressed states and persons, as he would himself. He might reduce those wandering Tartars in order, that infest China on the one side, Muscovy, Poland, on the other; and tame the vagabond Arabians that rob and spoil those eastern countries, that they should never use more caravans, or janizaries to conduct them. He might root out barbarism out of America, and fully discover *Terra Australis Incognita*,[1] find out the north-east and north-west passages, drain those mighty Mæotian fens, cut down those vast Hercynian woods, irrigate those barren Arabian deserts, etc., cure us of our epidemical diseases, *scorbutum, plica, morbus Neapolitanus*, etc., end all our idle controversies, cut off our tumultuous desires, inordinate lusts, root out atheism, impiety, heresy, schism, and superstition, which now so crucify the world, catechize gross ignorance, purge Italy of luxury and riot, Spain of superstition and jealousy, Germany of drunkenness, all our northern countries of gluttony and intemperance, castigate our hard-hearted parents, masters, tutors; lash disobedient children, negligent servants; correct these spendthrifts and prodigal sons, enforce idle persons to work, drive drunkards off the ale-house, repress thieves, visit corrupt and tyrannizing magistrates, etc. But as L. Licinius taxed Timolaus, you may us. These are vain, absurd, and ridiculous wishes not to be hoped: all must be as it is, Boccalinus may cite commonwealths to come before Apollo, and seek to reform the world itself by commissioners,[2] but there is no remedy, it may not be redressed, *desinent homines tum demum stultescere quando esse desinent* [men will cease to be fools only when they cease to be men], so long as they can wag their beards, they will play the knaves and fools.

Because, therefore, it is a thing so difficult, impossible, and far beyond Hercules' labours to be performed; let them be rude, stupid, ignorant, incult, *lapis super lapidem sedeat* [let stone sit on stone], and as the apologist will, *Resp. tussi et graveolentia laboret, mundus vitio*[3] [let the State cough and choke, the world be corrupt], let them be barbarous as they are, let them tyrannize, epicurize, oppress, luxuriate, consume themselves with factions, superstitions, lawsuits, wars, and contentions, live in riot, poverty, want, misery;[4] rebel, wallow as so many swine in their own dung, with Ulysses' companions, *stultos jubeo esse libenter* [I give them full permission to be fools]. I will yet, to satisfy and please myself, make an Utopia of mine own, a New Atlantis, a poetical commonwealth of mine own, in which I will freely domineer, build cities, make laws, statutes, as I list myself. And why may I not? *Pictoribus atque poetis*, etc.[5]—you know what liberty poets ever had, and besides, my predecessor Democritus was a politician, a recorder of Abdera, a law-maker, as some say; and why may not I presume so much as he did? Howsoever I will adventure. For the site, if you will needs urge me to it, I am not fully resolved, it may be in *Terra Australis Incognita*, there is room enough (for of my knowledge neither that hungry Spaniard,[1] nor Mercurius Britannicus, have yet discovered half of it), or else one of these floating islands in Mare del Zur,[2] which, like the Cyanean Isles in the Euxine Sea, alter their place, and are accessible only at set times, and to some few persons; or one of the Fortunate Isles, for who knows yet where, or which they are? There is room enough in the inner parts of America and northern coasts of Asia. But I will choose a site, whose latitude shall be forty-five degrees (I respect not minutes) in the midst of the temperate zone, or perhaps under the Equator, that paradise of the world, *ubi semper virens laurus* [where the laurel is ever green], etc., where is a perpetual spring:[3] the longitude for some reasons I will conceal. Yet "be it known to all men by these presents," that if any honest gentleman will send in so much money as Cardan allows an astrologer for casting a nativity, he shall be a sharer, I will acquaint him with my project; or if any worthy man will stand for any temporal or spiritual office or dignity (for, as he said of his archbishopric of Utopia, 'tis *sanctus ambitus* [a sacred ambition], and not amiss to be sought after), it shall be freely given without all intercessions, bribes, letters, etc., his own worth shall be the best spokesman; and because we shall admit of no deputies or advowsons; if he be sufficiently qualified, and as able as willing to execute the place himself, he shall have present possession. It shall be divided into twelve or thirteen provinces, and those by hills, rivers, roadways, or some more eminent limits exactly bounded. Each province shall have a metropolis, which shall be so placed as a centre almost in a circumference, and the rest at equal distances, some twelve Italian miles asunder, or thereabout, and in them shall be sold all things necessary for the use of man, *statis horis et diebus* [at stated hours and on stated days]; no market towns, markets or fairs, for they do but beggar cities (no village shall stand above six, seven, or eight miles from a city); except those emporiums which are by the seaside, general staples, marts, as Antwerp, Venice, Bergen of old, London, etc. Cities most part shall be situated upon navigable rivers or lakes, creeks, havens; and for their form, regular, round, square, or long square,[4] with fair, broad, and straight streets,[5] houses uniform, built of brick and stone, like

Bruges, Brussels, Rhegium Lepidi, Berne in Switzerland, Milan, Mantua, Crema, Cambalu in Tartary, described by M. Polus, or that Venetian Palma. I will admit very few or no suburbs, and those of baser building, walls only to keep out man and horse, except it be in some frontier towns, or by the seaside, and those to be fortified after the latest manner of fortification,[1] and situated upon convenient havens, or opportune places. In every so built city, I will have convenient churches, and separate places to bury the dead in, not in churchyards; a *citadella* (in some, not all) to command it, prisons for offenders, opportune market-places of all sorts, for corn, meat, cattle, fuel, fish, commodious courts of justice, public halls for all societies, bourses, meeting-places, armouries,[2] in which shall be kept engines for quenching of fire, artillery gardens, public walks, theatres, and spacious fields allotted for all gymnics, sports, and honest recreations, hospitals of all kinds, for children, orphans, old folks, sick men, madmen, soldiers, pest-houses, etc.; not built *precario* [as a favour], or by gouty benefactors, who, when by fraud and rapine they have extorted all their lives, oppressed whole provinces, societies, etc., give something to pious uses, build a satisfactory almshouse, school, or bridge, etc., at their last end, or before perhaps, which is no otherwise than to steal a goose and stick down a feather, rob a thousand to relieve ten; and those hospitals so built and maintained, not by collections, benevolences, donaries, for a set number (as in ours), just so many and no more at such a rate, but for all those who stand in need, be they more or less, and that *ex publico ærario* [at the public expense], and so still maintained; *non nobis solum nati sumus* [we are not born for ourselves alone], etc. I will have conduits of sweet and good water aptly disposed in each town, common granaries,[3] as at Dresden in Misnia, Stettin in Pomerland, Nuremberg, etc.; colleges of mathematicians, musicians, and actors, as of old at Lebedus in Ionia, alchemists,[4] physicians, artists, and philosophers, that all arts and sciences may sooner be perfected and better learned; and public historiographers, as amongst those ancient Persians, *qui in commentarios referebant quæ memorantu digna gerebantur*,[5] informed and appointed by the State to register all famous acts, and not by each insufficient scribbler, partial or parasitical pedant, as in our times. I will provide public schools of all kinds, singing, dancing, fencing, etc., especially of grammar and languages, not to be taught by those tedious precepts ordinarily used, but by use, example, conversation,[6] as travellers learn abroad, and nurses teach their children: as I will have all such places, so will I ordain public governors, fit officers to each place, treasurers, ædiles, quæstors, overseers of pupils, widows' goods, and all public houses, etc.,[1] and those once a year to make strict accounts of all receipts, expenses, to avoid confusion, *et sic fiet ut non absumant* (as Pliny to Trajan), *quod pudeat dicere* [and in this way there will be no squandering, if you will pardon my mentioning such a thing]. They shall be subordinate to those higher officers and governors of each city, which shall not be poor tradesmen and mean artificers, but noblemen and gentlemen, which shall be tied to residence in those towns they dwell next, at such set times and seasons: for I see no reason (which Hippolytus complains of[2]) "that it should be more dishonourable for noblemen to govern the city than the country, or unseemly to dwell there now than of old. I will have no bogs, fens, marshes, vast woods, deserts, heaths, commons, but all enclosed[3] (yet not depopulated, and therefore take heed you mistake me not); for that which is common, and every man's, is no man's; the richest countries are still enclosed, as Essex, Kent, with us, etc., Spain, Italy; and where enclosures are least in quantity, they are best husbanded, as about Florence in Italy, Damascus in Syria, etc., which are liker gardens than fields.[4] I will not have a barren acre in all my territories, not so much as the tops of mountains: where nature fails, it shall be supplied by art: lakes and rivers shall not be left desolate.[5] All common highways, bridges, banks, corrivations of waters, aqueducts, channels, public works, building, etc., out of a common stock,[6] curiously maintained and kept in repair; no depopulations, engrossings, alterations of wood, arable, but by the consent of some supervisors that shall be appointed for that purpose, to see what reformation ought to be had in all places, what is amiss, how to help it, *Et quid quæque ferat regio, et quid quæque recuset* [what each region will or will not produce], what ground is aptest for wood, what for corn, what for cattle, gardens, orchards, fishponds, etc., with a charitable division in every village (not one domineering house greedily to swallow up all, which is too common with us), what for lords, what for tenants;[7] and because they shall be better encouraged to improve such lands they hold, manure, plant trees, drain, fence, etc., they shall have long leases, a known rent, and known fine, to free them from those intolerable exactions of tyrannizing landlords. These supervisors shall likewise appoint what quantity of land in each manor is fit for the lord's demesnes, what for holding of tenants, how it ought to be husbanded—*Ut Magnetes equis, Minyæ gens cognita remis*[1] [as the Magnesians are famed for their horses, the Argonauts for oarsmanship]—how to be manured, tilled, rectified,

> *Hic segetes veniunt, illic felicius uvæ,*
> *Arborei fœtus alibi, atque injussa virescunt*
> *Gramina,*[2]

> [Here corn, and here the vine is better grown;
> Here fruits abound and grasses spring unsown,]

and what proportion is fit for all callings, because private professors are many times idiots, ill husbands, oppressors, covetous, and know not how to improve their own, or else wholly respect their own, and not public good.

Utopian parity is a kind of government to be wished for rather than effected, *Respub. Christianopolitana,*[3] Campanella's City of the Sun, and that New Atlantis,[4] witty fictions, but mere chimeras, and Plato's community in many things is impious, absurd, and ridiculous, it takes away all splendour and magnificence. I will have several orders, degrees of nobility, and those hereditary, not rejecting younger brothers in the meantime, for they shall be sufficiently provided for by pensions, or so qualified, brought up in some honest calling, they shall be able to live of themselves. I will have such a proportion of ground belonging to every barony; he that buys the land shall buy the barony, he that by riot consumes his patrimony and ancient demesnes shall forfeit his honours.[5] As some dignities shall be hereditary, so some again by election, or by gift (besides free offices, pensions, annuities), like our bishoprics, prebends, the bassas' palaces in Turkey, the procurators' houses and offices in Venice,[6] which, like the golden apple, shall be given to the worthiest and best deserving both in war and peace, as a reward of their worth and good service, as so many goals for all to aim at (*honos alit artes* [honour is an encouragement to art]), and encouragement to others. For I hate these severe, unnatural, harsh, German, French, and Venetian decrees, which exclude plebeians from honours; be they never so wise, rich, virtuous, valiant, and well qualified, they must not be patricians, but keep their own rank; this is *naturæ bellum inferre* [to make war on nature], odious to God and men, I abhor it. My form of government shall be monarchical;

> *Nunquam libertas gratior extat,*
> *Quam sub rege pio, etc.*[7]

> [Liberty is ne'er more sweet than when vouchsafed by a
> virtuous prince.]

Few laws, but those severely kept, plainly put down, and in the mother tongue, that every man may understand. Every city shall have a peculiar trade or privilege, by which it shall be chiefly maintained: and parents shall teach their children, one of three at least, bring up and instruct them in the mysteries of their own trade.[1] In each town these several tradesmen shall be so aptly disposed, as they shall free the rest from danger or offence: fire-trades, as smiths, forge-men, brewers, bakers, metal-men, etc., shall dwell apart by themselves: dyers, tanners, fellmongers, and such as use water, in convenient places by themselves: noisome or fulsome for bad smells, as butchers' slaughter-houses, chandlers, curriers, in remote places and some back lanes. Fraternities and companies I approve of, as merchants' bourses, colleges of druggers, physicians, musicians, etc., but all trades to be rated in the sale of wares, as our clerks of the market do bakers and brewers; corn itself, what scarcity soever shall come, not to exceed such a price. Of such wares as are transported or brought in, if they be necessary, commodious, and such as nearly concern man's life, as corn, wood, coal, etc.,[2] and such provision we cannot want, I will have little or no custom paid, no taxes; but for such things as are for pleasure, delight, or ornament, as wine, spice, tobacco, silk, velvet, cloth of gold, lace, jewels, etc., a greater impost. I will have certain ships sent out for new discoveries every year, and some discreet men appointed to travel into all neighbour kingdoms by land,[3] which shall observe what artificial inventions and good laws are in other countries, customs, alterations, or aught else, concerning war or peace, which may tend to the common good. Ecclesiastical discipline, *penes episcopos* [in the hands of the bishops], subordinate as the other. No impropriations, no lay patrons of church livings, or one private man, but common societies, corporations, etc., and those rectors of benefices to be chosen out of the universities, examined and approved, as the *literati* in China. No parish to contain above a thousand auditors. If it were possible, I would have such priests as should imitate Christ, charitable lawyers should love their neighbours as themselves, temperate and modest physicians, politicians contemn the world, philosophers should know themselves, noblemen live honestly, tradesmen leave lying and cozening, magistrates corruption etc.; but this is impossible, I must get such as I may. I will therefore have of lawyers, judges, advocates, physicians, chirurgeons, etc., a set number,[4] and every man, if it be possible

to plead his own cause, to tell that tale to the judge which he
doth to his advocate,[1] as at Fez in Africa, Bantam, Aleppo,
Ragusa, *suam quisque causam dicere tenetur* [every one is expected to plead his own cause].   Those advocates, chirurgeons,
and physicians [2] which are allowed, to be maintained out of the
common treasure,[3] no fees to be given or taken upon pain of
losing their places; or if they do, very small fees, and when the
cause is fully ended.[4] He that sues any man shall put in a
pledge, which, if it be proved he hath wrongfully sued his adversary, rashly or maliciously, he shall forfeit and lose.[5] Or else,
before any suit begin, the plaintiff shall have his complaint
approved by a set delegacy to that purpose; if it be of moment,
he shall be suffered as before to proceed, if otherwise, they shall
determine it. All causes shall be pleaded *suppresso nomine*,
the parties' names concealed, if some circumstances do not
otherwise require. Judges and other officers shall be aptly
disposed in each province, villages, cities, as common arbitrators
to hear causes and end all controversies, and those not single,
but three at least on the bench at once, to determine or give
sentence, and those again to sit by turns or lots, and not to
continue still in the same office. No controversy to depend
above a year, but without all delays and further appeals to be
speedily dispatched, and finally concluded in that time allotted.
These and all other inferior magistrates to be chosen as the
literati in China,[6] or by those exact suffrages of the Venetians,[7]
and such again not to be eligible, or capable of magistracies,
honours, offices, except they be sufficiently qualified for learning,[8]
manners, and that by the strict approbation of deputed
examinators: first scholars to take place, then soldiers; [9] for I
am of Vegetius his opinion, a scholar deserves better than a
soldier, because *unius ætatis sunt quæ fortiter fiunt, quæ vero
pro utilitate reipub. scribuntur, æterna:* a soldier's work lasts
for an age, a scholar's for ever. If they misbehave themselves,
they shall be deposed,[10] and accordingly punished, and whether
their offices be annual or otherwise,[11] once a year they shall be
called in question, and give an account; for men are partial
and passionate, merciless, covetous, corrupt, subject to love,
hate, fear, favour, etc., *omne sub regno graviore regnum* [every
throne is subject to a greater throne]: like Solon's Areopagites,
or those Roman censors, some shall visit others, and be visited
invicem [in turn] themselves,[12] they shall oversee that no
prowling officer, under colour of authority, shall insult over
his inferiors,[13] as so many wild beasts, oppress, domineer, flay,

grind, or trample on, be partial or corrupt, but that there be *æquabile jus*, justice equally done, live as friends and brethren together; and which Sesellius would have and so much desires in his kingdom of France,[1] "a diapason and sweet harmony of kings, princes, nobles, and plebeians so mutually tied and involved in love, as well as laws and authority, as that they never disagree, insult or encroach one upon another." If any man deserve well in his office he shall be rewarded,

> *Quis enim virtutem amplectitur ipsam,*
> *Præmia si tollas?*

> [For take away the prize, and who chooses virtue for its own sake?]

He that invents anything for public good in any art or science, writes a treatise, or performs any noble exploit at home or abroad,[2] shall be accordingly enriched,[3] honoured, and preferred.[4] I say with Hannibal in Ennius, *Hostem qui feriet erit mihi Carthaginensis* [whoever strikes down an enemy shall be in my eyes a Carthaginian], let him be of what condition he will, in all offices, actions, he that deserves best shall have best.

Tilianus in Philonius, out of a charitable mind no doubt, wished all his books were gold and silver, jewels and precious stones, to redeem captives, set free prisoners, and relieve all poor distressed souls that wanted means;[5] religiously done, I deny not, but to what purpose? Suppose this were so well done, within a little after, though a man had Crœsus' wealth to bestow, there would be as many more. Wherefore I will suffer no beggars, rogues, vagabonds, or idle persons at all,[6] that cannot give an account of their lives how they maintain themselves.[7] If they be impotent, lame, blind, and single, they shall be sufficiently maintained in several hospitals, built for that purpose; if married and infirm, past work, or by inevitable loss or some such-like misfortune cast behind, by distribution of corn, house-rent free, annual pensions or money,[8] they shall be relieved, and highly rewarded for their good service they have formerly done; if able, they shall be enforced to work. "For I see no reason" (as he said [9]) "why an epicure or idle drone, a rich glutton, a usurer, should live at ease, and do nothing, live in honour, in all manner of pleasures, and oppress others, when as in the meantime a poor labourer, a smith, a carpenter, an husbandman that hath spent his time in continual labour, as an ass to carry burdens, to do the commonwealth good, and without whom we cannot live, shall be left in his old age to beg or starve, and lead a miserable life worse than a jument."[1]   As all conditions shall be tied to their task, so none shall be over-tired, but have their set times of recreations and holidays, *indulgere genio* [to follow their own bent], feasts and merry meetings, even to the meanest artificer, or basest servant, once a week to sing or dance (though not all at once), or do whatso-ever he shall please;[2] like that *Sacarum festum*[3] amongst the Persians, those Saturnals in Rome, as well as his master.   If any be drunk, he shall drink no more wine or strong drink in a twelvemonth after.[4]   A bankrupt shall be *catomidiatus in Amphitheatro*,[5] publicly shamed, and he that cannot pay his debts, if by riot or negligence he have been impoverished, shall be for a twelvemonth imprisoned; if in that space his creditors be not satisfied, he shall be hanged.[6]   He that commits sacrilege shall lose his hands;[7] he that bears false witness, or is of perjury convict, shall have his tongue cut out, except he redeem it with his head.   Murder, adultery,[8] shall be punished by death, but not theft, except it be some more grievous offence, or notorious offenders:[9] otherwise they shall be con-demned to the galleys, mines, be his slaves whom they have offended, during their lives.   I hate all hereditary slaves, and that *duram Persarum legem* [hard law of the Persians], as Brisonius calls it;[10] or as Ammianus, *impendio formidatas et abominandas leges, per quas ob noxam unius omnis propinquitas perit*,[11] hard law that wife and children, friends and allies, should suffer for the father's offence.

No man shall marry until he be 25,[12] no woman till she be 20, *nisi aliter dispensatum fuerit*[13] [without a dispensation].   If one die, the other party shall not marry till six months after;[14] and because many families are compelled to live niggardly, exhaust and undone by great dowers, none shall be given at all,[15] or very little, and that by supervisors rated, they that are foul shall have a greater portion; if fair, none at all, or very little: howsoever, not to exceed such a rate as those supervisors shall think fit.[16]   And when once they come to those years, poverty shall hinder no man from marriage, or any other respect, but all shall be rather enforced than hindered,[17] except they be dismembered, or grievously deformed,[18] infirm, or visited with some enormous hereditary disease in body or mind; in such cases upon a great pain or mulct, man or woman shall not marry,[19] other order shall be taken for them to their content.[20] If people overabound, they shall be eased by colonies.[21]

No man shall wear weapons in any city.[22]   The same attire shall be kept, and that proper to several callings, by which they shall be distinguished. *Luxus funerum* [display at funerals] shall be taken away, that intempestive expense moderated,[1] and many others. Brokers, takers of pawns, biting usurers, I will not admit; yet because *hic cum hominibus non cum diis agitur*, we converse here with men, not with gods, and for the hardness of men's hearts, I will tolerate some kind of usury.[2] If we were honest, I confess, *si probi essemus*, we should have no use of it, but being as it is, we must necessarily admit it. Howsoever most divines contradict it (*Dicimus inficias, sed vox ea sola reperta est* [we say "no" with our lips, but do not mean it]), it must be winked at by politicians. And yet some great doctors approve of it, Calvin, Bucer, Zanchius, P. Martyr, because by so many grand lawyers, decrees of emperors, princes' statutes, customs of commonwealths, churches' approbations, it is permitted, etc., I will therefore allow it. But to no private persons, nor to every man that will, to orphans only, maids, widows, or such as by reason of their age, sex, education, ignorance of trading, know not otherwise how to employ it; and those so approved, not to let it out apart, but to bring their money to a common bank which shall be allowed in every city,[3] as in Genoa, Geneva, Nuremberg, Venice, at 5, 6, 7, not above 8 per centum,[4] as the supervisors, or *ærarii præfecti*, shall think fit. And as it shall not be lawful for each man to be an usurer that will, so shall it not be lawful for all to take up money at use, not to prodigals and spendthrifts, but to merchants, young tradesmen, such as stand in need, or know honestly how to employ it, whose necessity, cause, and condition the said supervisors shall approve of.[5]

I will have no private monopolies, to enrich one man and beggar a multitude, multiplicity of offices, of supplying by deputies;[6] weights and measures the same throughout, and those rectified by the *Primum mobile* and sun's motion, threescore miles to a degree according to observation, 1000 geometrical paces to a mile, five foot to a pace, twelve inches to a foot, etc., and from measures known it is an easy matter to rectify weights, etc., to cast up all, and resolve bodies by algebra, stereometry. I hate wars if they be not *ad populi salutem*, upon urgent occasion. *Odimus accipitrem, quia semper vivit in armis* [we hate the hawk, because it is for ever at war]. Offensive wars, except the cause be very just, I will not allow of.[7] For I do highly magnify that saying of Hannibal to Scipio, in Livy: "It had been a blessed thing for you and us, f God had given that mind to our predecessors, that you had been content with Italy, we with Africa. For neither Sicily nor Sardinia are worth such cost and pains, so many fleets and armies, or so many famous captains' lives." [1] *Omnia prius entanda*, fair means shall first be tried. *Peragit tranquilla potestas, Quod violenta nequit* [2] [peaceful pressure accomplishes more than violence]. I will have them proceed with all moderation: but hear you, Fabius my general, not Minucius, *nam qui consilio nititur plus hostibus nocet, quam qui sine animi ratione, viribus* [3] [for strategy can inflict greater blows on the enemy than uncalculating force]. And in such wars to abstain as much as is possible from depopulations, burning of towns, massacring of infants, etc. [4] For defensive wars, I will have forces still ready at a small warning, by land and sea, a prepared navy, soldiers *in procinctu, et quam Bonfinius apud Hungaros suos vult, virgam ferream* [5] [ready for action, and, as Bonfinius desired for his Hungarians, an iron rod], and money, which is *nervus elli* [the sinews of war], still in a readiness, and a sufficient revenue, a third part as in old Rome and Egypt, [6] reserved for the commonwealth; to avoid those heavy taxes and impositions, as well to defray this charge of wars, as also all other public defalcations, expenses, fees, pensions, reparations, chaste sports, feasts, donaries, rewards, and entertainments. All things in this nature especially I will have maturely done, and with great deliberation: [7] *ne quid temere, ne quid remisse ac timide fiat* [8] [without rashness, yet with courage and determination]; *sed quo feror hospes?* [but I am drifting too far]. To prosecute the rest would require a volume. *Manum de tabella* [I must call a halt], I have been over-tedious in this subject; I could have here willingly ranged, but these straits wherein I am included will not permit.

From commonwealths and cities I will descend to families, which have as many corsives and molestations, as frequent discontents as the rest. Great affinity there is betwixt a political and economical body; they differ only in magnitude and proportion of business (so Scaliger writes [9]); as they have both likely the same period, as Bodine [10] and Peucer [11] hold, out of Plato, six or seven hundred years, so many times they have the same means of their vexation and overthrows; as namely, riot, a common ruin of both, riot in building, riot in profuse spending, riot in apparel, etc., be it in what kind soever, it produceth the same effects. A chorographer of ours, [12] speaking *obiter* of ancient families, why they are so frequent in the north, continue so long, are so soon extinguished in the south, and so few, gives no other reason but this, *luxus omnia dissipavit*, riot hath consumed all. Fine clothes and curious buildings came into this island, as he notes in his annals, not so many years since; *non sine dispendio hospitalitatis*, to the decay of hospitality. Howbeit, many times that word is mistaken, and under the name of bounty and hospitality is shrouded riot and prodigality; and that which is commendable in itself well used, hath been mistaken heretofore, is become by his abuse the bane and utter ruin of many a noble family. For some men live like the rich glutton, consuming themselves and their substance by continual feasting and invitations, with Axylus in Homer, [1] keep open house for all comers, giving entertainment to such as visit them, keeping a table beyond their means, and a company of idle servants (though not so frequent as of old) are blown up on a sudden, and, as Actæon was by his hounds devoured by their kinsmen, friends, and multitude of followers. It is a wonder that Paulus Jovius relates of our northern countries, what an infinite deal of meat we consume on our tables; [3] that I may truly say, 'tis not bounty, not hospitality as it is often abused, but riot in excess, gluttony and prodigality; a mere vice; it brings in debt, want, and beggary, hereditary diseases, consumes their fortunes, and overthrows the good temperature of their bodies. To this I might here well add their inordinate expense in building, those phantastical houses, turrets, walks, parks, etc., gaming, excess of pleasure, and that prodigious riot in apparel, by which means they are compelled to break up house, and creep into holes. Sesellius in his Commonwealth of France, gives three reasons why the French nobility were so frequently bankrupts: "First, because they had so many lawsuits and contentions one upon another which were tedious and costly; by which means it came to pass that commonly lawyers bought them out of their possessions. A second cause was their riot; they lived beyond their means, and were therefore swallowed up by merchants." [4] (La Nove, a French writer, yields five reasons of his countrymen's poverty to the same effect almost, and thinks verily, if the gentry of France were divided into ten parts, eight of them would be found much impaired, by sales, mortgages, and debts, or wholly sunk in their estates.) "The last was immoderate excess in apparel, which consumed their revenues." How this concerns and agrees with our present state, look you. But of this elsewhere. As it is in a man's body, if either head, heart, stomach liver, spleen, or any one part be misaffected, all the rest suffer with it: so is it with this economical body. If the head be naught, a spendthrift, a drunkard, a whoremaster, a gamester, how shall the family live at ease? *Ipsa si cupiat salus servare, prorsus non potest hanc familiam,*[1] as Demea said in the comedy, Safety herself cannot save it. A good, honest, painful man many times hath a shrew to his wife, a sickly, dishonest, slothful, foolish, careless woman to his mate, a proud, peevish flirt, a liquorish, prodigal quean, and by that means all goes to ruin: or if they differ in nature, he is thrifty, she spends all, he wise, she sottish and soft; what agreement can there be? what friendship? Like that of the thrush and swallow in Æsop, instead of mutual love, kind compellations, whore and thief is heard, they fling stools at one another's heads. *Quæ intemperies vexat hanc familiam?*[2] [What madness has come over this family?] All enforced marriages commonly produce such effects, or if on their behalfs it be well, as to live and agree lovingly together, they may have disobedient and unruly children, that take ill courses to disquiet them, "their son is a thief, a spendthrift, their daughter a whore";[3] a stepmother[4] or a daughter-in-law distempers all; or else for want of means,[5] many tortures arise, debts, dues, fees, dowries, jointures, legacies to be paid, annuities issuing out, by means of which they have not wherewithal to maintain themselves in that pomp as their predecessors have done, bring up or bestow their children to their callings, to the birth and quality, and will not descend to their present fortunes.[6] Oftentimes, too, to aggravate the rest, concur many other inconveniences, unthankful friends, decayed friends, bad neighbours, negligent servants, *servi furaces, versipelles, callidi, occlusa sibi mille clavibus reserant, furtimque raptant, consumunt, liguriunt*[7] [thievish slaves, sly cunning varlets, they break through a thousand bolts, they steal, they eat up, they take the tit-bits]; casualties, taxes, mulcts, chargeable offices, vain expenses, entertainments, loss of stock, enmities, emulations, frequent invitations, losses, suretyship, sickness, death of friends, and that which is the gulf of all, improvidence, ill husbandry, disorder and confusion, by which means they are drenched on a sudden in their estates, and at unawares precipitated insensibly into an inextricable labyrinth of debts, cares, woes, want, grief, discontent, and melancholy itself.

I have done with families, and will now briefly run over some few sorts and conditions of men. The most secure, happy, jovial, and merry in the world's esteem are princes and great

men, free from melancholy: but for their cares, miseries, sus
picions, jealousies, discontents, folly and madness, I refer yo
to Xenophon's *Tyrannus*, where King Hiero discourseth a
large with Simonides the poet of this subject. Of all other
they are most troubled with perpetual fears, anxieties, insomuc
that, as he said in Valerius,[1] "If thou knewest with what care
and miseries this robe were stuffed, thou wouldst not stoop t
take it up." Or put case they be secure and free from fears an
discontents, yet they are void of reason too oft, and precipitat
in their actions;[2] read all our histories, *quos de stultis prodider
stulti* [which fools have written about fools], Iliads, Æneids
Annals, and what is the subject?

> *Stultorum regum, et populorum continet æstus.*
>
> [The giddy tumults and the foolish rage
> Of kings and people.]

How mad they are, how furious, and upon small occasions
rash and inconsiderate in their proceedings, how they dote
every page almost will witness:

> *Delirant reges, plectuntur Achivi.*
>
> [When doting monarchs urge
> Unsound resolves, their subjects feel the scourge.]

Next in place, next in miseries and discontents, in all manne
of hair-brain actions, are great men; *procul a Jove, procul
fulmine* [the farther from Jove, the farther from the lightning
the nearer the worse. If they live in court, they are up an
down, ebb and flow with their prince's favours, *Ingenium vult
statque caditque suo* [their talent rises or falls with his smile o
frown], now aloft, to-morrow down, as Polybius describes them
"like so many casting-counters, now of gold, to-morrow o
silver, that vary in worth as the computant will; now the
stand for units, to-morrow for thousands; now before al
and anon behind." Beside, they torment one another wit
mutual factions, emulations: one is ambitious, another en
amoured, a third in debt, a prodigal, overruns his fortunes,
fourth solicitous with cares, gets nothing, etc. But for thes
men's discontents, anxieties, I refer you to Lucian's tract, *L
mercede conductis*, Æneas Sylvius (*libidinis et stultitiæ servos*
[slaves of lust and folly] he calls them), Agrippa, and man
others.

Of philosophers and scholars *priscæ sapientiæ dictatores* [th
dictators of ancient learning], I have already spoken in gener

terms, those superintendents of wit and learning, **men above men**, those refined men, minions of the Muses,

mentemque habere queis bonam
Et esse corculis [1] *datum est.* [2]

[Who have been vouchsafed good brains and quick minds.]

These acute and subtle sophisters, so much honoured, have as much need of hellebore as others. [3] *O medici, mediam perundite venam* [4] [physicians, open the middle vein]. Read Lucian's *Piscator*, and tell how he esteemed them; Agrippa's Tract of the Vanity of Sciences; nay, read their own works, their absurd tenents, prodigious paradoxes, *et risum teneatis amici?* [and can you contain your laughter, friends?] You shall find that of Aristotle true, *nullum magnum ingenium sine mixura dementiæ* [no great wit without some admixture of madness], they have a worm as well as others; you shall find a phantastical strain, a fustian, a bombast, a vainglorious humour, an affected style, etc., like a prominent thread in an uneven woven cloth, run parallel throughout their works. And they that teach wisdom, patience, meekness, are the veriest dizzards, hair-brains, and most discontent. "In the multitude of wisdom is grief, and he that increaseth wisdom, increaseth sorrow." [5] I need not quote mine author. They that laugh and contemn others, condemn the world of folly, deserve to be mocked, are as giddy-headed, and lie as open as any other. Democritus, that common flouter of folly, [6] was ridiculous himself; barking Menippus, scoffing Lucian, satirical Lucilius, Petronius, Varro, Persius, etc., may be censured with the rest; *Loripedem rectus derideat, Æthiopem albus* [let the straight man deride the crookshank, the white man the blackamoor]. Bale, Erasmus, Hospinian, Vives, Kemnisius, explode as a vast ocean of *obs* and *sols*, [7] school divinity. A labyrinth of intricable questions, [8] unprofitable contentions, *incredibilem delirationem* [an incredible doting], one calls it. If school divinity be so censured, *subtilis Scotus, lima veritatis, Occam irrefragabilis, cujus ingenium vetera omnia ingenia subvertit* [9] [the subtle Scotus, who was the file of truth, the infallible Occam who confuted all the ancients], etc., Baconthorpe, Doctor Resolutus, and *Corculum Theologiæ* [the keenest of theological brains], Thomas himself, Doctor Seraphicus, *cui dictavit angelus* [10] [whose writings an angel dictated], etc., what shall become of humanity? *Ars stulta* [foolish art], what can she plead? what can her followers say for themselves? Much learning *cere-diminuit-brum*,[1] hath cracked their sconce, and taken such root that *tribus Anticyris caput insanabile*, hellebore itself can do no good, nor that renowned lanthorn of Epictetus,[2] by which if any man studied, he should be as wise as he was. But all will not serve; rhetoricians *in ostentationem loquacitatis multa agitant*, out of their volubility of tongue will talk much to no purpose; orators can persuade other men what they will, *quo volunt, unde volunt* [to go where they will, whence they will], move, pacify, etc., but cannot settle their own brains. What saith Tully? *Malo indisertam prudentiam quam loquacem stultitiam* [I prefer sense without eloquence to folly with it]; and, as Seneca seconds him,[3] a wise man's oration should not be polite or solicitous. Fabius esteems no better of most of them,[4] either in speech, action, gesture, than as men beside themselves, *insanos declamatores* [crazy rhetoricians]; so doth Gregory, *Non mihi sapit qui sermone, sed qui factis sapit* [I judge wisdom not from speech but from action]. Make the best of him, a good orator is a turncoat, an evil man, *bonus orator pessimus vir*, his tongue is set to sale, he is a mere voice, as he said of a nightingale,[5] *dat sine mente sonum* [all sound and no sense], an hyperbolical liar, a flatterer, a parasite, and as Ammianus Marcellinus will, a corrupting cozener, one that doth more mischief by his fair speeches than he that bribes by money;[6] for a man may with more facility avoid him that circumvents by money, than he that deceives with glozing terms; which made Socrates so much abhor and explode them.[7] Fracastorius, a famous poet, freely grants all poets to be mad;[8] so doth Scaliger;[9] and who doth not? *Aut insanit homo, aut versus facit* [he 's mad or making verses], Hor. *Sat.* 7, *lib.* 2. *Insanire lubet, i.e. versus componere* ['tis one's humour to be mad, i.e. to write verse], Virg. *Ecl.* 3, so Servius interprets it, all poets are mad, a company of bitter satirists, detractors, or else parasitical applauders: and what is poetry itself but, as Austin holds, *vinum erroris ab ebriis doctoribus propinatum* [the wine of error presented by drunken teachers]? You may give that censure of them in general which Sir Thomas More once did of Germanus Brixius' poems in particular:

> *Vehunter*
> *In rate stultitiæ, sylvam habitant furiæ.*

[They sail in the bark of folly, they inhabit the grove of madness.]

Budæus, in an epistle of his to Lupsetus, will have civil law

to be the tower of wisdom; another honours physic, the quintessence of nature: a third tumbles them both down, and sets
up the flag of his own peculiar science.   Your supercilious critics,
grammatical triflers, note-makers, curious antiquaries, find out
all the ruins of wit, *ineptiarum delicias* [exquisite follies],
amongst the rubbish of old writers; *Pro stultis habent nisi aliquid
sufficiant invenire, quod in aliorum scriptis vertant vitio*,[1] all
fools with them that cannot find fault; they correct others,
and are hot in a cold cause, puzzle themselves to find out how
many streets in Rome, houses, gates, towers, Homer's country,
Æneas' mother, Niobe's daughters, *an Sappho publica fuerit?
ovum prius exstiterit an gallina?* [2] *etc., et alia quæ dediscenda essent
scire, si scires* [whether Sappho was a courtesan; whether the
the egg came first or the hen; and similar nonsense which, even
if one had learnt it, ought to be forgotten], as Seneca holds;[3]
what clothes the senators did wear in Rome, what shoes, how
they sat, where they went to the close-stool, how many dishes
in a mess, what sauce, which for the present for an historian
to relate, according to Lodovic. Vives,[4] is very ridiculous, is
to them most precious elaborate stuff, they admired for it, and
as proud, as triumphant in the meantime for this discovery,
as if they had won a city, or conquered a province; as rich as
if they had found a mine of gold ore.   *Quosvis auctores absurdis
commentis suis percacant et stercorant*, one saith, they bewray
and daub a company of books and good authors with their
absurd comments, *correctorum sterquilinia* Scaliger calls them,[5]
and show their wit in censuring others, a company of foolish
note-makers, humble-bees, dors, or beetles, *inter stercora ut plurimum versantur*, they rake over all those rubbish and dunghills,
and prefer a manuscript many times before the Gospel itself,
Thesaurum criticum [6] before any treasure, and with their *delea-
turs, alii legunt sic, meus codex sic habet* [omit, some read, my MS.
reads], with their *postremæ editiones* [last editions], annotations,
castigations, etc., make books dear, themselves ridiculous, and
do nobody good, yet if any man dare oppose or contradict, they
are mad, up in arms on a sudden, how many sheets are written
in defence, how bitter invectives, what apologies! *Epiphyllides
hæ sunt et meræ nugæ* [7] [these are poor grapes, mere trifles].
But I dare say no more of, for, with, or against them, because
I am liable to their lash as well as others.   Of these and the
rest of our artists and philosophers, I will generally conclude
they are a kind of madmen, as Seneca esteems of them,[8] to
make doubts and scruples, how to read them truly, to mend

old authors, but will not mend their own lives, or teach us *ingenia sanare, memoriam officiorum ingerere, ac fidem in rebus humanis retinere*, to keep our wits in order, or rectify our manners. *Numquid tibi demens videtur, si istis operam impenderit?* Is not he mad that draws lines with Archimedes, whilst his house is ransacked and his city besieged, when the whole world is in combustion, or we whilst our souls are in danger (*mors sequitur, vita fugit* [death follows, life flies]), to spend our time in toys, idle questions, and things of no worth?

That lovers are mad, I think no man will deny.[1] *Amare simul et sapere* [to love and to be wise], *ipsi Jovi non datur*, Jupiter himself cannot intend both at once.

> *Non bene conveniunt, nec in una sede morantur*
> *Majestas et amor.*[2]
>
> [Majesty and love pull different ways;
> Where one is throned, the other never stays.]

Tully, when he was invited to a second marriage, replied, he could not *simul amare et sapere*, be wise and love both together. *Est Orcus ille, vis est immedicabilis, est rabies insana*,[3] love is madness, a hell, an incurable disease; *impotentem et insanam libidinem* Seneca calls it,[4] an impotent and raging lust. I shall dilate this subject apart; in the meantime let lovers sigh out the rest.

Nevisanus the lawyer holds it for an axiom, "most women are fools,"[5] *consilium feminis invalidum*[6] [women's judgment is weak]; Seneca, men, be they young or old; who doubts it? Youth is mad, as Elius in Tully, *stulti adolescentuli*, old age little better, *deliri senes*, etc. Theophrastus, in the 107th year of his age, said he then began to be wise, *tum sapere cœpit*, and therefore lamented his departure.[7] If wisdom came so late, where shall we find a wise man? Our old ones dote at threescore and ten. I would cite more proofs, and a better author; but for the present, let one fool point at another. Nevisanus hath as hard an opinion of rich men,[8] "Wealth and wisdom cannot dwell together,"[9] *stultitiam patiuntur opes* [wealth and folly can go together], and they do commonly *infatuare cor hominis*,[10] besot men;[11] and as we see it, "fools have fortune": *Sapientia non invenitur in terra suaviter viventium*[12] [wisdom is not found in the land of those who live at ease]. For beside a natural contempt of learning which accompanies such kind of men, innate idleness (for they will take no pains), and which Aristotle observes,[1] *ubi mens plurima, ibi minima fortuna* [where there is most wit there is least wealth], *ubi plurima fortuna, ibi mens perexigua*, great wealth and little wit go commonly together: they have as much brains some of them in their heads as in their heels; besides this inbred neglect of liberal sciences and all arts, which should *excolere mentem*, polish the mind, they have most part some gullish humour or other, by which they are led; one is an epicure, an atheist, a second a gamester, a third a whoremaster (fit subjects all for a satirist to work upon);

Hic nuptarum insanit amoribus, hic puerorum; [2]

[One burns to madness for the wedded dame;
Unnatural lusts another's heart inflame;]

one is mad of hawking, hunting, cocking; another of carousing, horse-riding, spending; a fourth of building, fighting, etc.[3] *Insanit veteres statuas Damasippus emendo* [Damasippus hath a craze for buying old statues], Damasippus hath an humour of his own, to be talked of: Heliodorus the Carthaginian another.[4] In a word, as Scaliger concludes of them all, they are *statuæ erectæ stultitiæ*, the very statues or pillars of folly. Choose out of all stories him that hath been most admired, you shall still find *multa ad laudem, multa ad vituperationem magnifica* [there is much to praise, but also much to blame], as Berosus of Semiramis; [5] *omnes mortales militia, triumphis, divitiis, etc., tum et luxu, cæde, cæterisque vitiis antecessit* [she surpassed all men in military achievements and wealth, but also in profligacy, cruelty, and other vices]; as she had some good, so had she many bad parts.

Alexander, a worthy man, but furious in his anger, overtaken in drink; Cæsar and Scipio, valiant and wise, but vainglorious, ambitious; Vespasian, a worthy prince, but covetous; Hannibal, as he had mighty virtues, so had he many vices: [6] *unam virtutem mille vitia comitantur* [one virtue accompanied by a thousand vices], as Machiavel of Cosmus Medices,[7] he had two distinct persons in him. I will determine of them all, they are like these double or turning pictures; stand before which, you see a fair maid on the one side, an ape on the other, an owl; look upon them at the first sight, all is well; but further examine, you shall find them wise on the one side and fools on the other; in some few things praiseworthy, in the rest incomparably faulty. I will say nothing of their diseases, emulations, discontents, wants, and such miseries: let Poverty plead the rest in Aristophanes' *Plutus*.

Covetous men, amongst others, are most mad, they have all

the symptoms of melancholy, fear, sadness, suspicion, etc.,[1] as
shall be proved in his proper place.

Danda est hellebori multo pars maxima avaris.

[Misers make whole Anticyra their own;
Its hellebore reserv'd for them alone.]

And yet methinks prodigals are much madder than they, be
of what condition they will, that bear a public or private purse;
as a Dutch writer censured Richard, the rich Duke of Cornwall,
suing to be emperor, for his profuse spending,[2] *qui effudit
pecuniam ante pedes principium Electorum sicut aquam,* that
scattered money like water; I do censure them. *Stulta Anglia*
(saith he), *quæ tot denariis sponte est privata, stulti principes
Alemanniæ, qui nobile jus suum pro pecunia vendiderunt* [foolish
Britain, to lose so much money without need; foolish princes
of Germany, to sell their proud privileges for pelf]. Spendthrifts, bribers, and bribe-takers are fools, and so are all they
that cannot keep, disburse, or spend their moneys well.[3]

I might say the like of angry, peevish, envious, ambitious;
Anticyras melior sorbere meracas [4] [you were better to swallow
the Anticyræ undiluted]; epicures, atheists, schismatics, heretics;
hi omnes habent imaginationem læsam [they have all a diseased
imagination] (saith Nymannus), "and their madness shall be
evident" (2 Tim. iii, 9). Fabatus, an Italian, holds seafaring
men all mad; "the ship is mad, for it never stands still; the
mariners are mad, to expose themselves to such imminent
dangers: the waters are raging mad, in perpetual motion; the
winds are as mad as the rest, they know not whence they
come, whither they would go: and those men are maddest of all
that go to sea; for one fool at home, they find forty abroad." [5]
He was a madman that said it, and thou peradventure as mad
to read it. Felix Platerus [6] is of opinion all alchemists are
mad, out of their wits; Athenæus [7] saith as much of fiddlers, *et
musarum luscinias* [and those nightingales of the Muses],
musicians, *omnes tibicines insaniunt* [all flute-players are mad],
ubi semel efflant, avolat illico mens, [8] in comes music at one ear,
out goes wit at another. Proud and vainglorious persons are
certainly mad; and so are lascivious; [9] I can feel their pulses
beat hither; horn-mad some of them, to let others lie with
their wives, and wink at it.

To insist in all particulars [10] were an Herculean task, to reckon
up [11] *insanas substructiones, insanos labores, insanum luxum,* [12]
mad labours, mad books, endeavours, carriages, gross ignorance,

ridiculous actions, absurd gestures; *insanam gulam, insana jurgia* [mad gluttony, mad disputes], *insaniam villarum,* as Tully terms them, madness of villages, stupend structures; as those Egyptian pyramids, labyrinths, and sphinxes, which a company of crowned asses, *ad ostentationem opum* [to show off their wealth], vainly built, when neither the architect nor king that made them, or to what use and purpose, are yet known: to insist in their hypocrisy, inconstancy, blindness, rashness, *dementem temeritatem,* fraud, cozenage, malice, anger, impudence, ingratitude, ambition, gross superstition, *tempora infecta et adulatione sordida,*[1] as in Tiberius' times, such base flattery, stupend, parasitical fawning and colloguing, etc., brawls, conflicts, desires, contentions, it would ask an expert Vesalius to anatomize every member. Shall I say Jupiter himself, Apollo, Mars, etc., doted? and monster-conquering Hercules, that subdued the world and helped others, could not relieve himself in this, but mad he was at last. And where shall a man walk, converse with whom, in what province, city, and not meet with Signior Deliro,[2] or Hercules Furens, Mænades, and Corybantes? Their speeches say no less. *E fungis nati homines*[3] [they were men born from mushrooms], or else they fetched their pedigree from those that were struck by Samson with the jawbone of an ass; or from Deucalion and Pyrrha's stones, for *durum genus sumus, marmorei sumus,*[4] we are stony-hearted, and savour too much of the stock: as if they had all heard that enchanted horn of Astolpho, that English duke in Ariosto, which never sounded but all his auditors were mad, and for fear ready to make away with themselves; or landed in the mad haven in the Euxine Sea of *Daphne insana,* which had a secret quality to dementate;[5] they are a company of giddy-heads, afternoon-men, it is midsummer moon still, and the dog-days last all the year long, they are all mad. Whom shall I then except? Ulricus Huttenus' *Nemo;*[6] *nam, Nemo omnibus horis sapit, Nemo nascitur sine vitiis, Crimine Nemo caret, Nemo sorte sua vivit contentus, Nemo in amore sapit, Nemo bonus, Nemo sapiens, Nemo est ex omni parti beatus* [Nobody; for Nobody is sensible at all times; Nobody is born without fault; Nobody is free from blame; Nobody lives content with his own lot; Nobody is sane in love; Nobody is good, Nobody wise; Nobody is completely happy], etc., and therefore Nicholas Nemo, or Monsieur Nobody, shall go free. *Quid valeat Nemo, Nemo referre potest* [Nobody can say what Nobody is capable of]. But whom shall I except in the second place? such as are silent; *vir sapit qui pauca*

I—* E 886

loquitur [he is a wise man who says little]; no better way to avoid folly and madness than by taciturnity.[1] Whom in a third? all senators, magistrates; for all fortunate men are wise, and conquerors valiant, and so are all great men, *non est bonum ludere cum diis* [it is not good to play tricks with the gods], they are wise by authority, good by their office and place, *his licet impune pessimos esse* [they are privileged to be as bad as they like] (some say), we must not speak of them, neither is it fit; *per me sint omnia protinus alba* [everything shall be stainless for all that I shall say], I will not think amiss of them. Whom next? Stoics? *Sapiens Stoicus* [the Stoic is wise], and he alone is subject to no perturbations, as Plutarch scoffs at him, "he is not vexed with torments, or burnt with fire, foiled by his adversary, sold of his enemy: though he be wrinkled, sand-blind, toothless, and deformed, yet he is most beautiful, and like a god, a king in conceit, though not worth a groat." [2] "He never dotes, never mad, never sad, drunk, because virtue cannot be taken away," as Zeno holds, "by reason of strong apprehension," [3] but he was mad to say so. *Anticyræ cœlo huic est opus aut dolabra* [4] [he needs either the climate of Anticyra or a pickaxe], he had need to be bored, and so had all his fellows, as wise as they would seem to be. Chrysippus himself liberally grants them to be fools as well as others, at certain times, upon some occasions, *amitti virtutem ait per ebrietatem, aut atribilarium morbum*, it [virtue] may be lost by drunkenness or melancholy; he may be sometimes crazed as well as the rest: *ad summum sapiens nisi quum pituita molesta* [5] [unfailingly wise save when troubled with the phlegm]. I should here except some Cynics, Menippus, Diogenes, that Theban Crates; or to descend to these times, that omniscious, only wise fraternity of the Rosy Cross,[6] those great theologues, politicians, philosophers, physicians, philologers, artists, etc., of whom St. Bridget, Abbas Joacchimus, Leicenbergius, and such divine spirits have prophesied, and made promise to the world, if at least there be any such (Hen. Neuhusius makes a doubt of it,[7] Valentinus Andreas,[8] and others), or an Elias Artifex their Theophrastian master; whom though Libavius and many deride and carp at, yet some will have to be "the renewer of all arts and sciences," [9] reformer of the world, and now living, for so Johannes Montanus Strigoniensis, that great patron of Paracelsus, contends, and certainly avers "a most divine man," [10] and the quintessence of wisdom wheresoever he is; for he, his fraternity, friends, etc., are all "betrothed to wisdom," [11] if we may believe their disciples and followers. I must needs except Lipsius and the Pope, and expunge their name out of the catalogue of fools. For besides that parasitical testimony of Dousa,

A sole exoriente Mæotidas usque paludes,
Nemo est qui Justo se æquiparare queat,

[From the rising sun to the Mæotid Sea, not one can put himself on a level with Justus [1]],

Lipsius saith of himself, that he was *humani generis quidam pædagogus voce et stylo,*[2] a grand signior, a master, a tutor of us all, and for thirteen years he brags how he sowed wisdom in the Low Countries, as Ammonius the philosopher sometime did in Alexandria, *cum humanitate literas et sapientiam cum prudentia* [3] [polite learning and practical philosophy]: *antistes sapientiæ* [a master of wisdom], he shall be *sapientum octavus* [the eighth wise man]. The Pope is more than a man, as his parasites[4] often make him, a demi-god, and besides His Holiness cannot err, *in Cathedra* belike: and yet some of them have been magicians, heretics, atheists, children, and as Platina saith of John XXII, *Etsi vir literatus, multa stoliditatem et lævitatem præ se ferentia egit, stolidi et socordis vir ingenii,* a scholar sufficient, yet many things he did foolishly, lightly. I can say no more then in particular, but in general terms to the rest, they are all mad, their wits are evaporated, and, as Ariosto feigns (*lib.* 34), kept in jars above the moon.

Some lose their wits with love, some with ambition,
Some following lords and men of high condition.[5]
Some in fair jewels rich and costly set,
Others in poetry their wits forget.
Another thinks to be an alchemist,
Till all be spent, and that his number's mist.

Convict fools they are, madmen upon record; and I am afraid past cure many of them, *crepunt inguina,*[6] the symptoms are manifest, they are all of Gotham parish:

Quum furor haud dubius, quum sit manifesta phrenesis.[7]

[Since their madness is incontestable, their delirium plain.]

What remains then but to send for *lorarios,* those officers to carry them all together for company to Bedlam, and set Rabelais to be their physician.[8]

If any man shall ask in the meantime, who I am that so boldly censure others, *Tu nullane habes vitia?* have I no faults? Yes, more than thou hast, whatsoever thou art.[9] *Nos numerus sumus* [I am of the number], I confess it again, I am as foolish, as mad as any one.

> *Insanus vobis videor, non deprecor ipse,*
> *Quo minus insanus,*[1]

[You think me mad, I make no objection,]

I do not deny it, *demens de populo dematur* [let the madman be removed from society]. My comfort is, I have more fellows, and those of excellent note. And though I be not so right or so discreet as I should be, yet not so mad, so bad neither, as thou perhaps takest me to be.

To conclude, this being granted, that all the world is melancholy, or mad, dotes, and every member of it, I have ended my task, and sufficiently illustrated that which I took upon me to demonstrate at first. At this present I have no more to say. *His sanam mentem Democritus* [Democritus wishes them sanity], I can but wish myself and them a good physician, and all of us a better mind.

And although, for the above-named reasons, I had a just cause to undertake this subject, to point at these particular species of dotage, that so men might acknowledge their imperfections, and seek to reform what is amiss; yet I have a more serious intent at this time; and to omit all impertinent digressions, to say no more of such as are improperly melancholy, or metaphorically mad, lightly mad, or in disposition, as stupid, angry, drunken, silly, sottish, sullen, proud, vainglorious, ridiculous, beastly, peevish, obstinate, impudent, extravagant, dry, doting, dull, desperate, harebrain, etc., mad, frantic, foolish, heteroclites, which no new hospital [2] can hold, no physic help: my purpose and endeavour is, in the following discourse to anatomize this humour of melancholy, through all his parts and species, as it is an habit, or an ordinary disease, and that philosophically, medicinally, to show the causes, symptoms, and several cures of it, that it may be the better avoided; moved thereunto for the generality of it, and to do good, it being a disease "so frequent," as Mercurialis observes, "in these our days";[3] "so often happening," saith Laurentius, "in our miserable times,"[4] as few there are that feel not the smart of it. Of the same mind is Ælian Montaltus, Melancthon,[5] and others; Julius Cæsar Claudinus calls it "the fountain of all other diseases, and so common in this crazed age of ours, that scarce one in a thousand is free from it";[6] and that splenetic, hypochondriacal wind especially, which proceeds from the spleen and short ribs. Being then a disease so grievous, so common, I know not wherein to do a more general service, and spend my time better, than to prescribe means how to prevent and cure so universal a malady, an epidemical disease, that so often, so much, crucifies the body and mind.

If I have overshot myself in this which hath been hitherto said, or that it is, which I am sure some will object, too phantastical, "too light and comical for a divine, too satirical for one of my profession," I will presume to answer, with Erasmus [1] in like case, 'Tis not I, but Democritus, *Democritus dixit*: you must consider what it is to speak in one's own or another's person, an assumed habit and name—a difference betwixt him that affects or acts a prince's, a philosopher's, a magistrate's, a fool's part, and him that is so indeed—and what liberty those old satirists have had; it is a cento collected from others; not I, but they that say it.

> *Dixero si quid forte jocosius, hoc mihi juris*
> *Cum veniá dabis.* [2]
>
> [Yet some indulgence I may justly claim,
> If too familiar with another's fame.]

Take heed you mistake me not. If I do a little forget myself, I hope you will pardon it. And to say truth, why should any man be offended, or take exceptions at it?

> *Licuit, semperque licebit,*
> *Parcere personis, dicere de vitiis.*
>
> It lawful was of old, and still will be,
> To speak of vice, but let the name go free.

I hate their vices, not their persons. If any be displeased, or take aught unto himself, let him not expostulate or cavil with him that said it (so did Erasmus excuse himself to Dorpius,[3] *si parva licet componere magnis* [to compare small things with great]), and so do I; "but let him be angry with himself, that so betrayed and opened his own faults in applying it to himself: if he be guilty and deserve it, let him amend, whoever he is, and not be angry." [4] "He that hateth correction is a fool" (Prov. xii, 1). If he be not guilty, it concerns him not; it is not my freeness of speech, but a guilty conscience, a galled back of his own that makes him winch.

> *Suspicione si quis errabit sua,*
> *Et rapiet ad se, quod erit commune omnium,*
> *Stulte nudabit animi conscientiam.*
>
> [If any, thinking that himself is meant,
> Shall take offence at what is aimed at large,
> The more fool he, for all the world will see
> His guilty conscience.]

I deny not this which I have said savours a little of Democritus; *quamvis ridentem dicere verum quid vetat?*[1] one may speak in jest, and yet speak truth.   It is somewhat tart, I grant it; *acriora orexim excitant embammata*, as he said, sharp sauces increase appetite, *nec cibus ipse juvat morsu fraudatus aceti*[2] [food is not enjoyable without a dash of vinegar].   Object then, and cavil what thou wilt, I ward all with Democritus' buckler, his medicine shall salve it;[3] strike where thou wilt, and when: *Democritus dixit*, Democritus will answer it.   It was written by an idle fellow, at idle times, about our Saturnalian or Dionysian feasts, when, as he said, *nullum libertati periculum est* [there is no danger to liberty], servants in old Rome had liberty to say and do what them list.   When our countrymen sacrificed to their goddess Vacuna,[4] and sat tippling by their Vacunal fires. I writ this, and published this.   Οὖτις ἔλεγεν [no one has said it], it is *neminis nihil* [nothing by nobody].   The time, place, persons, and all circumstances apologize for me, and why may I not then be idle with others, speak my mind freely?   If you deny me this liberty, upon these presumptions I will take it: I say again, I will take it.

> *Si quis est qui dictum in se inclementius*
> *Existimavit esse, sic existimet.*[5]

[If any one thinks he has been insulted, let him think so.]

If any man take exceptions, let him turn the buckle of his girdle,[6] I care not.   I owe thee nothing (reader), I look for no favour at thy hands, I am independent, I fear not.

No, I recant, I will not, I care, I fear, I confess my fault, acknowledge a great offence,

> *Motos præstat componere fluctus.*

[Let 's first assuage the troubled waves.]

I have overshot myself, I have spoken foolishly, rashly, unadvisedly, absurdly, I have anatomized mine own folly.   And now methinks upon a sudden I am awaked as it were out of a dream; I have had a raving fit, a phantastical fit, ranged up and down, in and out, I have insulted over most kind of men, abused some, offended others, wronged myself; and now being recovered, and perceiving mine error, cry with Orlando,[7] *Solvite me*, pardon, *O boni* [good friends], that which is past, and I will make you amends in that which is to come; I promise you a more sober discourse in my following treatise.

If through weakness, folly, passion, discontent,[8] ignorance,

I have said amiss, let it be forgotten and forgiven. I acknowledge that of Tacitus to be true,[1] *Asperæ facetiæ, ubi nimis ex vero traxere, acrem sui memoriam relinquunt*, a bitter jest leaves a sting behind it: and as an honourable man observes, "They fear a satirist's wit, he their memories."[2] I may justly suspect the worst; and though I hope I have wronged no man, yet in Medea's words I will crave pardon.

> *Illud jam voce extrema peto,*
> *Ne si qua noster dubius effudit dolor,*
> *Maneant in animo verba, sed melior tibi*
> *Memoria nostri subeat, hæc iræ data*
> *Obliterentur.*

> And in my last words this I do desire,
> That what in passion I have said, or ire,
> May be forgotten, and a better mind
> Be had of us, hereafter as you find.

I earnestly request every private man, as Scaliger did Cardan, not to take offence. I will conclude in his lines, *Si me cognitum haberes, non solum donares nobis has facetias nostras, sed etiam indignum duceres, tam humanum animum, lene ingenium, vel minimam suspicionem deprecari oportere.* If thou knewest my modesty and simplicity,[3] thou wouldst easily pardon and forgive what is here amiss, or by thee misconceived. If hereafter, anatomizing this surly humour, my hand slip, as an unskilful prentice I lance too deep, and cut through skin and all at unawares, make it smart, or cut awry, pardon a rude hand, an unskilful knife,[4] 'tis a most difficult thing to keep an even tone, a perpetual tenor, and not sometimes to lash out; *difficile est satiram non scribere* [it is hard not to write a satire], there be so many objects to divert, inward perturbations to molest, and the very best may sometimes err; *aliquando bonus dormitat Homerus* [sometimes that excellent Homer takes a nap], it is impossible not in so much to overshoot; *opere in longo fas est obrepere somnum* [over such a long work a little sleep is permissible]. But what needs all this? I hope there will no such cause of offence be given; if there be, *Nemo aliquid recognoscat, nos mentimur omnia*[5] [let no one take these things to himself, they are all but fiction]. I 'll deny all (my last refuge), recant all, renounce all I have said, if any man except, and with as much facility excuse as he can accuse; but I presume of thy good favour, and gracious acceptance (gentle reader). Out of an assured hope and confidence thereof, I will begin.

LECTORI MALE FERIATO

Tu vero cave, sis, edico quisquis es, ne temere sugilles auctorem hujusce operis, aut cavillator irrideas.   Immo ne vel ex aliorum censura tacite obloquaris (vis dicam verbo) ne quid nasutulus inepte improbes, aut falso fingas.   Nam si talis revera sit, qualem præ se fert Junior Democritus, seniori Democrito saltem affinis, aut ejus genium vel tantillum sapiat, actum de te, censorem æque ac delatorem aget e contra (*petulanti splene cum sit*), sufflabit te in jocos, comminuet in sales, addo etiam, et Deo Risui te sacrificabit.[1]

Iterum moneo, ne quid cavillere, ne dum Democritum Juniorem conviciis infames, aut ignominiose vituperes, de te non male sentientem, tu idem audias ab amico cordato, quod olim vulgus Abderitanum ab Hippocrate,[2] concivem bene meritum et popularem suum Democritum pro insano habens.   *Ne tu Democrite sapis, stulti autem et insani Abderitæ.*

Abderitanæ pectora plebis habes.[3]

Hæc te paucis admonitum volo (male feriate Lector) abi.

[TO THE READER WHO EMPLOYS HIS LEISURE ILL

Whoever you may be, I caution you against rashly defaming the author of this work, or cavilling in jest against him.   Nay, do not silently reproach him in consequence of others' censure, nor employ your wit in foolish disapproval or false accusation. For, should Democritus Junior prove to be what he professes, even a kinsman of his elder namesake, or be ever so little of the same kidney, it is all up with you: he will become both accuser and judge of you in his petulant spleen, will dissipate you in jests, pulverize you with witticisms, and sacrifice you, I can promise you, to the God of Mirth.

Again I warn you against cavilling, lest, while you calumniate or disgracefully disparage Democritus Junior, who has no animosity against you, you should hear from some judicious friend

the very words the people of Abdera heard of old from Hippocrates, when they held their well-deserving and popular fellow-
citizen to be a madman: "Truly, it is you, Democritus, that are
wise, while the people of Abdera are fools and madmen." You
have no more sense than the people of Abdera. Having given
you this warning in a few words, O reader who employ your
leisure ill, farewell.]

HERACLITE, fleas, misero sic convenit ævo,
  Nil nisi turpe vides, nil nisi triste vides.
Ride etiam, quantumque lubet, Democrite, ride
  Non nisi vana vides, non nisi stulta vides.
Is fletu, hic risu modo gaudeat, unus utrique
  Sit licet usque labor, sit licet usque dolor.
Nunc opus est (nam totus eheu jam desipit orbis)
  Mille Heraclitis, milleque Democritis.
Nunc opus est (tanta est insania) transeat omnis
  Mundus in Anticyras, gramen in helleborum.

[WEEP, Heraclitus; here is food for tears
In this sad world of ours, where naught appears
  Save what is vile and full of bitterness.
Yet thou, Democritus, with equal right
At this same world mayest laugh with all thy might
  To see such dotage and such craziness.
With tears and laughter, each as seemed him best,
These two one aim pursued, one grief expressed.
They for their day sufficed; but since, mankind
Is grown to be more vicious and more blind,
And now had need that there should come to life
A thousand such; now madness is so rife
That to Anticyra all the world should pass,
And hellebore should sprout instead of grass.]

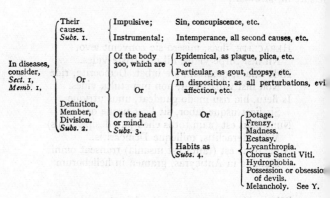

In diseases, consider, *Sect.* 1, *Memb.* 1,

Definition, Member, Division. *Subs.* 2.

Their causes. *Subs.* 1.

- Impulsive; — Sin, concupiscence, etc.
- Instrumental; — Intemperance, all second causes, etc.

Or

- Of the body 300, which are
  - Epidemical, as plague, plica, etc. or
  - Particular, as gout, dropsy, etc.

Or

- In disposition; as all perturbations, evi affection, etc.

- Of the head or mind. *Subs.* 3.

Or

- Dotage.
- Frenzy.
- Madness.
- Ecstasy.

Habits as *Subs.* 4.

- Lycanthropia.
- Chorus Sancti Viti.
- Hydrophobia.
- Possession or obsessio of devils.
- Melancholy. See Y.

Y Melancholy; in which consider

- Its Equivocations, in Disposition, Improper, etc. *Subsect.* 5.

Memb. 2. To its explication, a digression of anatomy in which observe parts of *Subs.* 1.

- Body hath parts *Subs.* 1.
  - contained as
    - Humours, 4. Blood, phlegm, ete
    - Spirits; vital, natural, animal.
  - or
  - containing
    - Similar; spermatical, or fles bones, nerves, etc. *Subs.* 3.
    - Dissimilar; brain, heart, liver, ete *Subs.* 4.
- Soul and its faculties, as
  - Vegetal. *Subs.* 5.
  - Sensible. *Subs.* 6, 7, 8.
  - Rational. *Subsect.* 9, 10, 11.

Memb. 3.
Its definition, name, difference, *Subs.* 1.
The part and parties affected, affection, etc. *Subs.* 2.
The matter of melancholy, natural, unnatural, etc. *Subs.* 4.

Species, or kinds, which are

- Proper to parts, as
  - Of the head alone, Hypochondriacal, or windy melancholy. Of the whole body.
  - with their sever causes, symptom prognostics, cure
- Or
- Indefinite; as love-melancholy, the subject of the thi Partition.

Its causes in general. *Sect.* 2, A.
Its symptoms or signs. *Sect.* 3, B.
Its prognostics or indications. *Sect.* 4, C.
Its cures; the subject of the second Partition.

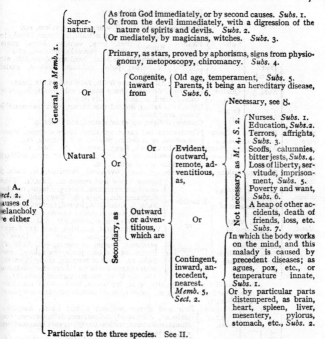

A.
ct. 2.
auses of
elancholy
e either

General, as *Memb.* 1.

Supernatural,
- As from God immediately, or by second causes. *Subs.* 1.
- Or from the devil immediately, with a digression of the nature of spirits and devils. *Subs.* 2.
- Or mediately, by magicians, witches. *Subs.* 3.

Natural

Or
- Primary, as stars, proved by aphorisms, signs from physiognomy, metoposcopy, chiromancy. *Subs.* 4.

Or
- Congenite, inward from
  - Old age, temperament, *Subs.* 5.
  - Parents, it being an hereditary disease, *Subs.* 6.

Secondary, as

Or
- Evident, outward, remote, adventitious, as,

as *M.* 4, *S.* 2.

Necessary, see 8.

Not necessary,
- Nurses. *Subs.* 1.
- Education, *Subs.* 2.
- Terrors, affrights, *Subs.* 3.
- Scoffs, calumnies, bitter jests, *Subs.* 4.
- Loss of liberty, servitude, imprisonment, *Subs.* 5.
- Poverty and want, *Subs.* 6.
- A heap of other accidents, death of friends, loss, etc. *Subs.* 7.

Outward or adventitious, which are

Or
- Contingent, inward, antecedent, nearest. *Memb.* 5, *Sect.* 2.
  - In which the body works on the mind, and this malady is caused by precedent diseases; as agues, pox, etc., or temperature innate, *Subs.* 1.
  - Or by particular parts distempered, as brain, heart, spleen, liver, mesentery, pylorus, stomach, etc., *Subs.* 2.

Particular to the three species. See II.

II
rticular
uses,
t. 2,
mb. 5,

Of head melancholy are, *Subs.* 3,

Inward
- Innate humour, or from distemperature adus
- A hot brain, corrupted blood in the brain.
- Excess of venery, or defect.
- Agues, or some precedent disease.
- Fumes arising from the stomach, etc.

or

Outward.
- Heat of the sun immoderate.
- A blow on the head.
- Overmuch use of hot wines, spices, garlic, onions, hot baths, overmuch waking, etc.
- Idleness, solitariness, or overmuch study, vehement labour, etc.
- Passions, perturbations, etc.

Of hypochondriacal, or windy melancholy are,

Inward
- Default of spleen, belly, bowels, stomach, mesentery, meseraic veins, liver, etc.
- Months or hemrods stopped, or any other ordinary evacuation.

or

Outward.
- Those six non-natural things abused.

Over all the body are, *Subs.* 5,

Inward
- Liver distempered, stopped, over-hot, apt to engender melancholy, temperature innate.

or

Outward.
- Bad diet, suppression of hemrods, etc., and such evacuations; passions, cares, etc.; those six non-natural things abused.

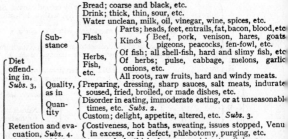

8
Necessary causes, as those six nonnatural things, which are, *Sect. 2, Memb. 2,*

Diet offending in, *Subs.* 3,

Substance

Bread; coarse and black, etc.
Drink; thick, thin, sour, etc.
Water unclean, milk, oil, vinegar, wine, spices, etc.

Flesh
Parts; heads, feet, entrails, fat, bacon, blood, etc.
Kinds { Beef, pork, venison, hares, goats, pigeons, peacocks, fen-fowl, etc.

Herbs, Fish, etc.
Of fish; all shell-fish, hard and slimy fish, etc.
Of herbs; pulse, cabbage, melons, garlic, onions, etc.
All roots, raw fruits, hard and windy meats.

Quality, as in
Preparing, dressing, sharp sauces, salt meats, indurate, soused, fried, broiled, or made dishes, etc.

Quantity
Disorder in eating, immoderate eating, or at unseasonable times, etc. *Subs.* 2.
Custom; delight, appetite, altered, etc. *Subs.* 3.

Retention and evacuation, *Subs.* 4. { Costiveness, hot baths, sweating, issues stopped, Venus in excess, or in defect, phlebotomy, purging, etc.

Air; hot, cold, tempestuous, dark, thick, foggy, moorish, etc. *Subs.* 5.

Exercise, *Sub.* 6. { Unseasonable, excessive, or defective, of body or mind, solitariness, idleness, a life out of action, etc.

Sleep and waking, unseasonable, inordinate, overmuch, overlittle, etc. *Subs.* 7

Memb. 3. *Sect.* 2. Passions and perturbations of the mind, *Subs.* 2, With a digression of the force of imagination, *Subs.* 2. and division of passions into, *Subs.* 3,

Irascible
Sorrow, cause and symptom, *Subs.* 4. Fear cause and symptom, *Subs.* 5. Shame, repulse, disgrace, etc., *Subs.* 6. Envy and malice, *Subs.* 7. Emulation, hatred, faction, desire of revenge, *Subs.* 8. Anger a cause, *Subs.* 9. Discontents, cares, miseries, etc. *Subs.* 10.

or

concupiscible.
Vehement desires, ambition, *Subs.* 11. Covetousness, φιλαργυρία, *Subs.* 12. Love of pleasures, gaming in excess, etc., *Subs.* 13 Desire of praise, pride, vainglory, etc. *Subs.* 14. Love of learning, study in excess, with a digression of the misery of scholars, and why the Muses are melancholy, *Subs.* 15.

B. Symptoms of melancholy are either, *Sect.* 3,

General, as of *Memb.* 1.

Body, as ill digestion, crudity, wind, dry brains, hard belly, thick blood, much waking, heaviness and palpitation of heart, leaping in many places, etc., *Subs.* 1.

or

Mind

Common to all or most.
Fear and sorrow without a just cause, suspicion, jealousy, discontent, solitariness, irksomeness, continual cogitations, restless thoughts, vain imaginations, etc. *Subs.* 2.

Or,

Celestial influences, as ♄, ♃, ♂, etc., parts of the body, heart, brain, liver, spleen, stomach, etc.

Humours
Sanguine are merry still, laughing, pleasant, meditating on plays, women, music, etc.
Phlegmatic, slothful, dull, heavy, etc.
Choleric, furious, impatient, subject to hear and see strange apparitions, etc.
Black, solitary, sad; they think they are bewitched, dead, etc.

Or mixed of these four humours adust, or not adust infinitely varied.

Particular to private persons, according to *Subs.* 3, 4.

Their several customs, conditions, inclinations, discipline, etc.
Ambitious thinks himself a king, lord; covetous runs on his money; lascivious on his mistress; religious has revelations, visions, is a prophet, troubled in mind; a scholar on his book, etc.

Continuance of time as the humour is intended or remitted, etc.
Pleasant at first, hardly discerned, afterwards harsh and intolerable, inveterate.

Hence some make three degrees, { 1. *Falso cogitat* 2. *Cogitata loqu* 3. *Exsequi locut*

By fits, or continuate, as the obj varies, pleasing, or displeasing.

Simple, or as it is mixed with other diseases, apoplexies, gout, *caninus appetit* etc., so the symptoms are various.

Particular symptoms to the three distinct species. *Sect. 3, Memb. 2.*

Head melancholy. *Subs. 1.*

In body — Headache, binding and heaviness, vertigo, lightness, singing of the ears, much waking, fixed eyes, high colour, red eyes, hard belly, dry body; no great sign of melancholy in the other parts.

Or

In mind. — Continual fear, sorrow, suspicion, discontent, superfluous cares, solicitude, anxiety, perpetual cogitation of such toys they are possessed with, thoughts like dreams, etc.

Hypochondriacal, or windy melancholy. *Subs. 2.*

In body — Wind, rumbling in the guts, belly-ache, heat in the bowels, convulsions, crudities, short wind, sour and sharp belchings, cold sweat, pain in the left side, suffocation, palpitation, heaviness of the heart, singing in the ears, much spittle, and moist, etc

Or

In mind. — Fearful, sad, suspicious, discontent, anxiety, etc. Lascivious by reason of much wind, troublesome dreams, affected by fits, etc.

Over all the body. *Subs. 3.*

In body — Black, most part lean, broad veins, gross, thick blood, their hemrods commonly stopped, etc.

Or

In mind. — Fearful, sad, solitary, hate light, averse from company, fearful dreams, etc.

Symptoms of nuns', maids', and widows' melancholy, in body and mind, etc.

A reason of these symptoms. *Memb. 3.*

Why they are so fearful, sad, suspicious without a cause, why solitary, why melancholy men are witty, why they suppose they hear and see strange voices, visions, apparitions.

Why they prophesy, and speak strange languages; whence comes their crudity, rumbling, convulsions, cold sweat, heaviness of heart, palpitation, cardiaca, fearful dreams, much waking, prodigious fantasies.

C Prognostics of melancholy. *Sect. 4.*

Tending to good, as — Morphew, scabs, itch, breaking out, etc. Black jaundice. If the hemrods voluntarily open. If varices appear.

Tending to evil, as — Leanness, dryness, hollow-eyed, etc. Inveterate melancholy is incurable. If cold, it degenerates often into epilepsy, apoplexy, dotage, or into blindness. If hot, into madness, despair, and violent death.

Corollaries and questions — The grievousness of this above all other diseases. The diseases of the mind are more grievous than those of the body. Whether it be lawful, in this case of melancholy, for a man to offer violence to himself. *Neg.* How a melancholy or mad man, offering violence to himself, is to be censured.

THE FIRST PARTITION

THE FIRST SECTION, MEMBER, SUBSECTION

Man's Excellency, Fall, Miseries, Infirmities; The causes of the

MAN, the most excellent and noble creature of the world, "the principal and mighty work of God, wonder of Nature," as Zoroaster calls him; *audacis naturæ miraculum* [Nature boldest and most marvellous stroke], "the marvel marvels,"[1] as Plato; "the abridgment and epitome of th world,"[2] as Pliny; *Microcosmus*, a little world, a model of th world, sovereign lord of the earth, viceroy of the world, so commander and governor of all the creatures in it;[3] to who empire they are subject in particular, and yield obedience; fa surpassing all the rest, not in body only, but in soul; *Imagin imago*,[4] created[5] to God's own image,[6] to that immortal an incorporeal substance, with all the faculties and powers belongir unto it; was at first pure, divine, perfect, happy, "created aft God in true holiness and righteousness";[7] *Deo congruens* [fitte for divinity], free from all manner of infirmities, and put Paradise, to know God, to praise and glorify Him, to do H will, *Ut dis consimiles parturiat deos* [that being like the go he may beget gods] (as an old poet saith) to propagate th Church.

But this most noble creature, *Heu tristis et lachrymo commutatio* (one exclaims[8]), O pitiful change! is fallen fro that he was, and forfeited his estate, become *miserabil homuncio*, a castaway, a caitiff, one of the most miserab creatures of the world, if he be considered in his own natur an unregenerate man, and so much obscured by his fa that (some few relics excepted) he is inferior to a beas "Man in honour that understandeth not, is like unto beas that perish,"[9] so David esteems him: a monster by stuper metamorphoses, a fox, a dog, a hog, what not?[10] *Quantu mutatus ab illo!* How much altered from that he was! befo blessed and happy, now miserable and accursed; "He mu eat his meat in sorrow,"[11] subject to death and all manner nfirmities, all kind of calamities. "Great travail is created for all men, and an heavy yoke on the sons of Adam, from the day that they go out of their mother's womb, unto that day they return to the mother of all things. Namely, their thoughts and fear of their hearts, and their imagination of things they wait for, and the day of death; from him that sitteth in the glorious throne, to him that sitteth beneath in the earth and ashes; from him that is clothed in blue silk and weareth a crown, to him that is clothed in simple linen. Wrath, envy, trouble, and unquietness, and fear of death, and rigour, and strife, and such things come to both man and beast, but seven-fold to the ungodly." [1] All this befalls him in this life, and peradventure eternal misery in the life to come.

The impulsive cause of these miseries in man, this privation or destruction of God's image, the cause of death and diseases, of all temporal and eternal punishments, was the sin of our first parent Adam, in eating of the forbidden fruit, by the devil's instigation and allurement.[2] His disobedience, pride, ambition, intemperance, incredulity, curiosity; from whence proceeded original sin and that general corruption of mankind, as from a fountain flowed all bad inclinations and actual transgressions, which cause our several calamities inflicted upon us for our sins. And this, belike, is that which our fabulous poets have shadowed unto us in the tale of Pandora's box, which, being opened through her curiosity, filled the world full of all manner of diseases.[3] It is not curiosity alone, but those other crying sins of ours, which pull these several plagues and miseries upon our heads. For *ubi peccatum, ibi procella* [where the sin is, there is the storm], as Chrysostom well observes.[4] "Fools, by reason of their transgression, and because of their iniquities, are afflicted." [5] Fear cometh like sudden desolation, and destruction like a whirlwind, affliction and anguish," [6] because they did not fear God. "Are you shaken with wars?" as Cyprian well urgeth Demetrius, "are you molested with dearth and famine? is our health crushed with raging diseases? is mankind generally tormented with epidemical maladies? 'tis all for your sins " [7] (Hag. i, 9, 10; Amos i; Jer. vii). God is angry, punisheth and threateneth, because of their obstinacy and stubbornness, they will not turn unto Him. "If the earth be barren then for want of rain, if dry and squalid, it yield no fruit, if your fountains be dried up, your wine, corn, and oil blasted, if the air be corrupted, and men troubled with diseases, 'tis by reason of their sins": [8] which like the blood of Abel cry loud to heaven

for vengeance. Lam. v, 15: "That we have sinned, therefore
our hearts are heavy." Is. lix, 11, 12: "We roar like bears,
and mourn like doves, and want health, etc., for our sins and
trespasses." But this we cannot endure to hear or to take
notice of (Jer. ii, 30): "We are smitten in vain and receive no
correction"; and (chap. v, 3): "Thou has stricken them, but they
have not sorrowed; they have refused to receive correction,
they have not returned." "Pestilence he hath sent, but they
have not turned to him" (Amos iv). Herod could not abide
John Baptist,[1] nor Domitian endure Apollonius to tell the
causes of the plague at Ephesus, his injustice, incest, adultery,
and the like.[2]

To punish therefore this blindness and obstinacy of ours as
a concomitant cause and principal agent, is God's just judgment in bringing these calamities upon us, to chastise us, I say
for our sins, and to satisfy God's wrath. For the law requires
obedience or punishment, as you may read at large (Deut. xxviii
15): "If they will not obey the Lord, and keep his command-
ments and ordinances, then all these curses shall come upon
them. Cursed in the town and in the field, etc.[3] Cursed in
the fruit of the body, etc.[4] The Lord shall send thee
trouble and shame, because of thy wickedness."[5] And a
little after, "The Lord shall smite thee with the botch of
Egypt, and with emrods, and scab, and itch, and thou canst
not be healed.[6] With madness, blindness, and astonishing of
heart."[7] This Paul seconds (Rom. ii, 9): "Tribulation and
anguish on the soul of every man that doth evil." Or else these
chastisements are inflicted upon us for our humiliation, to
exercise and try our patience here in this life, to bring us home,
to make us to know God ourselves, to inform and teach us
wisdom. "Therefore is my people gone into captivity, because
they had no knowledge; therefore is the wrath of the Lord
kindled against his people, and he hath stretched out his hand
upon them."[8] He is desirous of our salvation, *nostræ saluti
avidus*, saith Lemnius,[9] and for that cause pulls us by the ear
many times, to put us in mind of our duties: "That they which
erred might have understanding" (as Isaiah speaks, xxix, 24)
"and so to be reformed."[10] "I am afflicted, and at the point of
death," so David confesseth of himself (Ps. lxxxviii, 15, 9); "mine
eyes are sorrowful through mine affliction"; and that made
him turn unto God. Great Alexander in the midst of all his
prosperity, by a company of parasites deified, and now made
a god, when he saw one of his wounds bleed, remembered that

he was but a man, and remitted of his pride. *In morbo recolligit se animus*, as Pliny well perceived;[1] "In sickness the mind reflects upon itself, with judgment surveys itself, and abhors its former courses"; insomuch that he concludes to his friend Marius, "that it were the period of all philosophy, if we could so continue sound, or perform but a part of that which we promised to do, being sick."[2] "Whoso is wise, then, will consider these things," as David did (Ps. cvii, verse last); and whatso-ever fortune befall him, make use of it. If he be in sorrow, need, sickness, or any other adversity, seriously to recount with himself, why this or that malady, misery, this or that incurable disease is inflicted upon him; it may be for his good, *sic expedit*,[3] as Peter said of his daughter's ague. Bodily sick-ness is for his soul's health, *periisset nisi periisset*, had he not been visited, he had utterly perished; for "the Lord correcteth him whom he loveth, even as a father doth his child in whom he delighteth."[4] If he be safe and sound on the other side, and free from all manner of infirmity; *et cui*

> *Gratia, forma, valetudo contingat abunde*
> *Et mundus victus, non deficiente crumena;*[5]

> And that he have grace, beauty, favour, health,
> A cleanly diet, and abound in wealth;

yet in the midst of his prosperity, let him remember that caveat of Moses, "Beware that he do not forget the Lord his God";[6] that he be not puffed up, but acknowledge them to be his good gifts and benefits, and "the more he hath, to be more thankful"[7] (as Agapetianus adviseth), and use them aright.

Now the instrumental causes of these our infirmities are as diverse as the infirmities themselves; stars, heavens, elements, etc., and all those creatures which God hath made, are armed against sinners. They were indeed once good in themselves, and that they are now many of them pernicious unto us, is not in their nature, but our corruption, which hath caused it. For, from the fall of our first parent Adam, they have been changed, the earth accursed, the influence of stars altered, the four elements, beasts, birds, plants, are now ready to offend us. "The principal things for the use of man, are water, fire, iron, salt, meal, wheat, honey, milk, oil, wine, clothing, good to the godly, to the sinners turned to evil" (Ecclus. xxxix, 26). "Fire, and hail, and famine, and dearth, all these are created for vengeance" (Ecclus. xxxix, 29).

The heavens threaten us with their comets, stars, planets, with
their great conjunctions, eclipses, oppositions, quartiles, and
such unfriendly aspects; the air with his meteors, thunder
and lightning, intemperate heat and cold, mighty winds, tempests, unseasonable weather; from which proceed dearth, famine,
plague, and all sorts of epidemical diseases, consuming infinite
myriads of men. At Cairo in Egypt, every third year (as it is
related by Boterus,[1] and others), 300,000 die of the plague;
and 200,000 in Constantinople, every fifth or seventh at the
utmost. How doth the earth terrify and oppress us with
terrible earthquakes, which are most frequent in China, Japan,
and those eastern climes,[2] swallowing up sometimes six cities
at once! How doth the water rage with his inundations,
irruptions, flinging down towns, cities, villages, bridges, etc.,
besides shipwrecks! whole islands are sometimes suddenly overwhelmed with all their inhabitants in Zealand,[3] Holland, and
many parts of the continent drowned, as the Lake Erne in
Ireland.[4] *Nihilque præter arcium cadavera patenti cernimus
freto*[5] [we see nothing save the wreckage of cities upon the
spreading waters]. In the fens of Friesland, 1230, by reason
of tempests, the sea drowned *multa hominum millia, et jumenta
sine numero*[6] [many thousands of human beings and cattle
without number], all the country almost, men and cattle in it.
How doth the fire rage, that merciless element, consuming in
an instant whole cities! What town of any antiquity or note
hath not been once, again and again, by the fury of this merciless
element, defaced, ruinated, and left desolate? In a word,

> *Ignis pepercit, unda mergit, aeris*
> *Vis pestilentis æquori ereptum necat,*
> *Bello superstes, tabidus morbo perit.*[7]

> Whom fire spares, sea doth drown; whom sea,
> Pestilent air doth send to clay;
> Whom war 'scapes, sickness takes away.

To descend to more particulars, how many creatures are a
deadly feud with men! lions, wolves, bears, etc., some with
hoofs, horns, tusks, teeth, nails. How many noxious serpent
and venomous creatures, ready to offend us with stings, breath
sight, or quite kill us! How many pernicious fishes, plants
gums, fruits, seeds, flowers, etc., could I reckon up on a sudden
which by their very smell, many of them, touch, taste, cause
some grievous malady, if not death itself! Some make mention
of a thousand several poisons: but these are but trifles in respect
The greatest enemy to man is man, who by the devil's instiga

tion is still ready to do mischief, his own executioner, a wolf,
a devil to himself and others.[1]   We are all brethren in Christ,
or at least should be, members of one body, servants of one
Lord, and yet no fiend can so torment, insult over, tyrannize,
vex, as one man doth another.   Let me not fall therefore (saith
David, when wars, plague, famine were offered) into the hands
of men, merciless and wicked men:

> *Vix sunt homines hoc nomine digni,*
> *Quamque lupi sævæ plus feritatis habent.*[2]

> [Though men in shape, they scarce deserve the name;
> Their savagery doth put the wolves to shame.]

We can most part foresee these epidemical diseases, and likely
avoid them.   Dearths, tempests, plagues, our astrologers foretell
us; earthquakes, inundations, ruins of houses, consuming
fires, come by little and little, or make some noise beforehand;
but the knaveries, impostures, injuries, and villainies of men no
art can avoid.   We can keep our professed enemies from our
cities by gates, walls, and towers, defend ourselves from thieves
and robbers by watchfulness and weapons; but this malice of
men, and their pernicious endeavours, no caution can divert,
no vigilancy foresee, we have so many secret plots and devices
to mischief one another.

Sometimes by the devil's help, as magicians, witches; sometimes by impostures, mixtures,[3] poisons, stratagems, single
combats, wars, we hack and hew, as if we were *ad internecionem
nati*, like Cadmus' soldiers born to consume one another. 'Tis
an ordinary thing to read of an hundred and two hundred
thousand men slain in a battle; besides all manner of tortures,
brazen bulls, racks, wheels, strappadoes, guns, engines, etc. *Ad
unum corpus humanum supplicia plura quam membra:* we
have invented more torturing instruments than there be several
members in a man's body, as Cyprian well observes.[4] To come
nearer yet, our own parents by their offences, indiscretion, and
intemperance, are our mortal enemies.   "The fathers have eaten
our grapes, and the children's teeth are set on edge." [5] They
cause our grief many times, and put upon us hereditary diseases,
inevitable infirmities: they torment us, and we are ready to
injure our posterity:

> *mox daturi progeniem vitiosiorem,*[6]

> [And yet with crimes to us unknown,
> Our sons shall mark the coming age their own,]

and the latter end of the world, as Paul foretold,[7] is still like to

be the worst. We are thus bad by nature, bad by kind, but
far worse by art, every man the greatest enemy unto himself.
We study many times to undo ourselves, abusing those good
gifts which God hath bestowed upon us, health, wealth, strength,
wit, learning, art, memory to our own destruction: *Perditio tua
ex te* [1] [thy destruction is from thyself]. As Judas Maccabæus
killed Apollonius with his own weapons,[2] we arm ourselves to
our own overthrows; and use reason, art, judgment, all that
should help us, as so many instruments to undo us. Hector
gave Ajax a sword, which, so long as he fought against enemies,
served for his help and defence; but after he began to hurt
harmless creatures with it, turned to his own hurtless bowels.
Those excellent means God hath bestowed on us, well employed,
cannot but much avail us; but if otherwise perverted, they ruin
and confound us: and so by reason of our indiscretion and
weakness they commonly do, we have too many instances.
This St. Austin acknowledgeth of himself in his humble Confessions: "Promptness of wit, memory, eloquence, they were
God's good gifts, but he did not use them to His glory." If you
will particularly know how, and by what means, consult
physicians, and they will tell you that it is in offending in
some of those six non-natural things, of which I shall dilate
more at large;[3] they are the causes of our infirmities, our surfeiting and drunkenness, our immoderate, insatiable lust and
prodigious riot. *Plures crapula quam gladius* is a true saying,
the board consumes more than the sword. Our intemperance
it is that pulls so many several incurable diseases upon our
heads, that hastens old age,[4] perverts our temperature, and
brings upon us sudden death. And last of all, that which
crucifies us most, is our own folly, madness (*quos Jupiter perdit
dementat;* by subtraction of His assisting grace God permits it)
weakness, want of government, our facility and proneness in
yielding to several lusts, in giving way to every passion and
perturbation of the mind: by which means we metamorphose
ourselves and degenerate into beasts. All which that prince of
poets [5] observed of Agamemnon, that when he was well pleased
and could moderate his passion, he was *os oculosque Jovi par*
like Jupiter in feature, Mars in valour, Pallas in wisdom, another
god; but when he became angry, he was a lion, a tiger, a dog
etc., there appeared no sign or likeness of Jupiter in him; so
we, as long as we are ruled by reason, correct our inordinate
appetite, and conform ourselves to God's word, are as so many
saints: but if we give reins to lust, anger, ambition, pride, and

follow our own ways, we degenerate into beasts, transform ourselves, overthrow our constitutions, provoke God to anger,[1] and heap upon us this of melancholy, and all kinds of incurable diseases, as a just and deserved punishment of our sins.

SUBSECT. II.—*The Definition, Number, Division of Diseases*

What a disease is, almost every physician defines. Fernelius calleth it an "affection of the body contrary to nature";[2] Fuchsius and Crato, "an hindrance, hurt, or alteration of any action of the body, or part of it";[3] Tholosanus, "a dissolution of that league which is between body and soul, and a perturbation of it, as health [is] the perfection and makes to the preservation of it";[4] Labeo, in A. Gellius, "an ill habit of the body, opposite to nature, hindering the use of it";[5] others otherwise, all to this effect.

How many diseases there are, is a question not yet determined; Pliny reckons up 300 from the crown of the head to the sole of the foot:[6] elsewhere he saith, *morborum infinita multitudo*, their number is infinite. Howsoever it was in those times, it boots not; in our days I am sure the number is much augmented:

> *Macies et nova febrium*
> *Terris incubuit cohors.*[7]

[New wasting maladies have swarmed upon mankind.]

For besides many epidemical diseases unheard of, and altogether unknown to Galen and Hippocrates, as *scorbutum*, smallpox, *olica*, sweating sickness, *morbus Gallicus*, etc., we have many proper and peculiar almost to every part.

No man amongst us so sound, of so good a constitution, that hath not some impediment of body or mind. *Quisque suos patimur manes*, we have all our infirmities, first or last, more or less. There will be peradventure in an age, or one of a thousand, like Zenophilus the musician in Pliny,[8] that may haply live 105 years without any manner of impediment; a Pollio Romulus, that can preserve himself "with wine and oil";[9] a man as fortunate as Q. Metellus, of whom Valerius so much brags; a man as healthy as Otto Herwardus, a senator of Augsburg in Germany, whom Leovitius the astrologer brings in for an example and instance of certainty in his art;[10] who, because he had the significators in his geniture fortunate, and free from the hostile aspects of Saturn and Mars, being a very old man, "could not remember

that ever he was sick." [1] Paracelsus [2] may brag that he could
make a man live 400 years or more, if he might bring him up
from his infancy, and diet him as he list; and some physicians
hold, that there is no certain period of man's life; but it may
still by temperance and physic be prolonged. We find in the
meantime, by common experience, that no man can escape,
but that of Hesiod is true: [3]

> Πλείη μὲν γὰρ γαῖα κακῶν, πλείη δὲ θάλασσα,
> Νοῦσοι δ' ἀνθρώποισιν ἐφ' ἡμέρῃ ἠδ' ἐπὶ νυκτὶ
> Αὐτόματοι φοιτῶσι.
>
> Th' earth's full of maladies, and full the sea,
> Which set upon us both by night and day.

If you require a more exact division of these ordinary diseases
which are incident to men, I refer you to physicians; [4] they
will tell you of acute and chronic, first and secondary, *lethales,
salutares*, errant, fixed, simple, compound, connexed, or conse-
quent, belonging to parts or the whole, in habit, or in disposition, etc. My division at this time (as most befitting my
purpose) shall be into those of the body and mind. For them
of the body, a brief catalogue of which Fuschius hath made
(*Institut. lib.* 3, *sect.* 1, *cap.* 11), I refer you to the voluminous
tomes of Galen, Aretæus, Rhasis, Avicenna, Alexander, Paulus,
Aetius, Gordonerius; and those exact neoterics, Savanarola,
Capivaccius, Donatus Altomarus, Hercules de Saxonia, Mercurialis, Victorius Faventinus, Wecker, Piso, etc., that have
methodically and elaborately written of them all. Those of the
mind and head I will briefly handle, and apart.

SUBSECT. III.—*Division of the Diseases of the Head*

These diseases of the mind, forasmuch as they have their
chief seat and organs in the head, are commonly repeated
amongst the diseases of the head, which are divers, and vary
much according to their site. For in the head, as there be
several parts, so there be divers grievances, which according
to that division of Heurnius [5] (which he takes out of Arculanus)
are inward or outward (to omit all others which pertain to eyes
and ears, nostrils, gums, teeth, mouth, palate, tongue, wesel
chops, face, etc.) belonging properly to the brain, as baldness,
falling of hair, furfur, lice, etc. Inward belonging to the skins
next to the brain, called *dura* and *pia mater*, as all headaches
etc.,[6] or to the ventricles, cauls, kells, tunicles, creeks, and part

of it, and their passions, as *caro*,[1] vertigo, incubus, apoplexy,
falling sickness. The diseases of the nerves, cramps, stupor,
convulsion, tremor, palsy; or belonging to the excrements of
the brain, catarrhs, sneezing, rheums, distillations: or else those
that pertain to the substance of the brain itself, in which are
conceived frenzy, lethargy, melancholy, madness, weak memory,
sopor or coma, *vigilia* [sleeplessness], and *vigil coma*.[2] Out of these
again I will single such as properly belong to the phantasy,
or imagination, or reason itself, which Laurentius [3] calls the
diseases of the mind; and Hildesheim, *morbos imaginationis,
aut rationis læsæ* [diseases of the imagination, or of injured
reason], which are three or four in number, frenzy, madness,
melancholy, dotage, and their kinds: as hydrophobia, lycanthropia, *chorus Sancti Viti, morbi dæmoniaci* [St. Vitus's dance,
possession of devils], which I will briefly touch and point at,
insisting especially in this of melancholy, as more eminent than
the rest, and that through all his kinds, causes, symptoms,
prognostics, cures: as Lonicerus hath done *de apoplexia*, and
many other of such particular diseases. Not that I find fault
with those which have written of this subject before, as Jason
Pratensis, Laurentius, Montaltus, T. Bright, etc., they have
done very well in their several kinds and methods; yet that
which one omits, another may haply see; that which one contracts, another may enlarge. To conclude with Scribanius,[4]
"that which they had neglected, or perfunctorily handled, we
may more thoroughly examine; that which is obscurely delivered in them, may be perspicuously dilated and amplified by
us," and so made more familiar and easy for every man's
capacity, and the common good, which is the chief end of my
discourse.

Subsect. IV.—*Dotage, Madness, Frenzy, Hydrophobia, Lycanthropia, Chorus Sancti Viti, Ecstasis*

Dotage, fatuity, or folly, is a common name to all the
following species, as some will have it. Laurentius [5] and
Altomarus [6] comprehended madness, melancholy, and the rest
under this name, and call it the *summum genus* of them
all. If it be distinguished from them, it is natural or
ingenite, which comes by some defect of the organs, and overmuch brain, as we see in our common fools; and is for the most
part intended or remitted in particular men, and thereupon
some are wiser than others: or else it is acquisite, an appendix

or symptom of some other disease, which comes or goes; or if it
continue, a sign of melancholy itself.

Phrenitis, which the Greeks derive from the word φρήν,
is a disease of the mind, with a continual madness or dotage,
which hath an acute fever annexed, or else an inflammation of the brain, or the membranes or kells of it, with an
acute fever, which causeth madness and dotage. It differs
from melancholy and madness, because their dotage is without
an ague: this continual, with waking, or memory decayed, etc.
Melancholy is most part silent, this clamorous; and many such
like differences are assigned by physicians.

Madness, frenzy, and melancholy are confounded by
Celsus, and many writers; others leave out frenzy, and
make madness and melancholy but one disease, which
Jason Pratensis[1] especially labours, and that they differ only
secundum majus or *minus*, in quantity alone, the one being a
degree to the other, and both proceeding from one cause. They
differ *intenso et remisso gradu*, saith Gordonius,[2] as the humour is
intended or remitted. Of the same mind is Aretæus,[3] Alexander
Trallianus, Guianerius, Savonarola, Heurnius; and Galen
himself writes promiscuously of them both by reason of their
affinity: but most of our neoterics do handle them apart, whom
I will follow in this treatise. Madness is therefore defined to
be a vehement dotage, or raving without a fever, far more violent
than melancholy, full of anger and clamour, horrible looks,
actions, gestures, troubling the patients with far greater vehe-
mency both of body and mind, without all fear and sorrow, with
such impetuous force and boldness that sometimes three or
four men cannot hold them. Differing only in this from frenzy,
that it is without a fever, and their memory is most part better.
It hath the same causes as the other, as choler adust, and blood
incensed, brains inflamed, etc. Fracastorius adds a due
time and full age to this definition, to distinguish it from
children, and will have it confirmed impotency, to separate it
from such as accidentally come and go again, as by taking henbane, nightshade, wine, etc.[4] Of this fury there be divers
kinds: ecstasy, which is familiar with some persons, [5] as Cardan
saith of himself, he could be in one when he list; in which the
Indian priests deliver their oracles, and the witches in Lapland,
as Olaus Magnus writeth (*lib.* 3, *cap.* 18), *ecstasi omnia prædicere*,
answer all questions in an ecstasy you will ask; as what your
friends do, where they are, how they fare, etc. The other species
of this fury are enthusiasms, revelations, and visions, so often

mentioned by Gregory and Beda in their works; obsession or possession of devils, sibylline prophets, and poetical furies; such as
come by eating noxious herbs, tarantulas stinging, etc., which
some reduce to this. The most known are these: lycanthropia,
hydrophobia, *chorus Sancti Viti.*

Lycanthropia, which Avicenna calls *cucubuth,* others *lupinam
insaniam,* or wolf-madness, when men run howling about
graves and fields in the night, and will not be persuaded
but that they are wolves, or some such beasts. Aetius [1]
and Paulus [2] call it a kind of melancholy; but I should
rather refer it to madness as most do. Some make a doubt of it
whether there be any such disease. Donat. ab Altomari saith
that he saw two of them in his time.[3] Wierus tells a story of
such a one at Padua 1541,[4] that would not believe to the
contrary but that he was a wolf. He hath another instance of a
Spaniard, who thought himself a bear. Forestus confirms as
much by many examples; [5] one amongst the rest of which he
was an eye-witness at Alcmaar in Holland, a poor husbandman
that still hunted about graves, and kept in churchyards, of a
pale, black, ugly, and fearful look. Such belike, or little better,
were King Prœtus' daughters, that thought themselves kine.[6]
And Nebuchadnezzar in Daniel, as some interpreters hold, was
only troubled with this kind of madness. This disease perhaps
gave occasion to that bold assertion of Pliny, "some men were
turned into wolves in his time, and from wolves to men again"; [7]
and to that fable of Pausanias, of a man that was ten years a
wolf and afterwards turned to his former shape; to Ovid's tale
of Lycaon,[8] etc. He that is desirous to hear of this disease, or
more examples, let him read Austin in his 18th book *de Civitate
Dei, cap.* 5; Mizaldus, *cent.* 5, 77; Sckenkius, *lib.* 1; Hildesheim,
Spicil. 2, *de mania;* Forrestus, *lib.* 10, *de morbis cerebri;* Olaus
Magnus; Vincentius Bellovacensis, *Spec. nat. lib.* 31, *cap.* 122;
Pierius, Bodine, Zuinger, Zeilger, Peucer, Wierus, Sprenger, etc.
This malady, said Avicenna, troubleth men most in February,
and is nowadays frequent in Bohemia and Hungary, according
to Heurnius.[9] Scheretzius will have it common in Livonia.
They lie hid most part all day, and go abroad in the night, howling at graves and deserts; "they have usually hollow eyes,
scabbed legs and thighs, very dry and pale," [10] saith Altomarus; [11]
he gives a reason there of all the symptoms, and sets down a
brief cure of them.

Hydrophobia is a kind of madness, well known in every
village, which comes by the biting of a mad dog, or scratching,

saith Aurelianus; [1] touching or smelling alone sometimes, as
Sckenkius proves,[2] and is incident to many other creatures as
well as men: so called because the parties affected cannot endure
the sight of water, or any liquor, supposing still they see a mad
dog in it. And which is more wonderful, though they be very
dry (as in this malady they are), they will rather die than
drink. Cælius Aurelianus,[3] an ancient writer, makes a doubt
whether this hydrophobia be a passion of the body or the mind.
The part affected is the brain: the cause, poison that comes from
the mad dog, which is so hot and dry that it consumes all the
moisture in the body. Hildesheim [4] relates of some that died
so mad; and being cut up, had no water, scarce blood, or any
moisture left in them. To such as are so affected, the fear of
water begins at fourteen days after they are bitten, to some
again not till forty or sixty days after: commonly, saith Heurnius, they begin to rave, fly water and glasses, to look red and
swell in the face, about twenty days after (if some remedy be
not taken in the meantime) to lie awake, to be pensive, sad, to
see strange visions, to bark and howl, to fall into a swoon, and
oftentimes fits of the falling sickness. Some say, little things
like whelps will be seen in their urines.[5] If any of these signs
appear, they are past recovery. Many times these symptoms will
not appear till six or seven months after, saith Codronchus; [6] and
sometimes not till seven or eight years, as Guianerius; twelve
as Albertus; six or eight months after, as Galen holds. Baldus,
the great lawyer died of it: an Augustine friar and a woman in
Delft, that were Forestus' patients,[7] were miserably consumed
with it. The common cure in the country (for such at least as
dwell near the seaside) is to duck them over head and ears
in sea-water; some use charms: every goodwife can prescribe
medicines. But the best cure to be had in such cases is from the
most approved physicians; they that will read of them may
consult with Dioscorides, *lib.* 6, *cap.* 37, Heurnius, Hildesheim,
Capivaccius, Forestus, Sckenkius, and before all others
Codronchus, an Italian, who hath lately written two exquisite
books on the subject.

Chorus Sancti Viti, or St. Vitus' dance; the lascivious dance
Paracelsus calls it,[8] because they that are taken from it can do
nothing but dance till they be dead or cured. It is so called
for that the parties so troubled were wont to go to St. Vitus for
help, and after they had danced there awhile, they were certainly freed.[9] 'Tis strange to hear how long they will dance
and in what manner, over stools, forms, tables; even great

bellied women sometimes (and yet never hurt their children)
will dance so long that they can stir neither hand nor foot, but
seem to be quite dead. One in red clothes they cannot abide.
Music above all things they love, and therefore magistrates in
Germany will hire musicians to play to them, and some lusty
sturdy companions to dance with them. This disease hath
been very common in Germany, as appears by those relations of
Sckenkius,[1] and Paracelsus in his book of Madness, who brags
how many several persons he hath cured of it. Felix Platerus,
de mentis alienat. cap. 3, reports of a woman in Basil whom he
saw, that danced a whole month together. The Arabians call
it a kind of palsy. Bodine, in his 5th book *de Repub. cap.* 1,
speaks of this infirmity; Monavius in his last epistle to Scoltzius,
and in another to Dudithus, where you may read more of it.

The last kind of madness or melancholy, is that demoniacal
(if I may so call it) obsession or possession of devils, which
Platerus and others would have to be preternatural: stupend
things are said of them, their actions, gestures, contortions,
fasting, prophesying, speaking languages they were never
taught, etc. Many strange stories are related of them, which
because some will not allow (for Deacon and Darrel have written
large volumes on this subject pro and con) I voluntarily omit.

Fuchsius, *Institut. lib.* 3, *sec.* 1, *cap.* 11, Felix Plater,[2] Laurentius,[3] add to these another fury that proceeds from love,
and another from study, another divine or religious fury; but
these more properly belong to melancholy; of all which I will
speak apart,[4] intending to write a whole book of them.

SUBSECT. V.—*Melancholy in Disposition, improperly so called.*
Equivocations

Melancholy, the subject of our present discourse, is either in
disposition or habit. In disposition, is that transitory melancholy which goes and comes upon every small occasion of
sorrow, need, sickness, trouble, fear, grief, passion, or perturbation of the mind, any manner of care, discontent, or thought,
which causeth anguish, dullness, heaviness, and vexation of
spirit, any ways opposite to pleasure, mirth, joy, delight,
causing frowardness in us, or a dislike. In which equivocal
and improper sense, we call him melancholy that is dull,
sad, sour, lumpish, ill-disposed, solitary, anyway moved or displeased. And from these melancholy dispositions, no man living
is free, no Stoic, none so wise, none so happy, none so patient,

so generous, so godly, so divine, that can vindicate himself;
so well composed, but more or less, some time or other, he feel
the smart of it. Melancholy in this sense is the character o
mortality. "Man that is born of a woman, is of short con
tinuance, and full of trouble." [2] Zeno, Cato, Socrates himsel
whom Ælian so highly commends for a moderate temper, tha
"nothing could disturb him, but going out, and coming in, sti
Socrates kept the same serenity of countenance, what miser
soever befell him," [3] (if we may believe Plato his disciple) wa
much tormented with it. Q. Metellus, in whom Valerius give
instance of all happiness, "the most fortunate man then living
born in that most flourishing city of Rome, of noble parentage
a proper man of person, well qualified, healthful, rich, honour
able, a senator, a consul, happy in his wife, happy in his children,
etc.,[4] yet this man was not void of melancholy, he had hi
share of sorrow. Polycrates Samius,[5] that flung his ring int
the sea, because he would participate of discontent with other
and had it miraculously restored to him again shortly after, b
a fish taken as he angled, was not free from melancholy dis
positions. No man can cure himself; the very gods had bitte
pangs, and frequent passions, as their own poets put upon them
In general, "as the heaven, so is our life, sometimes fai
sometimes overcast, tempestuous and serene; as in
rose, flowers and prickles; in the year itself, a temperat
summer sometimes, a hard winter, a drouth, and then agai
pleasant showers: so is our life intermixed with joys, hope
fears, sorrows, calumnies." [7] *Invicem cedunt dolor et volupta*
there is a succession of pleasure and pain.

Medio de fonte leporum,
Surgit amari aliquid quod in ipsis floribus angat.[8]

[From out the very fountain of delight,
Rises some gall, our merriment to blight.]

"Even in the midst of laughing there is sorrow" (as Solomo
holds [9]): even in the midst of all our feasting and jollity, a
Austin infers in his Com. on the Forty-first Psalm,[10] there
grief and discontent. *Inter delicias semper aliquid sævi ne*
strangulat [in the midst of our enjoyment something hars
chokes us]; for a pint of honey thou shalt here likely find
gallon of gall, for a dram of pleasure a pound of pain, for a
inch of mirth an ell of moan; as ivy doth an oak, these miseri
encompass our life, and 'tis most absurd and ridiculous fo
any mortal man to look for a perpetual tenor of happiness i

is life. Nothing so prosperous and pleasant, but it hath some
bitterness in it, some complaining, some grudging;[1] it is all
λυκύπικρον [bitter-sweet], a mixed passion, and like a chequer-
able, black and white men; families, cities, have their falls and
vanes, now trines, sextiles, then quartiles and oppositions. We
are not here as those angels, celestial powers and bodies, sun
and moon, to finish our course without all offence, with such
constancy, to continue for so many ages: but subject to
infirmities, miseries, interrupt, tossed and tumbled up and
down, carried about with every small blast, often molested and
disquieted upon each slender occasion, uncertain, brittle, and so
is all that we trust unto.[2] "And he that knows not this is not
armed to endure it, is not fit to live in this world" (as one condoles
our time), "he knows not the condition of it, where with a
reciprocal tie pleasure and pain are still united, and succeed
one another in a ring."[3] *Exi e mundo*, get thee gone hence,
if thou canst not brook it; there is no way to avoid it, but to
arm thyself with patience, with magnanimity,[4] to oppose thyself
unto it, to suffer affliction as a good soldier of Christ, as Paul
adviseth,[5] constantly to bear it. But forasmuch as so few can
embrace this good counsel of his, or use it aright, but rather as
so many brute beasts give a way to their passion, voluntarily
subject and precipitate themselves into a labyrinth of cares,
woes, miseries, and suffer their souls to be overcome by them,
cannot arm themselves with that patience as they ought to do,
it falleth out oftentimes that these dispositions become habits, and
"many affects contemned" (as Seneca notes [6]) "make a disease."
Even as "one distillation, not yet grown to custom, makes
a cough, but continual and inveterate causeth a consumption of
the lungs"; so do these our melancholy provocations: and
according as the humour itself is intended or remitted in men,
as their temperature of body, or rational soul, is better able to
make resistance; so are they more or less affected. For that
which is but a flea-biting to one, causeth insufferable torment
to another; and which one by his singular moderation and well-
composed carriage can happily overcome, a second is no whit
able to sustain, but upon every small occasion of misconceived
abuse, injury, grief, disgrace, loss, cross, rumour, etc. (if solitary
or idle), yields so far to passion, that his complexion is altered,
his digestion hindered, his sleep gone, his spirits obscured, and
his heart heavy, his hypochondries misaffected; wind, crudity
on a sudden overtake him, and he himself overcome with
melancholy. As it is with a man imprisoned for debt, if once

in the jail, every creditor will bring his action against him, an
there likely hold him; if any discontent seize upon a patient
in an instant all other perturbations (for *qua data porta ruun*
[they rush out wherever there is an opening]) will set upo
him, and then like a lame dog or broken-winged goose he droop
and pines away, and is brought at last to that ill habit o
malady of melancholy itself. So that as the philosophers mak
eight degrees of heat and cold,[1] we may make eighty-eight o
melancholy, as the parts affected are diversely seized with i
or have been plunged more or less into this infernal gulf, o
waded deeper into it. But all these melancholy fits, howsoeve
pleasing at first, or displeasing, violent and tyrannizing ove
those whom they seize on for the time; yet these fits I say, o
men affected, are but improperly so called, because they con
tinue not, but come and go, as by some objects they are moved
This melancholy of which we are to treat, is a habit, *morbi
sonticus* or *chronicus*, a chronic or continuate disease, a settle
humour, as Aurelianus [3] and others [4] call it, not errant, bu
fixed; and as it was long increasing, so now being (pleasant, o
painful) grown to an habit, it will hardly be removed.

SECT. I. MEMB. II.

SUBSECT. I.—*Digression of Anatomy*

BEFORE I proceed to define the disease of melancholy, what
is, or to discourse further of it, I hold it not impertinent to mak
a brief digression of the anatomy of the body and faculties o
the soul, for the better understanding of that which is to follov
because many hard words will often occur, as myrach, hyp
condries, hemrods, etc., imagination, reason, humours, spirit
vital, natural, animal, nerves, veins, arteries, chylus, pituita
which by the vulgar will not so easily be perceived, what the
are, how cited, and to what end they serve. And besides,
may peradventure give occasion to some men to examine mo
accurately, search farther into this most excellent subject, ar
thereupon with that royal prophet to praise God ("for a ma
is fearfully and wonderfully made, and curiously wrought"[5
that have time and leisure enough, and are sufficiently informe
in all other worldly businesses as to make a good bargain, bu
and sell, to keep and make choice of a fair hawk, hound, hors
etc. But for such matters as concern the knowledge of ther

elves, they are wholly ignorant and careless; they know not
what this body and soul are, how combined, of what parts and
faculties they consist, or how a man differs from a dog. And
what can be more ignominious and filthy (as Melancthon well
inveighs[1]) "than for a man not to know the structure and
composition of his own body, especially since the knowledge of
it tends so much to the preservation of his health and information of his manners?" To stir them up therefore to this study,
to peruse those elaborate works of Galen,[2] Bauhinus, Plater,
Vesalius, Fallopius, Laurentius, Remelinus, etc., which have
written copiously in Latin; or that which some of our industrious
countrymen have done in our mother tongue, not long since,
as that translation of Columbus,[3] and *Microcosmographia*,[4] in
thirteen books, I have made this brief digression. Also because
Vecker,[5] Melancthon,[6] Fernelius,[7] Fuchsius,[8] and those tedious
tracts *de Anima* (which have more compendiously handled and
written of this matter) are not at all times ready to be had, to
give them some small taste, or notice of the rest, let this
epitome suffice.

SUBSECT. II.—*Division of the Body, Humours, Spirits*

Of the parts of the body there may be many divisions: the
most approved is that of Laurentius,[9] out of Hippocrates: which
, into parts contained, or containing. Contained, are either
humours or spirits.

A humour is a liquid or fluent part of the body, comprehended
in it, for the preservation of it; and is either innate or born
with us, or adventitious and acquisite. The radical or innate is
daily supplied by nourishment, which some call cambium, and
make those secondary humours of ros and gluten to maintain
: or acquisite, to maintain these four first primary humours,
coming and proceeding from the first concoction in the liver, by
which means chylus is excluded. Some divide them into profitable and excrementitious. But Crato,[10] out of Hippocrates,
will have all four to be juice, and not excrements, without which
no living creature can be sustained: which four, though they
be comprehended in the mass of blood, yet they have their
several affections, by which they are distinguished from one
another, and from those adventitious, peccant, or diseased
humours, as Melancthon calls them.[11]

Blood is a hot, sweet, temperate, red humour, prepared in
the meseraic veins, and made of the most temperate parts of

the chylus in the liver, whose office is to nourish the whole body
to give it strength and colour, being dispersed by the vein
through every part of it. And from it spirits are first begotten
in the heart, which afterwards by the arteries are communicated
to the other parts.

Pituita, or phlegm, is a cold and moist humour, begotten o
the colder part of the chylus (or white juice coming out of the
meat digested in the stomach), in the liver; his office is to
nourish and moisten the members of the body which, as the
tongue, are moved, that they be not over-dry.

Choler is hot and dry, bitter, begotten of the hotter parts o
the chylus, and gathered to the gall: it helps the natural hea
and senses, and serves to the expelling of excrements.

Melancholy, cold and dry, thick, black, and sour, begotten o
the more feculent part of nourishment, and purged from the
spleen, is a bridle to the other two hot humours, blood and
choler, preserving them in the blood, and nourishing the bones
These four humours have some analogy with the four elements
and to the four ages in man.

To these humours you may add serum, which is the matter
of urine, and those excrementitious humours of the third
concoction, sweat and tears.

Spirit is a most subtle vapour, which is expressed from the
blood, and the instrument of the soul, to perform all his actions
a common tie or medium between the body and the soul, as some
will have it; or as Paracelsus, a fourth soul of itself.[1] Melanc
thon holds the fountain of these spirits to be the heart, begotten
there; and afterward conveyed to the brain, they take another
nature to them. Of these spirits there be three kinds, according
to the three principal parts, brain, heart, liver; natural, vital
animal. The natural are begotten in the liver, and thenc
dispersed through the veins, to perform those natural actions
The vital spirits are made in the heart of the natural, which by
the arteries are transported to all the other parts: if the spirit
cease, then life ceaseth, as in a syncope or swooning. The
animal spirits, formed of the vital, brought up to the brain
and diffused by the nerves to the subordinate members, give
sense and motion to them all.

Subsect. III.—*Similar Parts*

Containing parts, by reason of their more solid substance
are either homogeneal or heterogeneal, similar or dissimilar

so Aristotle divides them, *lib. 1, cap. 1, de hist. animal.*;
Laurentius, *cap. 20, lib. 1.* Similar, or homogeneal, are such
as, if they be divided, are still severed into parts of the same
nature, as water into water. Of these some be spermatical,
some fleshy or carnal. Spermatical are such as are immediately
begotten of the seed, which are bones, gristles, ligaments,
membranes, nerves, arteries, veins, skins, fibres or strings, fat.[1]

The bones are dry and hard, begotten of the thickest
of the seed, to strengthen and sustain other parts: some say
there be 304, some 307, or 313 in man's body. They have
no nerves in them, and are therefore without sense.

A gristle is a substance softer than bone, and harder than the
rest, flexible, and serves to maintain the parts of motion.

Ligaments are they that tie the bones together, and other
parts to the bones, with their subserving tendons. Membranes'
office is to cover the rest.

Nerves, or sinews, are membranes without, and full of marrow
within; they proceed from the brain, and carry the animal
spirits for sense and motion. Of these some be harder, some
softer; the softer serve the senses, and there be seven pair of
them. The first be the optic nerves, by which we see; the
second move the eyes; the third pair serve for the tongue to
taste; the fourth pair for the taste in the palate; the fifth belong
to the ears; the sixth pair is most ample, and runs almost over
all the bowels; the seventh pair moves the tongue. The harder
sinews serve for the motion of the inner parts, proceeding from
the marrow in the back, of whom there be thirty combinations,
seven of the neck, twelve of the breast, etc.

Arteries are long and hollow, with a double skin to
convey the vital spirits; to discern which the better, they say
that Vesalius the anatomist was wont to cut up men alive.
They arise in the left side of the heart, and are principally two,
from which the rest are derived, aorta and venosa:[2] aorta is
the root of all the other, which serve the whole body; the other
goes to the lungs, to fetch air to refrigerate the heart.

Veins are hollow and round, like pipes, arising from the
liver, carrying blood and natural spirits; they feed all the
parts. Of these there be two chief, *vena porta* and *vena cava*,
from which the rest are corrivated. That *vena porta* is a vein
coming from the concave of the liver, and receiving those
meseraical veins, by whom he takes the chylus from the stomach
and guts, and conveys it to the liver. The other derives blood
from the liver to nourish all the other dispersed members. The

branches of that *vena porta* are the meseraical and hæmor-
rhoids. The branches of the *cava* are inward or outward.
Inward, seminal or emulgent. Outward, in the head, arms,
feet, etc., and have several names.

Fibræ are strings, white and solid, dispersed through the
whole member, and right, oblique, transverse, all which have
their several uses. Fat is a similar part, moist, without
blood, composed of the most thick and unctuous matter of
the blood. The skin covers the rest, and hath *cuticulam*, or
a little skin, under it.[1] Flesh is soft and ruddy, composed of
the congealing of blood, etc.

SUBSECT. IV.—*Dissimilar Parts*

Dissimilar parts are those which we call organical or instrumental, and they be inward or outward. The chiefest outward
parts are situate forward or backward: forward, the crown and
foretop of the head, skull, face, forehead, temples, chin, eyes,
ears, nose, etc., neck, breast, chest, upper and lower part of
the belly, hypochondries, navel, groin, flank, etc.; backward,
the hinder part of the head, back, shoulders, sides, loins, hip
bones, *os sacrum*, buttocks, etc. Or joints, arms, hands, feet,
legs, thighs, knees, etc. Or common to both, which, because
they are obvious and well known, I have carelessly repeated
*eaque præcipua et grandiora tantum; quod reliquum ex libris de
anima qui volet, accipiat* [and then only the larger and more
important; the rest can be found in books on anatomy].

Inward organical parts, which cannot be seen, are divers in
number, and have several names, functions, and divisions; but
that of Laurentius is most notable, into noble or ignoble parts.
Of the noble there be three principal parts, to which all the rest
belong, and whom they serve—brain, heart, liver; according to
whose site, three regions, or a threefold division, is made of the
whole body. As first of the head, in which the animal organs
are contained, and brain itself, which by his nerves gives sense
and motion to the rest, and is, as it were, a privy counsellor
and chancellor to the heart. The second region is the chest
or middle belly, in which the heart as king keeps his court, and
by his arteries communicates life to the whole body. The third
region is the lower belly, in which the liver resides as a legate *a
latere*, with the rest of those natural organs, serving for concoction, nourishment, expelling of excrements. This lower
region is distinguished from the upper by the midriff, or

diaphragma, and is subdivided again by some[1] into three concavities or regions, upper, middle, and lower. The upper of
the hypochondries, in whose right side is the liver, the left the
spleen; from which is denominated hypochondriacal melancholy.
The second of the navel and flanks, divided from the first by
the rim. The last of the watercourse, which is again subdivided
into three other parts. The Arabians make two parts of this
region, epigastrium and hypogastrium, upper or lower. Epigastrium they call *myrach*, from whence comes *myrachialis melancholia*, sometimes mentioned of them. Of these several regions
I will treat in brief apart; and first of the third region, in which
the natural organs are contained.

But you that are readers, in the meantime "suppose you were
now brought into some sacred temple, or majestical palace" (as
Melancthon saith), "to behold not the matter only, but the
singular art, workmanship, and counsel of this our great Creator.
And 'tis a pleasant and profitable speculation, if it be considered
aright."[2] The parts of this region, which present themselves
to your consideration and view, are such as serve to nutrition
or generation. Those of nutrition serve to the first or second
concoction; as the œsophagus or gullet, which brings meat and
drink into the stomach. The ventricle or stomach, which is
seated in the midst of that part of the belly beneath the midriff,
the kitchen, as it were, of the first concoction, and which turns
our meat into chylus. It hath two mouths, one above, another
beneath. The upper is sometimes taken for the stomach itself;
the lower and nether door (as Wecker calls it) is named pylorus.
This stomach is sustained by a large kell or caul, called omen-
um; which some will have the same with peritoneum, or rim of
the belly. From the stomach to the very fundament are produced the guts, or intestina, which serve a little to alter and
distribute the chylus and convey away the excrements. They
are divided into small and great, by reason of their site and
substance, slender or thicker: the slender is duodenum, or whole
gut, which is next to the stomach, some twelve inches long,
saith Fuchsius.[3] Jejunum, or empty gut, continuate to the
other, which hath many meseraic veins annexed to it, which
take part of the chylus to the liver from it. Ilion, the third,
which consists of many crinkles, which serves with the rest to
receive, keep, and distribute the chylus from the stomach..
The thick guts are three, the blind gut, colon, and right gut.
The blind is a thick and short gut, having one mouth, in which
the ilion and colon meet: it receives the excrements, and conveys

them to the colon. This colon hath many windings, that the excrements pass not away too fast: the right gut is straight, and conveys the excrements to the fundament, whose lower part is bound up with certain muscles called sphincters, that the excrements may be the better contained, until such time as a man be willing to go to the stool. In the midst of these guts is situated the mesenterium or midriff, composed of many veins, arteries, and much fat, serving chiefly to sustain the guts. All these parts serve the first concoction. To the second, which is busied either in refining the good nourishment or expelling the bad, is chiefly belonging the liver, like in colour to congealed blood, the shop of blood, situate in the right hypochondry, in figure like to a half-moon—*generosum membrum*, Melancthon styles it, a generous part; it serves to turn the chylus to blood, for the nourishment of the body. The excrements of it are either choleric or watery, which the other subordinate parts convey. The gall, placed in the concave of the liver, extracts choler to it: the spleen, melancholy; which is situate on the left side, over against the liver, a spongy matter, that draws this black choler to it by a secret virtue, and feeds upon it, conveying the rest to the bottom of the stomach, to stir up appetite, or else to the guts as an excrement. That watery matter the two kidneys expurgate by those emulgent veins and ureters. The emulgent draw this superfluous moisture from the blood; the two ureters convey it to the bladder, which, by reason of his site in the lower belly, is apt to receive it, having two parts, neck and bottom: the bottom holds the water, the neck is constringed with a muscle, which, as a porter, keeps the water from running out against our will.

Members of generation are common to both sexes, or peculiar to one; which, because they are impertinent to my purpose, I do voluntarily omit.

Next in order is the middle region, or chest, which comprehends the vital faculties and parts; which (as I have said) is separated from the lower belly by the diaphragma or midriff, which is a skin consisting of many nerves, membranes; and amongst other uses it hath, is the instrument of laughing. There is also a certain thin membrane, full of sinews, which covereth the whole chest within, and is called pleura, the seat of the disease called pleurisy, when it is inflamed; some add a third skin, which is termed mediastinus, which divides the chest into two parts, right and left. Of this region the principal part is the heart, which is the seat and fountain of life, of heat, of spirits, of pulse and respiration, the sun of our body, the king and sole commander of it, the seat and organ of all passions and affections. *Primum vivens, ultimum moriens*, it lives first and dies last in all creatures. Of a pyramidical form, and not much unlike to a pineapple; a part worthy of admiration, that can yield such variety of affections, by whose motion it is dilated or contracted, to stir and command the humours in the body:[1] as in sorrow, melancholy; in anger, choler; in joy, to send the blood outwardly; in sorrow, to call it in; moving the humours as horses do a chariot. This heart, though it be one sole member, yet it may be divided into two creeks right and left. The right is like the moon increasing, bigger than the other part, and receives blood from *vena cava*, distributing some of it to the lungs to nourish them; the rest to the left side, to engender spirits. The left creek hath the form of a cone, and is the seat of life, which, as a torch doth oil, draws blood unto it, begetting of it spirits and fire; and as fire in a torch, so are spirits in the blood; and by that great artery called aorta it sends vital spirits over the body, and takes air from the lungs by that artery which is called venosa; so that both creeks have their vessels, the right two veins, the left two arteries, besides those two common anfractuous ears, which serve them both; the one to hold blood, the other air, for several uses. The lungs is a thin, spongy part, like an ox-hoof (saith Fernelius[2]), the town-clerk or crier (one terms it), the instrument of voice, as an orator to a king;[3] annexed to the heart, to express his thoughts by voice. That it is the instrument of voice is manifest, in that no creature can speak, or utter any voice, which wanteth these lights. It is, besides, the instrument of respiration, or breathing; and its office is to cool the heart, by sending air unto it, by the venosal artery, which vein comes to the lungs by that *aspera arteria*, which consists of many gristles, membranes, nerves, taking in air at the nose and mouth, and by it likewise exhales the fumes of the heart.

In the upper region serving the animal faculties, the chief organ is the brain, which is a soft, marrowish, and white substance, engendered of the purest part of seed and spirits, included by many skins, and seated within the skull or brain-pan; and it is the most noble organ under heaven, the dwelling-house and seat of the soul, the habitation of wisdom, memory, judgment, reason, and in which man is most like unto God; and therefore nature hath covered it with a skull of hard bone, and two skins or membranes, whereof the one is called *dura mater*, or

meninx, the other *pia mater*. The *dura mater* is next to the
skull, above the other, which includes and protects the brain.
When this is taken away, the *pia mater* is to be seen, a thin
membrane, the next and immediate cover of the brain, and not
covering only, but entering into it. The brain itself is divided
into two parts, the fore and hinder part; the fore part is much
bigger than the other, which is called the little brain in respect
of it. This fore part hath many concavities distinguished
by certain ventricles, which are the receptacles of the spirits,
brought hither by the arteries from the heart, and are there
refined to a more heavenly nature, to perform the actions of
the soul. Of these ventricles there be three—right, left, and
middle. The right and left answer to their site, and beget
animal spirits; if they be anyway hurt, sense and motion
ceaseth. These ventricles, moreover, are held to be the seat
of the common sense. The middle ventricle is a common
concourse and cavity of them both, and hath two passages—
the one to receive pituita, and the other extends itself to the
fourth creek; in this they place imagination and cogitation,
and so the three ventricles of the fore part of the brain are
used. The fourth creek behind the head is common to the
cerebel, or little brain, and marrow of the backbone, the last
and most solid of all the rest, which receives the animal spirits
from the other ventricles, and conveys them to the marrow in
the back, and is the place where they say the memory is seated.

Subsect. V.—*Of the Soul and her Faculties*

According to Aristotle,[1] the soul is defined to be ἐντελέχεια,
*perfectio et actus primus corporis organici, vitam habentis in
potentia*, the perfection or first act of an organical body, having
power of life, which most philosophers approve.[2] But many
doubts arise about the essence, subject, seat, distinction, and
subordinate faculties of it. For the essence and particular
knowledge, of all other things it is most hard (be it of man or
beast) to discern, as Aristotle himself,[3] Tully,[4] Picus Mirandula,[5]
Tolet,[6] and other neoteric philosophers confess. "We can understand all things by her, but what she is we cannot apprehend." [7]
Some therefore make one soul, divided into three principal
faculties; others, three distinct souls: which question of late
hath been much controverted by Piccolomineus and Zabarel.
Paracelsus will have four souls, adding to the three grand
faculties a spiritual soul:[8] which opinion of his Campanella

in his book *de sensu rerum*,[1] much labours to demonstrate and
prove, because carcasses bleed at the sight of the murderer;
with many such arguments; and some again, one soul of all
creatures whatsoever, differing only in organs;[2] and that beasts
have reason as well as men, though, for some defect of organs,
not in such measure. Others make a doubt whether it be all
in all, and all in every part; which is amply discussed in Zabarel
amongst the rest. The common division of the soul is into three
principal faculties — vegetal, sensitive, and rational,[3] which
make three distinct kinds of living creatures: vegetal plants,
sensible beasts, rational men. How these three principal
faculties are distinguished and connected, *humano ingenio
inaccessum videtur*, is beyond human capacity, as Taurellus,[4]
Philip, Flavius, and others suppose. The inferior may be alone,
but the superior cannot subsist without the other; so sensible
includes vegetal, rational both; which are contained in it (saith
Aristotle) *ut trigonus in tetragono*, as a triangle in a quadrangle.

Vegetal, the first of the three distinct faculties, is defined
to be a "substantial act of an organical body, by which it
is nourished, augmented, and begets another like unto itself."
In which definition, three several operations are specified—
altrix, auctrix, procreatrix; the first is nutrition, whose object
is nourishment, meat, drink, and the like;[5] his organ the liver
in sensible creatures; in plants, the root or sap. His office is
to turn the nutriment into the substance of the body nourished,
which he performs by natural heat. This nutritive operation
hath four other subordinate functions or powers belonging to
it: attraction, retention, digestion, expulsion.

Attraction is a ministering faculty, which, as a loadstone
doth iron, draws meat into the stomach, or as a lamp doth
oil;[6] and this attractive power is very necessary in plants,
which suck up moisture by the root, as another mouth, into the
sap, as a like stomach.

Retention keeps it, being attracted unto the stomach until
such time it be concocted; for if it should pass away straight,
the body could not be nourished.

Digestion is performed by natural heat; for as the flame
of a torch consumes oil, wax, tallow, so doth it alter and digest
the nutritive matter. Indigestion is opposite unto it, for want
of natural heat. Of this digestion there be three differences:
maturation, elixation, assation.

Maturation is especially observed in the fruits of trees; which
are then said to be ripe when the seeds are fit to be sown

again.. Crudity is opposed to it, which gluttons, epicures, and idle persons are most subject unto, that use no exercise to stir natural heat, or else choke it, as too much wood puts out a fire.

Elixation is the seething of meat in the stomach, by the said natural heat, as meat is boiled in a pot; to which corruption or putrefaction is opposite.

Assation is a concoction of the inward moisture by heat; his opposite is semiustulation.

Besides these three several operations of digestion there is a four-fold order of concoction: mastication, or chewing in the mouth; chylification of this so chewed meat in the stomach; the third is in the liver, to turn this chylus into blood, called sanguification; the last is assimilation, which is in every part.

Expulsion is a power of nutrition by which it expels all superfluous excrements, and relics of meat and drink, by the guts, bladder, pores; as by purging, vomiting, spitting, sweating, urine, hairs, nails, etc.

As this nutritive faculty serves to nourish the body, so doth the augmenting faculty (the second operation or power of the vegetal faculty) to the increasing of it in quantity according to all dimensions, long, broad, thick, and to make it grow till it come to his due proportion and perfect shape; which hath his period of augmentation, as of consumption; and that most certain, as the poet observes:

> *Stat sua cuique dies, breve et irreparabile tempus*
> *Omnibus est vitæ.*
>
> A term of life is set to every man,
> Which is but short, and pass it no one can.

The last of these vegetal faculties is generation, which beget another by means of seed like unto itself, to the perpetual preservation of the species. To this faculty they ascribe three subordinate operations: the first to turn nourishment into seed, etc.

Necessary concomitants or affections of this vegetal faculty are life, and his privation, death. To the preservation of life the natural heat is most requisite, though siccity and humidity, and those first qualities, be not excluded. This heat is likewise in plants, as appears by their increasing, fructifying, etc., though not so easily perceived. In all bodies it must have radical moisture to preserve it, that it be not consumed;[1] to which preservation our clime, country, temperature, and the good or bad use of those six non-natural things avail much. For as this natural heat and moisture decays, so doth our life itself; and if not prevented before by some violent accident, or interrupted through our own default, is in the end dried up by old age, and extinguished by death for want of matter, as a lamp for defect of oil to maintain it.

Subsect. VI.—*Of the Sensible Soul*

Next in order is the sensible faculty, which is as far beyond the other in dignity as a beast is preferred to a plant, having those vegetal powers included in it. 'Tis defined "an act of an organical body, by which it lives, hath sense, appetite, judgment, breath, and motion." His object in general is a sensible or passible quality, because the sense is affected with it. The general organ is the brain, from which principally the sensible operations are derived. This sensible soul is divided into two parts, apprehending or moving. By the apprehensive power we perceive the species of sensible things, present or absent, and retain them as wax doth the print of a seal. By the moving the body is outwardly carried from one place to another, or inwardly moved by spirits and pulse. The apprehensive faculty is subdivided into two parts, inward or outward. Outward, as the five senses, of touching, hearing, seeing, smelling, tasting, to which you may add Scaliger's sixth sense of titillation, if you please; or that of speech, which is the sixth external sense, according to Lullius. Inward are three—common sense, phantasy, memory. Those five outward senses have their object in outward things only, and such as are present, as the eye sees no colour except it be at hand, the ear [no] sound. Three of these senses are of commodity, hearing, sight, and smell; two of necessity, touch and taste, without which we cannot live. Besides the sensitive power is active or passive; active in sight, the eye sees the colour; passive when it is hurt by his object, as the eye by the sunbeams; according to that axiom, *Visibile forte destruit sensum* [excessive brightness in an object destroys the sight]; or if the object be not pleasing, as a bad sound to the ear, a stinking smell to the nose, etc.

Of these five senses, sight is held to be most precious, and the best, and that by reason of his object; it sees the whole body at once; by it we learn, and discern all things, a sense most excellent for use. To the sight three things are required, the object, the organ, and the medium. The object in general is visible, or that which is to be seen, as colours, and all shining bodies. The medium is the illumination of the air which comes from light,[1] commonly called *diaphanum*; for in dark we cannot see. The organ is the eye, and chiefly the apple of it, which by those optic nerves, concurring both in one, conveys the sight to the common sense. Betwixt the organ and object a true distance is required, that it be not too near, or too far off. Many excellent questions appertain to this sense, discussed by philosophers: as whether this sight be caused *intra mittendo, vel extra mittendo*, etc., by receiving in the visible species, or sending of them out, which Plato,[2] Plutarch,[3] Macrobius,[4] Lactantius,[5] and others dispute. And besides it is the subject of the perspectives, of which Alhazen the Arabian, Vitellio, Roger Bacon, Baptista Porta, Guidus Ubaldus, Aquilonius, etc., have written whole volumes.

Hearing, a most excellent outward sense, "by which we learn and get knowledge." His object is sound, or that which is heard; the medium, air; organ, the ear. To the sound, which is a collision of the air, three things are required: a body to strike, as the hand of a musician; the body strucken, which must be solid and able to resist, as a bell, lute-string, not wool, or sponge; the medium, the air, which is inward or outward; the outward, being struck or collided by a solid body, still strikes the next air, until it come to that inward natural air, which as an exquisite organ is contained in a little skin formed like a drum-head, and struck upon by certain small instruments like drum-sticks, conveys the sound by a pair of nerves, appropriated to that use, to the common sense, as to a judge of sounds. There is a great variety and much delight in them; for the knowledge of which consult with Boethius and other musicians.

Smelling is an "outward sense, which apprehends by the nostrils drawing in air"; and of all the rest it is the weakest sense in men. The organ in the nose, or two small hollow pieces of flesh a little above it: the medium, the air to men, as water to fish: the object, smell, arising from a mixed body resolved, which, whether it be a quality, fume, vapour, or exhalation, I will not now dispute, or of their differences, and how they are caused. This sense is an organ of health, as sight and hearing, saith A. Gellius,[6] are of discipline; and that by avoiding bad smells, as by choosing good, which do as much alter and affect the body many times as diet itself.

Taste, a necessary sense, "which perceives all savours by the tongue and palate, and that by means of a thin spittle, or watery juice." His organ is the tongue with his tasting nerves;

the medium, a watery juice; the object, taste or savour, which
is a quality in the juice, arising from the mixture of things tasted.
Some make eight species or kinds of savour, bitter, sweet, sharp,
salt, etc., all which sick men (as in an ague) cannot discern, by
reason of their organs misaffected.

Touch, the last of the senses, and most ignoble, yet of as great
necessity as the other, and of as much pleasure. This sense
is exquisite in men, and by his nerves dispersed all over the body,
perceives any tactile quality. His organ the nerves; his object
those first qualities, hot, dry, moist, cold; and those that follow
them, hard, soft, thick, thin, etc. Many delightsome questions
are moved by philosophers about these five senses, their organs,
objects, mediums, which for brevity I omit.

SUBSECT. VII.—*Of the Inward Senses*

Inner senses are three in number, so called because they be
within the brain-pan, as common sense, phantasy, memory.
Their objects are not only things present, but they perceive
the sensible species of things to come, past, absent, such as were
before in the sense. This common sense is the judge or moderator of the rest, by whom we discern all differences of objects;
for by mine eye I do not know that I see, or by mine ear that I
hear, but by my common sense, who judgeth of sounds and
colours: they are but the organs to bring the species to be
censured; so that all their objects are his, and all their offices
are his. The fore-part of the brain is his organ or seat.

Phantasy, or imagination, which some call estimative, or
cogitative (confirmed, saith Fernelius,[1] by frequent meditation), is an inner sense which doth more fully examine the
species perceived by common sense, of things present or absent,
and keeps them longer, recalling them to mind again, or making
new of his own. In time of sleep this faculty is free, and many
times conceive strange, stupend, absurd shapes, as in sick men
we commonly observe. His organ is the middle cell of the
brain; his objects all the species communicated to him by the
common sense, by comparison of which he feigns infinite other
unto himself. In melancholy men this faculty is most powerful
and strong, and often hurts, producing many monstrous and
prodigious things, especially if it be stirred up by some terrible
object, presented to it from common sense or memory. In
poets and painters imagination forcibly works, as appears by
their several fictions, antics, images: as Ovid's house of Sleep,

Psyche's palace in Apuleius, etc. In men it is subject and governed by reason, or at least should be; but in brutes it hath no superior, and is *ratio brutorum*, all the reason they have.

Memory lays up all the species which the senses have brought in, and records them as a good register, that they may be forthcoming when they are called for by phantasy and reason. His object is the same with phantasy, his seat and organ the back part of the brain.

The affections of these senses are sleep and waking, common to all sensible creatures. "Sleep is a rest or binding of the outward senses, and of the common sense, for the preservation of body and soul" (as Scaliger defines it [1]); for when the common sense resteth, the outward senses rest also. The phantasy alone is free, and his commander, reason: as appears by those imaginary dreams, which are of divers kinds, natural, divine, demoniacal, etc., which vary according to humours, diet, actions, objects, etc., of which Artemidorus, Cardanus, and Sambucus, with their several interpretators, have written great volumes. This ligation of senses proceeds from an inhibition of spirits, the way being stopped by which they should come; this stopping is caused of vapours arising out of the stomach, filling the nerves, by which the spirits should be conveyed. When these vapours are spent, the passage is open, and the spirits perform their accustomed duties: so that "waking is the action and motion of the senses, which the spirits dispersed over all parts cause."

SUBSECT. VIII.—*Of the Moving Faculty*

This moving faculty is the other power of the sensitive soul which causeth all those inward and outward animal motions in the body. It is divided into two faculties, the power of appetite and of moving from place to place. This of appetite is three-fold, so some will have it; natural, as it signifies any such inclination, as of a stone to fall downward, and such actions as retention, expulsion, which depend not on sense, but are vegetal, as the appetite of meat and drink, hunger and thirst. Sensitive is common to men and brutes. Voluntary, the third, or intellective, which commands the other two in men, and is a curb unto them, or at least should be, but for the most part is captivated and overruled by them; and men are led like beasts by sense, giving reins to their concupiscence and several lusts. For by this appetite the soul is led or inclined to follow that good which the senses shall approve, or avoid that which they hold evil: his object being good or evil, the one he embraceth, the other he rejecteth; according to that aphorism, *omnia appetunt bonum*, all things seek their own good, or at least seeming good. This power is inseparable from sense, for where sense is, there is likewise pleasure and pain. His organ is the same with the common sense, and is divided into two powers or inclinations, concupiscible or irascible: or (as one translates it [1]) "coveting, anger invading, or impugning." Concupiscible covets always pleasant and delightsome things, and abhors that which is distasteful, harsh, and unpleasant. Irascible, *quasi aversans per iram et odium*,[2] as avoiding it with anger and indignation. All affections and perturbations arise out of these two fountains, which, although the Stoics make light of, we hold natural, and not to be resisted. The good affections are caused by some object of the same nature; and if present, they procure joy, which dilates the heart and preserves the body: if absent, they cause hope, love, desire, and concupiscence. The bad are simple or mixed: simple for some bad object present, as sorrow, which contracts the heart, macerates the soul, subverts the good estate of the body, hindering all the operations of it, causing melancholy, and many times death itself; or future, as fear. Out of these two arise those mixed affections and passions of anger, which is a desire of revenge; hatred, which is inveterate anger; zeal, which is offended with him who hurts that he loves; and ἐπιχαιρεκακία, a compound affection of joy and hate, when we rejoice at other men's mischief, and are grieved at their prosperity; pride, self-love, emulation, envy, shame, etc., of which elsewhere.

Moving from place to place is a faculty necessarily following the other. For in vain were it otherwise to desire and to abhor, if we had not likewise power to prosecute or eschew, by moving the body from place to place: by this faculty therefore we locally move the body, or any part of it, and go from one place to another. To the better performance of which, three things are requisite: that which moves; by what it moves; that which is moved. That which moves is either the efficient cause, or end. The end is the object which is desired or eschewed; as in a dog to catch a hare, etc. The efficient cause in man is reason, or his subordinate phantasy, which apprehends good or bad objects: in brutes imagination alone, which moves the appetite, the appetite this faculty, which by an admirable league of nature, and by mediation of the spirit, commands the organ by which it moves: and that consists of nerves, muscles, cords, dispersed through the whole body, contracted and relaxed as the spirits will, which move the muscles, or nerves in the midst of them,[1] and draw the cord, and so *per consequens* the joint, to the place intended. That which is moved is the body or some member apt to move. The motion of the body is diverse, as going, running, leaping, dancing, sitting, and such-like, referred to the predicament of *situs* [position]. Worms creep, birds fly, fishes swim; and so of parts, the chief of which is respiration or breathing, and is thus performed. The outward air is drawn in by the vocal artery, and sent by mediation of the midriff to the lungs, which, dilating themselves as a pair of bellows, reciprocally fetch it in and send it out to the heart to cool it; and from thence now being hot, convey it again, still taking in fresh. Such a like motion is that of the pulse, of which, because many have written whole books, I will say nothing.

Subsect. IX.—*Of the Rational Soul*

In the precedent subsections I have anatomized those inferior faculties of the soul; the rational remaineth, "a pleasant, but a doubtful subject" (as one terms it [2]), and with the like brevity to be discussed. Many erroneous opinions are about the essence and original of it; whether it be fire, as Zeno held; harmony, as Aristoxenus; number, as Xenocrates; whether it be organical or inorganical; seated in the brain, heart, or blood; mortal or immortal; how it comes into the body. Some hold that it is *ex traduce,* as Phil. 1 *de Anima,* Tertullian, Lactantius, *de opific. Dei, cap.* 19; Hugo, *lib. de Spiritu et Anima;* Vincentius Bellovac. *Spec. natural. lib.* 23, *cap.* 2 *et* 11; Hippocrates, Avicenna, and many late writers; [3] that one man begets another, body and soul; or as a candle from a candle, to be produced from the seed: otherwise, say they, a men begets but half a man, and is worse than a beast that begets both matter and form; and besides the three faculties of the soul must be together infused, which is most absurd, as they hold, because in beasts they are begot, the two inferior I mean, and may not be well separated in men. Galen supposeth the soul *crasin esse,* to be the temperature itself; [4] Trismegistus, Musæus, Orpheus, Homer, Pindarus Pherecydes Syrius, Epictetus, with the Chaldees and Egyptians affirmed the soul to be immortal, as did those British Druid. of old.[5] The Pythagoreans defend metempsychosis and *palingenesia,* that souls go from one body to another,[6] *epote prius Lethes unda* [after a draught of the waters of Lethe], as men into wolves, bears, dogs, hogs, as they were inclined in their lives, or participated in conditions:

> *Inque ferinas*
> *Possumus ire domus, pecudumque in corpora condi.*[1]

> [In beasts and cattle we may find abode,
>   And in their shapes become incorporate.]

Lucian's cock[2] was first Euphorbus, a captain:

> *Ille ego* (*nam memini*) *Trojani tempore belli,*
> *Panthoides Euphorbus eram,*[3]

> [At Troy, I well recall, in former life,
>   Euphorbus, son of Panthous, was I,]

a horse, a man, a sponge. Julian the Apostate thought Alexander's soul was descended into his body:[4] Plato *in Timæo*, and in his *Phædo* (for aught I can perceive), differs not much from this opinion, that it was from God at first, and knew all, but being enclosed in the body, it forgets, and learns anew, which he calls *reminiscentia*, or recalling, and that it was put into the body for a punishment; and thence it goes into a beast's, or man's, as appears by his pleasant fiction *de sortitione animarum* [of the allotment of souls], *lib.* 10 *de Rep.*, and after ten thousand years is to return into the former body again.[5]

> *Post varios annos, per mille figuras,*
> *Rursus ad humanæ fertur primordia vitæ.*[6]

> [After many years, and many transformations, he again
>   commences life as a human being.]

Others deny the immortality of it, which Pomponatius of Padua decided out of Aristotle not long since, Plinius Avunculus,[7] *cap.* 7, *lib.* 2, *et lib.* 7, *cap.* 55; Seneca, *lib.* 7, *Epist. ad Lucilium*, *pist.* 55; Dicæarchus *in Tull. Tusc.*; Epicurus, Aratus, Hippocrates, Galen; Lucretius, *lib.* 1:

> *Præterea gigni pariter cum corpore, et una*
> *Crescere sentimus, pariterque senescere mentem;*

> [The mind, we see, is with the body born,
>   Grows with its growth, and with its years is worn;]

Averroes, and I know not how many neoterics. "This question of the immortality of the soul is diversely and wonderfully impugned and disputed, especially among the Italians of late,"[8] saith Jab. Colerus, *lib. de immort. animæ, cap.* 1. The Popes themselves have doubted of it: Leo Decimus, that Epicurean Pope, as some record of him,[9] caused this question to be discussed pro and con before him, and concluded at last, as a profane and atheistical moderator, with that verse of Cornelius Gallus, *Et redit in nihilum, quod fuit ante nihil:* it began of nothing and in nothing it ends. Zeno and his Stoics, as Austin quotes him,[1] supposed the soul so long to continue, till the body was fully putrefied, and resolved into *materia prima*: but after that, *in fumos evanescere*, to be extinguished and vanished; and in the meantime, whilst the body was consuming, it wandered all abroad, *et e longinquo multa annunciare* [announced many things from afar], and (as that Clazomenian Hermotimus averred) saw pretty visions, and suffered I know not what.

> *Errant exsangues sine corpore et ossibus umbræ.*[2]
>
> [As bloodless shades, devoid of bone and flesh,
> They flit about.]

Others grant the immortality thereof, but they make many fabulous fictions in the meantime of it, after the departure from the body: like Plato's Elysian Fields, and that Turkey paradise. The souls of good men they deified; the bad (saith Austin) became devils,[3] as they supposed; with many such absurd tenents, which he hath confuted. Hierome, Austin, and other Fathers of the Church, hold that the soul is immortal, created of nothing, and so infused into the child or embryo in his mother's womb, six months after the conception;[4] not as those of brutes, which are *ex traduce*, and dying with them vanish into nothing. To whose divine treatises, and to the Scriptures themselves, I rejourn all such atheistical spirits, as Tully did Atticus, doubting of this point, to Plato's *Phædo*. Or if they desire philosophical proofs and demonstrations, I refer them to Niphus', Nic. Faventinus' tracts of this subject, to Fran. and John Picus *in digress. sup.* 3 *de Anima*, Tholosanus, Eugubinus, to Soto, Canus, Thomas, Pererius, Dandinus, Colerus, to that elaborate tract in Zanchius, to Tolet's sixty reasons, and Lessius' twenty-two arguments, to prove the immortality of the soul. Campanella, *lib. de sensu rerum*, is large in the same discourse, Albertinus the Schoolman, Jacob. Nactantus, *tom.* 2 *op.*, handleth it in four questions, Antony Brunus, Aonius Palearius, Marinus Marcennus, with many others. This reasonable soul, which Austin calls a spiritual substance moving itself, is defined by philosophers to be "the first substantial act of a natural, human, organical body, by which a man lives, perceives, and understands, freely doing all things, and with election." Out of which definition we may gather that this rational soul includes

the powers, and performs the duties, of the two other which are
contained in it, and all three faculties make one soul, which is
inorganical of itself, although it be in all parts, and incorporeal,
using their organs, and working by them. It is divided into
two chief parts, differing in office only, not in essence: the
understanding, which is the rational power apprehending; the
will, which is the rational power moving: to which two all the
other rational powers are subject and reduced.

SUBSECT. X.—*Of the Understanding*

"Understanding is a power of the soul, by which we perceive,
know, remember, and judge, as well singulars as universals,
having certain innate notices or beginnings of arts, a reflecting
action, by which it judgeth of his own doings and examines
them." [1] Out of this definition (besides his chief office, which
is to apprehend, judge all that he performs, without the help of
any instruments or organs) three differences appear betwixt a
man and a beast. As first, the sense only comprehends singularities, the understanding universalities. Secondly, the sense
hath no innate notions. Thirdly, brutes cannot reflect upon
themselves. Bees indeed make neat and curious works, and
many other creatures besides; but when they have done, they
cannot judge of them. His object is God, *Ens*, all nature, and
whatsoever is to be understood: which successively it apprehends.
The object first moving the understanding is some sensible
thing; after, by discoursing, the mind finds out the corporeal
substance, and from thence the spiritual. His actions (some
say) are apprehension, composition, division, discoursing,
reasoning, memory, which some include in invention, and
judgment. The common divisions are, of the understanding:
agent and patient; speculative and practic; in habit or in
act; simple or compound. The agent is that which is called
the wit of man, acumen or subtlety, sharpness of invention, when
he doth invent of himself without a teacher, or learns anew,
which abstracts those intelligible species from the phantasy,
and transfers them to the passive understanding, "because
there is nothing in the understanding which was not first in
the sense." [2] That which the imagination hath taken from the
sense, this agent judgeth of, whether it be true or false; and
being so judged he commits it to the passible to be kept. The
agent is a doctor or teacher, the passive a scholar; and his
office is to keep and further judge of such things as are

committed to his charge; as a bare and razed table[1] at first,
capable of all forms and notions. Now these notions are two-
fold, actions or habits: actions, by which we take notions of and
perceive things; habits, which are durable lights and notions,
which we may use when we will. Some reckon up eight kinds
of them: sense, experience, intelligence, faith, suspicion, error,
opinion, science; to which are added art, prudency, wisdom:
as also synteresis,[2] *dictamen rationis* [the dictate of reason],
conscience; so that in all there be fourteen species of the understanding, of which some are innate, as the three last mentioned;
the other are gotten by doctrine, learning, and use. Plato will
have all to be innate: Aristotle reckons up but five intellectual
habits: two speculative, as that intelligence of the principles and
science of conclusion; two practic, as prudency, whose end is to
practise, art to fabricate; wisdom to comprehend the use and
experiments of all notions and habits whatsoever. Which division
of Aristotle (if it be considered aright) is all one with the precedent;
for three being innate, and five acquisite, the rest are improper,
imperfect, and in a more strict examination excluded. Of all
these I should more amply dilate, but my subject will not permit.
Three of them I will only point at, as more necessary to my
following discourse.

Synteresis, or the purer part of the conscience, is an innate
habit, and doth signify "a conservation of the knowledge of the
law of God and Nature, to know good or evil." And (as our
divines hold) it is rather in the understanding than in the will.
This makes the major proposition in a practic syllogism.
The *dictamen rationis* is that which doth admonish us to do good
or evil, and is the minor in the syllogism. The conscience is
that which approves good or evil, justifying or condemning our
actions, and is the conclusion of the syllogism: as in that familiar
example of Regulus the Roman, taken prisoner by the Cartha-
ginians, and suffered to go to Rome, on that condition he should
return again, or pay so much for his ransom. The synteresis
proposeth the question; his word, oath, promise, is to be
religiously kept, although to his enemy, and that by the law of
nature. "Do not that to another which thou wouldest not have
done to thyself."[3] *Dictamen* applies it to him, and dictate
this or the like: "Regulus, thou wouldst not another man should
falsify his oath, or break promise with thee"; conscience concludes, "Therefore, Regulus, thou dost well to perform thy
promise, and oughtest to keep thine oath." More of this in
Religious Melancholy.

SUBSECT. XI.—*Of the Will*

Will is the other power of the rational soul, "which covets or
avoids such things as have been before judged and apprehended
by the understanding." [1] If good, it approves; if evil, it abhors
it: so that his object is either good or evil. Aristotle calls this
our rational appetite; for as, in the sensitive, we are moved to
good or bad by our appetite, ruled and directed by sense; so
in this we are carried by reason. Besides, the sensitive appetite
hath a particular object, good or bad; this an universal, immaterial: that respects only things delectable and pleasant;
this honest. Again, they differ in liberty. The sensual appetite
seeing an object, if it be a convenient good, cannot but desire
it; if evil, avoid it; but this is free in his essence, "much now
depraved, obscured, and fallen from his first perfection; yet in
some of his operations still free," [2] as to go, walk, move at his
pleasure, and to choose whether it will do or not do, steal or not
steal. Otherwise, in vain were laws, deliberations, exhortations,
counsels, precepts, rewards, promises, threats and punishments:
and God should be the author of sin. But in spiritual things
we will no good,[3] prone to evil (except we be regenerate, and
led by the spirit), we are egged on by our natural concupiscence,
and there is ἀταξία, a confusion in our powers, "our whole will
is averse from God and His law," [4] not in natural things only,
as to eat and drink, lust, to which we are led headlong by our
temperature and inordinate appetite,

> *Nec nos obniti contra, nec tendere tantum*
> *Sufficimus,*[5]
>
> [To make a stand and manfully resist
>   Our force avails not,]

we cannot resist, our concupiscence is originally bad, our heart
evil, the seat of our affections captivates and enforceth our will;
so that in voluntary things we are averse from God and goodness,
bad by nature, by ignorance worse,[6] by art, discipline, custom,
we get many bad habits, suffering them to domineer and
tyrannize over us; and the devil is still ready at hand with his
evil suggestions, to tempt our depraved will to some ill-disposed
action, to precipitate us to destruction, except our will be swayed
and counterpoised again with some divine precepts and good
notions of the spirit, which many times restrain, hinder, and
check us, when we are in the full career of our dissolute courses.
So David corrected himself, when he had Saul at a vantage.

Revenge and malice were as two violent oppugners on the one side; but honesty, religion, fear of God, withheld him on the other.

The actions of the will are *velle* and *nolle*, to will and nill: which two words comprehend all, and they are good or bad, accordingly as they are directed, and some of them freely performed by himself; although the Stoics absolutely deny it, and will have all things inevitably done by destiny, imposing a fatal necessity upon us, which we may not resist; yet we say that our will is free in respect of us, and things contingent, howsoever (in respect of God's determinate counsel) they are inevitable and necessary. Some other actions of the will are performed by the inferior powers which obey him, as the sensitive and moving appetite; as to open our eyes, to go hither and thither, not to touch a book, to speak fair or foul: but this appetite is many times rebellious in us, and will not be contained within the lists of sobriety and temperance. It was (as I said) once well agreeing with reason, and there was an excellent consent and harmony betwixt them, but that is now dissolved, they often jar, reason is overborne by passion: *Fertur equis auriga, nec audit currus habenas* [the driver is whirled along, the steeds obey not the rein], as so many wild horses run away with a chariot, and will not be curbed. We know many times what is good, but will not do it, as she said:

> *Trahit invitam nova vis, aliudque cupido,*
> *Mens aliud suadet.*[1]

Lust counsels one thing, reason another, there is a new reluctancy in men.

> *Odi, nec possum cupiens non esse quod odi.*[2]
>
> [I loathe it, yet cannot abate
> To be the very thing I hate.]

We cannot resist, but as Phædra confessed to her nurse, *quæ loqueris, vera sunt, sed furor suggerit sequi pejora* [3] [thou speakest truth, yet my passion drives me to follow the worse course]: she said well and true, she did acknowledge it, but headstrong passion and fury made her to do that which was opposite. So David knew the filthiness of his fact, what a loathsome, foul crying sin adultery was, yet notwithstanding he would commit murder, and take away another man's wife, enforced against reason, religion, to follow his appetite.

Those natural and vegetal powers are not commanded by will at all; for "who can add one cubit to his stature?" These other may, but are not: and thence come all those headstrong passions violent perturbations of the mind; and many times vicious habits, customs, feral diseases; because we give so much way to our appetite, and follow our inclination, like so many beasts. The principal habits are two in number, virtue and vice, whose peculiar definitions, descriptions, differences, and kinds are handled at large in the ethics, and are, indeed, the subject of moral philosophy.

MEMB. III

SUBSECT. I.—*Definition of Melancholy, Name, Difference*

HAVING thus briefly anatomized the body and soul of man, as a preparative to the rest, I may now freely proceed to treat of my intended subject, to most men's capacity; and after many ambages, perspicuously define what this melancholy is, show his name and differences. The name is imposed from the matter, and disease denominated from the material cause: as Bruel observes, Μελανχολία, *quasi* Μέλαινα χολή, from black choler. And whether it be a cause or an effect, a disease or symptom, let Donatus Altomarus and Salvianus decide; I will not contend about it. It hath several descriptions, notations, and definitions. Fracastorius, in his second book of Intellect, calls those melancholy "whom abundance of that same depraved humour of black choler hath so misaffected, that they become mad thence, and dote in most things, or in all, belonging to election, will, or other manifest operations of the understanding." [1] Melanelius out of Galen, Ruffus, Aetius, describe it to be "a bad and peevish disease, which makes men degenerate into beasts"; [2] Galen, "a privation or infection of the middle cell of the head," etc., defining it from the part affected, which Hercules de Saxonia approves, [3] *lib.* 1, *cap.* 16, calling it "a depravation of the principal function"; Fuchsius, *lib.* 1, *cap.* 23; Arnoldus, *Breviar. lib.* 1, *cap.* 18; Guianerius, and others: "by reason of black choler," Paulus adds. Halyabbas simply calls it a "commotion of the mind"; Aretæus, "a perpetual anguish of the soul, fastened on one thing, without an ague"; [4] which definition of his Mercurialis, *de affect. cap. lib.* 1, *cap.* 10, taxeth: but Ælianus Montaltus defends, *lib. de morb. cap.* 1, *de melan.*, for sufficient and good. The common sort define it to be "a kind of dotage without a fever, having for his ordinary

companions fear and sadness, without any apparent occasion.
So doth Laurentius, *cap.* 4; Piso, *lib.* 1, *cap.* 43; Donatus Altomarus, *cap.* 7 *Art. medic.*; Jacchinus, *in com. in lib.* 9 *Rhasis
ad Almansor. cap.* 15; Valesius, *Exerc.* 17; Fuchsius, *Institut.* 13,
sec. 1, *cap.* 11, etc., which common definition, howsoever approved
by most, Hercules de Saxonia will not allow of,[1] nor David
Crusius, *Theat. morb. Herm. lib.* 2, *cap.* 6; he holds it unsufficient,
"as rather showing what it is not, than what it is,"[2] as omitting
the specifical difference, the phantasy and brain: but I descend
to particulars. The *summum genus* is dotage, or "anguish of
the mind," saith Aretæus; "of a principal part," Hercules
de Saxonia adds, to distinguish it from cramp and palsy, and
such diseases as belong to the outward sense and motions;
"depraved," to distinguish it from folly and madness[3] (which
Montaltus makes *angor animi*, to separate), in which those
functions are not depraved, but rather abolished; "without an
ague" is added by all, to sever it from frenzy, and that melancholy which is in a pestilent fever. "Fear and sorrow" make
it differ from madness; "without a cause" is lastly inserted, to
specify it from all other ordinary passions of "fear and sorrow."
We properly call that dotage, as Laurentius interprets it, "when
some one principal faculty of the mind, as imagination or
reason, is corrupted, as all melancholy persons have."[4]   It is
without a fever, because the humour is most part cold and dry,
contrary to putrefaction. Fear and sorrow are the true characters and inseparable companions of most melancholy, not all,
as Hercules de Saxonia, *tract. posthumo de Melancholia, cap.* 2,
well excepts; for to some it is most pleasant, as to such as
laugh most part; some are bold again, and free from all manner
of fear and grief, as hereafter shall be declared.

SUBSECT. II.—*Of the Part affected. Affection. Parties affected*

Some difference I find amongst writers, about the principal
part affected in this disease, whether it be the brain, or heart
or some other member. Most are of opinion that it is the
brain: for being a kind of dotage, it cannot otherwise be but
that the brain must be affected, as a similar part, be it by
consent or essence,[5] not in his ventricles, or any obstruction
in them, for then it would be an apoplexy, or epilepsy, as
Laurentius well observes,[6] but in a cold, dry distemperature of
it in his substance, which is corrupt and become too cold, or
too dry, or else too hot, as in madmen and such as are incline

to it: and this Hippocrates confirms,[1] Galen, [the] Arabians, and
most of our new writers. Marcus de Oddis (in a consultation
of his, quoted by Hildesheim[2]) and five others there cited are
of the contrary part; because fear and sorrow, which are passions,
be seated in the heart. But this objection is sufficiently
answered by Montaltus,[3] who doth not deny that the heart is
affected (as Melanelius proves out of Galen[4]) by reason of his
vicinity, and so is the midriff and many other parts. They do
compati [sympathize], and have a fellow-feeling by the law of
nature: but forasmuch as this malady is caused by precedent
imagination, with the appetite, to whom spirits obey, and are
subject to those principal parts, the brain must needs primarily
be misaffected, as the seat of reason; and then the heart, as the
seat of affection. Capivaccius[5] and Mercurialis have copiously
discussed this question, and both conclude the subject is the
inner brain, and from thence it is communicated to the heart
and other inferior parts, which sympathize and are much
troubled, especially when it comes by consent, and is caused
by reason of the stomach, or myrach, as the Arabians term it,
whole body, liver, or spleen, which are seldom free,[6] pylorus,
meseraic veins, etc. For our body is like a clock; if one wheel
be amiss, all the rest are disordered, the whole fabric suffers:
with such admirable art and harmony is a man composed, such
excellent proportion, as Lodovicus Vives in his Fable of Man
hath elegantly declared.

As many doubts almost arise about the affection,[7] whether
it be imagination or reason alone, or both. Hercules de Saxonia
proves it out of Galen, Aetius, and Altomarus, that the sole fault
is in imagination.[8] Bruel is of the same mind. Montaltus in his
second chapter of Melancholy confutes this tenent of theirs, and
illustrates the contrary by many examples: as of him that thought
himself a shell-fish, of a nun, and of a desperate monk that
would not be persuaded but that he was damned; reason was in
fault as well as imagination, which did not correct this error:
they make away themselves oftentimes, and suppose many
absurd and ridiculous things. Why doth not reason detect
the fallacy, settle and persuade, if she be free? Avicenna
therefore holds both corrupt,[9] to whom most Arabians subscribe. The same is maintained by Aretæus,[10] Gordonius,[11]
Guianerius, etc. To end the controversy, no man doubts of
imagination, but that it is hurt and misaffected here; for the
other I determine with Albertinus Bottonus,[12] a doctor of
Padua, that it is "first in imagination, and afterwards in reason,

if the disease be inveterate, or as it is more or less of continuance";
but by accident, as Herc. de Saxonia adds: "Faith, opinion,
discourse, ratiocination, are all accidentally depraved by the
default of imagination."[1]

To the part affected, I may here add the parties, which shall
be more opportunely spoken of elsewhere, now only signified.
Such as have the Moon, Saturn, Mercury misaffected in their
genitures; such as live in over-cold or over-hot climes; such as
are born of melancholy parents; as offend in those six non-
natural things, are black, or of a high sanguine complexion,
that have little heads,[2] that have a hot heart, moist brain, hot
liver and cold stomach, have been long sick; such as are
solitary by nature, great students, given to much contemplation, lead a life out of action, are most subject to melancholy.
Of sexes both, but men more often; yet women misaffected are
far more violent, and grievously troubled.[3] Of seasons of the
year, the autumn is most melancholy. Of peculiar times: old
age, from which natural melancholy is almost an inseparable
accident; but this artificial malady is more frequent in such as
are of a middle age.[4] Some assign forty years, Gariopontus
thirty. Jobertus excepts neither young nor old from this
adventitious. Daniel Sennertus involves all of all sorts, out of
common experience, *in omnibus omnino corporibus cujuscunque
constitutionis dominatur*[5] [it attacks all persons of whatever
constitution]. Aetius and Aretæus[6] ascribe into the number
"not only discontented, passionate, and miserable persons,
swarthy, black; but such as are most merry and pleasant
scoffers, and high coloured."[7] "Generally," saith Rhasis, "the
finest wits and most generous spirits are before other obnoxious
to it";[8] I cannot except any complexion, any condition, sex
or age, but fools[9] and Stoics, which, according to Synesius,
are never troubled with any manner of passion, but as Anacreon
cicada, *sine sanguine et dolore; similes fere diis sunt* [without
blood or feeling; they are almost like the gods]. Erasmus
vindicates fools from this melancholy catalogue, because they
have most part moist brains and light hearts; "they are free
from ambition, envy, shame, and fear; they are neither troubled
in conscience, nor macerated with cares, to which our whole life
is most subject."[11]

SUBSECT. III.—*Of the Matter of Melancholy*

Of the matter of melancholy, there is much question betwixt Avicenna and Galen, as you may read in Cardan's Contradictions,[1] Valesius' Controversies,[2] Montanus, Prosper Calenus, Capivaccius, Bright,[3] Ficinus,[4] that have written either whole tracts, or copiously of it in their several treatises of this subject. "What this humour is, or whence it proceeds, how it is engendered in the body, neither Galen nor any old writer hath sufficiently discussed,"[5] as Jacchinus thinks: the neoterics cannot agree. Montanus, in his Consultations, holds melancholy to be material or immaterial: and so doth Arculanus. The material is one of the four humours before mentioned, and natural; the immaterial or adventitious, acquisite, redundant, unnatural, artificial; which Hercules de Saxonia will have reside in the spirits alone, and to proceed from a "hot, cold, dry, moist distemperature, which, without matter, alters the brain and functions of it."[6] Paracelsus wholly rejects and derides this division of four humours and complexions, but our Galenists generally approve of it, subscribing to this opinion of Montanus.

This material melancholy is either simple or mixed; offending in quantity or quality, varying according to his place, where it settleth, as brain, spleen, meseraic veins, heart, womb, and stomach; or differing according to the mixture of those natural humours amongst themselves, or four unnatural adust humours, as they are diversely tempered and mingled. If natural melancholy abound in the body, which is cold and dry, "so that it be more than the body is well able to bear, it must needs be distempered," saith Faventius, "and diseased";[7] and so the other, if it be depraved, whether it arise from that other melancholy of choler adust, or from blood, produceth the like effects, and is, as Montaltus contends, if it come by adustion of humours, most part hot and dry. Some difference I find, whether this melancholy matter may be engendered of all four humours, about the colour and temper of it. Galen holds it may be engendered of three alone, excluding phlegm, or pituita, whose true assertion Valesius and Menardus[8] stiffly maintain, and so doth Fuchsius,[9] Montaltus, Montanus.[10] How (say they) can white become black? But Hercules de Saxonia, *lib. post. de mela. cap.* 8, and Cardan[11] are of the opposite part (it may be engendered of phlegm, *etsi raro contingat*, though it seldom come to pass); so is Guianerius,[12] and Laurentius, *cap.* 1, with Melancthon in his book *de Anima*, and chap. of Humours; he calls

it *asininam*, dull, swinish melancholy, and saith that he was
an eye-witness of it: so is Wecker.[1] From melancholy adust
ariseth one kind; from choler another, which is most brutish;
another from phlegm, which is dull; and the last from blood,
which is best. Of these some are cold and dry, others hot and
dry, varying according to their mixtures, as they are intended
and remitted.[2] And indeed, as Rodericus à Fons., *cons.* 12, *lib.* 1,
determines, ichors and those serous matters being thickened
become phlegm, and phlegm degenerates into choler, choler
adust becomes *æruginosa melancholia* [rusty melancholy], as
vinegar out of purest wine putrefied or by exhalation of purer
spirits is so made, and becomes sour and sharp; and from the
sharpness of this humour proceeds much waking, troublesome
thoughts and dreams, etc., so that I conclude as before. If
the humour be cold, it is, saith Faventinus, "a cause of dotage,
and produceth milder symptoms: if hot, they are rash, raving
mad, or inclining to it." [3] If the brain be hot, the animal
spirits are hot; much madness follows, with violent actions: if
cold, fatuity and sottishness (Capivaccius).[4] "The colour of
this mixture varies likewise according to the mixture, be it hot
or cold; 'tis sometimes black, sometimes not " [5] (Altomarus).
The same Melanelius proves out of Galen; and Hippocrates in
his book of Melancholy (if at least it be his), giving instance in
a burning coal, "which when it is hot, shines; when it is cold,
looks black; and so doth the humour." [6] This diversity of melancholy matter produceth diversity of effects. If it be within the
body, and not putrefied, it causeth black jaundice; [7] if putrefied,
a quartan ague; if it break out to the skin, leprosy; if to parts,
several maladies, as scurvy, etc. If it trouble the mind, as it is
diversely mixed, it produceth several kinds of madness and
dotage: of which in their place.

SUBSECT. IV.—*Of the Species or Kinds of Melancholy*

When the matter is diverse and confused, how should it otherwise be but that the species should be diverse and confused?
Many new and old writers have spoken confusedly of it, con-
founding melancholy and madness, as Heurnius,[8] Guianerius,
Gordonius, Sallustius Salvianus, Jason Pratensis, Savonarola,
that will have madness no other than melancholy in extent,
differing (as I have said) in degrees. Some make two distinct
species, as Ruffus Ephesius, an old writer, Constantinus Africanus,
Aretæus, Aurelianus,[9] Paulus Ægineta: others acknowledge a

multitude of kinds, and leave them indefinite, as Aetius in his
Tetrabiblos,[1] Avicenna,[2] *lib. 3, fen. 1, tract 4, cap.* 18; Arculanus,
cap. 16, *in* 9 *Rhasis*; Montanus, *Med. part.* 1. "If natural melancholy
be adust, it maketh one kind; if blood, another; if choler, a third,
differing from the first; and so many several opinions there are
about the kinds, as there be men themselves."[3] Hercules de
Saxonia sets down two kinds, "material and immaterial; one from
spirits alone, the other from humours and spirits."[4] Savonarola,
rub. 11, *tract.* 6, *cap.* 1, *de ægritud. capitis*, will have the kinds
to be infinite; one from the myrach, called *myrachialis* of the
Arabians; another *stomachalis*, from the stomach; another from
the liver, heart, womb, hemrods: "one beginning, another consummate."[5] Melancthon seconds him:[6] "As the humour is
diversely adust and mixed, so are the species diverse"; but what
these men speak of species I think ought to be understood of
symptoms, and so doth Arculanus interpret himself:[7] infinite
species, *id est*, symptoms; and in that sense, as Jo. Gorrhæus
acknowledgeth in his Medicinal Definitions, the species are
infinite, but they may be reduced to three kinds by reason of
their seat; head, body, and hypochondries. This threefold
division is approved by Hippocrates in his book of Melancholy
(if it be his, which some suspect), by Galen, *lib.* 3 *de loc. affectis*,
cap. 6; by Alexander, *lib.* 1, *cap.* 16; Rhasis, *lib.* 1 *Continent.*,
Tract. 9, *lib.* 1, *cap.* 16; Avicenna, and most of our new writers.
Th. Erastus makes two kinds; one perpetual, which is head-
melancholy; the other interrupt, which comes and goes by fits,
which he subdivides into the other two kinds, so that all comes
to the same pass. Some again make four or five kinds, with
Rodericus à Castro, *de morbis mulier. lib.* 2, *cap.* 3, and Lod.
Mercatus, who in his second book *de mulier. affect. cap.* 4, will
have that melancholy of nuns, widows, and more ancient maids
to be a peculiar species of melancholy differing from the rest:
some will reduce enthusiasts, ecstatical and demoniacal persons
to this rank, adding love-melancholy to the first,[8] and lycanthropia. The most received division is into three kinds. The
first proceeds from the sole fault of the brain, and is called
head-melancholy; the second sympathetically proceeds from
the whole body, when the whole temperature is melancholy:
the third ariseth from the bowels, liver, spleen, or membrane
called mesenterium, named hypochondriacal or windy melancholy, which Laurentius[9] subdivides into three parts, from those
three members, hepatic, splenetic, meseraic. Love-melancholy,
which Avicenna calls *ilishi*, and lycanthropia, which he calls

cucubuth, are commonly included in head-melancholy; but of
this last, which Gerardus de Solo calls amorous, and most
knight-melancholy, with that of religious melancholy, *virginum
et viduarum* [of maids and widows], maintained by Rod. à
Castro and Mercatus, and the other kinds of love-melancholy,
I will speak of apart by themselves in my third partition. The
three precedent species are the subject of my present discourse,
which I will anatomize and treat of through all their causes,
symptoms, cures, together and apart; that every man that is
in any measure affected with this malady may know how to
examine it in himself, and apply remedies unto it.

It is a hard matter, I confess, to distinguish these three
species one from the other, to express their several causes,
symptoms, cures, being that they are so often confounded
amongst themselves, having such affinity that they can scarce
be discerned by the most accurate physicians, and so often
intermixed with other diseases that the best experienced have
been plunged. Montanus, *consil.* 26, names a patient that had
this disease of melancholy and *caninus appetitus* both together;
and, *consil.* 23, with vertigo; Julius Cæsar Claudinus with stone,
gout, jaundice;[1] Trincavellius with an ague, jaundice, *caninus
appetitus*, etc. Paulus Regoline,[2] a great doctor in his time,
consulted in this case, was so confounded with a confusion of
symptoms, that he knew not to what kind of melancholy to
refer it. Trincavellius,[3] Fallopius, and Francanzanus, famous
doctors in Italy, all three conferred with about one party at
the same time, gave three different opinions. And in another
place, Trincavellius being demanded what he thought of a
melancholy young man to whom he was sent for, ingenuously
confessed that he was indeed melancholy, but he knew not to
what kind to reduce it. In his seventeenth consultation there
is the like disagreement about a melancholy monk. Those
symptoms, which others ascribe to misaffected parts and
humours, Herc. de Saxonia[4] attributes wholly to distempered
spirits, and those immaterial, as I have said. Sometimes they
cannot well discern this disease from others. In Reinerus
Solenander's Counsels, *sect.* 3, *consil.* 5, he and Dr. Brande both
agreed that the patient's disease was hypochondriacal melancholy. Dr. Matholdus said it was asthma, and nothing else
Solenander and Guarionius,[5] lately sent for to the melancholy
Duke of Cleve, with others, could not define what species it was
or agree amongst themselves. The species are so confounded
as in Cæsar Claudinus his forty-fourth consultation for a Poloniar

count; in his judgment "he laboured of head melancholy, and that which proceeds from the whole temperature, both at once."[1] I could give instance of some that have had all three kinds *semel et simul* [all together], and some successively. So that I conclude of our melancholy species, as many politicians do of their pure forms of commonwealths,[2] monarchies, aristocracies, democracies, are most famous in contemplation, but in practice they are temperate and usually mixed (so Polybius informeth us[3]), as the Lacedæmonian, the Roman of old, German now, and many others. What physicians say of distinct species in their books it much matters not, since that in their patients' bodies they are commonly mixed. In such obscurity, therefore, variety and confused mixture of symptoms, causes, how difficult a thing is it to treat of several kinds apart; to make any certainty or distinction among so many casualties, distractions, when seldom two men shall be like affected *per omnia* [in all respects] ! 'Tis hard, I confess, yet nevertheless I will adventure through the midst of these perplexities, and, led by the clue or thread of the best writers, extricate myself out of a labyrinth of doubts and errors, and so proceed to the causes.

SECT. II. MEMB. I.

SUBSECT. I.—*Causes of Melancholy. God a Cause*

"IT is in vain to speak of cures, or think of remedies, until such time as we have considered of the causes," so Galen prescribes Glauco:[4] and the common experience of others confirms that those cures must be imperfect, lame, and to no purpose, wherein the causes have not first been searched, as Prosper Calenius well observes in his tract *de atra bile* to Cardinal Cæsius.[5] Insomuch that Fernelius puts "a kind of necessity in the knowledge of the causes, and without which it is impossible to cure or prevent any manner of disease."[6] Empirics may ease, and sometimes help, but not throughly root out; *sublata causa tollitur effectus*, as the saying is, if the cause be removed, the effect is likewise vanquished. It is a most difficult thing (I confess) to be able to discern these causes whence they are, and in such variety to say what the beginning was.[7] He is happy that can perform it aright.[8] I will adventure to guess as near as I can, and rip them all up, from the first to the

last, general and particular, to every species, that so they may
the better be described.

General causes are either supernatural or natural. Supernatural are from God and His angels, or by God's permission
from the devil and his ministers. That God Himself is a
cause for the punishment of sin, and satisfaction of His justice,
many examples and testimonies of holy Scriptures make evident
unto us. Ps. cvii, 17: "Foolish men are plagued for their offence,
and by reason of their wickedness." Gehazi was strucken with
leprosy (2 Reg. v, 27); Jehoram with dysentery and flux, and
great diseases of the bowels (2 Chron. xxi, 15); David plagued
for numbering his people (1 Chron. xxi); Sodom and Gomorrah
swallowed up. And this disease is peculiarly specified (Ps.
cvii, 12), "He brought down their heart through heaviness";
(Deut. xxviii, 28), "He struck them with madness, blindness,
and astonishment of heart"; "An evil spirit was sent by the
Lord upon Saul, to vex him";[1] Nebuchadnezzar did eat grass
like an ox, and his "heart was made like the beasts of the
field."[2] Heathen stories are full of such punishments. Lycurgus, because he cut down the vines in the country, was by
Bacchus driven into madness: so was Pentheus and his mother
Agave for neglecting their sacrifice. Censor Fulvius ran mad
for untiling Juno's temple, to cover a new one of his own, which
he had dedicated to Fortune,[3] "and was confounded to death
with grief and sorrow of heart."[4] When Xerxes would have
spoiled Apollo's temple at Delphi of those infinite riches it
possessed, a terrible thunder came from heaven and struck
four thousand men dead, the rest ran mad.[5] A little after, the
like happened to Brennus, lightning, thunder, earthquakes, upon
such a sacrilegious occasion.[6] If we may believe our pontifical
writers, they will relate unto us many strange and prodigious
punishments in this kind, inflicted by their saints. How Clodo-
veus, sometime King of France, the son of Dagobert, lost his
wits for uncovering the body of St. Denis;[7] and how a sacrilegious Frenchman, that would have stolen a silver image of
St. John, at Birgburge, became frantic on a sudden, raging,
and tyrannizing over his own flesh;[8] of a Lord of Radnor,
that coming from hunting late at night, put his dogs into St.
Avan's Church (Llan Avan they called it), and rising betimes
next morning, as hunters use to do, found all his dogs
mad, himself being suddenly strucken blind;[9] of Tiridates, an
Armenian king, for violating some holy nuns, that was punished
in like sort, with loss of his wits. But poets and papists may

go together for fabulous tales; let them free their own credits:
howsoever they feign of their Nemesis, and of their saints, or
by the devil's means may be deluded, we find it true that
ultor a tergo Deus,[1] "He is God the avenger," as David styles
Him;[2] and that it is our crying sins that pull this and many
other maladies on our own heads; that He can by His angels,
which are His ministers, strike and heal (saith Dionysius) whom
He will;[3] that He can plague us by His creatures, sun, moon,
and stars, whom He useth as His instruments, as a husbandman
(saith Zanchius) doth a hatchet: hail, snow, winds, etc.—*Et
conjurati veniunt in classica venti*[4] [the winds in a band answer
His summons]—as in Joshua's time, as in Pharaoh's reign in
Egypt, they are but as so many executioners of His justice.
He can make the proudest spirits stoop, and cry out with
Julian the Apostate, *Vicisti, Galilæe*;[5] or with Apollo's priest in
Chrysostom,[6] *O cœlum! O terra!* [O heaven! O earth!] *unde
hostis hic?* what an enemy is this? and pray with David,
acknowledging his power, "I am weakened and sore broken,
I roar for the grief of mine heart, mine heart panteth,"
etc. (Ps. xxxviii, 8); "O Lord, rebuke me not in thine
anger, neither chastise me in thy wrath" (Ps. xxxviii, 1);
"Make me to hear joy and gladness, that the bones which
thou hast broken may rejoice" (Ps. li, 8); "Restore to me
the joy of thy salvation, and stablish me with thy free spirit"
(Ps. li, 12). For these causes belike Hippocrates[7] would have
a physician take special notice whether the disease come not
from a divine supernatural cause, or whether it follow the
course of nature. But this is further discussed by Fran. Valesius,
de sacr. philos. cap. 8, Fernelius,[8] and J. Cæsar Claudinus,[9]
to whom I refer you, how this place of Hippocrates is to be
understood. Paracelsus is of opinion that such spiritual diseases
(for so he calls them) are spiritually to be cured, and not otherwise. Ordinary means in such cases will not avail: *Non est
reluctandum cum Deo* [we must not struggle with God]. When
that monster-taming Hercules overcame all in the Olympics,
Jupiter at last in an unknown shape wrestled with him; the
victory was uncertain, till at length Jupiter descried himself,
and Hercules yielded. No striving with supreme powers. *Nil
uvat immensos Cratero promittere montes* [it avails not to promise
Craterus gold mines for a cure], physicians and physic can
do no good, "we must submit ourselves unto the mighty hand
of God, acknowledge our offences, call to Him for mercy."[10]
If He strike us, *una eademque manus vulnus opemque feret* [the

same hand will inflict the wound and provide the remedy], as
it is with them that are wounded with the spear of Achilles,
He alone must help; otherwise our diseases are incurable, and
we not to be relieved.

SUBSECT. II.—*A Digression of the Nature of Spirits, Bad Angels, or Devils, and how they cause Melancholy*

How far the power of spirits and devils doth extend, and
whether they can cause this, or any other disease, is a serious
question, and worthy to be considered: for the better understanding of which, I will make a brief digression of the nature
of spirits. And although the question be very obscure, according to Postellus, "full of controversy and ambiguity," [1] beyond
the reach of human capacity, *fateor excedere vires intentionis
meæ*, saith Austin,[2] I confess I am not able to understand it,
finitum de infinito non potest statuere [the finite cannot decide
about the infinite], we can sooner determine with Tully (*De
nat. deorum*), *quid non sint, quam quid sint* [what they are not
than what they are], our subtle schoolmen, Cardans, Scaligers,
profound Thomists, *Fracastoriana et Ferneliana acies*, are weak,
dry, obscure, defective in these mysteries, and all our quickest
wits, as an owl's eyes at the sun's light, wax dull, and are
not sufficient to apprehend them; yet, as in the rest, I will
adventure to say something to this point. In former times, as
we read (Acts xxiii), the Sadducees denied that there were any
such spirits, devils, or angels. So did Galen the physician, the
Peripatetics, even Aristotle himself, as Pomponatius stoutly
maintains, and Scaliger in some sort grants, though Dandinus
the Jesuit, *Com. in lib. 2 de anima*, stiffly denies it; *substantiæ
separatæ* [abstract substances] and intelligences are the same
which Christians call angels, and Platonists devils, for they
name all the spirits *dæmones*, be they good or bad angels, as
Julius Pollux, *Onomasticon, lib. 1, cap. 1*, observes. Epicures
and atheists are of the same mind in general, because they
never saw them. Plato, Plotinus, Porphyrius, Iamblichus,
Proclus, insisting in the steps of Trismegistus, Pythagoras, and
Socrates, make no doubt of it: nor Stoics, but that there are
such spirits, though much erring from the truth. Concerning
the first beginning of them, the Talmudists say that Adam had
a wife called Lilis, before he married Eve, and of her he begat
nothing but devils.[3] The Turks' Alcoran is altogether as absurd
and ridiculous in this point: [4] but the Scripture informs us

Christians, how Lucifer, the chief of them, with his associates,
fell from heaven for his pride and ambition;[1] created of God,
placed in heaven, and sometime an angel of light, now cast
down into the lower aerial sublunary parts, or into hell, "and
delivered into chains of darkness to be kept unto damnation"
(2 Pet. ii, 4). There is a foolish opinion which some hold, that
they are the souls of men departed; good and more noble were
deified, the baser grovelled on the ground, or in the lower parts,
and were devils; the which, with Tertullian, Porphyrius the
philosopher, M. Tyrius, *ser.* 27, maintains. "These spirits," he
saith, "which we call angels and devils, are naught but souls
of men departed, which either through love and pity of their
friends yet living, help and assist them, or else persecute their
enemies, whom they hated," [2] as Dido threatened to persecute
Æneas:

Omnibus umbra locis adero: dabis, improbe, pœnas.

[My angry ghost, arising from the deep,
Shall haunt thee waking, and disturb thy sleep.]

They are (as others suppose) appointed by those higher powers
to keep men from their nativity, and to protect or punish them
as they see cause: and are called *boni* and *mali genii* by the
Romans; heroes, lares if good, lemures or larvæ if bad, by
the Stoics; governors of countries, men, cities, saith Apuleius:
*Deos appellant qui ex hominum numero juste ac prudenter vitæ
curriculo gubernato, pro numine, postea ab hominibus præditi
fanis et ceremoniis vulgo admittuntur, ut in Ægypto Osiris* [3]
[they call gods those who, having as men lived justly and wisely
on earth, are after their death deified, and honoured with temples
and rites, like Osiris in Egypt], etc. *Præstites* [protectors],
Capella calls them, "which protected particular men as well
as princes." Socrates had his *dæmonium saturninum et igneum*
[saturnine and fiery familiar spirit], which of all spirits is
best *ad sublimes cogitationes animum erigentem* [for stirring the
mind to sublime reflections], as the Platonists supposed;
Plotinus his; and we Christians our assisting angel, as Andreas
Victorellus, a copious writer of this subject, Lodovicus de La-
Cerda, the Jesuit, in his voluminous tract *de Angelo Custode,*
Zanchius, and some divines think. But this absurd tenent of
Tyrius, Proclus confutes at large in his book *de anima et dæmone.*
Psellus,[4] a Christian, and sometime tutor (saith Cuspinian)
to Michael Parapinatius, Emperor of Greece, a great observer
of the nature of devils, holds they are corporeal, and have

"aerial bodies, that they are mortal, live and die," [1] (which
Martianus Capella likewise maintains, but our Christian philosophers explode), "that they are nourished and have excrements,
that they feel pain if they be hurt" (which Cardan confirms, and
Scaliger justly laughs him to scorn for; *Si pascantur aere, cur
non pugnant ob puriorem aera?* [If they feed on air, why do
they not fight for purer air?], etc.) "or stroken": [2] and if their
bodies be cut, with admirable celerity they come together
again. Austin, *in Gen. lib.* 3, *lib. arbit.*, approves as much,
mutato casu corpora in deteriorem qualitatem aeris spissioris
[conversely, their bodies can be changed to an air of inferior
and coarser quality]; so doth Hierome, *Comment. in Epist. ad
Ephes. cap.* 3, Origen, Tertullian, Lactantius, and many ancient
Fathers of the Church: that in their fall their bodies were changed
into a more aerial and gross substance. Bodine, *lib.* 4 *Theatri
Naturæ*, and David Crusius, *Hermeticæ Philosophiæ lib.* 1, *cap.* 4,
by several arguments proves angels and spirits to be corporeal:
*Quicquid continetur in loco corporeum est: At spiritus continetur
in loco, ergo* [whatever occupies space is corporeal; spirit occupies
space, therefore, etc.]. *Si spiritus sunt quanti, erunt corporei:
At sunt quanti, ergo. Sunt finiti, ergo quanti* [If spirits are
quantities, they must be corporeal; but they are quantities,
therefore . . . They are finite, therefore quantitative], etc.
Bodine goes farther yet, and will have these *animæ separatæ*
[abstract souls], genii, spirits, angels, devils, and so likewise
souls of men departed, if corporeal (which he most eagerly
contends), to be of some shape, and that absolutely round, like
sun and moon, because that is the most perfect form, *quæ nihil
habet asperitatis, nihil angulis incisum, nihil anfractibus invo-
lutum, nihil eminens, sed inter corpora perfecta est perfectissimum* [3]
[which has no rough edges, no corners, no twists, no projections,
but is the most perfect of shapes]; therefore all spirits are
corporeal, he concludes, and in their proper shapes round.
That they can assume other aerial bodies, all manner of shapes
at their pleasures, appear in what likeness they will themselves,
that they are most swift in motion, can pass many miles in an
instant, and so likewise transform bodies of others into what
shape they please, and with admirable celerity remove them
from place to place [4] (as the angel did Habakkuk to Daniel,
and as Philip the Deacon was carried away by the Spirit, when
he had baptized the eunuch; so did Pythagoras and Apollonius
remove themselves and others, with many such feats); that
they can represent castles in the air, palaces, armies, spectrums

prodigies, and such strange objects to mortal men's eyes, cause
smells, savours, etc.,[1] deceive all the senses; most writers of
this subject credibly believe; and that they can foretell future
events, and do many strange miracles. Juno's image spake
to Camillus, and Fortune's statue to the Roman matrons, with
many such. Zanchius, Bodine, Spondanus, and others, are of
opinion that they cause a true metamorphosis, as Nebuchadnezzar was really translated into a beast, Lot's wife into a
pillar of salt, Ulysses' companions into hogs and dogs by
Circe's charms; turn themselves and others, as they do witches,
into cats, dogs, hares, crows, etc. Strozzius Cicogna hath
many examples, *lib. 3 Omnif. mag. cap.* 4 *et* 5, which he
there confutes, as Austin likewise doth, *de Civ. Dei, lib.* 18.
That they can be seen when, and in what shape, and to whom
they will, saith Psellus, *tametsi nil tale viderim, nec optem videre,*
though he himself never saw them nor desired it; and use sometimes carnal copulation (as elsewhere I shall prove more at
large [2]) with women and men. Many will not believe they can
be seen, and if any man shall say, swear, and stiffly maintain,
though he be discreet and wise, judicious and learned, that he
hath seen them, they account him a timorous fool, a melancholy
dizzard, a weak fellow, a dreamer, a sick or a mad man, they
contemn him, laugh him to scorn, and yet Marcus of his credit
told Psellus that he had often seen them. And Leo Suavius,
a Frenchman, *cap.* 8, *in Commentar. lib.* 1 *Paracelsi de vita longa,*
out of some Platonists, will have the air to be as full of them as
snow falling in the skies, and that they may be seen, and withal
sets down the means how men may see them: *Si irreverberatis
oculis sole splendente versus cœlum continuaverint obtutus* [by
looking steadfastly at the sky, in bright sunshine, without
blinking], etc., and saith moreover he tried it, *præmissorum
feci experimentum,* and it was true that the Platonists said.
Paracelsus confesseth that he saw them divers times, and
conferred with them, and so doth Alexander ab Alexandro,
"that he so found it by experience, whenas before he doubted
of it."[3] Many deny it, saith Lavater, *de spectris, part.* 1, *cap.* 2,
and *part.* 2, *cap.* 11, "because they never saw them themselves";
but as he reports at large all over his book, especially *cap.* 19, *part.*
1, they are often seen and heard, and familiarly converse with
men, as Lod. Vives assureth us, innumerable records, histories,
and testimonies evince in all ages, times, places, and all travellers besides;[4] in the West Indies and our northern climes,
nihil familiarius quam in agris et urbibus spiritus videre, audire

qui vetent, jubeant [nothing is more common than to see spirits both in town and country, and to hear them ordering or forbidding something], etc. Hieronymus, *vita Pauli*, Basil, *ser.* 40, Nicephorus, Eusebius, Socrates, Sozomenus,[1] Jacobus Boissardus in his tract *de spirituum apparitionibus*, Petrus Loyerus, *lib. de spectris*, Wierus, *lib.* 1, have infinite variety of such examples of apparitions of spirits, for him to read that further doubts, to his ample satisfaction. One alone I will briefly insert. A nobleman in Germany was sent ambassador to the King of Sweden (for his name, the time, and such circumstances, I refer you to Boissardus, mine author[2]). After he had done his business, he sailed to Livonia, on set purpose to see those familiar spirits, which are there said to be conversant with men and do their drudgery works. Amongst other matters, one of them told him where his wife was, in what room, in what clothes, what doing, and brought him a ring from her, which at his return, *non sine omnium admiratione* [to the general surprise], he found to be true; and so believed that ever after, which before he doubted of. Cardan, *lib.* 19 *de subtil.*, relates of his father, Facius Cardan, that after the accustomed solemnities, *ann.* 1491, 13 August, he conjured up seven devils in Greek apparel, about forty years of age, some ruddy of complexion, and some pale, as he thought; he asked them many questions, and they made ready answer, that they were aerial devils, that they lived and died as men did, save that they were far longer lived (seven or eight hundred years[3]); they did as much excel men in dignity as we do juments, and were as far excelled again of those that were above them; our governors and keepers they are, moreover,[4] which Plato in *Critias* delivered of old,[5] and subordinate to one another, *ut enim homo homini, sic dæmon dæmoni dominatur* [for as man rules man, so devil rules devil], they rule themselves as well as us, and the spirits of the meaner sort had commonly such offices, as we make horsekeepers, neatherds, and the basest of us overseers of our cattle; and that we can no more apprehend their natures and functions than a horse a man's. They knew all things, but might not reveal them to men; and ruled and domineered over us, as we do over our horses; the best kings amongst us, and the most generous spirits, were not comparable to the basest of them. Sometimes they did instruct men, and communicate their skill, reward and cherish, and sometimes again terrify and punish, to keep them in awe, as they thought fit, *nihil magis cupientes* (saith Lysius, *Phys. Stoicorum*) *quam adorationem hominum* [longing

for nothing more than the worship of mankind]. The same
author, Cardan, in his *Hyperchen*, out of the doctrine of Stoics,
will have some of these genii (for so he calls them) to be desirous
of men's company, very affable and familiar with them, as
dogs are; others, again, to abhor as serpents, and care not for
them.[1] The same, belike, Trithemius calls *igneos et sublunares,
qui nunquam demergunt ad inferiora, aut vix ullum habent in
terris commercium* [fiery and sublunar, who never descend to
the lower sphere, and have little to do with the earth]. "Generally they far excel men in worth, as a man the meanest worm,
though some of them are inferior to those of their own rank in
worth as the black guard in a prince's court, and to men again
as some degenerate, base, rational creatures are excelled of
brute beasts." [2]

That they are mortal, besides these testimonies of Cardan,
Martianus, etc., many other divines and philosophers hold, *post
prolixum tempus moriuntur omnes* [they all die after a great
lapse of time]; the Platonists [3] and some Rabbins, Porphyrius,
and Plutarch, as appears by that relation of Thamus: "The
great God Pan is dead"; [4] Apollo Pythius ceased; and so the rest.
St. Hierome, in the life of Paul the Eremite, tells a story how
one of them appeared to St. Anthony in the wilderness, and
told him as much. Paracelsus, of our late writers, stiffly maintains that they are mortal, live and die as other creatures do.[5]
Zozimus, *lib.* 2, farther adds, that religion and policy dies and
alters with them. The Gentiles' gods, he saith, were expelled
by Constantine,[6] and together with them *imperii Romani
majestas et fortuna interiit, et profligata est,* the fortune and
majesty of the Roman Empire decayed and vanished; as that
heathen in Minucius formerly bragged, when the Jews were
overcome by the Romans, the Jews' God was likewise captivated
by that of Rome; [7] and Rabshakeh to the Israelites, no God
should deliver them out of the hands of the Assyrians. But
these paradoxes of their power, corporeity, mortality, taking
of shapes, transposing bodies, and carnal copulations, are
sufficiently confuted by Zanch. *cap.* 10, *lib.* 4; Pererius, in his
Comment, and Tostatus' questions on the 6th of Gen.; Th. Aquin.,
St. Austin, Wierus, Th. Erastus, Delrio, *tom.* 2, *lib.* 2, *quæst.* 29;
Sebastian Michaelis, *cap.* 2 *de spiritibus*, Dr. Rainolds, *Lect.* 47.
They may deceive the eyes of men, yet not take true bodies, or
make a real metamorphosis; but as Cicogna proves at large,
they are *illusoriæ et præstigiatrices transformationes* [8] (*Omnif.
mag. lib.* 4, *cap.* 4), mere illusions and cozenings, like that tale

of *Pasetis obolus* in Suidas, or that of Autolycus, Mercury's son that dwelt in Parnassus, who got so much treasure by cozenage and stealth. His father Mercury, because he could leave him no wealth, taught him many fine tricks to get means, for he could drive away men's cattle, and if any pursued him, turn them into what shapes he would,[1] and so did mightily enrich himself, *hoc astu maximam prædam est adsecutus*. This, no doubt, is as true as the rest; yet thus much in general Thomas, Durand, and others grant, that they have understanding far beyond men, can probably conjecture and foretell many things;[2] they can cause and cure most diseases, deceive our senses; they have excellent skill in all arts and sciences; and that the most illiterate devil is *quovis homine scientior* (more knowing than any man), as Cicogna maintains out of others.[3] They know the virtues of herbs, plants, stones, minerals, etc., of all creatures, birds, beasts, the four elements, stars, planets; can aptly apply and make use of them as they see good; perceiving the causes of all meteors, and the like. *Dant se coloribus* (as Austin hath it[4]), *accommodant se figuris, adhærent sonis, subjiciunt se odoribus, infundunt se saporibus* [they insert themselves into colours, shapes, sounds, smells, and tastes], *omnes sensus etiam ipsam intelligentiam dæmones fallunt*, they deceive all our senses, even our understanding itself at once. They can produce miraculous alterations in the air, and most wonderful effects, conquer armies, give victories, help, further, hurt, cross, and alter human attempts and projects (*Dei permissu*) as they see good themselves.[5] When Charles the Great intended to make a channel betwixt the Rhine and Danubius, look what his workmen did in the day, these spirits flung down in the night,[6] *ut conatu rex desisteret, pervicere* [they succeeded in making the king desist from his attempt]. Such feats can they do. But that which Bodine, *lib. 4 Theat. nat.*, thinks (following Tyrius belike, and the Platonists), they can tell the secrets of a man's heart, *aut cogitationes hominum*, is most false; his reasons are weak, and sufficiently confuted by Zanch., *lib. 4, cap.* 9; Hierome, *lib.* 2 *Com. in Mat. ad cap.* 15, Athanasius, *Quæst.* 27 *ad Antiochum Principem*, and others.

As for those orders of good and bad devils, [that] which the Platonists hold is altogether erroneous, and those ethnics' *boni* and *mali genii* [good and bad genii] are to be exploded: these heathen writers agree not in this point among themselves, as Dandinus notes, *An sint mali non conveniunt*[7] [they are not agreed as to whether there are any bad]; some will have all spirits good or bad to us by a mistake; as if an ox or horse could discourse, he would say the butcher was his enemy because he killed him, the grazier his friend because he fed him; an hunter preserves and yet kills his game, and is hated nevertheless of his game; *nec piscatorem piscis amare potest* [the fish cannot love the fisherman], etc. But Iamblichus, Psellus, Plutarch, and most Platonists acknowledge bad, *et ab eorum maleficiis cavendum* [and we should beware of their wickedness], for they are enemies of mankind, and this Plato learned in Egypt, that they quarrelled with Jupiter, and were driven by him down to hell.[1] That which Apuleius,[2] Xenophon, and Plato contend of Socrates' *dæmonium*, is most absurd: that which Plotinus of his, that he had likewise *deum pro dæmonio* [a god for his familiar spirit]; and that which Porphyry concludes of them all in general, if they be neglected in their sacrifice they are angry; nay more, as Cardan in his *Hyperchen* will, they feed on men's souls: *Elementa sunt plantis elementum, animalibus plantæ, hominibus animalia, erunt et homines aliis, non autem diis, nimis enim remota est eorum natura a nostra, quapropter dæmonibus* [minerals are food for plants, plants for animals, animals for men; men will also be food for other creatures, but not for gods, for their nature is far removed from ours; it must therefore be for devils]; and so, belike, that we have so many battles fought in all ages, countries, is to make them a feast, and their sole delight: but to return to that I said before, if displeased they fret and chafe (for they feed, belike, on the souls of beasts, as we do on their bodies), and send many plagues amongst us; but if pleased, then they do much good; is as vain as the rest, and conjuted by Austin, *lib. 9, cap. 8, de Civ. Dei.*, Euseb., *lib. 4 Præpar. Evang. cap. 6*, and others. Yet thus much I find, that our schoolmen and other divines make nine kinds of bad spirits,[3] as Dionysius hath done of angels. In the first rank are those false gods of the Gentiles, which were adored heretofore in several idols, and gave oracles at Delphi, and elsewhere; whose prince is Beelzebub. The second rank is of liars and equivocators, as Apollo Pythius and the like. The third are those vessels of anger, inventors of all mischief; as that Theuth in Plato; Esay calls them vessels of fury;[4] their prince is Belial. The fourth are malicious revenging devils; and their prince is Asmodæus. The fifth kind are cozeners, such as belong to magicians and witches; their prince is Satan. The sixth are those aerial devils that corrupt the air and cause plagues, thunders, fires, etc.; spoken of in the Apocalypse,[5]

and Paul to the Ephesians names them the princes of the air;
Meresin[1] is their prince.   The seventh is a destroyer, captain
of the Furies, causing wars, tumults, combustions, uproars,
mentioned in the Apocalypse, and called Abaddon.   The eighth
is that accusing or calumniating devil, whom the Greeks call
Διάβολος, that drives men to despair.   The ninth are those
tempters in several kinds, and their prince is Mammon.   Psellus
makes six kinds, yet none above the moon; Wierus, in his
Pseudomonarchia Dæmonis, out of an old book, makes many
more divisions and subordinations, with their several names,
numbers, offices, etc., but Gazæus, cited by Lipsius,[2] will have
all places full of angels, spirits, and devils, above and beneath
the moon,[3] ætherial and aerial, which Austin cites out of
Varro, *lib. 7 de Civ. Dei, cap.* 6, "the celestial devils above, and
aerial beneath," or, as some will, gods above, *semidei* or half-
gods beneath, lares, heroes, genii, which climb higher, if they
lived well, as the Stoics held, but grovel on the ground as they
were baser in their lives, nearer to the earth: and are manes,
lemures, lamiæ, etc.   They will have no place void, but all full
of spirits, devils, or some other inhabitants;[4] *plenum cœlum,
aer, aqua, terra, et omnia sub terra* [full is the sky, the air, the
sea, the earth, and all beneath the earth], saith Gazæus;
though Anthony Rusca, in his book *de Inferno, lib.* 5, *cap.* 7,
would confine them to the middle region, yet they will have
them everywhere, "not so much as an hairbreadth empty in
heaven, earth, or waters, above or under the earth."[5]   The air
is not so full of flies in summer as it is at all times of invisible
devils: this Paracelsus[6] stiffly maintains, and that they have
every one their several chaos; others will have infinite worlds
and each world his peculiar spirits, gods, angels, and devils
to govern and punish it.

> *Singula nonnulli credunt quoque sidera posse
> Dici orbes, terramque appellant sidus opacum,
> Cui minimus divum præsit.*[7]

> [Some, too, believe that each star may also be called a
> world, and regard this earth as a dark star over
> which the least of the gods presides.]

Gregorius Tholosanus makes seven kinds of ætherial spirits or
angels,[8] according to the number of the seven planets, Saturnine, Jovial, Martial, of which Cardan discourseth, *lib.* 20 *d.
subtil.*; he calls them *substantias primas* [primary substances]
Olympicos dæmones Trithemius, qui præsunt zodiaco [Trithemiu

calls them Olympian spirits which rule the zodiac], etc.,
and will have them to be good angels above, devils beneath
the moon; their several names and offices he there sets down,
and, which Dionysius of angels, will have several spirits for
several countries, men, offices, etc., which live about them,
and as so many assisting powers cause their operations; will
have, in a word, innumerable, as many of them as there be stars
in the skies. Marsilius Ficinus seems to second this opinion,[1]
out of Plato, or from himself, I know not (still ruling their
inferiors, as they do those under them again, all subordinate,
and the nearest to the earth rule us, whom we subdivide into
good and bad angels, call gods or devils, as they help or hurt
us, and so adore, love or hate), but it is most likely from Plato,
for he, relying wholly on Socrates, *quem mori potius quam mentiri
voluisse scribit* [who, he says, would rather die than tell a false-
hood], out of Socrates' authority alone, made nine kinds of them;
which opinion, belike, Socrates took from Pythagoras, and he
from Trismegistus, he from Zoroaster: 1, God; 2, Ideæ; 3, Intelligences; 4, Archangels; 5, Angels; 6, Devils; 7, Heroes; 8, Principalities; 9, Princes: of which some were absolutely good, as
gods, some bad, some indifferent *inter deos et homines* [between
gods and men], as heroes and dæmons, which ruled men, and
were called genii, or as Proclus[2] and Iamblichus will, the
middle betwixt God and men, principalities and princes, which
commanded and swayed kings and countries, and had several
places in the spheres perhaps, for as every sphere is higher, so
hath it more excellent inhabitants: which, belike, is that Galilæus
à Galilæo and Kepler aims at in his *Nuncio Sidereo*, when he
will have Saturnine and Jovial inhabitants:[3] and which Tycho
Brahe doth in some sort touch or insinuate in one of his epistles:
but these things Zanchius justly explodes, *cap*. 3, *lib*. 4;[4] P.
Martyr *in* 1 *Sam*. 28.

So that according to these men the number of ætherial spirits
must needs be infinite; for if that be true that some of our
mathematicians say: if a stone could fall from the starry heaven,
or eighth sphere, and should pass every hour an hundred miles,
it would be 65 years, or more, before it would come to ground,
by reason of the great distance of heaven from earth, which
contains, as some say, 170 millions 803 miles, besides those other
heavens, whether they be crystalline or watery, which Maginus
adds, which peradventure holds as much more; how many such
spirits may it contain? And yet for all this Thomas,[5] Albertus,
and most, hold that there be far more angels than devils.

But be they more or less, *Quod supra nos nihil ad nos* [what is beyond our comprehension does not concern us]. Howsoever, as Martianus foolishly supposeth, *Ætherii dæmones non curant res humanas*, they care not for us, do not attend our actions, or look for us, those ætherial spirits have other worlds to reign in, belike, or business to follow. We are only now to speak in brief of those sublunary spirits or devils: for the rest, our divines determine that the devil had no power over stars or heavens. *Carminibus cœlo possunt deducere lunam*[1] [by their charms (verses) they can seduce the moon from the heavens], etc.—those are poetical fictions; and that they can *sistere aquam fluviis, et vertere sidera retro*[2] [stop rivers and turn the stars backward in their courses], etc., as Canidia in Horace, 'tis all false. They are confined until the day of judgment to this sublunary world, and can work no farther than the four elements, and as God permits them.[3] Wherefore of these sublunary devils, though others divide them otherwise according to their several places and offices, Psellus makes six kinds, fiery, aerial, terrestrial, watery, and subterranean devils, besides those fairies, satyrs, nymphs, etc.

Fiery spirits or devils are such as commonly work by blazing stars, fire-drakes, or *ignes fatui*; which lead men often *in flumina aut præcipitia* [into rivers or over precipices], saith Bodine, *lib. 2 Theat. naturæ, fol.* 221. *Quos, inquit, arcere si volunt viatores, clara voce Deum appellare aut prona facie terram contingente adorare oportet, et hoc amuletum majoribus nostris acceptum ferre debemus* [whom if travellers wish to keep off they must pronounce the name of God with a clear voice, or adore Him with their faces in contact with the ground], etc.; likewise they counterfeit suns and moons, stars oftentimes, and sit on ship-masts: *in navigiorum summitatibus visuntur*; and are called *Dioscuri*, as Eusebius, *lib. contra Philosophos, cap.* 48, informeth us, out of the authority of Zenophanes; or little clouds, *ad motum nescio quem volantes* [scudding along all ways]; which never appear, saith Cardan, but they signify some mischief or other to come unto men, though some again will have them to pretend good, and victory to that side they come towards in sea fights; St. Elmo's fires they commonly call them, and they do likely appear after a sea storm; Radzivilius, the Polonian duke, calls this apparition *Sancti Germani sidus* [the star of St. Germanus]; and saith moreover that he saw the same after or in a storm, as he was sailing, 1582, from Alexandria to Rhodes.[4] Our stories are full of such apparitions in all kinds

Some think they keep their residence in that Hecla, a mountain in Iceland, Ætna in Sicily, Lipari, Vesuvius, etc. These devils were worshipped heretofore by that superstitious Πυρομαντεία [divination by fire] and the like.

Aerial spirits or devils are such as keep quarter most part in the air,[1] cause many tempests, thunder, and lightnings, tear oaks, fire steeples, houses, strike men and beasts, make it rain stones, as in Livy's time, wool, frogs, etc., counterfeit armies in the air, strange noises, swords, etc., as at Vienna before the coming of the Turks, and many times in Rome, as Scheretzius, *lib. de spect. cap. 1, part. 1*; Lavater, *de spect. part. 1, cap. 17*; Julius Obsequens, an old Roman, in his book of prodigies, *ab urb. cond. 505*. Machiavel hath illustrated by many examples,[2] and Josephus, in his book *de bello Judaico*, before the destruction of Jerusalem. All which Guil. Postellus, in his first book, *cap. 7, de orbis concordia*, useth as an effectual argument (as indeed it is) to persuade them that will not believe there be spirits or devils. They cause whirlwinds on a sudden, and tempestuous storms; which though our meteorologists generally refer to natural causes, yet I am of Bodine's mind, *Theat. Nat. lib. 2*, they are more often caused by those aerial devils, in their several quarters; for *tempestatibus se ingerunt* [they ride on the storm], saith Rich. Argentine;[3] as when a desperate man makes away himself, which by hanging or drowning they frequently do, as Kornmannus observes, *de mirac. mort. part. 7, cap. 76, tripudium agentes*, dancing and rejoicing at the death of a sinner. These can corrupt the air, and cause plagues, sickness, storms, shipwrecks, fires, inundations. At Mons Draconis in Italy, there is a most memorable example in Jovianus Pontanus:[4] and nothing so familiar (if we may believe those relations of Saxo Grammaticus, Olaus Magnus, Damianus à Goes) as for witches and sorcerers, in Lapland, Lithuania, and all over Scandia, to sell winds to mariners, and cause tempests, which Marcus Paulus the Venetian relates likewise of the Tartars. These kind of devils are much delighted in sacrifices (saith Porphyry),[5] held all the world in awe, and had several names, idols, sacrifices, in Rome, Greece, Egypt, and at this day tyrannize over and deceive those ethnics and Indians, being adored and worshipped for gods.[6] For the Gentiles' gods were devils (as Trismegistus confesseth in his *Asclepius*[7]), and he himself could make them come to their images by magic spells: and are now as much "respected by our papists" (saith Pictorius) "under the name of saints."[8] These are they which Cardan thinks desire so much carnal copulation with witches (incubi and succubi), transform bodies, and are so very cold if they be touched; and that serve magicians. His father had one of them (as he is not ashamed to relate[1]), an aerial devil, bound to him for twenty and eight years. As Agrippa's dog had a devil tied to his collar; some think that Paracelsus (or else Erastus belies him) had one confined to his sword pummel; others wear them in rings, etc. Jannes and Jambres did many things of old by their help; Simon Magus, Cinops, Apollonius Tyanæus, Iamblichus, and Trithemius of late, that showed Maximilian the emperor his wife, after she was dead; *et verrucam in collo ejus* (saith Godelman)[2] so much as the wart on her neck. Delrio, *lib.* 2, hath divers examples of their feats; Cicogna, *lib.* 3, *cap.* 3, and Wierus in his book *de præstig. dæmonum*; Boissardus, *de magis et veneficis*.

Water-devils are those naiades or water-nymphs[3] which have been heretofore conversant about waters and rivers. The water (as Paracelsus thinks) is their chaos, wherein they live; some call them fairies, and say that Habundia is their queen; these cause inundations, many times shipwrecks, and deceive men divers ways, as succubæ, or otherwise, appearing most part (saith Trithemius) in women's shapes. Paracelsus[4] hath several stories of them that have lived and been married to mortal men and so continued for certain years with them, and after, upon some dislike, have forsaken them. Such a one was Egeria with whom Numa was so familiar, Diana, Ceres, etc. Olaus Magnus[5] hath a long narration of one Hotherus, a king of Sweden, that having lost his company, as he was hunting one day met with these water-nymphs or fairies, and was feasted by them and Hector Boethius, of Macbeth and Banquo, two Scottish lords, that, as they were wandering in the woods, had their fortunes told them by three strange women. To these, heretofore, they did use to sacrifice, by that ὑδρομαντεία or divination by waters.

Terrestrial devils are those lares,[6] genii, fauns, satyrs, wood-nymphs,[7] foliots, fairies, Robin Goodfellows, *trolli* [trolls] etc., which as they are most conversant with men, so they do them most harm. Some think it was they alone that kept the heathen people in awe of old, and had so many idols and temples erected to them. Of this range was Dagon amongst the Philistines, Bel amongst the Babylonians, Astarte amongst the Sidonians, Baal amongst the Samaritans, Isis and Osiris amongst the Egyptians, etc.; some put our fairies[8] into this rank, which have been in former times adored with much superstition, with sweeping their houses, and setting of a pail of clean water, good victuals, and the like, and then they should not be pinched, but find money in their shoes, and be fortunate in their enterprises. These are they that dance on heaths and greens, as Lavater thinks[1] with Trithemius, and, as Olaus Magnus adds,[2] leave that green circle, which we commonly find in plain fields, which others hold to proceed from a meteor falling, or some accidental rankness of the ground, so Nature sports herself; they are sometimes seen by old women and children. Hieronym. Pauli, in his description of the city of Barcino in Spain, relates how they have been familiarly seen near that town, about fountains and hills. *Nonnunquam* (saith Trithemius) *in sua latibula montium simpliciores homines ducunt, stupenda mirantibus ostendentes miracula, nolarum sonitus, spectacula,* [sometimes they lead simple-minded peasants into their hiding-places in the mountains, where they show them marvellous sights, make them hear bells, and astonish them in other ways], etc. Giraldus Cambrensis gives instance in a monk of Wales that was so deluded. Paracelsus reckons up many places in Germany, where they do usually walk in little coats, some two foot long.[3] A bigger kind there is of them called with us hobgoblins, and Robin Goodfellows, that would in those superstitious times grind corn for a mess of milk, cut wood, or do any manner of drudgery work. They would mend old irons in those Æolian isles of Lipari, in former ages, and have been often seen and heard. Tholosanus[4] calls them *trollos* and *getulos*, and saith that in his days they were common in many places of France. Dithmarus Bleskenius, in his description of Iceland, reports for a certainty, that almost in every family they have yet some such familiar spirits; and Felix Malleolus, in his book *de crudel. læmon.*, affirms as much, that these *trolli* or *telchines* are very common in Norway, "and seen to do drudgery work"; [5] to draw water, saith Wierus, *lib.* 1, *cap.* 22, dress meat, or any such thing. Another sort of these there are, which frequent forlorn houses,[6] which the Italians call foliots, most part innoxious, Cardan holds: [7] "They will make strange noises in the night, howl sometimes pitifully, and then laugh again, cause great flame and sudden lights, fling stones, rattle chains, shave men, open doors and shut them, fling down platters, stools, chests, sometimes appear in the likeness of hares, crows, black dogs, etc.," [8] of which read Pet. Thyræus the Jesuit, in his tract *de locis infestis, part.* 1, *cap.* 1 *et cap.* 4, who will have them to be devils

or the souls of damned men that seek revenge, or else souls out
of purgatory that seek ease;[1] for such examples peruse Sigis-
mundus Scheretzius, *lib. de spectris, part.* 1, *cap.* 1, which he
saith he took out of Luther most part; there be many instances.
Plinius Secundus[2] remembers such a house at Athens, which
Athenodorus the philosopher hired, which no man durst inhabit
for fear of devils. Austin, *de Civ. Dei, lib.* 22, *cap.* 8, relates
as much of Hesperius the tribune's house at Zubeda, near their
city of Hippo, vexed with evil spirits, to his great hindrance,
cum afflictione animalium et servorum suorum [and to the great
distress of his animals and slaves]. Many such instances are
to be read in Niderius, *Formicar. lib.* 5, *cap.* 12, 13, etc. Whether
I may call these Zim and Ochim, which Isaiah, chap. xiii, 21,
speaks of, I make a doubt. See more of these in the said
Scheretz., *lib.* 1 *de spect. cap.* 4; he is full of examples. These
kind of devils many times appear to men, and affright them out
of their wits, sometimes walking at noonday,[3] sometimes at
nights, counterfeiting dead men's ghosts, as that of Caligula,
which (saith Suetonius) was seen to walk in Lavinia's garden;
where his body was buried, spirits haunted, and [in] the house
where he died; *nulla nox sine terrore transacta, donec incendio con-
sumpta;*[4] every night this happened, there was no quietness
till the house was burned. About Hecla, in Iceland, ghosts
commonly walk, *animas mortuorum simulantes* [resembling
the dead], saith Joh. Anan., *lib.* 3 *de nat. dæm.*, Olaus, *lib.* 2
cap. 2, Natal. Tallopid., *lib. de apparit. spir.*, Kornmannus, *de
mirac. mort. part.* 1, *cap.* 44. Such sights are frequently seen
circa sepulchra et monasteria, saith Lavater, *lib.* 1, *cap.* 19, in
monasteries and about churchyards, *loca paludinosa, ampl.
ædificia, solitaria, et cæde hominum notata,* [marshes, great buildings, solitary places, or places remarkable as the scene of some
murder] etc. Thyræus adds, *ubi gravius peccatum est commissum,
impii pauperum oppressores et nequiter insignes habitant* [where
some very heinous crime was committed, there the impious
and infamous generally dwell]. These spirits often foretell
men's deaths by several signs, as knocking, groanings, etc.
though Rich. Argentine, *cap.* 18 *de præstigiis dæmonum*, will
ascribe these predictions to good angels, out of the authority of
Ficinus and others; *prodigia in obitu principum sæpius con-
tingunt* [prodigies frequently occur at the deaths of illustrious
men], etc., as in the Lateran Church in Rome,[6] the Popes' deaths
are foretold by Sylvester's tomb. Near Rupes Nova in Finland,
in the kingdom of Sweden, there is a lake, in which, before the

governor of the castle dies, a spectrum, in the habit of Arion
with his harp, appears and makes excellent music; like those
blocks in Cheshire,[1] which (they say) presage death to the
master of the family; or that oak in Lanthadran Park in Cornwall,[2] which foreshows as much.   Many families in Europe are
so put in mind of their last by such predictions, and many men
are forewarned (if we may believe Paracelsus) by familiar spirits
in divers shapes, as cocks, crows, owls, which often hover about
sick men's chambers, *vel quia morientium fœditatem sentiunt*
[either because they smell a corpse], as Baracellus conjectures,[3]
et ideo super tectum infirmorum crocitant [and therefore they
croak over a house where someone is lying ill], because they
smell a corse; or for that (as Bernardinus de Bustis thinketh[4])
God permits the devil to appear in the form of crows and such-
like creatures, to scare such as live wickedly here on earth.   A
little before Tully's death (saith Plutarch) the crows made a
mighty noise about him, *tumultuose perstrepentes*, they pulled
the pillow from under his head.   Rob. Gaguinus, *Hist. Franc.
lib.* 8, telleth such another wonderful story at the death of
Johannes de Monteforti, a French lord, *anno* 1345; *tanta cor-
vorum multitudo œdibus morientis insedit, quantam esse in Gallia
nemo judicasset* [a multitude of crows alighted on the house of
the dying man, such as no one imagined existed in France].
Such prodigies are very frequent in authors.   See more of these
in the said Lavater, Thyræus, *de locis infestis, part.* 3, *cap.* 58,
Pictorius, Delrio, Cicogna, *lib.* 3, *cap.* 9.   Necromancers take
upon them to raise and lay them at their pleasures.   And so likewise those which Mizaldus calls *ambulones*, that walk about
midnight on great heaths and desert places, which (saith
Lavater[5]) "draw men out of the way, and lead them all night a
by-way, or quite bar them of their way"; these have several
names in several places; we commonly call them Pucks.   In the
deserts of Lop, in Asia, such illusions of walking spirits are
often perceived, as you may read in M. Paulus the Venetian,
his travels; if one lose his company by chance, these devils will
call him by his name, and counterfeit voices of his companions
to seduce him.   Hieronym. Pauli, in his book of the hills of
Spain, relates of a great mount in Cantabria,[6] where such
spectrums are to be seen; Lavater and Cicogna have variety of
examples of spirits and walking devils in this kind.   Sometimes
they sit by the highway side, to give men falls, and make their
horses stumble and start as they ride (if you will believe the
relation of that holy man Ketellus in Nubrigensis,[7] that had an

especial grace to see devils, *gratiam divinitus collatam*, and talk with them, *et impavidus cum spiritibus sermonem miscere*, without offence); and if a man curse or spur his horse for stumbling they do heartily rejoice at it; with many such pretty feats.

Subterranean devils are as common as the rest, and do as much harm. Olaus Magnus, *lib.* 6, *cap.* 19, makes six kinds of them; some bigger, some less. These (saith Munster[1]) are commonly seen about mines of metals, and are some of them noxious; some again do no harm. The metal-men in many places account it good luck, a sign of treasure and rich ore when they see them. Georgius Agricola, in his book *de subterraneis animantibus*, *cap.* 37, reckons two more notable kinds of them, which he calls *getuli* and *cobali*; both "are clothed after the manner of metal-men, and will many times imitate their works."[2] Their office, as Pictorius and Paracelsus think, is to keep treasure in the earth, that it be not all at once revealed; and besides, Cicogna avers that they are the frequent causes of those horrible earthquakes "which often swallow up, not only houses, but whole islands and cities";[3] in his third book, *cap.* 11, he gives many instances.

The last are conversant about the centre of the earth, to torture the souls of damned men to the day of judgment; their egress and regress some suppose to be about Ætna, Lipari, Mons Hecla in Iceland, Vesuvius, Terra del Fuego, etc., because many shrieks and fearful cries are continually heard thereabouts, and familiar apparitions of dead men, ghosts, and goblins.

Thus the devil reigns, and in a thousand several shapes, "as a roaring lion still seeks whom he may devour" (1 Pet. v), by earth, sea, land, air, as yet unconfined, though some will have his proper place the air;[4] all that space between us and the moon for them that transgressed least, and hell for the wickedest of them; *Hic velut in carcere ad finem mundi, tunc in locum funestiorum trudendi* [here they are confined as in a prison till the end of the world; then they are to be thrust forth into a still more dreadful place], as Austin holds, *de Civit. Dei*, *cap.* 22 *lib.* 14, *cap.* 3 *et* 23; but be where he will, he rageth while he may to comfort himself, as Lactantius thinks,[5] with other men's falls, he labours all he can to bring them into the same pit of perdition with him. For "men's miseries, calamities, and ruins are the devil's banqueting dishes."[6] By many temptations and several engines, he seeks to captivate our souls. The Lord of Lies, saith Austin,[7] "as he was deceived himself, he seeks to deceive others"; the ringleader to all naughtiness, as he did

by Eve and Cain, Sodom and Gomorrah, so would he do by all
the world. Sometimes he tempts by covetousness, drunkenness, pleasure, pride, etc., errs, dejects, saves, kills, protects,
and rides some men as they do their horses. He studies our
overthrow, and generally seeks our destruction; and although
he pretend many times human good, and vindicate himself
for a god by curing of several diseases, *ægris sanitatem, et cæcis
luminis usum restituendo* [by restoring health to the sick and
sight to the blind] as Austin declares, *lib.* 10 *de Civit. Dei, cap.* 6,
as Apollo, Æsculapius, Isis, of old have done; divert plagues,
assist them in wars, pretend their happiness, yet *nihil his
impurius, scelestius, nihil humano generi infestius*, nothing so
impure, nothing so pernicious, as may well appear by their
tyrannical and bloody sacrifices of men to Saturn and Moloch,
which are still in use among those barbarous Indians, their
several deceits and cozenings to keep men in obedience, their
false oracles, sacrifices, their superstitious impositions of fasts,
penury, etc., heresies, superstitious observations of meats,
times, etc., by which they crucify the souls of mortal men,[1] as
shall be showed in our Treatise of Religious Melancholy. *Modico
lhuc tempore sinitur malignari*, as Bernard expresseth it,[2] by
God's permission he rageth awhile, hereafter to be confined
to hell and darkness, "which is prepared for him and his
angels" (Matt. xxv).

How far their power doth extend it is hard to determine;
what the ancients held of their effects, force, and operations
will briefly show you. Plato in *Critias*, and after him his
followers, gave out that these spirits or devils "were men's
governors and keepers, our lords and masters, as we are of our
cattle. They govern provinces and kingdoms by oracles,
auguries, dreams, rewards and punishments,"[3] prophecies, in-
spirations, sacrifices, and religious superstitions, varied in as
many forms as there be diversity of spirits; they send wars,
plagues, peace, sickness, health, dearth, plenty, *adstantes hic
cum nobis, spectantes, et arbitrantes*[4] [standing by us here and
now, watching and judging us], etc., as appears by those
stories of Thucydides, Livius, Dionysius Halicarnasseus, with
many others that are full of their wonderful stratagems, and
were therefore by those Roman and Greek commonwealths
adored and worshipped for gods with prayers and sacrifices, etc.
In a word, *nihil magis quærunt quam metum et admirationem
hominum*[5] [they seek nothing more eagerly than the fear and
admiration of men]; and as another hath it, *dici non potest,*

quam impotenti ardore in homines dominium, et divinos cultu
maligni spiritus affectent [it is impossible to describe the ardou
with which evil spirits seek to obtain dominion over men an
the honours of divine worship]. Trithemius, in his book *a*
septem secundis, assigns names to such angels as are governor
of particular provinces, by what authority I know not, an
gives them several jurisdictions. Asclepiades a Grecian, Rabl
Achiba the Jew, Abraham Avenezra and Rabbi Azarie
Arabians (as I find them cited by Cicogna[1]), farther add, tha
they are not our governors only, *sed ex eorum concordia*
discordia, boni et mali affectus promanant, but as they agree, s
do we and our princes, or disagree; stand or fall. Juno was
bitter enemy to Troy, Apollo a good friend, Jupiter indifferen
Æqua Venus Teucris, Pallas iniqua fuit [Venus was for th
Trojans, Pallas against]; some are for us still, some against u
Premente deo, fert deus alter opem [when one god threaten
another comes to the rescue]. Religion, policy, public an
private quarrels, wars are procured by them, and they a
delighted perhaps to see men fight, as men are with cock
bulls and dogs, bears, etc.[2] Plagues, dearths depend on ther
our *bene* and *male esse*, and almost all our other peculiar actio
(for as Anthony Rusca contends, *lib.* 5, *cap.* 18, every man ha
a good and a bad angel attending on him in particular all h
life long, which Iamblichus calls *dæmonem*), preferments, losse
weddings, deaths, rewards and punishments, and as Procl
will,[3] all offices whatsoever, *alii genetricem, alii opificem pote*
tatem habent [some help in childbirth, others in manual labour
etc., and several names they give them according to the
offices, as *Lares, Indigetes, Præstites*, etc. When the Arcad
in that battle at Chæronea, which was fought against Ki
Philip for the liberty of Greece, had deceitfully carried ther
selves, long after, in the very same place, *diis Græciæ ultorib*
[through the avenging gods of Greece] (saith mine auth
they were miserably slain by Metellus the Roman: so likewi
in smaller matters, they will have things fall out, as these bo
and *mali genii* favour or dislike us. *Saturnini non conveniu*
Jovialibus, etc. He that is *Saturninus* shall never likely
preferred. That base fellows are often advanced, undeservi
Gnathos, and vicious parasites, whereas discreet, wise, virtuo
and worthy men are neglected and unrewarded,[4] they refer
those domineering spirits, or subordinate genii; as they
inclined, or favour men, so they thrive, are ruled and ov
come; for, as Libanius supposeth, in our ordinary conflicts a

contentions, *Genius genio cedit et obtemperat*,[1] one genius yields
and is overcome by another. All particular events almost they
refer to these private spirits; and (as Paracelsus adds) they
direct, teach, inspire, and instruct men. Never was any man
extraordinary famous in any art, action, or great commander,
that had not *familiarem dæmonem* [a familiar spirit] to inform
him, as Numa, Socrates, and many such (as Cardan illustrates,
cap. 128, *Arcanis prudentiæ civilis*); *speciali siquidem gratia se
à Deo donari asserunt magi, a geniis cœlestibus instrui, ab iis
doceri* [2] [the Magians assert that they are vouchsafed from God
a special grace, that they are trained and instructed by the
heavenly spirits]. But these are most erroneous paradoxes,
ineptæ et fabulosæ nugæ, rejected by our divines and Christian
churches. 'Tis true they have, by God's permission, power
over us, and we find by experience that they can hurt not our
fields only, cattle, goods, but our bodies and minds.[3] At
Hammel in Saxony, *ann.* 1484, 20 *Junii*, the devil, in likeness
of a pied piper, carried away 130 children that were never
after seen. Many times men are affrighted out of their wits,
carried away quite, as Scheretzius illustrates, *lib.* 1, *cap.* 4, and
severally molested by his means. Plotinus the Platonist, *lib.* 14
Advers. Gnost., laughs them to scorn that hold the devil or
spirits can cause any such diseases.[4] Many think he can
work upon the body, but not upon the mind. But experience
pronounceth otherwise, that he can work both upon body and
mind. Tertullian is of this opinion, *cap.* 22, "that he can cause
both sickness and health," [5] and that secretly. Taurellus adds,
"By clancular poisons he can infect the bodies, and hinder the
operations of the bowels, though we perceive it not," [6] "closely
creeping into them," saith Lipsius,[7] and so crucify our souls:
nociva melancholia furiosos efficit [and makes people mad from
noxious melancholy]. For being a spiritual body, he struggles
with our spirits, saith Rogers, and suggests (according to Cardan [8])
verba sine voce, species sine visu [words without speaking,
sights without showing anything], envy, lust, anger, etc., as
he sees men inclined.

The manner how he performs it, Biarmannus, in his Oration
against Bodine, sufficiently declares. "He begins first with the
phantasy, and moves that so strongly that no reason is able
to resist." [9] Now the phantasy he moves by mediation of
humours; although many physicians are of opinion that the devil
can alter the mind, and produce this disease of himself." *Qui-
sdam medicorum visum*, saith Avicenna, *quod melancholia*

contingat a dæmonio [1] [some doctors have held that melancholy
is from the devil]. Of the same mind is Psellus, and Rhasis
the Arab, *lib.* 1, *tract.* 9, *Cont.*, "that this disease proceeds
especially from the devil, and from him alone." [2] Arculanus,
cap. 6, *in* 9 *Rhasis*; Ælianus Montaltus in his 9th *cap.*; Daniel
Sennertus, *lib.* 1, *part.* 2, *cap.* 11, confirm as much, that the
devil can cause this disease; by reason many times that the
parties affected prophesy, speak strange language, but *non sine
interventu humoris*, not without the humour, as he interprets
himself; no more doth Avicenna: *Si contingat a dæmonio, sufficit
nobis ut convertat complexionem ad choleram nigram, et sit causa
ejus propinqua cholera nigra* [if it is from the devil, the sufficient
sign is that it turns the humour to black bile and that its
immediate cause is black bile]; the immediate cause is choler
adust, which Pomponatius likewise labours to make good:
Galgerandus of Mantua, a famous physician, so cured a dæmoniacal woman in his time, that spake all languages, by purging
black choler; and thereupon, belike, this humour of melancholy
is called *balneum diaboli*, the devil's bath; the devil, spying
his opportunity of such humours, drives them many times to
despair, fury, rage, etc., mingling himself amongst these humours.
This is that which Tertullian avers, *Corporibus infligunt acerbo
casus, animæque repentinos, membra distorquent, occulte repente*
[they cause grievous bodily and mental harm; they distort
the limbs, coming on stealthily], etc., and which Lemnius goes
about to prove, *Immiscent se mali genii pravis humoribus, atque
atræ bili* [evil spirits insert themselves in depraved humour
and black bile], etc. And Jason Pratensis, "that the devil
being a slender incomprehensible spirit, can easily insinuate
and wind himself into human bodies, and, cunningly couched in
our bowels, vitiate our healths, terrify our souls with fearful
dreams, and shake our mind with furies." [4] And in another
place, "These unclean spirits settled in our bodies, and now
mixed with our melancholy humours, do triumph as it were
and sport themselves as in another heaven." [5] Thus he argues,
and that they go in and out of our bodies, as bees do in a hive,
and so provoke and tempt us as they perceive our temperature
inclined of itself, and most apt to be deluded. Agrippa [6] and
Lavater [7] are persuaded that this humour invites the devil
to it, wheresoever it is in extremity, and, of all other, melancholy persons are most subject to diabolical temptations and
illusions, and most apt to entertain them, and the devil be
able to work upon them. But whether by obsession, or pos-

session, or otherwise, I will not determine; 'tis a difficult question.
Delrio the Jesuit, *tom.* 3, *lib.* 6; Sprenger and his colleague,
Mall. Malef.;[1] Pet. Thyræus the Jesuit, *lib. de dæmoniacis, de
locis infestis, de terrificationibus nocturnis*; Hieronymus Mengus,
Flagel. dæm., and others of that rank of pontifical writers, it
seems, by their exorcisms and conjurations approve of it, having
forged many stories to that purpose. A nun did eat a lettuce
without grace or signing it with the sign of the cross, and
was instantly possessed.[2] Durand, *lib.* 6 *Rational. cap.* 86,
num. 8, relates that he saw a wench possessed in Bononia with
two devils, by eating an unhallowed pomegranate, as she did
afterwards confess, when she was cured by exorcisms. And
therefore our papists do sign themselves so often with the sign
of the cross, *ne dæmon ingredi ausit* [that the demon may not dare
to enter], and exorcise all manner of meats, as being unclean or
accursed otherwise, as Bellarmine defends. Many such stories
I find amongst pontifical writers, to prove their assertions; let
them free their own credits; some few I will recite in this kind
out of most approved physicians. Cornelius Gemma, *lib.* 2
e nat. mirac. cap. 4, related of a young maid, called Katherine
Gualter, a cooper's daughter, *anno* 1571, that had such strange
passions and convulsions, three men could not sometimes hold
her; she purged a live eel, which he saw, a foot and a half long,
and touched himself; but the eel afterwards vanished; she
vomited some twenty-four pounds of fulsome stuff of all colours,
twice a day for fourteen days; and after that she voided great
balls of hair, pieces of wood, pigeon's dung, parchment, goose
dung, coals; and after them two pound of pure blood, and then
again coals and stones, of which some had inscriptions, bigger
than a walnut, some of them pieces of glass, brass, etc., besides
paroxysms of laughing, weeping and ecstasies, etc. *Et hoc
(inquit) cum horrore vidi,* "this I saw with horror." They could
do no good on her by physic, but left her to the clergy. Marcellus
Donatus, *lib.* 2, *cap.* 1, *de med. mirab.*, hath such another story of
a country fellow, that had four knives in his belly, *instar serræ
dentatos*, indented like a saw, every one a span long, and a
wreath of hair like a globe, with much baggage of like sort,
wonderful to behold: how it should come into his guts, he
concludes, *certo non alio quam dæmonis astutia et dolo* [could
assuredly only have been through the artifice of the devil].
Langius, *Epist. med. lib.* 1, *epist.* 38, hath many relations to
this effect, and so hath Christopherus à Vega: Wierus, Sckenkius,
Scribanius, all agree that they are done by the subtlety and

illusion of the devil. If you shall ask a reason of this, 'tis to exercise our patience; for as Tertullian holds,[1] *Virtus non es virtus, nisi comparem habet aliquem, in quo superando vim suam ostendat* [virtue is not worthy of the name till it has over come an antagonist worthy of its steel]; 'tis to try us and our faith, 'tis for our offences, and for the punishment of our sins by God's permission they do it, *carnifices vindictæ justæ Dei* as Tholosanus styles them,[2] executioners of His will; or rather as David (Ps. lxxviii, 49), "He cast upon them the fiercenes of his anger, indignation, wrath, and vexation, by sending out of evil angels"; so did He afflict Job, Saul, the lunatics and dæmoniacal persons whom Christ cured (Matt. iv, 8; Luke iv, 11 Luke xiii; Mark ix; Tobit viii, 3, etc.). This, I say, happeneth for a punishment of sin, for their want of faith, incredulity weakness, distrust, etc.

SUBSECT. III.—*Of Witches and Magicians, how they cause Melancholy*

You have heard what the devil can do of himself, now you shall hear what he can perform by his instruments, who are many times worse (if it be possible) than he himself, and to satisfy their revenge and lust cause more mischief. *Multa enim mala non egisset dæmon, nisi provocatus a sagis,* as Erastus thinks;[3] much harm had never been done, had he not been provoked by witches to it. He had not appeared in Samuel's shape, if the Witch of Endor had let him alone; or represented those serpents in Pharaoh's presence, had not the magicians urged him unto it; *nec morbos vel hominibus vel brutis infligere* (Erastus maintains) *si sagæ quiescerent:* men and cattle might go free, if the witches would let him alone. Many deny witches at all, or if there be any they can do no harm; of this opinion is Wierus, *lib. 3, cap. 53, de præstig. dæm.,* Austin Lerchemer, Dutch writer, Biarmannus, Ewichius, Euwaldus, our country man Scot;[4] with him in Horace,

> *Somnia, terrores magicos, miracula, sagas,*
> *Nocturnos lemures, portentaque Thessala risu*
> *Excipiunt.*

> [They laugh indignant at the schemes
> Of magic terrors, visionary dreams,
> Portentous wonders, witching imps of hell,
> The nightly goblin, and enchanting spell.]

They laugh at all such stories; but on the contrary are most lawyers, divines, physicians, philosophers, Austin, Hemingius, Danæus, Chytræus, Zanchius, Aretæus, etc., Delrio, Sprenger, Niderius, *lib. 5 Formicar.*,[1] Cujacius, Bartolus, *consil. 6, tom. 1,* Bodine, *Dæmoniant. lib. 2, cap. 8,* Godelman, Damhoderius, etc., Paracelsus, Erastus, Scribanius, Camerarius, etc.   The parties by whom the devil deals may be reduced to these two: such as command him in show at least, as conjurors, and magicians, whose detestable and horrid mysteries are contained in their book called *Arbatell*;[2] *dæmones enim advocati præsto sunt, seque exorcismis et conjurationibus quasi cogi patiuntur, ut miserum magorum genus in impietate detineant* [the demons are always on the alert, and obey the call of incantations and charms, in order that they may confirm the accursed tribe of magicians in their impiety]; or such as are commanded, as witches, that deal *ex parte implicite*, or *explicite*, as the king hath well defined;[3] many subdivisions there are, and many several species of sorcerers, witches, enchanters, charmers, etc.   They have been tolerated heretofore some of them; and magic hath been publicly professed in former times, in Salamanca,[4] Cracovia,[5] and other places, though after censured by several universities,[6] and now generally contradicted, though practised by some still, maintained and excused, *tanquam res secreta quæ non nisi viris magnis et peculiari beneficio de cœlo instructis communicatur* [like a great secret, only to be communicated to notable men specially favoured by Heaven] (I use Boissardus his words[7]), and so far approved by some princes, *ut nihil ausi aggredi in politicis, in sacris, in consiliis, sine eorum arbitrio*; they consult still with them, and dare indeed do nothing without their advice.   Nero and Heliogabalus, Maxentius and Julianus postata, were never so much addicted to magic of old as some of our modern princes and popes themselves are nowadays. Erricus, King of Sweden, had an enchanted cap,[8] by virtue of which, and some magical murmur or whispering terms, he could command spirits, trouble the air, and make the wind stand which way he would, insomuch that when there was any great wind or storm, the common people were wont to say, the king now had on his conjuring cap.   But such examples are infinite. That which they can do, is as much almost as the devil himself, who is still ready to satisfy their desires, to oblige them the more unto him.   They can cause tempests, storms, which is familiarly practised by witches in Norway, Iceland, as I have proved.   They can make friends enemies, and enemies friends by philters; *turpes amores conciliare*,[9] enforce love, tell any

man where his friends are, about what employed though in t
most remote places; and if they will, "bring their sweethea
to them by night, upon a goat's back flying in the air"
(Sigismund Scheretzius, *part.* 1, *cap.* 9, *de spect.*, reports con
dently that he conferred with sundry such, that had been
carried many miles, and that he heard witches themselv
confess as much); hurt and infect men and beasts, vines, cor
cattle, plants, make women abortive, not to conceive, barre
men and women unapt and unable,[2] married and unmarrie
fifty several ways, saith Bodine, *lib.* 2, *cap.* 2, fly in the air, me
when and where they will, as Cicogna proves, and Lavat.
spec. part. 2, *cap.* 17, "steal young children out of their cradl
ministerio dæmonum [with the help of the demons] and p
deformed in their rooms, which we call changelings," sai
Scheretzius, *part.* 1, *cap.* 6,[3] make men victorious, fortuna
eloquent; and therefore in those ancient monomachies and cor
bats they were searched of old, they had no magical charms
they can make stick frees,[5] such as shall endure a rapier's poir
musket-shot, and never be wounded: of which read more
Boissardus, *cap.* 6 *de Magia*, the manner of the adjuratic
and by whom 'tis made, where and how to be used *in expec
tionibus bellicis, præliis, duellis* [in military expeditions, battl
wars], etc., with many peculiar instances and examples; th
can walk in fiery furnaces, make men feel no pain on the rac
aut alias torturas sentire [or feel other tortures]; they can stan
blood, represent dead men's shapes, alter and turn themselv
and others into several forms, at their pleasures.[6]   Agaberta,
famous witch in Lapland,[7] would do as much publicly to
spectators, *modo pusilla, modo anus, modo procera ut querci
modo vacca, avis, coluber, etc.*, now young, now old, high, lo
like a cow, like a bird, a snake, and what not? she could repr
sent to others what forms they most desired to see, show the
friends absent, reveal secrets, *maxima omnium admiratione* [
the great astonishment of all], etc.   And yet for all this subtle
of theirs, as Lipsius well observes, *Physiolog. Stoicor. lib.*
cap. 17, neither these magicians nor devils themselves can ta
away gold or letters out of mine or Crassus' chest, *et cliente
suis largiri* [and make presents to their followers], for they a
base, poor, contemptible fellows most part; as Bodine note
they can do nothing *in judicum decreta aut pœnas, in regu
concilia vel arcana, nihil in rem nummariam aut thesauros*, th
cannot give money to their clients, alter judges' decrees,
councils of kings, these *minuti genii* cannot do it, *altiores ger*

hoc sibi adservarunt, the higher powers reserve these things to themselves. Now and then peradventure there may be some more famous magicians like Simon Magus, Apollonius Tyanæus,[1] Pases,[2] Iamblichus, Eudo de Stellis,[3] that for a time can build castles in the air, represent armies, etc., as they are said to have done,[4] command wealth and treasure, feed thousands with all variety of meats upon a sudden, protect themselves and their followers from all princes' persecutions, by removing from place to place in an instant, reveal secrets, future events, tell what is done in far countries, make them appear that died long since, etc., and do many such miracles, to the world's terror, admiration, and opinion of deity to themselves, yet the devil forsakes them at last, they come to wicked ends, and *raro aut nunquam* [rarely or never] such impostors are to be found. The vulgar sort of them can work no such feats. But to my purpose, they can, last of all, cure and cause most diseases to such as they love or hate, and this of melancholy amongst the rest.[5] Paracelsus, *tom. 4, de morbis amentium, tract.* 1, in express words affirms, *Multi fascinantur in melancholiam*, many are bewitched into melancholy, out of his experience. The same saith Danæus, *lib. 3 de sortiariis. Vidi, inquit, qui melancholicos morbos gravissimos induxerunt:* I have seen those that have caused melancholy in the most grievous manner, dried up women's paps, cured gout, palsy; this and apoplexy, falling sickness, which no physic could help, *solo tactu*, by touch alone.[6] Ruland, in his 3rd *cent., cura* 91, gives an instance of one David Helde, a young man, who by eating cakes which a witch gave him, *mox delirare cœpit*, began to dote on a sudden, and was instantly mad:[7] F. H. D. in Hildesheim,[8] consulted about a melancholy man, thought his disease was partly magical, and partly natural, because he vomited pieces of iron and lead, and spake such languages as he had never been taught; but such examples are common in Scribanius, Hercules de Saxonia, and others. The means by which they work are usually charms, images, as that in Hector Boethius of King Duff; characters stamped of sundry metals, and at such and such constellations, knots, amulets, words, philters, etc., which generally make the parties affected melancholy;[9] as Monavius discourseth at large in an epistle of his to Acolsius, giving instance in a Bohemian baron that was so troubled by a philter taken. Not that there is any power at all in those spells, charms, characters, and barbarous words; but that the devil doth use such means to delude them, *Ut fideles inde magos* (saith Libanius[10]) *in officio retineat, tum in*

I—H 886

consortium malefactorum vocet [that he may keep the Mag•
true to their allegiance, and then summon them to join the
company of evil-doers].

SUBSECT. IV.—*Stars a Cause. Signs from Physiognomy, Metoposcopy, Chiromancy*

Natural causes are either primary and universal, or secondary
and more particular. Primary causes are the heavens, planets
stars, etc., by their influence (as our astrologers hold) producing
this and such-like effects. I will not here stand to discus•
obiter, whether stars be causes, or signs; or to apologize fo•
judicial astrology. If either Sextus Empiricus, Picus Miran•
dula, Sextus ab Heminga, Pererius, Erastus, Chambers, etc.
have so far prevailed with any man, that he will attribut•
no virtue at all to the heavens, or to sun, or moon, more tha•
he doth to their signs at an innkeeper's post, or tradesman'•
shop, or generally condemn all such astrological aphorism•
approved by experience: I refer him to Bellantius, Pirovanu•
Marascallerus, Goclenius, Sir Christopher Heydon, etc. If tho•
shalt ask me what I think, I must answer, *nam et doctis hisc•
erroribus versatus sum* [for I too am conversant with these learne•
errors], they do incline, but not compel; no necessity at al•
agunt non cogunt: [1] and so gently incline, that a wise man ma•
resist them; *sapiens dominabitur astris* [a wise man will rul•
the stars]; they rule us, but God rules them. All this (me•
thinks) Joh. de Indagine hath comprised in brief: [2] *Quæris a m•
quantum in nobis operantur astra?* etc. "Wilt thou know ho•
far the stars work upon us? I say they do but incline, an•
that so gently, that if we will be ruled by reason, they have n•
power over us; but if we follow our own nature, and be led b•
sense, they do as much in us as in brute beasts, and we ar•
no better." So that, I hope, I may justly conclude wit•
Cajetan,[3] *Cælum est vehiculum divinæ virtutis*, etc., that th•
heaven is God's instrument, by mediation of which He goverr•
and disposeth these elementary bodies; or a great book, whos•
letters are the stars (as one calls it), wherein are written man•
strange things for such as can read, "or an excellent harp, mac•
by an eminent workman, on which he that can but play wi•
make most admirable music." [4] But to the purpose.

Paracelsus is of opinion "that a physician without the know•
ledge of stars can neither understand the cause or cure of an•
disease, either of this or gout, not so much as toothache; excep•

we see the peculiar geniture and scheme of the party affected." [1]
And for this proper malady, he will have the principal and
primary cause of it proceed from the heaven, ascribing more
to stars than humours, "and that the constellation alone many
times produceth melancholy, all other causes set apart." [2] He
gives instance in lunatic persons, that are deprived of their
wits by the moon's motion; and in another place refers all to
the ascendant, and will have the true and chief cause of it to
be sought from the stars. Neither is it his opinion only, but
of many Galenists and philosophers, though they [do] not so
peremptorily maintain as much. "This variety of melancholy
symptoms proceeds from the stars," saith Melancthon: [3] the
most generous melancholy, as that of Augustus, comes from the
conjunction of Saturn and Jupiter in Libra: the bad, as that
of Catiline's, from the meeting of Saturn and the Moon in Scorpio.
Jovianus Pontanus, in his tenth book and thirteenth chapter
e rebus cœlestibus, discourseth to this purpose at large: *Ex
atra bile varii generantur morbi*, etc., "many diseases proceed
from black choler, as it shall be hot or cold; and though it be
cold in its own nature, yet it is apt to be heated, as water may
be made to boil, and burn as bad as fire; or made cold as ice:
and thence proceed such variety of symptoms, some mad, some
solitary, some laugh, some rage," etc.[4] The cause of all which
intemperance he will have chiefly and primarily proceed from
the heavens, "from the position of Mars, Saturn, and Mercury." [5]
His aphorisms be these: "Mercury in any geniture, if he shall be
found in Virgo, or Pisces his opposite sign, and that in the horoscope, irradiated by those quartile aspects of Saturn or Mars,
the child shall be mad or melancholy." [6] Again, "He that
shall have Saturn and Mars, the one culminating, the other in
the fourth house, when he shall be born, shall be melancholy,
of which he shall be cured in time, if Mercury behold them.[7]
If the Moon be in conjunction or opposition at the birth time
with the Sun, Saturn or Mars,[8] or in a quartile aspect with
them" (*e malo cœli loco* [from a malign quarter of the heaven],
Leovitius adds), "many diseases are signified, especially the head
and brain is like to be misaffected with pernicious humours, to
be melancholy, lunatic, or mad"; Cardan adds, *quarta luna natos*
[those born on the fourth day after the new moon], [or in] eclipses,
earthquakes. Garcæus and Leovitius will have the chief judgment
to be taken from the lord of the geniture, or when there is an
aspect between the Moon and Mercury, and neither behold the
horoscope, or Saturn and Mars shall be lord of the present

conjunction or opposition in Sagittary or Pisces, of the Sun or Moon, such persons are commonly epileptic, dote, dæmoniacal melancholy: but see more of these aphorisms in the above-named Pontanus; Garcæus, *cap.* 23 *de Jud. genitur.*; Scheiner, *lib.* 1 *cap.* 8, which he hath gathered out of Ptolemy;[1] Albubater and some other Arabians, Junctine, Ranzovius, Lindhout Origan, etc. But these men you will reject peradventure, as astrologers, and therefore partial judges; then hear the testimony of physicians, Galenists themselves. Crato confesseth the influence of stars to have a great hand to this peculiar disease,[2] so doth Jason Pratensis, Lonicerus, *præfat. de Apoplexia*, Ficinus, Fernelius, etc. P. Cnemander acknowledgeth the stars an universal cause, the particular from parents, and the use of the six non-natural things.[3] Baptista Porta, *Mag. lib.* 1 *cap.* 10, 12, 15, will have them causes to every particular *individuum*. Instances and examples, to evince the truth of those aphorisms, are common amongst those astrologian treatises Cardan, in his thirty-seventh geniture, gives instance in Math Bolognius, Camerar., *Hor. natalit. centur.* 7, *genit.* 6 *et* 7, of Daniel Gare, and others; but see Garcæus, *cap.* 33, Luc. Gauricus, *Tract* 6, *de Azimenis*, etc. The time of this melancholy is, when the significators of any geniture are directed according to art, as the hor., moon, hylech, etc., to the hostile beams or terms of ♀ and ♂ especially, or any fixed star of their nature, or if ♄ be his revolution, or *transitus*, shall offend any of those radical promissors in the geniture.

Other signs there are taken from physiognomy, metoposcopy, chiromancy, which because Joh. de Indagine, and Rotman, the Landgrave of Hesse his mathematician, not long since in his Chiromancy, Baptista Porta in his Celestial Physiognomy have proved to hold great affinity with astrology, to satisfy the curious, I am the more willing to insert.

The general notions physiognomers[4] give, be these: "black colour argues natural melancholy; so doth leanness, hirsuteness broad veins, much hair on the brows," saith Gratarolus *cap.* 7, and a little head, out of Aristotle; high, sanguine, red colour, shows head melancholy;[5] they that stutter and are bald will be soonest melancholy (as Avicenna supposeth), by reason of the dryness of their brains; but he that will know more of the several signs of humour and wits out of physiognomy, let him consult with old Adamantus and Polemus, that comment, or rather paraphrase, upon Aristotle's Physiognomy, Baptista Porta's four pleasant books, Michael Scot *de secretis naturæ*

John de Indagine, Montaltus, Antony Zara, *Anat. ingeniorum*, sect. 1, memb. 13, *et lib.* 4.

Chiromancy hath these aphorisms to foretell melancholy. Taisnier, *lib.* 5, *cap.* 2, who hath comprehended the sum of John de Indagine, Tricassus, Corvinus, and others in his book, thus hath it: "The saturnine line going from the rascetta through the hand to Saturn's mount, and there intersected by certain little lines, argues melancholy; [1] so if the vital and natural make an acute angle" (Aphorism 100). "The saturnine, hepatic, and natural lines, making a gross triangle in the hand, argue as much"; which Goclenius, *cap.* 5 *Chiros.*, repeats verbatim out of him. In general they conclude all, that if Saturn's mount be full of many small lines and intersections, "such men are most part melancholy, miserable and full of disquietness, care and trouble, continually vexed with anxious and bitter thoughts, always sorrowful, fearful, suspicious; they delight in husbandry, buildings, pools, marshes, springs, woods, walks, etc." [2] Thaddæus Haggesius, in his *Metoposcopia*, hath certain aphorisms derived from Saturn's lines in the forehead, by which he collects a melancholy disposition; and Baptista Porta [3] makes observations from those other parts of the body, as if a spot be over the spleen; "or in the nails, [4] if it appear black, it signifieth much care, grief, contention, and melancholy"; the reason he refers to the humours, and gives instance in himself, that for seven years' space he had such black spots in his nails, and all that while was in perpetual lawsuits, controversies for his inheritance, fear, loss of honour, banishment, grief, care, etc., and when his miseries ended, the black spots vanished. Cardan, in his book *de libris propriis*, tells such a story of his own person, that a little before his son's death, he had a black spot, which appeared in one of his nails, and dilated itself as he came nearer to his end. But I am over-tedious in these toys, which howsoever, in some men's too severe censures, they may be held absurd and ridiculous, I am the bolder to insert, as not borrowed from circumforanean rogues and gipsies, but out of the writings of worthy philosophers and physicians, yet living some of them, and religious professors in famous universities, who are able to patronize that which they have said, and vindicate themselves from all cavillers and ignorant persons.

SUBSECT. V.—*Old Age a Cause*

Secondary peculiar causes efficient, so called in respect of th
other precedent, are either *congenitæ*, *internæ*, *innatæ*, as the
term them, inward, innate, inbred; or else outward and adven
titious, which happen to us after we are born: congenite, o
born with us, are either natural, as old age, or *præter natura*
[unnatural] (as Fernelius calls it [1]), that distemperature whic
we have from our parents' seed, it being an hereditary diseas
The first of these, which is natural to all, and which no ma
living can avoid, is old age,[2] which being cold and dry, and o
the same quality as melancholy is, must needs cause it, b
diminution of spirits and substance, and increasing of adus
humours; therefore Melancthon avers out of Aristotle,[3] as a
undoubted truth, *senes plerumque delirasse in senecta*, that ol
men familiarly dote, *ob atram bilem*, for black choler, which
then superabundant in them: and Rhasis, that Arabian phys
cian, in his *Cont. lib.* 1, *cap.* 9, calls it "a necessary and insepa
able accident"[4] to all old and decrepit persons. After sevent
years (as the Psalmist saith) "all is trouble and sorrow";[5] an
common experience confirms the truth of it in weak and ol
persons, especially such as have lived in action all their live
had great employment, much business, much command, an
many servants to oversee, and leave off *ex abrupto*, as Charl
the Fifth did to King Philip, resign up all on a sudden;[6] the
are overcome with melancholy in an instant: or if they o
continue in such courses, they dote at last (*senex bis puer* [a
old man is in his second boyhood]), and are not able to mana
their estates through common infirmities incident in their ag
full of ache, sorrow, and grief, children again, dizzards, the
carle many times as they sit, and talk to themselves, they a
angry, waspish, displeased with everything, "suspicious of a
wayward, covetous, hard" (saith Tully[7]), "self-willed, supe
stitious, self-conceited, braggers, and admirers of themselves,"
Balthasar Castilio hath truly noted of them.[8] This natur
infirmity is most eminent in old women, and such as are poc
solitary, live in most base esteem and beggary, or such as a
witches; insomuch that Wierus,[9] Baptista Porta, Ulricus Molit
Edwicus, do refer all that witches are said to do, to imaginatio
alone, and this humour of melancholy. And whereas it
controverted, whether they can bewitch cattle to death, ri
in the air upon a cowl-staff out of a chimney-top, transfor
themselves into cats, dogs, etc., translate bodies from place

lace, meet in companies and dance, as they do, or have carnal opulation with the devil, they ascribe all to this redundant melancholy, which domineers in them, to somniferous potions,[1] nd natural causes, the devil's policy. *Non lædunt omnino* saith Wierus) *aut quid mirum faciunt* (*de Lamiis, lib.* 3, *cap.* 36), *t putatur, solam vitiatam habent phantasiam;* they do no such onders at all, only their brains are crazed.[2] "They think hey are witches, and can do hurt, but do not."[3] But this pinion Bodine, Erastus, Danæus, Scribanius, Sebastian Iichaelis, Campanella, *de sensu rerum, lib.* 4, *cap.* 9, Dandinus he Jesuit, *lib.* 2 *de Anima,*[4] explode; Cicogna confutes at large.[5] 'hat witches are melancholy they deny not, but not out of a orrupt phantasy alone, so to delude themselves and others, or produce such effects.

Subsect. VI.—*Parents a Cause by Propagation*

That other inward, inbred cause of melancholy is our tem-erature, in whole or part, which we receive from our parents, hich Fernelius calls *præter naturam,*[6] or unnatural, it being a hereditary disease; for as he justifies, *Quale parentum maxime atris semen obtigerit, tales evadunt similares spermaticæque partes, iocunque etiam morbo pater quum generat tenetur, cum semine ansfert in prolem;*[7] such as the temperature of the father is, uch is the son's, and look what disease the father had when he :got him, his son will have after him; " and is as well inheritor of s infirmities as of his lands."[8] "And where the complexion id constitution of the father is corrupt, there" (saith Roger acon) "the complexion and constitution of the son must needs : corrupt, and so the corruption is derived from the father to ie son."[9] Now this doth not so much appear in the composi-n of the body, according to that of Hippocrates, "in habit, roportion, scars, and other lineaments; but in manners and nditions of the mind,"[10] *Et patrum in natos abeunt cum semine ores* [the character of the parents is transmitted to the children rough the seed].

Seleucus had an anchor on his thigh, so had his posterity, as ogus records, *lib.* 15. Lepidus, in Pliny, *lib.* 7, *cap.* 17, was arblind, so was his son. That famous family of Aenobarbi were own of old, and so surnamed from their red beards; the ustrian lip, and those Indians' flat noses are propagated, the avarian chin, and goggle eyes amongst the Jews, as Buxtorfius serves;[11] their voice, pace, gesture, looks, is likewise derived

with all the rest of their conditions and infirmities; such a mother
such a daughter; their very affections Lemnius contends "t
follow their seed, and the malice and bad conditions of children
are many times wholly to be imputed to their parents";[1] I need
not therefore make any doubt of melancholy, but that it is an
hereditary disease.   Paracelsus in express words affirms it,
lib. de morb. amentium, to. 4, *tr.* 1; so doth Crato in an epistle
of his to Monavius.[3]   So doth Bruno Seidelius in his book *de
morbo incurab.*   Montaltus proves, *cap.* 11, out of Hippocrate
and Plutarch, that such hereditary dispositions are frequent
et hanc (*inquit*) *fieri reor ob participatam melancholicam intem
perantiam* (speaking of a patient), "I think he became so by
participation of melancholy."   Daniel Sennertus, *lib.* 1, *part.* 2
cap. 9, will have his melancholy constitution derived not only
from the father to the son, but to the whole family sometimes
quandoque totis familiis hæreditativam.   Forestus, in his medicina
observations,[4] illustrates this point, with an example of a mer
chant, his patient, that had this infirmity by inheritance; s
doth Rodericus à Fonseca, *tom.* 1, *consul.* 69, by an instance of
a young man that was so affected *ex matre melancholica*, had
melancholy mother, *et victu melancholico*, and bad diet together
Lodovicus Mercatus, a Spanish physician, in that excellen
tract which he hath lately written of hereditary diseases, *tom.
oper. lib.* 5, reckons up leprosy, as those Galbots in Gascony,
hereditary lepers, pox, stone, gout, epilepsy, etc.   Amongst th
rest, this and madness after a set time comes to many, which h
calls a miraculous thing in nature, and sticks for ever to the
as an incurable habit.   And that which is more to be wondere
at, it skips in some families the father, and goes to the son
"or takes every other, and sometimes every third in a line
descent, and doth not always produce the same, but some lik
and a symbolizing disease."[6]   These secondary causes hen
derived are commonly so powerful, that (as Wolfius holds
sæpe mutant decreta siderum, they do often alter the primar
causes, and decrees of the heavens.   For these reasons, belik
the Church and commonwealth, human and divine laws, ha
conspired to avoid hereditary diseases, forbidding such marriag
as are any whit allied; and as Mercatus adviseth all famili
to take such, *si fieri possit, quæ maxime distant natura
possible, as are most distant in nature], and to mal
choice of those that are most differing in complexion fro
them, if they love their own, and respect the common goo
And sure, I think, it hath been ordered by God's especi

providence, that in all ages there should be (as usually there is)
once in six hundred years, a transmigration of nations,[1] to
amend and purify their blood, as we alter seed upon our land,
and that there should be, as it were, an inundation of those
northern Goths and Vandals, and many such-like people which
came out of that continent of Scandia and Sarmatia (as some
suppose) and overran, as a deluge, most part of Europe and
Africa, to alter for our good our complexions, which were much
defaced with hereditary infirmities, which by our lust and intemperance we had contracted.   A sound generation of strong
and able men were sent amongst us, as those northern men
usually are, innocuous, free from riot, and free from diseases;
to qualify and make us as those poor naked Indians are generally
at this day, and those about Brazil (as a late writer observes [2]),
in the Isle of Maragnan, free from all hereditary diseases or
other contagion, whereas without help of physic they live
commonly 120 years or more, as in the Orcades and many other
places.   Such are the common effects of temperance and
intemperance; but I will descend to particulars, and show by
what means, and by whom especially, this infirmity is derived
unto us.

Filii ex senibus nati, raro sunt firmi temperamenti, old men's
children are seldom of a good temperament, as Scoltzius supposeth, *consult.* 177, and therefore most apt to this disease; and
as Levinus Lemnius farther adds, old men beget most part
wayward, peevish, sad, melancholy sons, and seldom merry.[3]
He that begets a child on a full stomach will either have a sick
child or a crazed son (as Cardan thinks,[4] *Contradict. med. lib.* 1,
contradict. 18), or if the parents be sick, or have any great pain
of the head, or megrim, headache (Hieronymus Wolfius doth
instance in a child of Sebastian Castalio's [5]), or if a drunken man
get a child, it will never likely have a good brain, as Gellius
argues, *lib.* 12, *cap.* 1.   *Ebrii gignunt ebrios,* one drunkard begets
another, saith Plutarch,[6] *Symp. lib.* 1, *quest.* 5, whose sentence
Lemnius approves, *lib.* 1, *cap.* 4; [7] Alsarius Crucius Gen., *de
quæsit. med. cent.* 3, *fol.* 182; Macrobius, *lib.* 1; Avicenna, *lib.* 3,
fen. 21, *tract.* 1, *cap.* 8; and Aristotle himself, *sect.* 2, *prob.* 4.
Foolish, drunken, or hairbrain women most part bring forth
children like unto themselves, *morosos et languidos* [morose and
feeble], and so likewise he that lies with a menstruous woman.
*Intemperantia veneris, quam in nautis præsertim insectatur
Lemnius,[8] qui uxores ineunt, nulla menstrui decursus ratione
habita, nec observato interlunio, præcipua causa est, noxia,*

I—*H 886

*perniciosa (concubitum hunc exitialem ideo, et pestiferum vocat
Rodericus a Castro, Lusitanus,[1] detestantur ad unum omnes medici),
tum et quarta luna concepti, infelices plerumque et amentes,
deliri, stolidi, morbosi, impuri, invalidi, tetra lue sordidi, minime
vitales, omnibus bonis corporis atque animi destituti: ad laborem
nati, si seniores, inquit Eustathius, ut Hercules, et alii. Judæi
maxime insectantur fœdum hunc et immundum apud Christianos
concubitum, ut illicitum abhorrent, et apud suos prohibent; et
quod Christiani toties leprosi, amentes, tot morbilli, impetigines,
alphi, psoræ, cutis et faciei decolorationes, tam multi morbi
epidemici, acerbi, et venenosi sint, in hunc immundum concubitum
rejiciunt, et crudeles in pignora vocant, qui quarta luna profluente
hac mensium illuvie concubitum hunc non perhorrescunt.[2]
Damnavit olim divina lex et morte mulctavit hujusmodi homines
(Lev. xviii, xx), et inde nati, si qui deformes aut mutili, pater
dilapidatus, quod non contineret ab immunda muliere.[3] Gregorius Magnus, petenti Augustino numquid apud Britannos
hujusmodi concubitum toleraret, severe prohibuit viris suis tum
misceri feminas in consuetis suis menstruis, etc.[4]* I spare to
English this which I have said. Another cause some give,
inordinate diet, as if a man eat garlic, onions, fast overmuch,
study too hard, be over-sorrowful, dull, heavy, dejected in
mind, perplexed in his thoughts, fearful, etc., "their children"
(saith Cardan, *Subtil. lib.* 18) "will be much subject to madness
and melancholy; for if the spirits of the brain be fuzzled or misaffected by such means at such a time, their children will be
fuzzled in the brain: they will be dull, heavy, timorous, discontented all their lives."[5] Some are of opinion, and maintain
that paradox or problem, that wise men beget commonly fools;
Suidas gives instance in Aristarchus the Grammarian, *duos
reliquit filios, Aristarchum et Aristachorum, ambos stultos* [he left
two sons, Aristarchus and Aristachorus, both stupid]; and
which Erasmus urgeth in his *Moria*,[6] fools beget wise men.
Cardan, *Subt. lib.* 12, gives this cause, *quoniam spiritus sapientum
ob studium resolvuntur, et in cerebrum feruntur a corde:* because
their natural spirits are resolved by study, and turned into
animal; drawn from the heart, and those other parts, to the
brain. Lemnius subscribes to that of Cardan, and assigns this
reason, *quod persolvant debitum languide, et oscitanter, und
fœtus a parentum generositate desciscit:* they pay their debt (as
Paul calls it) to their wives remissly, by which means their
children are weaklings, and many times idiots and fools.

Some other causes are given, which properly pertain to, and de proceed from, the mother. If she be over-dull, heavy, angry, peevish, discontented, and melancholy, not only at the time of conception, but even all the while she carries the child in her womb (saith Fernelius, *Path. lib.* 1, 11), her son will be so likewise affected, and worse, as Lemnius adds,[1] *lib.* 4, *cap.* 7. If she grieve overmuch, be disquieted, or by any casualty be affrighted and terrified by some fearful object heard or seen, she endangers her child, and spoils the temperature of it; for the strange imagination of a woman works effectually upon her infant, that, as Baptista Porta proves, *Physiog. cœlestis, lib.* 5, *cap.* 2, she leaves a mark upon it, which is most especially seen in such as prodigiously long for such and such meats; the child will love those meats, saith Fernelius, and be addicted to like humours: "if a great-bellied woman see a hare, her child will often have an hare-lip," [2] as we call it. Garcæus, *de judiciis geniturarum, cap.* 33, hath a memorable example of one Thomas Nickell, born in the city of Brandenburg, 1551, "that went reeling and staggering all the days of his life, as if he would fall to the ground, because his mother being great with child saw a drunken man reeling in the street." [3] Such another I find in Martin Wenrichius, *Com. de ortu monstrorum, cap.* 17. "I saw" (saith he) "at Wittenberg, in Germany, a citizen that looked like a carcass; I asked him the cause, he replied, "His mother, when she bore him in her womb, saw a carcass by chance, and was so sore affrighted with it, that *ex eo fœtus ei assimilatus*, from a ghastly impression the child was like it." [4]

So many several ways are we plagued and punished for our fathers' defaults; insomuch that, as Fernelius truly saith, "It is the greatest part of our felicity to be well born, and it were happy for humankind, if only such parents as are sound of body and mind should be suffered to marry." [5] An husbandman will sow none but the best and choicest seed upon his land, he will not rear a bull or a horse, except he be right shapen in all parts, or permit him to cover a mare, except he be well assured of his breed; we make choice of the best rams for our sheep, rear the neatest kine, and keep the best dogs, *quanto id diligentius in procreandis liberis observandum!* and how careful then should we be in begetting of our children ! In former times some countries have been so chary in this behalf, so stern, that if a child were crooked or deformed in body or mind, they made him away: [6] so did the Indians of old by the relation of Curtius, and many other well-governed commonwealths, according to the discipline of those times. Heretofore in

Scotland, saith Hect. Boethius, "if any were visited with the
falling sickness, madness, gout, leprosy, or any such dangerous
disease, which was likely to be propagated from the father to
the son, he was instantly gelded; a woman kept from all company of men; and if by chance, having some such disease, she
were found to be with child, she with her brood were buried
alive:[1] and this was done for the common good, lest the whole
nation should be injured or corrupted." A severe doom, you
will say, and not to be used amongst Christians, yet more to
be looked into than it is. For now, by our too much facility
in this kind, in giving way for all to marry that will, too much
liberty and indulgence in tolerating all sorts, there is a vast
confusion of hereditary diseases, no family secure, no man,
almost, free from some grievous infirmity or other, when no
choice is had, but still the eldest must marry, as so many
stallions of the race; or if rich, be they fools or dizzards, lame
or maimed, unable, intemperate, dissolute, exhaust through
riot, as he said,[2] *jure hæreditario sapere jubentur*; they must be
wise and able by inheritance: it comes to pass that our generation is corrupt, we have many weak persons, both in body and
mind, many feral diseases raging amongst us, crazed families,
parentes peremptores [our parents are our ruin], our fathers
bad, and we are like to be worse.

MEMB. II

Subsect. I.—*Bad Diet a Cause. Substance. Quality of Meats*

According to my proposed method, having opened hitherto
these secondary causes, which are inbred with us, I must now
proceed to the outward and adventitious, which happen unto
us after we are born. And those are either evident, remote, or
inward, antecedent, and the nearest: continent causes some
call them. These outward, remote, precedent causes are subdivided again into necessary and not necessary. Necessary
(because we cannot avoid them, but they will alter us, as they
are used or abused) are those six non-natural things, so much
spoken of amongst physicians, which are principal causes of
this disease. For almost in every consultation, whereas they
shall come to speak of the causes, the fault is found, and this
most part objected to the patient: *Peccavit circa res sex non*
naturales, he hath still offended in one of those six. Montanus
consil. 22, consulted about a melancholy Jew, gives that sentence

so did Frisimelica in the same place; and in his 244th counsel, censuring a melancholy soldier, assigns that reason of his malady, "He offended in all those six non-natural things, which were the outward causes, from which came those inward obstructions"; [1] and so in the rest.

These six non-natural things are diet, retention, and evacuation, which are more material than the other because they make new matter, or else are conversant in keeping or expelling of it; the other four are air, exercise, sleeping, waking, and perturbations of the mind, which only alter the matter. The first of these is diet, which consists in meat and drink, and causeth melancholy, as it offends in substance or accidents, that is quantity, quality, or the like. And well it may be called a material cause, since that, as Fernelius holds, "it hath such a power in begetting of diseases, and yields the matter and sustenance of them; for neither air, nor perturbations, nor any of those other evident causes take place, or work this effect, except the constitution of body and preparation of humours do concur; that a man may say this diet is the mother of diseases, let the father be what he will; and from this alone melancholy and frequent other maladies arise." [2] Many physicians, I confess, have written copious volumes of this one subject, of the nature and qualities of all manner of meats; as namely, Galen, Isaac the Jew; Halyabbas, Avicenna, Mesue, also four [3] Arabians; Gordonius, Villanovanus, Wecker, Johannes Bruerinus, *Sitologia de Esculentis et Poculentis*, Michael Savonarola, *tract. 2, cap.* 8, Anthony Fumanellus, *lib. de regimine senum*, Curio in his Comment on Schola Salerna, Godefridus Stegius *Arte med.*, Marsilius Cognatus, Ficinus, Ranzovius, Fonseca, Lessius, Magninus, *Regim. sanitatis*, Freitagius, Hugo Fridevallius, etc., besides many other in English; [4] and almost every peculiar physician discourseth at large of all peculiar meats in his chapter of melancholy: yet because these books are not at hand to every man, I will briefly touch of what kind of meats engender this humour, through their several species, and which are to be avoided. How they alter and change the matter, spirits first, and after humours, by which we are preserved, and the constitution of our body, Fernelius and others will show you. I hasten to the thing itself: and first of such diet as offends in substance.

Beef, a strong and hearty meat (cold in the first degree, dry in the second, saith Galen, *lib.* 3, *cap.* 1, *de alim. fac.*), is condemned by him and all succeeding authors to breed gross melancholy blood: good for such as are sound and of a strong constitution, for labouring men if ordered aright, corned, young, of an ox (for all gelded meats in every species are held best), or if old, such as have been tired out with labour are preferred.[1]   Aubanus and Sabellicus commend Portugal beef to be the most savoury, best and easiest of digestion; we commend ours: but all is rejected and unfit for such as lead a resty life, anyways inclined to melancholy, or dry of complexion; *Tales* (Galen thinks) *de facili melancholicis ægritudinibus capiuntur* [such easily fall a prey to the ailments of melancholy].

Pork, of all meats, is most nutritive in his own nature, but altogether unfit for such as live at ease, are anyways unsound of body or mind:[2] too moist, full of humours, and therefore *noxia delicatis*, saith Savonarola, *ex earum usu ut dubitetur an febris quartana generetur :* naught for queasy stomachs, insomuch that frequent use of it may breed a quartan ague.

Savonarola discommends goat's flesh, and so doth Bruerinus,[3] *lib.* 13, *cap.* 19, calling it a filthy beast, and rammish: and therefore supposeth it will breed rank and filthy substance; yet kid, such as are young and tender, Isaac accepts, Bruerinus, and Galen, *lib.* 1, *cap.* 1, *de alimentorum facultatibus.*

Hart and red deer hath an evil name: it yields gross nutriment:[4] a strong and great-grained meat, next unto a horse.   Which, although some countries eat, as Tartars, and they of China, yet Galen condemns.[5]   Young foals are as commonly eaten in Spain as red deer, and to furnish their navies, about Malaga especially, often used; but such meats ask long baking or seething to qualify them, and yet all will not serve.

All venison is melancholy, and begets bad blood; a pleasant meat: in great esteem with us (for we have more parks in England than there are in all Europe besides) in our solemn feasts.   'Tis somewhat better hunted than otherwise, and well prepared by cookery; but generally bad, and seldom to be used.

Hare, a black meat, melancholy, and hard of digestion; it breeds *incubus*, often eaten, and causeth fearful dreams, so doth all venison, and is condemned by a jury of physicians.   Mizaldus and some others say that hare is a merry meat, and that it will make one fair, as Martial's epigram testifies to Gellia; but this is *per accidens*, because of the good sport it makes, merry company and good discourse that is commonly at the eating of it, and not otherwise to be understood.

Conies are of the nature of hares.[6]   Magninus compares them to beef, pig, and goat, *Reg. sanit. part.* 3, *cap.* 17; yet young rabbits by all men are approved to be good.

Generally, all such meats as are hard of digestion breed
melancholy. Aretæus, *lib.* 7, *cap.* 5, reckons up heads and feet,
bowels, brains, entrails, marrow, fat, blood, skins, and those
inward parts, as heart, lungs, liver, spleen, etc.[1] They are
rejected by Isaac, *lib.* 2, *part.* 3; Magninus, *part.* 3, *cap.* 17;
Bruerinus, *lib.* 12; Savonarola, *rub.* 32, *tract.* 2.

Milk, and all that comes of milk, as butter and cheese, curds,
etc., increase melancholy (whey only excepted, which is most
wholesome): some except asses' milk.[2] The rest, to such as
are sound, is nutritive and good, especially for young children,
but because soon turned to corruption, not good for those that
have unclean stomachs, are subject to headache, or have green
wounds, stone, etc.[3] Of all cheeses, I take that kind which we
call Banbury cheese to be the best; *ex vetustis pessimus,* the
older, stronger, and harder, the worst, as Langius discourseth in
his epistle to Melancthon, cited by Mizaldus, Isaac, *part.* 5, Galen,
lib. 3, *de cibis boni succi,* etc.

Amongst fowl, peacocks and pigeons, all fenny fowl are
forbidden, as ducks, geese, swans, herons, cranes, coots, didap-
pers, waterhens, with all those teals, currs, sheldrakes, and peckled
fowls, that come hither in winter out of Scandia, Muscovy,
Greenland, Friesland, which half the year are covered all over
with snow and frozen up.[4] Though these be fair in feathers,
pleasant in taste, and have a good outside, like hypocrites,
white in plumes, and soft, their flesh is hard, black, unwholesome, dangerous, melancholy meat; *Gravant et putrefaciunt
stomachum* [they overload and spoil the stomach], saith Isaac,
part. 5, *de vol.*; their young ones are more tolerable, but young
pigeons he quite disapproves.

Rhasis and Magninus[5] discommend all fish, and say they
breed viscosities, slimy nutriment, little and humorous nourishment. Savonarola adds cold; moist and phlegmatic, Isaac;
and therefore unwholesome for all cold and melancholy complexions: others make a difference, rejecting only, amongst
freshwater fish, eel, tench, lamprey, crawfish (which Bright
approves, *cap.* 6), and such as are bred in muddy and standing
waters, and have a taste of mud, as Franciscus Bonsuetus
poetically defines, *lib. de aquatilibus*:

> *Nam pisces omnes, qui stagna lacusque frequentant,*
>   *Semper plus succi deterioris habent.*

All fish, that standing pools and lakes frequent,
   Do ever yield bad juice and nourishment.

Lampreys, Paulus Jovius, *cap.* 34, *de piscibus fluvial.,* highly

magnifies, and saith, none speak against them, but *inepti* [fools
and *scrupulosi*, some scrupulous persons; but eels, *cap.* 33, "he abhorreth in all places, at all times, all physicians detest them
especially about the solstice."[1] Gomesius, *lib.* 1, *cap.* 22, *de
sale*, doth immoderately extol sea-fish, which others as much
vilify, and above the rest, dried, soused, indurate fish, as ling,
fumadoes, red-herrings, sprats, stock-fish, haberdine, poor-john,
all shell-fish. Tim. Bright excepts lobster and crab.[2] Mes-
sarius commends salmon, which Bruerinus contradicts, *lib.* 22,
cap. 17. Magninus rejects conger, sturgeon, turbot, mackerel,
skate.

Carp is a fish of which I know not what to determine. Franciscus Bonsuetus accounts it a muddy fish. Hippolytus Salvianus
in his book *de piscium natura et præparatione*, which was printed
at Rome in folio, 1554, with most elegant pictures, esteems carp
no better than a slimy, watery meat. Paulus Jovius, on the
other side, disallowing tench, approves of it; so doth Dubravius
in his books of Fish-ponds. Freitagius extols it for an excellent
wholesome meat, and puts it amongst the fishes of the best
rank;[3] and so do most of our country gentlemen, that store
their ponds almost with no other fish. But this controversy is
easily decided, in my judgment, by Bruerinus, *lib.* 22, *cap.* 13.
The difference riseth from the site and nature of pools, sometimes muddy, sometimes sweet;[4] they are in taste as the place
is from whence they be taken. In like manner almost we may
conclude of other fresh fish. But see more in Rondeletius,
Bellonius, Oribasius, *lib.* 7, *cap.* 22, Isaac, *lib.* 1, especially
Hippolytus Salvianus, who is *instar omnium solus*, etc. Howsoever they may be wholesome and approved, much use of them
is not good; P. Forestus, in his Medicinal Observations, relates
that Carthusian friars, whose living is most part fish, are more
subject to melancholy than any other Order, and that he found
by experience, being sometime their physician ordinary at
Delft, in Holland.[5] He exemplifies it with an instance of one
Buscodnese, a Carthusian of a ruddy colour, and well liking,
that by solitary living and fish-eating became so misaffected.

Amongst herbs to be eaten I find gourds, cucumbers, cole-
worts, melons, disallowed, but especially cabbage. It causeth
troublesome dreams, and sends up black vapours to the brain,
Galen, *Loc. affect. lib.* 3, *cap.* 6, of all herbs condemns cabbage
and Isaac, *lib.* 2, *cap.* 1, *animæ gravitatem facit*, it brings heaviness to the soul. Some are of opinion that all raw herbs and
sallets breed melancholy blood, except bugloss and lettuce

Crato, *consil.* 21, *lib.* 2, speaks against all herbs and worts, except borage, bugloss, fennel, parsley, dill, balm, succory; Magninus, *Regim. sanitatis, part.* 3, *cap.* 31, *Omnes herbæ simpliciter malæ, via cibi;* all herbs are simply evil to feed on (as he thinks). So did that scoffing cook in Plautus hold: [1]

> *Non ego cænam condio ut alii coqui solent,*
> *Qui mihi condita prata in patinis proferunt,*
> *Boves qui convivas faciunt, herbasque aggerunt.*

> Like other cooks I do not supper dress,
>   That put whole meadows into a platter,
> And make no better of their guests than beeves,
>   With herbs and grass to feed them fatter.

Our Italians and Spaniards do make a whole dinner of herbs and sallets (which our said Plautus calls *cænas terrestres* [earthy meals], Horace, *cænas sine sanguine* [bloodless meals]), by which means, as he follows it:

> *Hic homines tam brevem vitam colunt . . .*
> *Qui herbas hujusmodi in alvum suum congerunt,*
> *Formidolosum dictu, non esu modo,*
> *Quas herbas pecudes non edunt, homines edunt.* [2]

> Their lives, that eat such herbs, must needs be short,
>   And 'tis a fearful thing for to report,
> That men should feed on such a kind of meat,
>   Which very juments would refuse to eat.

They are windy, and not fit, therefore, to be eaten of all men raw, though qualified with oil, but in broths, or otherwise.[3] See more of these in every husbandman and herbalist.[4]

Roots, *etsi quorundam gentium opes sint,* saith Bruerinus, the wealth of some countries, and sole food, are windy and bad, or troublesome to the head: as onions, garlic, scallions, turnips, carrots, radishes, parsnips: Crato, *lib.* 2, *consil.* 11, disallows all roots, though some approve of parsnips and potatoes.[5] Magninus is of Crato's opinion, "They trouble the mind, sending gross fumes to the brain, make men mad,"[6] especially garlic, onions, if a man liberally feed on them a year together.[7] Guianerius, *tract.* 15, *cap.* 2, complains of all manner of roots, and so doth Bruerinus, even parsnips themselves, which are the best, *lib.* 9, *cap.* 14, *Pastinacarum usus succos gignit improbos* [indulgence in parsnips creates harmful juices]. Crato, *consil.* 21, *lib.* 1, utterly forbids all manner of fruits, as pears, apples, plums, cherries, strawberries, nuts, medlars, serves, etc. *Sanguinem inficiunt,* saith Villanovanus, they infect the blood, and putrefy it, Magninus holds, and must not therefore be taken *via cibi, aut quantitate magna,* not to make a meal of, or in any great

quantity. Cardan makes that a cause of their continual sickness at Fez in Africa, "because they live so much on fruits,
eating them thrice a day." [1] Laurentius approves of many
fruits, in his Tract of Melancholy, which others disallow, and
amongst the rest apples, which some likewise commend, sweet-
ings, pearmains, pippins, as good against melancholy; but to
him that is any way inclined to, or touched with this malady,
Nicholas Piso, in his Practics,[2] forbids all fruits, as windy, or
to be sparingly eaten at least, and not raw. Amongst other
fruits, Bruerinus,[3] out of Galen, excepts grapes and figs, but
I find them likewise rejected.

All pulse are naught, beans, pease, fitches, etc., they fill the
brain (saith Isaac) with gross fumes, breed black, thick blood,
and cause troublesome dreams. And therefore, that which
Pythagoras said to his scholars of old may be for ever applied
to melancholy men, *A fabis abstinete*, eat no pease, nor beans;
yet to such as will needs eat them, I would give this counsel, to
prepare them according to those rules that Arnoldus Villanovanus and Freitagius prescribe, for eating, and dressing, fruits,
herbs, roots, pulse, etc.

Spices cause hot and head melancholy, and are for that cause
forbidden by our physicians to such men as are inclined to this
malady, as pepper, ginger, cinnamon, cloves, mace, dates, etc.,
honey, and sugar. Some except honey;[4] to those that are cold
it may be tolerable, but *Dulcia se in bilem vertunt* [5] [sweets turn
into bile], they are obstructive. Crato therefore forbids all
spice, in a consultation of his, for a melancholy schoolmaster,
omnia aromatica, et quicquid sanguinem adurit [all spices, and
whatever dries up the blood]: so doth Fernelius, *consil.* 45;
Guianerius, *tract.* 15, *cap.* 2; Mercurialis, *cons.* 189. To these
I may add all sharp and sour things, luscious and over-sweet,
or fat, as oil, vinegar, verjuice, mustard, salt; as sweet things
are obstructive, so these are corrosive. Gomesius, in his books
de sale, lib. 1, *cap.* 21, highly commends salt; so doth Codronchus
in his tract *de sale absinthii*, Lemn. *lib.* 3, *cap.* 9, *de occult. nat.
mir.*; yet common experience finds salt, and salt-meats, to be
great procurers of this disease. And for that cause belike those
Egyptian priests abstained from salt, even so much as in their
bread, *ut sine perturbatione anima esset*, saith mine author, that
their souls might be free from perturbations.

Bread that is made of baser grain, as pease, beans, oats, rye,
or over-hard baked, crusty,[6] and black, is often spoken against,
as causing melancholy juice and wind. Joh. Major, in the

first book of his History of Scotland, contends much for the
wholesomeness of oaten bread: it was objected to him, then
living at Paris in France, that his countrymen fed on oats and
base grain, as a disgrace; but he doth ingenuously confess,
Scotland, Wales, and a third part of England did most part
use that kind of bread, that it was as wholesome as any grain,
and yielded as good nourishment. And yet Wecker, out of
Galen, calls it horse-meat, and fitter for juments than men to
feed on. But read Galen himself, *lib.* I *de cibis boni et mali
succi,* more largely discoursing of corn and bread.

All black wines, over-hot, compound, strong, thick drinks, as
muscadine, malmsey, alicant, rumney, brown bastard, methe-
glin, and the like, of which they have thirty several kinds in
Muscovy, all such made drinks are hurtful in this case, to such
as are hot, or of a sanguine, choleric complexion, young, or
inclined to head-melancholy. For many times the drinking of
wine alone causeth it. Arculanus, *cap.* 16, *in* 9 *Rhasis,* puts in
wine for a great cause,[1] especially if it be immoderately used.
Guianerius, *tract.* 15, *cap.* 2, tells a story of two Dutchmen, to
whom he gave entertainment in his house, "that in one month's
space were both melancholy by drinking of wine, one did naught
but sing, the other sigh."[2] Galen, *lib. de causis morb., cap.* 3;
Matthiolus on Dioscorides; and above all other Andreas Bachius,
lib. 3, *cap.* 18, 19, 20, have reckoned upon those inconveniences
that come by wine: yet notwithstanding all this, to such as are
cold, or sluggish melancholy, a cup of wine is good physic, and
so doth Mercurialis grant, *consil.* 25; in that case, if the temperature be cold, as to most melancholy men it is, wine is much
commended, if it be moderately used.

Cider and perry are both cold and windy drinks, and for
that cause to be neglected, and so are all those hot, spiced,
strong drinks.

Beer, if it be over-new, or over-stale, over-strong, or not
sod, smell of the cask, sharp, or sour, is most unwholesome,
frets, and galls, etc. Henricus Ayrerus, in a consultation of
his,[3] for one that laboured of hypochondriacal melancholy,
discommends beer. So doth Crato, in that excellent counsel
of his, *lib.* 2, *consil.* 21, as too windy, because of the hop.[4]
But he means, belike, that thick, black Bohemian beer used in
some other parts of Germany:[5]

> *Nil spissius illa*
> *Dum bibitur, nil clarius est dum mingitur, unde*
> *Constat, quod multas fæces in corpore linquat.*

Nothing comes in so thick,
Nothing goes out so thin,
It must needs follow then
The dregs are left within.

As that old poet [1] scoffed, calling it *Stygiæ monstrum conforme paludi*, a monstrous drink, like the River Styx.   But let them say as they list, to such as are accustomed unto it, "'tis a most wholesome" (so Polydore Virgil calleth it [2]) "and a pleasant drink," it is more subtile and better for the hop that rarefies it, hath an especial virtue against melancholy, as our herbalists confess, Fuchsius approves, *lib. 2, sec. 3, Instit. cap.* 11, and many others.

Standing waters, thick and ill-coloured, such as come forth of pools and moats where hemp hath been steeped or slimy fishes live, are most unwholesome, putrefied, and full of mites, creepers, slimy, muddy, unclean, corrupt, impure, by reason of the sun's heat and still standing; they cause foul distempera-tures in the body and mind of man, are unfit to make drink of, to dress meat with, or to be used about men inwardly or out-wardly.[3]   They are good for many domestic uses, to wash horses, water cattle, etc., or in time of necessity, but not other-wise.   Some are of opinion that such fat, standing waters make the best beer, and that seething doth defecate it, as Cardan holds, *lib.* 13 *Subtil.*, "It mends the substance and savour of it,"[4] but it is a paradox.   Such beer may be stronger, but not so wholesome as the other, as Jobertus truly justifieth out of Galen, *Paradox. dec. 1, paradox.* 5, that the seething of such impure waters doth not purge or purify them;[5] Pliny, *lib.* 31, *cap.* 3, is of the same tenent, and P. Crescentius, *Agricult. lib.* 1 *et lib.* 4, *cap.* 11 *et cap.* 45.   Pamphilius Herilachus, *lib.* 4 *de nat. aquarum*, such waters are naught, not to be used, and by the testimony of Galen, "breed agues, dropsies, pleurisies, splenetic and melancholy passions, hurt the eyes, cause a bad temperature and ill disposition of the whole body, with bad colour."[6]   This Jobertus stiffly maintains, *Paradox. lib. 1, part.* 5, that it causeth blear eyes, bad colour, and many loathsome diseases to such as use it: this which they say, stands with good reason; for as geographers relate, the water of Astracan breeds worms in such as drink it.   Axius, or as now called Verduri,[7] the fairest river in Macedonia, makes all cattle black that taste of it. [8]   Aliac-mon, now Peleca, another stream in Thessaly, turns cattle most part white, *si potui ducas* [if you take them to drink there]. J. Aubanus Bohemus refers that *struma* or poke of the Bava-

rians and Styrians to the nature of their waters,[1] as Munster
doth that of the Valesians in the Alps,[2] and Bodine supposeth
the stuttering of some families in Aquitania, about Labden, to
proceed from the same cause, "and that the filth is derived
from the water to their bodies." [3]   So that they that use filthy,
standing, ill-coloured, thick, muddy water, must needs have
muddy, ill-coloured, impure, and infirm bodies.   And because
the body works upon the mind, they shall have grosser under-
standings, dull, foggy, melancholy spirits, and be readily subject
to all manner of infirmities.

To these noxious simples we may reduce an infinite number
of compound, artificial, made dishes, of which our cooks afford
us a great variety, as tailors do fashions in our apparel.   Such
are puddings stuffed with blood, or otherwise composed;[4] baked
meats, soused indurate meats, fried and broiled, buttered meats,
condite, powdered, and over-dried; all cakes, simnels, buns,
cracknels made with butter, spice, etc., fritters, pancakes, pies,
sausages, and those several sauces, sharp, or over-sweet,[5] of
which *scientia popinæ* [the learning of the cookshop], as Seneca
calls it, hath served those Apician tricks and perfumed dishes,
which Adrian the Sixth, Pope, so much admired in the accounts
of his predecessor Leo Decimus,[6] and which prodigious riot and
prodigality have invented in this age.[7]   These do generally
engender gross humours, fill the stomach with crudities, and all
those inward parts with obstructions.   Montanus, *consil.* 22,
gives instance in a melancholy Jew, that by eating such tart
sauces, made dishes, and salt meats, with which he was overmuch delighted, became melancholy, and was evil-affected.
Such examples are familiar and common.

SUBSECT. II.—*Quantity of Diet a Cause*

There is not so much harm proceeding from the substance
itself of meat, and quality of it, in ill dressing and preparing, as
there is from the quantity, disorder of time and place, unseasonable use of it, intemperance, overmuch or overlittle taking of
it.[8]   A true saying it is, *Plures crapula quam gladius*, this
gluttony kills more than the sword, this *omnivorans et homicida
gula*, this all-devouring and murdering gut.   And that of Pliny
is truer, "Simple diet is the best; heaping up of several meats
is pernicious, and sauces worse; many dishes bring many
diseases." [9]   Avicen cries out, that "nothing is worse than to
feed on many dishes, or to protract the time of meats longer

than ordinary; from thence proceed our infirmities, and 'tis the
fountain of all diseases, which arise out of the repugnancy of
gross humours." [1] Thence, saith Fernelius, come crudities,
wind, oppilations, cacochymia, plethora, cachexia, bradypepsia,[2]
Hinc subitæ mortes, atque intestata senectus,[3] sudden death, etc.
and what not.

As a lamp is choked with a multitude of oil, or a little fire
with overmuch wood quite extinguished, so is the natural heat
with immoderate eating strangled in the body. *Perniciosa
sentina est abdomen insaturabile*, one saith, an insatiable paunch
is a pernicious sink, and the fountain of all diseases, both of
body and mind. Mercurialis will have it a peculiar cause of
this private disease; [4] Solenander, *consil*. 5, *sect*. 3, illustrates
this of Mercurialis with an example of one so melancholy, *ab in-
tempestivis commessationibus*, [from] unseasonable feasting. Crato
confirms as much, in that often cited counsel, 21, *lib*. 2, putting
superfluous eating for a main cause.[5] But what need I seek
farther for proofs? Hear Hippocrates himself, *lib*. 2, *aphor*. 10:
"Impure bodies, the more they are nourished, the more they are
hurt, for the nourishment is putrefied with vicious humours." [6]

And yet for all this harm, which apparently follows surfeiting
and drunkenness, see how we luxuriate and rage in this kind,
read what Johannes Stuckius hath written lately of this subject,
in his great volume *de Antiquorum Conviviis*, and of our present
age; *Quam portentosæ cœnæ*,[7] [what] prodigious suppers, *Qui dum
invitant ad cœnam efferunt ad sepulchrum*[8] [who in inviting
us to supper conduct us to our graves], what Fagos, Epicures,
Apiciuses, Heliogables, our times afford! Lucullus' ghost walks
still, and every man desires to sup in Apollo; Æsop's costly dish
is ordinarily served up. *Magis illa juvant, quæ pluris emunter*
[the more they cost, the more we enjoy them]. The dearest
cates are best, and 'tis an ordinary thing to bestow twenty or
thirty pound on a dish, some thousand crowns upon a dinner,
Muley-Hamet, King of Fez and Morocco, spent three pound
on the sauce of a capon: [10] it is nothing in our times, we scorn
all that is cheap. "We loathe the very light" (some of us, as
Seneca notes) "because it comes free, and we are offended with
the sun's heat, and those cool blasts, because we buy them not." [11]
This air we breathe is so common, we care not for it; nothing
pleaseth but what is dear. And if we be witty in anything, it
is *ad gulam*; [12] if we study at all, it is *erudito luxu* [the learning
of luxury], to please the palate, and to satisfy the gut. "A
cook of old was a base knave" (as Livy complains), "but now

great man in request; cookery is become an art, a noble science; cooks are gentlemen"; [1] *Venter Deus* [their belly is their god]. They wear "their brains in their bellies, and their guts in their heads," as Agrippa [2] taxed some parasites of his time, rushing on their own destruction, as if a man should run upon the point of a sword, *usque dum rumpantur comedunt* [they eat till they burst]: all day, all night,[3] let the physician say what he will, imminent danger and feral diseases are now ready to seize upon them, that will eat till they vomit, *Edunt ut vomant, vomunt ut edant* [they eat to vomit and vomit to eat], saith Seneca (which Dion relates of Vitellius, *Solo transitu ciborum nutriri judicatus:* his meat did pass through and away), or till they burst again. *Strage animantium ventrem onerant* [4] [they load their bellies with the spoil of the animal world], and rake over all the world, as so many slaves,[5] belly-gods, and land-serpents, *et totus orbis ventri nimis angustus,* the whole world cannot satisfy their appetite. "Sea, land, rivers, lakes, etc., may not give content to their raging guts." [6] To make up the mess, what immoderate drinking in every place! *Senem potum pota trahebat anus* [old men, old women drunk go arm in arm], how they flock to the tavern! as if they were *fruges consumere nati,* born to no other end but to eat and drink, like Offellius Bibulus, that famous Roman parasite, *qui dum vixit, aut bibit aut minxit*; as so many casks to hold wine, yea worse than a cask, that mars wine, and itself is not marred by it, yet these are brave men, *Silenus ebrius* [drunken Silenus] was no braver. *Et quæ fuerunt vitia, mores sunt* [what once was vice is now highly moral]: 'tis now the fashion of our times, an honour: *Nunc vero res ista eo rediit* (as Chrysost., *serm.* 30 *in* 5 *Ephes.*, comments) *ut effeminatæ ridendæque ignaviæ loco habeatur, nolle inebriari;* 'tis now come to that pass that he is no gentleman, a very milksop, a clown, of no bringing-up, that will not drink; fit for no company; he is your only gallant that plays it off finest, no dis-paragement now to stagger in the streets, reel, rave, etc., but much to his fame and renown; as in like case Epidicus told Thesprio his fellow-servant, in the poet.[7] *Edepol facinus improbum* [in truth, a very wrong action], one urged; the other replied, *At jam alii fecere idem, erit illi illa res honori,* 'tis now no fault, there be so many brave examples to bear one out; 'tis a credit to have a strong brain, and carry his liquor well; 'tis the sole contention who can drink most, and fox his fellow the soonest. 'Tis the *summum bonum* of our tradesmen, their felicity, life, and soul (*Tanta dulcedine affectant,* saith Pliny, *lib.*

14, *cap*. 12, *ut magna pars non aliud vitæ præmium intelligat*
[strong drink gives such pleasure that many people think there
is nothing else worth living for]), their chief comfort, to be
merry together in an alehouse or tavern, as our modern Mus-
covites do in their mead-inns, and Turks in their coffa-houses,
which much resemble our taverns; they will labour hard all
day long to be drunk at night, and spend *totius anni labores* [the
earnings of a whole year], as St. Ambrose adds, in a tippling
feast; convert day into night, as Seneca taxes some in his
times, *Pervertunt officia noctis et lucis* [they turn day into night
and night into day]; when we rise, they commonly go to bed,
like our antipodes:

> *Nosque ubi primus equis oriens afflavit anhelis,*
> *Illis sera rubens accendit lumina vesper.*

> [When dawn for us pants up the East on high,
> For them the eve glows in the western sky.]

So did Petronius in Tacitus, Heliogabalus in Lampridius.

> *Noctes vigilabat ad ipsum*
> *Mane, diem totum stertebat.*[1]

> [He drank the night away
> Till rising dawn, then snor'd out all the day.]

Smindyrides the Sybarite never saw the sun rise or set so much
as once in twenty years. Verres, against whom Tully so much
inveighs, in winter he never was *extra tectum* [out of his house],
vix extra lectum, never almost out of bed, still wenching and
drinking;[2] so did he spend his time, and so do myriads in our
days. They have *gymnasia bibonum* [training grounds for
topers], schools and rendezvous; these Centaurs and Lapithæ
toss pots and bowls as so many balls; invent new tricks, as
sausages, anchovies, tobacco, caviare, pickled oysters, herrings,
fumadoes, etc., innumerable salt meats to increase their appetite,
and study how to hurt themselves by taking antidotes "to carry
their drink the better";[3] "and when naught else serves, they will
go forth, or be conveyed out, to empty their gorge, that they
may return to drink afresh."[4] They make laws, *insanos leges
contra bibendi fallacias* [crazy laws against attempts to shirk
drinking], and brag of it when they have done,[5] crowning that
man that is soonest gone, as their drunken predecessors have
done (*Quid ego video? Ps. Cum corona Pseudolum ebrium
tuum.*[6] [What do I see? Your friend Pseudolus, drunk

and garlanded]), and when they are dead, will have a can of
wine with Maron's old woman[1] to be engraven on their tombs.
So they triumph in villainy, and justify their wickedness with
Rabelais, that French Lucian: drunkenness is better for the body
than physic, because there be more old drunkards than old
physicians. Many such frothy arguments they have, inviting
and encouraging others to do as they do,[2] and love them dearly
for it (no glue like to that of good fellowship). So did Alcibiades in Greece; Nero, Bonosus, Heliogabalus in Rome, or
Alegabalus rather, as he was styled of old (as Ignatius proves
out of some old coins[3]). So do many great men still, as Heres-
bachius observes.[4] When a prince drinks till his eyes stare,
like Bitias in the poet,

> *Ille impiger hausit*
> *Spumantem vino pateram,*[5]

[Eager he drained the bowl, brimming with wine,]

and comes off clearly, sound trumpets, fife and drums, the
spectators will applaud him, "the bishop himself" (if he belie
them not) "with his chaplain will stand by and do as much,"[6]
O dignum principe haustum, 'twas done like a prince. "Our
Dutchmen invite all comers with a pail and a dish, *velut
infundibula integras obbas exhauriunt, et in monstrosis poculis
ipsi monstrosi monstrosius epotant* [they take in whole beakers
like funnels, and swill hugely out of huge goblets], making
barrels of their bellies."[7] *Incredible dictu,* as one of their own
countrymen complains, *quantum liquoris immodestissima gens
capiat* [the amount of liquor these heavy drinkers can
consume is incredible], etc.; "how they love a man that will be
drunk, crown him and honour him for it, hate him that will
not pledge him, stab him, kill him":[8] a most intolerable offence,
and not to be forgiven. "He is a mortal enemy that will not
drink with him,"[9] as Munster relates of the Saxons. So in
Poland, he is the best servitor, and the honestest fellow, saith
Alexander Gaguinus, that drinketh most healths to the honour
of his master;[10] he shall be rewarded as a good servant, and held
the bravest fellow that carries his liquor best, whenas a brewer's
horse will bear much more than any sturdy drinker; yet for his
noble exploits in this kind he shall be accounted a most valiant
man, for *Tam inter epulas fortis vir esse potest ac in bello,*[11] as
much valour is to be found in feasting as in fighting, and some of
our city captains and carpet knights will make this good, and
prove it. Thus they many times wilfully pervert the good

temperature of their bodies, stifle their wits, strangle nature, and degenerate into beasts.

Some again are in the other extreme, and draw this mischief on their heads by too ceremonious and strict diet, being over-precise, cockney-like, and curious in their observation of meats, times, as that *medicina statica* [regimen of diet] prescribes, just so many ounces at dinner, which Lessius enjoins, so much at supper, not a little more, nor a little less, of such meat, and at such hours, a diet-drink in the morning, cock-broth, china-broth, at dinner plum-broth, a chicken, a rabbit, rib of a rack of mutton, wing of a capon, the merry-thought of a hen, etc.; to sounder bodies this is too nice and most absurd. Others offend in over-much fasting: pining adays, saith Guianerius,[1] and waking anights, as many Moors and Turks in these our times do. "Anchorites, monks, and the rest of that superstitious rank" (as the same Guianerius witnesseth, that he hath often seen to have happened in his time) "through immoderate fasting, have been frequently mad." Of such men belike Hippocrates speaks, 1 *Aphor.* 5, whenas he saith, "They more offend in too sparing diet, and are worse damnified, than they that feed liberally and are ready to surfeit." [2]

SUBSECT. III.—*Custom of Diet, Delight, Appetite, Necessity, how they cause or hinder*

No rule is so general, which admits not some exception; to this, therefore, which hath been hitherto said (for I shall otherwise put most men out of commons), and those inconveniences which proceed from the substance of meats, an intemperate or unseasonable use of them, custom somewhat detracts and qualifies, according to that of Hippocrates, 2 *Aphoris.* 50, "Such things as we have been long accustomed to, though they be evil in their own nature, yet they are less offensive." [3] Otherwise it might well be objected that it were a mere tyranny to live after those strict rules of physic; [4] for custom doth alter nature itself,[5] and to such as are used to them it makes bad meats wholesome, and unseasonable times to cause no disorder. Cider and perry are windy drinks, so are all fruits windy in themselves, cold most part, yet in some shires of England,[6] Normandy in France, Guipuscoa in Spain, 'tis their common drink, and they are no whit offended with it. In Spain, Italy, and Africa, they live most on roots, raw herbs, camel's milk,[7] and it agrees well with them: which to a stranger will cause much grievance. In Wales, *lacticiniis vescuntur*, as Humphrey Llwyd confesseth, a Cambro-Briton himself, in his elegant epistle to Abraham Ortelius, they live most on white meats; in Holland on fish, roots, butter;[1] and so at this day in Greece, as Bellonius observes, they had much rather feed on fish than flesh.[2] With us, *maxima pars victus in carne consistit*, we feed on flesh most part, saith Polydore Virgil,[3] as all northern countries do; and it would be very offensive to us to live after their diet, or they to live after ours. We drink beer, they wine; they use oil, we butter; we in the north are great eaters,[4] they most sparing in those hotter countries; and yet they and we following our own customs are well pleased. An Ethiopian of old, seeing an European eat bread, wondered, *quomodo stercoribus vescentes viverimus*, how we could eat such kind of meats: so much differed his countrymen from ours in diet, that, as mine author infers,[5] *si quis illorum victum apud nos æmulari vellet*, if any man should so feed with us, it would be all one to nourish as cicuta, aconitum, or hellebore itself. At this day in China the common people live in a manner altogether on roots and herbs, and to the wealthiest, horse, ass, mule, dog's, cat-flesh, is as delightsome as the rest, so Mat. Riccius the Jesuit relates,[6] who lived many years amongst them. The Tartars eat raw meat, and most commonly horse-flesh, drink milk and blood, as the Nomades of old:[7] *Et lac concretum cum sanguine potat equino* [he drinks milk thickened with horse's blood]. They scoff at our Europeans for eating bread, which they call tops of weeds, and horse-meat, not fit for men; and yet Scaliger accounts them a sound and witty nation, living an hundred years; even in the civilest country of them they do thus, as Benedict the Jesuit observed in his travels from the Great Mogor's court by land to Paquin,[8] which Riccius contends to be the same with Cambalu in Cataia. In Scandia their bread is usually dried fish, and so likewise in the Shetland Isles; and their other fare, as in Iceland, saith Dithmarus Bleskenius,[9] "butter, cheese, and fish; their drink water, their lodging on the ground." In America in many places their bread is roots, their meat palmitos, pinas, potatoes, etc., and such fruits. There be of them too that familiarly drink salt sea-water all their lives,[10] eat raw meat, grass, and that with delight.[11] With some, fish, serpents, spiders; and in divers places they eat man's flesh[12] raw and roasted, even the Emperor Metazuma himself.[13] In some coasts, again, one tree yields them coco-nuts, meat and drink, fire, fuel, apparel with his leaves, oil, vinegar, cover for houses, etc.,[14] and yet these men, going naked, feeding coarse, live commonly an hundred years, are seldom or never sick; all which diet our physicians forbid. In Westphalia they feed most part on fat meats and worts, knuckle-deep, and call it *cerebrum Jovis*[1] [Jupiter's brain]; in the Low Countries with roots; in Italy frogs and snails are used. The Turks, saith Busbequius, delight most in fried meats. In Muscovy, garlic and onions are ordinary meat and sauce, which would be pernicious to such as are unaccustomed unto them, delightsome to others; and all is because they have been brought up unto it.[2] Husbandmen, and such as labour, can eat fat bacon, salt gross meat, hard cheese, etc. (*O dura messorum ilia!* [what tough insides have these mowers!]), coarse bread at all times, go to bed and labour upon a full stomach, which to some idle persons would be present death, and is against the rules of physic, so that custom is all in all. Our travellers find this by common experience when they come in far countries and use their diet; they are suddenly offended,[3] as our Hollanders and Englishmen, when they touch upon the coasts of Africa, those Indian capes and islands, are commonly molested with calentures, fluxes, and much distempered by reason of their fruits. *Peregrina, etsi suavia, solent vescentibus perturbationes insignes adferre;*[4] strange meats, though pleasant, cause notable alterations and distempers. On the other side, use or custom mitigates or makes all good again. Mithridates by often use, which Pliny wonders at, was able to drink poison; and a maid, as Curtius records, sent to Alexander from King Porus, was brought up with poison from her infancy. The Turks, saith Bellonius *lib.* 3, *cap.* 15, eat opium familiarly, a dram at once, which we dare not take in grains. Garcias ab Horto writes[5] of one whom he saw at Goa in the East Indies, that took ten drams of opium in three days; and yet *consulto loquebatur*, spake understandingly, so much can custom do. Theophrastus speaks of a shepherd that could eat hellebore in substance.[6] And therefore Cardan concludes out of Galen, *Consuetudinem utcunque ferendam, nisi valde malam*, custom is howsoever to be kept, except it be extremely bad: he adviseth all men to keep their old customs, and that by the authority of Hippocrates himself,[7] *Dandum aliquid tempori, ætati, regioni, consuetudini* [regard must be had to season, age, district, and habit], and therefore to continue as they began, be it diet, bath, exercise, etc., or whatsoever else.[8]

Another exception is delight, or appetite, to such and such meats. Though they be hard of digestion, melancholy, yet, as

Fuchsius excepts, *cap.* 6, *lib.* 2 *Instit. sect.* 2, "The stomach
doth readily digest and willingly entertain such meats we love
most and are pleasing to us, abhors on the other side such as
we distaste." [1] Which Hippocrates confirms, *Aphoris.* 2, 38.
Some cannot endure cheese, out of a secret antipathy; or to see
a roasted duck, which to others is a delightsome meat.[2]

The last exception is necessity, poverty, want, hunger, which
drives men many times to do that which otherwise they are
loath, cannot endure, and thankfully to accept of it: as beverage
in ships, and in sieges of great cities to feed on dogs, cats, rats,
and men themselves.   Three outlaws in Hector Boethius,[3] being
driven to their shifts, did eat raw flesh, and flesh of such fowl
as they could catch, in one of the Hebrides for some few months.
These things do mitigate or disannul that which hath been
said of melancholy meats, and make it more tolerable; but to
such as are wealthy, live plenteously, at ease, may take their
choice, and refrain if they will, these viands are to be forborne,
if they be inclined to, or suspect melancholy, as they tender
their healths: otherwise if they be intemperate, or disordered in
their diet, at their peril be it.   *Qui monet amat, Ave atque cave.*

> [He who advises is your friend
> Farewell, and to your health attend.]

SUBSECT. IV.—*Retention and Evacuation a Cause, and how*

Of retention and evacuation there be divers kinds, which are
either concomitant, assisting, or sole causes many times of
melancholy. Galen reduceth defect and abundance to this
head; [4] others, "all that is separated, or remains." [5]

In the first rank of these, I may well reckon up costiveness,
and keeping in of our ordinary excrements, which as it often
causeth other diseases, so this of melancholy in particular. Celsus,
lib. 1, *cap.* 3, saith, "It produceth inflammation of the head, dullness, cloudiness, headache, etc." [6] Prosper Calenus, *lib. de atra
bile,* will have it distemper not the organ only, "but the mind itself
by troubling of it"; [7] and sometimes it is a sole cause of madness,
as you may read in the first book of Sckenkius his Medicinal Observations.[8] A young merchant going to Nordeling Fair in Germany,
for ten days' space never went to stool; at his return he was
grievously melancholy,[9] thinking that he was robbed, and would
not be persuaded but that all his money was gone; his friends
thought he had some philtrum given him, but Cnelinus a physician

being sent for, found his costiveness alone to be the cause,[1] and thereupon gave him a clyster, by which he was speedily recovered. Trincavellius, *consult.* 35, *lib.* 1, saith as much of a melancholy lawyer, to whom he administered physic, and Rodericus à Fonseca, *consult.* 85, *tom.* 2, of a patient of his, that for eight days was bound,[2] and therefore melancholy affected. Other retentions and evacuations there are, not simply necessary, but at some times, as Fernelius accounts them, *Path. lib.* 1, *cap.* 15; as suppression of hemrods, monthly issues in women, bleeding at nose,[3] immoderate or no use at all of Venus, or any other ordinary issues.

Detention of hemrods, or monthly issues, Villanovanus, *Breviar. lib.* 1, *cap.* 18; Arculanus, *cap.* 16, *in* 9 *Rhasis*; Victorius Faventinus, *Pract. mag. tract.* 2, *cap.* 15; Bruel, etc., put for ordinary causes. Fuchsius, *lib.* 2, *sect.* 5, *cap.* 30, goes farther, and saith that "many men unseasonably cured of the hemrods have been corrupted with melancholy; seeking to avoid Scylla, they fall into Charybdis."[4] Galen, *lib. de hum. commen.* 3, *ad text.* 26, illustrates this by an example of Lucius Martius, whom he cured of madness, contracted by this means: and Sckenkius hath two other instances of two melancholy and mad women, so caused from the suppression of their months.[5] The same may be said of bleeding at the nose, if it be suddenly stopped, and have been formerly used, as Villanovanus urgeth:[6] and Fuchsius, *lib.* 2, *sect.* 5, *cap.* 33, stiffly maintains "that without great danger such an issue may not be stayed."[7]

Venus omitted produceth like effects. Matthiolus, *epist.* 5, *lib. penult.*, avoucheth of his knowledge, "that some through bashfulness abstained from venery, and thereupon became very heavy and dull; and some others that were very timorous, melancholy, and beyond all measure sad."[8] Oribasius, *Med. collect. lib.* 6, *cap.* 37, speaks of some, "that if they do not use carnal copulation, are continually troubled with heaviness and headache; and some in the same case by intermission of it."[9] Not use of it hurts many; Arculanus, *cap.* 6, *in* 9 *Rhasis*, and Magninus, *part.* 3, *cap.* 5, think, because it "sends up poisoned vapours to the brain and heart."[10] And so doth Galen himself hold, "that if this natural seed be over-long kept (in some parties) it turns to poison."[11] Hieronymus Mercurialis, in his chapter of Melancholy, cites it for an especial cause of this malady, priapismus, satyriasis, etc.[12] Halyabbas, 5 *Theor. cap.* 36, reckons up this and many other diseases. Villanovanus, *Breviar. lib.* 1, *cap.* 18, saith, he "knew many monks and widows grievously

troubled with melancholy, and that from this sole cause." [1]
Lodovicus Mercatus, *lib. 2 de mulierum affect. cap.* 4, and
Rodericus à Castro, *de morbis mulier. lib. 2, cap.* 3, treat largely of
this subject, and will have it produce a peculiar kind of melancholy in stale maids, nuns, and widows; [2] *Ob suppressionem mensium et venerem omissam, timidæ, anxiæ, verecundæ, suspiciosæ,
languentes, consilii inopes, cum summa vitæ et rerum meliorum
desperatione,* etc., they are melancholy in the highest degree,
and all for want of husbands. Ælianus Montaltus, *cap.* 37 *de
melanchol.,* confirms as much out of Galen; so doth Wierus.
Christopherus à Vega, *de art. med. lib. 3, cap.* 14, relates many such
examples of men and women, that he had seen so melancholy.
Felix Plater, in the first book of his Observations, tells a
story of an ancient gentleman in Alsatia, that "married a young
wife, and was not able to pay his debts in that kind for a long
time together, by reason of his several infirmities: but she,
because of this inhibition of Venus, fell into a horrible fury,
and desired every one that came to see her, by words, looks,
and gestures, to have to do with her," etc. [3] Bernardus
Paternus, a physician, saith, he knew "a good honest godly
priest, that because he would neither willingly marry, nor
make use of the stews, fell into grievous melancholy fits." [4]
Hildesheim, *Spicil.* 2, hath such another example of an Italian
melancholy priest, in a consultation had *anno* 1580. Jason
Pratensis gives instance in a married man, that, from his wife's
death "abstaining after marriage, became exceedingly melancholy"; [5] Rodericus à Fonseca in a young man so misaffected,
tom. 2, *consult.* 85. To these you may add, if you please,
that conceited tale of a Jew, so visited in like sort, and so
cured, out of Poggius Florentinus.

Intemperate Venus is all out as bad in the other extreme.
Galen, *lib. 6 de morbis popular. sect.* 5, *text.* 26, reckons up
melancholy amongst those diseases which are "exasperated by
venery": [6] so doth Avicenna, 2, 3, *cap.* 11; Oribasius, *loc. citat.*;
Ficinus, *lib. 2 de sanitate tuenda*; Marsilius Cognatus; Mon-
altus, *cap.* 27; Guianerius, *tract.* 3, *cap.* 2. [7] Magninus, *cap.* 5,
art. 3, gives the reason, because "it infrigidates and dries up
the body, consumes the spirits"; and would therefore have all
such as are cold and dry to take heed of and to avoid it as a
mortal enemy. [8] Jacchinus, *in* 9 *Rhasis, cap.* 15, ascribes
the same cause, and instanceth in a patient of his, that
married a young wife in a hot summer, "and so dried himself
with chamber-work, that he became in short space, from

melancholy, mad": he cured him by moistening remedies.[1]
The like example I find in Lælius à Fonte Eugubinus, *consult.*
129, of a gentleman of Venice, that upon the same occasion
was first melancholy, afterwards mad. Read in him the story
at large.

Any other evacuation stopped will cause it, as well as these
above named, be it bile, ulcer,[2] issue, etc. Hercules de Saxonia,
lib. 1, *cap.* 16, and Gordonius, verify this out of their experience.
They saw one wounded in the head who, as long as the sore was
open, *lucida habuit mentis intervalla*, was well; but when it
was stopped, *rediit melancholia*, his melancholy fit seized on
him again.

Artificial evacuations are much like in effect, as hot-houses,
baths, blood-letting, purging, unseasonably and immoderately
used. Baths dry too much, if used in excess, be they natural
or artificial, and offend extreme hot, or cold;[3] one dries,[4] the
other refrigerates overmuch. Montanus, *consil.* 137, saith they
over-heat the liver. Joh. Struthius, *Stigmat. artis, lib.* 4, *cap.* 9,
contends, "that if one stay longer than ordinary at the bath,
go in too oft, or at unseasonable times, he putrefies the humours
in his body."[5] To this purpose writes Magninus, *lib.* 3, *cap.* 5,
Guianerius, *tract.* 15, *cap.* 21, utterly disallows all hot baths in
melancholy adust. "I saw" (saith he) "a man that laboured
of the gout, who to be freed of his malady came to the bath, and
was instantly cured of his disease, but got another worse, and
that was madness."[6] But this judgment varies as the humour
doth, in hot or cold: baths may be good for one melancholy
man, bad for another; that which will cure it in this party
may cause it in a second.

Phlebotomy, many times neglected, may do much harm to
the body, when there is a manifest redundance of bad humours
and melancholy blood; and when these humours heat and boil,
if this be not used in time, the parties affected, so inflamed, are
in great danger to be mad; but if it be unadvisedly, importunely,
immoderately used, it doth as much harm by refrigerating the
body, dulling the spirits, and consuming them. As Joh. Curio
in his 10th chapter [7] well reprehends, such kind of letting blood
doth more hurt than good; "the humours rage much more
than they did before; and is so far from avoiding melancholy,
that it increaseth it, and weakeneth the sight."[8] Prosper
Calenus [9] observes as much of all phlebotomy, except they keep
a very good diet after it; yea, and as Leonartus Jacchinus
speaks out of his own experience,[10] "the blood is much blacker

many men after their letting of blood than it was at first." [1]
for this cause belike Sallust. Salvianus, *lib. 2, cap.* 1, will admit
he hear of no blood-letting at all in this disease, except it be
manifest it proceed from blood: he was (it appears) by his own
words in that place, master of an hospital of madmen, "and
found by long experience that this kind of evacuation, either
in head, arm, or any other part, did more harm than good." [2]
To this opinion of his Felix Plater [3] is quite opposite: "Though
some wink at, disallow and quite contradict all phlebotomy in
melancholy, yet by long experience I have found innumerable
so saved, after they had been twenty, nay, sixty times let
blood, and to live happily after it. It was an ordinary thing of
old, in Galen's time, to take at once from such men six pound
of blood, which now we dare scarce take in ounces." *Sed viderint
medici* [but this is a matter for the doctors]; great books are
written of this subject.

Purging upward and downward, in abundance of bad humours
omitted, may be for the worst; so likewise as in the precedent,
if overmuch, too frequent or violent, it weakeneth their strength,[4]
saith Fuchsius, *lib. 2, sect. 2, cap.* 17, or if they be strong or able
to endure physic, yet it brings them to an ill habit, they make
their bodies no better than apothecaries' shops; this and such-
like infirmities must needs follow.

SUBSECT. V.—*Bad Air a Cause of Melancholy*

Air is a cause of great moment in producing this or any
other disease, being that it is still taken into our bodies by
respiration, and our more inner parts. "If it be impure and
foggy, it dejects the spirits, and causeth diseases by infection
of the heart," [5] as Paulus hath it, *lib.* 1, *cap.* 49; Avicenna,
lib. 1; Gal. *de san. tuenda*; Mercurialis, Montaltus, etc. Fernelius
saith, "A thick air thickeneth the blood and humours." [6]
Lemnius [7] reckons up two main things most profitable and most
pernicious to our bodies: air and diet; and this peculiar disease
nothing sooner causeth (Jobertus holds [8]) than the air wherein
we breathe and live. Such as is the air, such be our spirits;
and as our spirits, such are our humours.[9] It offends commonly
if it be too hot and dry,[10] thick, fuliginous, cloudy, blustering,
or a tempestuous air. Bodine, in his fifth book, *De repub.
cap.* 1 and 5, of his Method of History, proves that hot countries
are most troubled with melancholy, and that there are therefore in Spain, Africa, and Asia Minor, great numbers of

madmen, insomuch that they are compelled in all cities of note
to build peculiar hospitals for them. Leo Afer, *lib.* 3, *de Fess.
urbe*,[1] Ortelius, and Zuinger confirm as much: they are ordinarily
so choleric in their speeches, that scarce two words pass without
railing or chiding in common talk, and often quarrelling in their
streets. Gordonius will have every man take notice of it:
"Note this" (saith he) "that in hot countries it is far more familiar
than in cold." Although this we have now said be not continually so, for, as Acosta truly saith,[3] under the Equator itself
is a most temperate habitation, wholesome air, a paradise of
pleasure: the leaves ever green, cooling showers. But it holds
in such as are intemperately hot, as Johannes à Meggen found
in Cyprus,[4] others in Malta, Apulia,[5] and the Holy Land, where
at some seasons of the year is nothing but dust, their rivers
dried up, the air scorching hot, and earth inflamed; insomuch
that many pilgrims, going barefoot for devotion sake from
Joppa to Jerusalem upon the hot sands, often run mad; or else
quite overwhelmed with sand, *profundis arenis*, as in many
parts of Africa, Arabia Deserta, Bactriana, now Chorassan,
when the west wind blows, *involuti arenis transeuntes necantur*
[travellers are sometimes buried by clouds of sand]. Hercules
de Saxonia,[7] a professor in Venice, gives this cause why so many
Venetian women are melancholy, *quod diu sub sole degant*,
they tarry too long in the sun. Montanus, *consil.* 21, amongst
other causes assigns this, why that Jew his patient was mad,
quod tam multum exposuit se calori et frigori: he exposed himself
so much to heat and cold. And for that reason in Venice there
is little stirring in those brick-paved streets in summer about
noon, they are most part then asleep: as they are likewise in
the Great Mogor's countries, and all over the East Indies. At
Aden in Arabia, as Lodovicus Vertomannus relates in his
travels,[8] they keep their markets in the night, to avoid extremity
of heat; and in Ormus, like cattle in a pasture, people of all
sorts lie up to the chin in water all day long. At Braga in
Portugal, Burgos in Castile, Messina in Sicily, all over Spain
and Italy, their streets are most part narrow, to avoid the sunbeams. The Turks wear great turbans *ad fugandos solis radios*,
to refract the sunbeams; and much inconvenience that hot
air of Bantam in Java yields to our men that sojourn there for
traffic; where it is so hot, "that they that are sick of the pox lie
commonly bleaching in the sun, to dry up their sores."[9] Such
complaint I read of those isles of Cape Verde, fourteen degrees
from the Equator, they do *male audire* [have a bad name].

ne [1] calls them the unhealthiest clime of the world, for fluxes,
fevers, frenzies, calentures, which commonly seize on seafaring
men that touch at them, and all by reason of a hot distemperature of the air. The hardiest men are offended with this heat,
and stiffest clowns cannot resist it, as Constantine affirms,
Agricult. lib. 2, cap. 45. They that are naturally born in such
air, may not endure it,[2] as Niger records of some part of Mesopotamia, now called Diarbecha:[3] *Quibusdam in locis sævienti
æstui adeo subjecta est, ut pleraque animalia fervore solis et cœli
extinguantur,* 'tis so hot there in some places, that men of the
country and cattle are killed with it; and Adricomius of Arabia
Felix,[4] by reason of myrrh, frankincense, and hot spices there
growing, the air is so obnoxious to their brains, that the very
inhabitants at some times cannot abide it, much less weaklings
and strangers.[5] Amatus Lusitanus, *cent.* 1, *curat.* 45, reports
of a young maid, that was one Vincent a currier's daughter,
some thirteen years of age, that would wash her hair in the heat
of the day (in July) and so let it dry in the sun, "to make it
yellow, but by that means tarrying too long in the heat, she
inflamed her head, and made herself mad." [6]

Cold air in the other extreme is almost as bad as hot, and so
both Montaltus esteem of it, *cap.* 11, if it be dry withal. In
those northern countries, the people are therefore generally
dull, heavy, and many witches, which (as I have before quoted)
Saxo Grammaticus, Olaus, Baptista Porta ascribe to melancholy. But these cold climes are more subject to natural
melancholy (not this artificial) which is cold and dry: for which
cause Mercurius Britannicus [7] belike puts melancholy men to
inhabit just under the Pole. The worst of the three is a thick,
cloudy, misty, foggy air,[8] or such as come from fens, moorish
grounds, lakes, muckhills, draughts, sinks, where any carcasses
or carrion lies, or from whence any stinking fulsome smell comes:
Galen, Avicenna, Mercurialis, new and old physicians, hold that
such air is unwholesome, and engenders melancholy, plagues,
and what not? Alexandretta, an haven-town in the Mediter-
ranean Sea,[9] Saint John de Ulloa, an haven in Nova Hispania,
are much condemned for a bad air, so are Durazzo in Albania,
Lithuania, Ditmarsh, Pomptinæ Paludes [10] in Italy, the territories about Pisa, Ferrara, etc., Romney Marsh with us, the
hundreds in Essex, the fens in Lincolnshire. Cardan, *de rerum
varietate, lib.* 17, *cap.* 96, finds fault with the site of those rich and
most populous cities in the Low Countries, as Bruges, Ghent,
Amsterdam, Leyden, Utrecht, etc., the air is bad; and so at

Stockholm in Sweden, Rhegium in Italy, Salisbury with us, Hul
and Lynn; they may be commodious for navigation, this nev
kind of fortification, and many other good necessary uses; bu
are they so wholesome? Old Rome hath descended from th
hills to the valley, 'tis the site of most of our new cities, an
held best to build in plains, to take the opportunity of rivers
Leander Albertus pleads hard for the air and site of Venice
though the black moorish lands appear at every low water
the sea, fire, and smoke (as he thinks) qualify the air; and som
suppose that a thick foggy air helps the memory, as in ther
of Pisa in Italy;[1] and our Camden, out of Plato, commend
the site of Cambridge, because it is so near the fens. But le
the site of such places be as it may, how can they be excuse
that have a delicious seat, a pleasant air, and all that natu
can afford, and yet through their own nastiness and sluttisl
ness, immund and sordid manner of life, suffer their air t
putrefy, and themselves to be choked up? Many cities i
Turkey do *male audire* [have a bad name] in this kind: Co
stantinople itself, where commonly carrion lies in the stree
Some find the same fault in Spain, even in Madrid, the king
seat; a most excellent air, a pleasant site, but the inhabitan
are slovens, and the streets uncleanly kept.

A troublesome tempestuous air is as bad as impure, roug
and foul weather, impetuous winds, cloudy dark days, as it
commonly with us, *cœlum visu fœdum*, Polydore calls it,[2]
filthy sky, *et in quo facile generantur nubes* [where the clou
rapidly collect]; as Tully's brother Quintus wrote to him
Rome, being then Quæstor in Britain. "In a thick and cloud
air" (saith Lemnius[3]) "men are tetric, sad, and peevish: and
the western winds blow, and that there be a calm, or a fair su
shine day, there is a kind of alacrity in men's minds; it chee
up men and beasts: but if it be a turbulent, rough, cloud
stormy weather, men are sad, lumpish, and much dejecte
angry, waspish, dull, and melancholy." This was Virgi
experiment of old:[4]

> *Verum ubi tempestas, et cœli mobilis humor*
> *Mutavere vices, et Jupiter humidus Austro,*
> *Vertuntur species animorum, et pectore motus*
> *Concipiunt alios.*

> But when the face of heaven changed is
>   To tempests, rain, from season fair:
> Our minds are altered, and in our breasts
>   Forthwith some new conceits appear.

and who is not weather-wise against such and such conjunctions of planets, moved in foul weather, dull and heavy in such tempestuous seasons? *Gelidum contristat Aquarius annum* [1] [chill, cheerless days Aquarius brings]: the time requires, and the autumn breeds it; winter is like unto it, ugly, foul, squalid; the air works on all men, more or less, but especially on such as are melancholy, or inclined to it, as Lemnius holds: "They are most moved with it, and those which are already mad rave downright, either in or against a tempest. Besides, the devil many times takes his opportunity of such storms, and when the humours by the air be stirred, he goes in with them, exagitates our spirits, and vexeth our souls; as the sea-waves, so are the spirits and humours in our bodies tossed with tempestuous winds and storms." [2] To such as are melancholy, therefore, Montanus, *consil.* 24, will have tempestuous and rough air to be avoided, and, *consil.* 27, all night air, and would not have them to walk abroad but in a pleasant day. Lemnius, *lib.* 3, *cap.* 3, discommends the south and eastern winds, commends the north. Montanus, *consil.* 31, will not any windows to be opened in the night.[3] *Consil.* 229, *et consil.* 230, he discommends especially the south wind, and nocturnal air: so doth Plutarch.[4] The night and darkness makes men sad, the like do all subterranean vaults, dark houses in caves and rocks; desert places cause melancholy in an instant, especially such as have not been used to it, or otherwise accustomed. Read more of air in Hippocrates; Aetius, *lib.* 3, *a cap.* 171 *ad* 175; Oribasius, *a cap.* 1 *ad* 21; Avicen, *lib.* 1, *can. fen.* 2, *doc.* 2, *n.* 1, *cap.* 123, to the 12, etc.

SUBSECT. VI.—*Immoderate Exercise a Cause, and how.*
Solitariness, Idleness

Nothing so good but it may be abused: nothing better than exercise (if opportunely used) for the preservation of the body; nothing so bad if it be unseasonable, violent, or overmuch. Fernelius, out of Galen, *Path. lib.* 1, *cap.* 16, saith, "that much exercise and weariness consumes the spirits and substance, refrigerates the body; and such humours which nature would have otherwise concocted and expelled, it stirs up and makes them rage: which being so enraged, diversely affect and trouble the body and mind." [5] So doth it, if it be unseasonably used, upon a full stomach, or when the body is full of crudities, which Fuchsius so much inveighs against, *lib.* 2 *Instit. sect.* 2, *cap.* 4,

giving that for a cause why schoolboys in Germany are so
often scabbed, because they use exercise presently after meats.
Bayerus puts in a caveat against such exercise,[1] because "it
corrupts the meat in the stomach, and carries the same juice
raw, and as yet undigested, into the veins" (saith Lemnius)
"which there putrefies and confounds the animal spirits."
Crato, *consil.* 21, *lib.* 2, protests against all such exercise after
meat, as being the greatest enemy to concoction that may
be, and cause of corruption of humours, which produce this
and many other diseases.[3] Not without good reason then doth
Sallust. Salvianus, *lib.* 2, *cap.* 1, and Leonartus Jacchinus *in*
Rhasis, Mercurialis, Arculanus, and many other, set down
immoderate exercise[4] as a most forcible cause of melancholy.

Opposite to exercise is idleness (the badge of gentry) or want
of exercise, the bane of body and mind, the nurse of naughtiness,
stepmother of discipline, the chief author of all mischief, one
of the seven deadly sins, and a sole cause of this and many
other maladies, the devil's cushion, as Gualter calls it,[5] his
pillow and chief reposal. "For the mind can never rest, but still
meditates on one thing or other; except it be occupied about
some honest business, of his own accord it rusheth into melancholy." "As too much and violent exercise offends on the one
side, so doth an idle life on the other" (saith Crato), "it fills the
body full of phlegm, gross humours, and all manner of obstructions, rheums, catarrhs, etc."[6] Rhasis, *Cont. lib.* 1, *tract.*
accounts of it as the greatest cause of melancholy. "I have
often seen" (saith he) "that idleness begets this humour more
than anything else."[7] Montaltus, *cap.* 1, seconds him out of his
experience: "They that are idle are far more subject to melancholy than such as are conversant or employed about any office
or business."[8] Plutarch reckons up idleness for a sole cause
of the sickness of the soul: "There are they" (saith he) "troubled
in mind, that have no other cause but this."[9] Homer, Iliad
brings in Achilles eating of his own heart in his idleness, because
he might not fight. Mercurialis, *consil.* 86, for a melancholy
young man, urgeth it is a chief cause; why was he melancholy?
because idle.[10] Nothing begets it sooner, increaseth and continueth it oftener, than idleness;[11] a disease familiar to all idle
persons, an inseparable companion to such as live at ease,
pingui otio desidiose agentes, a life out of action, and have no
calling or ordinary employment to busy themselves about, that
have small occasions; and though they have, such is the
laziness, dullness, they will not compose themselves to do aught.

hey cannot abide work, though it be necessary, easy, as to dress
hemselves, write a letter, or the like; yet, as he that is benumbed
vith cold sits still shaking, that might relieve himself with a little
xercise or stirring, do they complain, but will not use the
acile and ready means to do themselves good; and so are still
ormented with melancholy. Especially if they have been
ormerly brought up to business, or to keep much company,
nd upon a sudden come to lead a sedentary life, it crucifies
heir souls, and seizeth on them in an instant; for whilst they
.re anyways employed, in action, discourse, about any business,
port or recreation, or in company to their liking, they are
·ery well; but if alone or idle, tormented instantly again; one
ay's solitariness, one hour's sometimes, doth them more harm
han a week's physic, labour, and company can do good. Melan-
holy seizeth on them forthwith being alone, and is such a tor-
ure that, as wise Seneca well saith, *Malo mihi male quam*
olliter esse, I had rather be sick than idle. This idleness is
ither of body or mind. That of body is nothing but a kind
f benumbing laziness, intermitting exercise, which, if we may
elieve Fernelius, "causeth crudities, obstructions, excremental
umours, quencheth the natural heat, dulls the spirits, and
nakes them unapt to do anything whatsoever." [1]

Neglectis urenda filix innascitur agris. [2]

[Neglected fields yield bracken for burning.]

.s fern grows in untilled grounds, and all manner of weeds, so
·o gross humours in an idle body, *Ignavum corrumpunt otia*
orpus. A horse in a stable that never travels, a hawk in a mew
nat seldom flies, are both subject to diseases; which, left unto
nemselves, are most free from any such encumbrances. An
lle dog will be mangy, and how shall an idle person think to
scape? Idleness of the mind is much worse than this of the
ody; wit without employment is a disease, *ærugo animi, rubigo*
igenii: [3] the rust of the soul, a plague, a hell itself,[4] *maximum*
nimi nocumentum,[5] Galen calls it. "As in a standing pool
·orms and filthy creepers increase" (*et vitium capiunt ni move-*
ntur aquæ, the water itself putrefies, and air likewise, if it be
·ot continually stirred by the wind), "so do evil and corrupt
noughts in an idle person," [6] the soul is contaminated. In a
·ommonwealth, where is no public enemy, there is, likely, civil
·ars, and they rage upon themselves: this body of ours, when
· is idle and knows not how to bestow itself, macerates and
·exeth itself with cares, griefs, false fears, discontents, and

suspicions; it tortures and preys upon his own bowels, and i
never at rest. Thus much I dare boldly say: he or she tha
is idle, be they of what condition they will, never so rich, s
well allied, fortunate, happy, let them have all things in abun
dance and felicity that heart can wish and desire, all contentment
so long as he or she or they are idle, they shall never be pleased
never well in body and mind, but weary still, sickly still, vexe
still, loathing still, weeping, sighing, grieving, suspecting
offended with the world, with every object, wishing themselve
gone or dead, or else carried away with some foolish phantas
or other. And this is the true cause that so many great mer
ladies, and gentlewomen, labour of this disease in country an
city; for idleness is an appendix to nobility; they count it
disgrace to work, and spend all their days in sports, recreation
and pastimes, and will therefore take no pains, be of no voca
tion: they feed liberally, fare well, want exercise, action, employ
ment (for to work, I say, they may not abide), and compan
to their desires, and thence their bodies become full of gros
humours, wind, crudities, their minds disquieted, dull, heavy
etc.; care, jealousy, fear of some diseases, sullen fits, weepin
fits, seize too familiarly on them.[1] For what will not fear an
phantasy work in an idle body? what distempers will they no
cause? When the children of Israel murmured against Pharao
in Egypt,[2] he commanded his officers to double their task, an
let them get straw themselves, and yet make their full numbe
of bricks; for the sole cause why they mutiny, and are evil a
ease, is, "they are idle." When you shall hear and see so man
discontented persons in all places where you come, so man
several grievances, unnecessary complaints, fear, suspicions
the best means to redress it is to set them awork, so to bus
their minds; for the truth is, they are idle. Well they ma
build castles in the air for a time, and soothe up themselves wit
phantastical and pleasant humours, but in the end they wi
prove as bitter as gall, they shall be still, I say, disconten
suspicious, fearful, jealous, sad, fretting and vexing of ther
selves;[4] so long as they be idle, it is impossible to please ther
Otio qui nescit uti, plus habet negotii quam qui negotium in n
gotio, as that A. Gellius could observe:[5] he that knows not ho
to spend his time, hath more business, care, grief, anguish of mir
than he that is most busy in the midst of all his business. *Otios*
animus nescit quid volet: an idle person (as he follows it) knov
not when he is well, what he would have, or whither he wou
go; *quum illuc ventum est, [ire] illinc lubet* [as soon as he com

to a place, he wants to leave it], he is tired out with every-thing, displeased with all, weary of his life; *nec bene domi, nec militiæ,* [happy] neither at home nor abroad, *errat, et præter vitam vivitur,* he wanders and lives besides himself. In a word, what the mischievous effects of laziness and idleness are, I do not find anywhere more accurately expressed, than in these verses of Philolaches in the comical poet,[1] which for their elegancy I will in part insert.

> *Novarum ædium esse arbitror similem ego hominem,*
> *Quando hic natus est. Ei rei argumenta dicam.*
> *Ædes quando sunt ad amussim expolitæ,*
> *Quisque laudat fabrum, atque exemplum expetit,* etc.
> *At ubi illo migrat nequam homo indiligensque,* etc.
> *Tempestas venit, confringit tegulas, imbricesque,*
> *Putrefacit aer operam fabri,* etc.
> *Dicam ut homines similes esse ædium arbitremini,*
> *Fabri parentes fundamentum substruunt liberorum,*
> *Expoliunt, docent literas, nec parcunt sumptui,*
> *Ego autem sub fabrorum potestate frugi fui,*
> *Postquam autem migravi in ingenium meum,*
> *Perdidi operam fabrorum illico, oppido,*
> *Venit ignavia, ea mihi tempestas fuit,*
> *Adventuque suo grandinem et imbrem attulit,*
> *Illa mihi virtutem deturbavit,* etc.

A young man is like a fair new house; the carpenter leaves it well built, in good repair, of solid stuff; but a bad tenant lets it rain in, and for want of reparation fall to decay, etc. Our parents, tutors, friends, spare no cost to bring us up in our youth in all manner of virtuous education; but when we are left to ourselves, idleness as a tempest drives all virtuous motions out of our minds, *et nihili sumus;* on a sudden, by sloth and such bad ways, we come to naught.

Cousin-german to idleness, and a concomitant cause which goes hand in hand with it, is *nimia solitudo,* too much solitariness, by the testimony of all physicians,[2] cause and symptom both; but as it is here put for a cause, it is either coact, enforced, or else voluntary. Enforced solitariness is commonly seen in students, monks, friars, anchorites, that by their order and course of life must abandon all company, society of other men, and betake themselves to a private cell: *Otio superstitioso seclusi* [recluses through superstition], as Bale and Hospinian well term it, such as are the Carthusians of our time, that eat no flesh (by their order), keep perpetual silence, never go abroad; such as live in prison, or some desert place, and cannot have company, as many of our country gentlemen do in solitary houses, they must either be alone without companions, or live beyond their means, and entertain all comers as so many hosts, or else converse with their servants and hinds, such as are unequal, inferior to them, and of a contrary disposition: or else, as some do to avoid solitariness, spend their time with lewd fellows in taverns and in alehouses, and thence addict themselves to some unlawful disports, or dissolute courses. Divers again are cast upon this rock of solitariness for want of means, or out of a strong apprehension of some infirmity, disgrace, or through bashfulness, rudeness, simplicity, they cannot apply themselves to others' company. *Nullum solum infelici gratius solitudine, ubi nullus sit qui miseriam exprobret* [to the wretched no spot is more welcome than one where there is no one to upbraid his misery]. This enforced solitariness takes place, and produceth his effect soonest, in such as have spent their time jovially, peradventure in all honest recreations, in good company, in some great family or populous city, and are upon a sudden confined to a desert country cottage far off, restrained of their liberty, and barred from their ordinary associates; solitariness is very irksome to such, most tedious, and a sudden cause of great inconvenience.

Voluntary solitariness is that which is familiar with melancholy, and gently brings on like a siren, a shoeing-horn, or some sphinx to this irrevocable gulf; a primary cause, Piso calls it.[1] Most pleasant it is at first, to such as are melancholy given, to lie in bed whole days, and keep their chambers, to walk alone in some solitary grove, betwixt wood and water, by a brook side, to meditate upon some delightsome and pleasant subject, which shall affect them most; *amabilis insania* [a pleasing dotage], and *mentis gratissimus error* [a most flattering delusion]. A most incomparable delight it is so to melancholize, and build castles in the air, to go smiling to themselves, acting an infinite variety of parts, which they suppose and strongly imagine they represent, or that they see acted or done. *Blandum quidem ab initio* [it is delightful at first], saith Lemnius, to conceive and meditate of such pleasant things sometimes, "present, past, or to come," [2] as Rhasis speaks. So delightsome these toys are at first, they could spend whole days and nights without sleep, even whole years alone in such contemplations and phantastical meditations, which are like unto dreams, and they will hardly be drawn from them, or willingly interrupt; so pleasant their vain conceits are, that they hinder their ordinary tasks and necessary business, they cannot address themselves to

them, or almost to any study or employment, these phantastical
and bewitching thoughts so covertly, so feelingly, so urgently,
so continually set upon, creep in, insinuate, possess, overcome,
distract, and detain them, they cannot, I say, go about their
more necessary business, stave off or extricate themselves, but
are ever musing, melancholizing, and carried along; as he (they
say) that is led round about a heath with a Puck in the night,
they run earnestly on in this labyrinth of anxious and solicitous
melancholy meditations, and cannot well or willingly refrain,
or easily leave off, winding and unwinding themselves as so
many clocks, and still pleasing their humours, until at last the
scene is turned upon a sudden by some bad object, and they,
being now habituated to such vain meditations and solitary
places, can endure no company, can ruminate of nothing but
harsh and distasteful subjects. Fear, sorrow, suspicion, *subrusticus pudor* [a rustic bashfulness], discontent, cares, and
weariness of life surprise them in a moment, and they can
think of nothing else, continually suspecting; no sooner are
their eyes open, but this infernal plague of melancholy seizeth
on them, and terrifies their souls, representing some dismal
object to their minds, which now by no means, no labour, no
persuasions they can avoid, *hæret lateri lethalis arundo* [the
deadly arrow still remains in their side], they may not be rid
of it, they cannot resist.[1] I may not deny but that there is
some profitable meditation, contemplation, and kind of solitariness to be embraced, which the Fathers so highly commended,
Hierome,[2] Chrysostom, Cyprian, Austin, in whole tracts, which
Petrarch, Erasmus, Stella, and others so much magnify in their
books; a paradise, a heaven on earth, if it be used aright, good
for the body, and better for the soul: as many of those old
monks used it, to divine contemplations; as Simulus, a courtier
in Hadrian's time, Dioclesian the emperor, retired themselves,
etc., in that sense, *Vatia solus scit vivere*, Vatia lives alone,
which the Romans were wont to say when they commended
a country life. Or to the bettering of their knowledge, as
Democritus, Cleanthes, and those excellent philosophers have
ever done, to sequester themselves from the tumultuous world,
or as in Pliny's Villa Laurentana, Tully's Tusculan, Jovius'
study, that they might better *vacare studiis et Deo*, serve God
and follow their studies. Methinks, therefore, our too zealous
innovators were not so well advised in that general subversion
of abbeys and religious houses, promiscuously to fling down
all; they might have taken away those gross abuses crept in

amongst them, rectified such inconveniences, and not so far to have raved and raged against those fair buildings and ever-lasting monuments of our forefathers' devotion, consecrated to pious uses; some monasteries and collegiate cells might have been well spared, and their revenues otherwise employed, here and there one, in good towns or cities at least, for men and women of all sorts and conditions to live in, to sequester themselves from the cares and tumults of the world, that were not desirous or fit to marry, or otherwise willing to be troubled with common affairs, and know not well where to bestow themselves, to live apart in, for more conveniency, good education, better company sake, to follow their studies (I say), to the perfection of arts and sciences, common good, and, as some truly devoted monks of old had done, freely and truly to serve God. For these men are neither solitary nor idle, as the poet made answer to the husbandman in Æsop that objected idleness to him: he was never so idle as in his company; or that Scipio Africanus in Tully,[1] *Nunquam minus solus, quam cum solus; nunquam minus otiosus, quam quum esset otiosus:* never less solitary than when he was alone, never more busy than when he seemed to be most idle. It is reported by Plato in his dialogue *de Amore*, in that prodigious commendation of Socrates, how a deep meditation coming into Socrates' mind by chance, he stood still musing, *eodem vestigio cogitabundus*, from morning to noon, and whenas then he had not yet finished his meditation, *perstabat cogitans*, he so continued till the evening; the soldiers (for he then followed the camp) observed him with admiration, and on set purpose watched all night, but he persevered immovable *ad exortum solis*, till the sun rose in the morning, and then, saluting the sun, went his ways. In what humour constant Socrates did thus, I know not, or how he might be affected, but this would be pernicious to another man; what intricate business might so really possess him, I cannot easily guess. But this is *otiosum otium* [a vacant idleness], it is far otherwise with these men, according to Seneca, *Omnia nobis mala solitudo persuadet* [solitude leads us into all sorts of evil]; this solitude undoeth us, *pugnat cum vita sociali* [it is the foe of the social life]; 'tis a destructive solitariness. These men are devils alone, as the saying is, *Homo solus aut deus, aut dæmon:* a man alone is either a saint or a devil; *mens ejus aut languescit, aut tumescit* [he becomes either slow-witted or conceited]; and *Væ soli*[2] in this sense, woe be to him that is so alone. These wretches do frequently degenerate from men, and of sociable creatures become beasts, monsters, inhuman, ugly to behold, *misanthropi*; they do even loathe themselves, and hate the company of men, as so many Timons, Nebuchadnezzars, by too much indulging to these pleasing humours, and through their own default. So that which Mercurialis, *consil. II*, sometime expostulated with his melancholy patient, may be justly applied to every solitary and idle person in particular. *Natura de te videtur conqueri posse,* etc.[1] "Nature may justly complain of thee, that whereas she gave thee a good wholesome temperature, a sound body, and God hath given thee so divine and excellent a soul, so many good parts and profitable gifts, thou hast not only contemned and rejected, but hast corrupted them, polluted them, overthrown their temperature, and perverted those gifts with riot, idleness, solitariness, and many other ways; thou art a traitor to God and nature, an enemy to thyself and to the world. *Perditio tua ex te:* thou hast lost thyself wilfully, cast away thyself, thou thyself art the efficient cause of thine own misery, by not resisting such vain cogitations, but giving way unto them."

SUBSECT. VII.—*Sleeping and Waking, Causes*

What I have formerly said of exercise, I may now repeat of sleep. Nothing better than moderate sleep, nothing worse than it if it be in extremes or unseasonably used. It is a received opinion, that a melancholy man cannot sleep overmuch; *somnus supra modum prodest* [extra sleep is beneficial], as an only antidote, and nothing offends them more, or causeth this malady sooner, than waking; yet in some cases sleep may do more harm than good, in that phlegmatic, swinish, cold, and sluggish melancholy which Melancthon speaks of, that thinks of waters, sighing most part, etc. It dulls the spirits, if overmuch, and senses;[2] fills the head full of gross humours; causeth distillations, rheums, great store of excrements in the brain, and all the other parts, as Fuchsius speaks of them,[3] that sleep like so many dormice. Or if it be used in the daytime, upon a full stomach, the body ill-composed to rest, or after hard meats, it increaseth fearful dreams, *incubus*, night-walking, crying out, and much unquietness; "such sleep prepares the body," as one observes,[4] "to many perilous diseases." But, as I have said, waking overmuch is both a symptom and an ordinary cause. "It causeth dryness of the brain, frenzy, dotage, and makes the

body dry, lean, hard, and ugly to behold," as Lemnius hath it; [1]
"the temperature of the brain is corrupted by it, the humours
adust, the eyes made to sink into the head, choler increased,
and the whole body inflamed": and, as may be added out of
Galen, 3 *de sanitate tuenda*, Avicenna, 3, 1, "it overthrows the
natural heat, it causeth crudities, hurts concoction," [2] and what
not? Not without good cause therefore Crato, *consil*. 21, *lib*. 2,
Hildesheim, *Spicil*. 2, *de delir. et mania*, Jacchinus, Arculanus
on Rhasis, Guianerius, and Mercurialis reckon up this overmuch
waking as a principal cause.

MEMB. III

SUBSECT. I.—*Passions and Perturbations of the Mind, how they cause Melancholy*

As that gymnosophist in Plutarch [3] made answer to Alexander
(demanding which spake best), Every one of his fellows did
speak better than the other: so may I say of these causes to
him that shall require which is the greatest, every one is more
grievous than other, and this of passion the greatest of all. A
most frequent and ordinary cause of melancholy, *fulmen pertur-
bationum* (Piccolomineus calls it [4]), this thunder and lightning
of perturbation, which causeth such violent and speedy alterations in this our microcosm, and many times subverts the good
estate and temperature of it. For as the body works upon the
mind by his bad humours, troubling the spirits, sending gross
fumes into the brain, and so *per consequens* [consequently]
disturbing the soul, and all the faculties of it,

Corpus onustum
Hesternis vitiis animum quoque prægravat una,[5]

[By yesterday's excesses still oppressed,
The body suffers not the mind to rest,]

with fear, sorrow, etc., which are ordinary symptoms of this
disease: so, on the other side, the mind most effectually works
upon the body, producing by his passions and perturbations
miraculous alterations, as melancholy, despair, cruel diseases,
and sometimes death itself; insomuch that it is most true
which Plato saith in his *Charmides*, *omnia corporis mala ab
anima procedere*, all the mischiefs of the body proceed from the
soul: [6] and Democritus in Plutarch urgeth,[7] *Damnatam iri*

animam a corpore, if the body should in this behalf bring an
action against the soul, surely the soul would be cast and convicted, that by her supine negligence had caused such inconveniences, having authority over the body, and using it for an
instrument as a smith doth his hammer (saith Cyprian[1]), im-
puting all those vices and maladies to the mind.   Even so doth
Philostratus, *Non coinquinatur corpus, nisi consensu animæ:*[2]
the body is not corrupted but by the soul.   Lodovicus Vives
will have such turbulent commotions proceed from ignorance
and indiscretion.[3]   All philosophers impute the miseries of the
body to the soul, that should have governed it better, by
command of reason, and hath not done it.   The Stoics are
altogether of opinion (as Lipsius[4] and Piccolomineus[5] record),
that a wise man should be ἀπαθής, without all manner of passions
and perturbations whatsoever, as Seneca reports of Cato,[6] the
Greeks of Socrates,[7] and Jo. Aubanus of a nation in Africa,[8] so
free from passion, or rather so stupid, that if they be wounded
with a sword, they will only look back.   Lactantius, 2 *Instit.*,
will exclude fear from a wise man;[9] others except all, some the
greatest passions.   But let them dispute how they will, set down
in thesi [in a thesis], give precepts to the contrary; we find that of
Lemnius true by common experience: "No mortal man is free
from these perturbations: or if he be so, sure he is either a god
or a block."[10]   They are born and bred with us, we have them
from our parents by inheritance, *A parentibus habemus malum
hunc assem*, saith Pelezius,[11] *nascitur una nobiscum, aliturque*
[it is born and grows with us], 'tis propagated from Adam :
Cain was melancholy, as Austin[12] hath it, and who is not?
Good discipline, education, philosophy, divinity (I cannot deny),
may mitigate and restrain these passions in some few men at
some times, but most part they domineer, and are so violent,
that as a torrent (*torrens velut aggere rupto*) bears down all before,
and overflows his banks, *sternit agros, sternit sata* [lays waste
the fields, prostrates the crops], they overwhelm reason, judgment, and pervert the temperature of the body;[13] *Fertur equis
auriga, nec audit currus habenas*[14] [the driver is whirled along,
the steeds obey not the rein].   Now such a man (saith Austin)
"that is so led, in a wise man's eye is no better than he that
stands upon his head."[15]   It is doubted by some, *gravioresne
morbi a perturbationibus, an ab humoribus*, whether humours or
perturbations cause the more grievous maladies.   But we find
that of our Saviour (Matt. xxvi, 41) most true, "The spirit is
willing, the flesh is weak," we cannot resist; and this of

Philo Judæus, "Perturbations often offend the body, and are most frequent causes of melancholy, turning it out of the hinges of his health." [1] Vives compares them to "winds upon the sea, some only move as those great gales, but others turbulent quite overturn the ship." [2] Those which are light, easy, and more seldom, to our thinking do us little harm, and are therefore contemned of us: yet if they be reiterated, "as the rain" (saith Austin "doth a stone, so do these perturbations penetrate the mind": [3] and (as one observes) "produce a habit of melancholy at the last, which, having gotten the mastery in our souls, may well be called diseases." [4]

How these passions produce this effect, Agrippa hath handled at large, *Occult. Philos. lib.* 11, *cap.* 63; [5] Cardan, *lib.* 14 *Subtil.*; Lemnius, *lib.* 1, *cap.* 12, *de occult. nat. mir., et lib.* 1, *cap.* 16; Suarez, *Met. disput.* 18, *sect.* 1, *art.* 25; T. Bright, *cap.* 12 of his Melancholy Treatise; Wright the Jesuit, in his Book of the Passions of the Mind, etc. Thus, in brief, to our imagination cometh, by the outward sense of memory, some object to be known (residing in the foremost part of the brain), which he, misconceiving or amplifying, presently communicates to the heart, the seat of all affections. The pure spirits forthwith flock from the brain to the heart by certain secret channels, and signify what good or bad object was presented; which immediately bends itself to prosecute or avoid it, [6] and, withal, draweth with it other humours to help it: so in pleasure, concur great store of purer spirits; in sadness, much melancholy blood; in ire, choler. If the imagination be very apprehensive, intent, and violent, it sends great store of spirits to or from the heart, and makes a deeper impression and greater tumult; as the humours in the body be likewise prepared, and the temperature itself ill or well disposed, the passions are longer and stronger; so that the first step and fountain of all our grievances in this kind is *læsa imaginatio* [7] [a disordered imagination], which, misinforming the heart, causeth all these distemperatures, alteration and confusion of spirits and humours; by means of which, so disturbed, concoction is hindered, and the principal parts are much debilitated; as Dr. Navarra well declared, being consulted by Montanus about a melancholy Jew.[8] The spirits so confounded, the nourishment must needs be abated, bad humours increased, crudities and thick spirits engendered, with melancholy blood. The other parts cannot perform their functions, having the spirits drawn from them by vehement passion, but fail in sense and motion; so we look upon a thing, and see it not; hear, and observe not; which otherwise would much affect us, had we been free. I may therefore conclude with Arnoldus,[1] *Maxima vis est phantasiæ, et huic uni fere, non autem corporis intemperiei, omnis melancholiæ causa est ascribenda:* great is the force of imagination, and much more ought the cause of melancholy to be ascribed to this alone, than to the distemperature of the body. Of which imagination, because it hath so great a stroke in producing this malady, and is so powerful of itself, it will not be improper to my discourse to make a brief digression, and speak of the force of it, and how it causeth this alteration. Which manner of digression howsoever some dislike, as frivolous and impertinent, yet I am of Beroaldus his opinion, "Such digressions do mightily delight and refresh a weary reader, they are like sauce to a bad stomach, and I do therefore most willingly use them." [2]

SUBSECT. II.—*Of the Force of Imagination*

What imagination is I have sufficiently declared in my digression of the anatomy of the soul. I will only now point at the wonderful effects and power of it; which, as it is eminent in all, so most especially it rageth in melancholy persons, in keeping the species of objects so long, mistaking, amplifying them by continual and strong meditation,[3] until at length it produceth in some parties real effects, causeth this and many other maladies. And although this phantasy of ours be a subordinate faculty to reason, and should be ruled by it, yet in many men, through inward or outward distemperature, defect of organs, which are inapt or hindered, or otherwise contaminated, it is likewise inapt, hindered, and hurt. This we see verified in sleepers, which by reason of humours and concourse of vapours troubling the phantasy, imagine many times absurd and prodigious things, and in such as are troubled with *incubus*, or witch-ridden (as we call it); if they lie on their backs, they suppose an old woman rides and sits so hard upon them that they are almost stifled for want of breath; when there is nothing offends but a concourse of bad humours, which trouble the phantasy. This is likewise evident in such as walk in the night in their sleep, and do strange feats: these vapours move the phantasy, the phantasy the appetite, which moving the animal spirits causeth the body to walk up and down as if they were awake.[4] Fracastorius, *lib. 3 de intellect.*, refers all ecstasies to this force of imagination, such as lie whole days together in a trance: as that priest whom Celsus

speaks of, that could separate himself from his senses when he
list, and lie like a dead man, void of life and sense.[1] Cardan
brags of himself that he could do as much, and that when he
list. Many times such men, when they come to themselves,
tell strange things of heaven and hell, what visions they have
seen; as that St. Owen, in Matthew Paris, that went into
St. Patrick's Purgatory, and the monk of Evesham in the same
author. Those common apparitions in Bede and Gregory,
St. Bridget's revelations, Wier., *lib.* 3 *de lamiis, cap.* 11, Cæsar
Vaninus in his Dialogues, etc., reduceth (as I have formerly
said), with all these tales of witches' progresses, dancing, riding,
transformations, operations, etc., to the force of imagination,[2]
and the devil's illusions.[3] The like effects almost are to be
seen in such as are awake: how many chimeras, antics, golden
mountains, and castles in the air do they build unto themselves!
I appeal to painters, mechanicians, mathematicians. Some
ascribe all vices to a false and corrupt imagination, anger,
revenge, lust, ambition, covetousness, which prefers falsehood
before that which is right and good, deluding the soul with
false shows and suppositions. Bernardus Penottus [4] will have
heresy and superstition to proceed from this fountain; as he
falsely imagineth, so he believeth; and as he conceiveth of it, so
it must be, and it shall be, *contra gentes* [against the world], he
will have it so. But most especially in passions and affections
it shows strange and evident effects: what will not a fearful
man conceive in the dark? what strange forms of bugbears,
devils, witches, goblins? Lavater imputes the greatest cause
of spectrums, and the like apparitions, to fear, which above all
other passions begets the strongest imagination (saith Wierus [5])
and so likewise love, sorrow, joy, etc. Some die suddenly, as
she that saw her son come from the battle at Cannæ, etc. Jacob
the patriarch, by force of imagination, made peckled lambs,
laying peckled rods before his sheep. Persina, that Ethiopian
queen in Heliodorus, by seeing the picture of Perseus and
Andromeda, instead of a blackamoor, was brought to bed of a
fair, white child. In imitation of whom, belike, an hard-favoured
fellow in Greece, because he and his wife were both deformed
to get a good brood of children, *elegantissimas imagines in
thalamo collocavit*, etc., hung the fairest pictures he could buy
for money in his chamber, "that his wife, by frequent sight of
them, might conceive and bear such children." And if we may
believe Bale, one of Pope Nicholas the Third's concubines, by
seeing of a bear, was brought to bed of a monster.[6] "If a

woman" (saith Lemnius), "at the time of her conception think of
another man present or absent, the child will be like him." [1]
Great-bellied women, when they long, yield prodigious examples
in this kind, as moles, warts, scars, harelips, monsters, especially
caused in their children by force of a depraved phantasy in them.
Ipsam speciem quam animo effigiat, fœtui inducit: she imprints
that stamp upon her child which she conceives unto herself.[2]
And therefore, Lodovicus Vives, *lib. 2 de Christ. fem.*, gives a
special caution to great-bellied women, "that they do not admit
such absurd conceits and cogitations, but by all means avoid
those horrible objects, heard or seen, or filthy spectacles." [3]
Some will laugh, weep, sigh, groan, blush, tremble, sweat, at
such things as are suggested unto them by their imagination.
Avicenna speaks of one that could cast himself into a palsy when
he list; and some can imitate the tunes of birds and beasts, that
they can hardly be discerned. Dagobertus' and St. Francis'
scars and wounds, like those of Christ's (if at the least any such
were), Agrippa supposeth to have happened by force of imagination:[4] that some are turned to wolves, from men to women,
and women again to men (which is constantly believed) to the
same imagination; or from men to asses, dogs, or any other
shapes. Wierus[5] ascribes all those famous transformations to
imagination; that in hydrophobia they seem to see the picture
of a dog still in their water, that melancholy men and sick men
conceive so many phantastical visions, apparitions to themselves,
and have such absurd suppositions, as that they are kings, lords,
cocks, bears, apes, owls;[6] that they are heavy, light, trans-
parent, great and little, senseless and dead (as shall be showed
more at large in our section of symptoms[7]), can be imputed
to naught else but to a corrupt, false, and violent imagination.
It works not in sick and melancholy men only, but even most
forcibly sometimes in such as are sound: it makes them suddenly
sick, and alters their temperature in an instant.[8] And sometimes a strong conceit or apprehension, as Valesius proves, will
take away diseases:[9] in both kinds it will produce real effects.
Men, if they see but another man tremble, giddy, or sick of
some fearful disease, their apprehension and fear is so strong
in this kind that they will have the same disease. Or if by
some soothsayer, wise man, fortune-teller, or physician they be
told they shall have such a disease, they will so seriously apprehend it that they will instantly labour of it. A thing familiar
in China (saith Riccius the Jesuit): "If it be told them they
shall be sick on such a day, when that day comes they will

surely be sick, and will be so terribly afflicted that sometime they die upon it." [1] Dr. Cotta, in his Discovery of Ignoran Practitioners of Physic, *cap.* 8, hath two strange stories to thi purpose, what fancy is able to do: the one of a parson's wif in Northamptonshire, *anno* 1607, that, coming to a physiciar and told by him that she was troubled with the sciatica, as h conjectured (a disease she was free from), the same night afte her return, upon his words, fell into a grievous fit of a sciatica and such another example he hath of another goodwife, that wa so troubled with the cramp, after the same manner she came b it, because her physician did but name it. Sometimes deat itself is caused by force of phantasy. I have heard of one tha coming by chance in company of him that was thought to b sick of the plague (which was not so), fell down suddenly dead Another was sick of the plague with conceit. One, seeing hi fellow let blood, falls down in a swoon. Another (saith Carda out of Aristotle) fell down dead (which is familiar to women a any ghastly sight), seeing but a man hanged. [2] A Jew i France (saith Lodovicus Vives) came by chance over a dan gerous passage or plank that lay over a brook, in the dar without harm, the next day, perceiving what danger he was ir fell down dead. [3] Many will not believe such stories to be tru but laugh commonly, and deride when they hear of them; bu let these men consider with themselves, as Peter Byarus illu trates it, [4] if they were set to walk upon a plank on high, the would be giddy, upon which they dare securely walk upon th ground. Many (saith Agrippa), "strong-hearted men otherwis tremble at such sights, dazzle, and are sick, if they look but dow from a high place, and what moves them but conceit?" [5] A some are so molested by phantasy; so some again, by fancy alon and a good conceit, are as easily recovered. We see common the toothache, gout, falling sickness, biting of a mad dog, an many such maladies cured by spells, words, characters, an charms, and many green wounds by that now so much use *unguentum armarium* [weapon-salve] magnetically cured, whic Crollius and Goclenius in a book of late hath defended, Libavius a just tract as stiffly contradicts, and most men controvert. A the world knows there is no virtue in such charms or cures, but strong conceit and opinion alone, as Pomponatius holds, "whic forceth a motion of the humours, spirits, and blood, whic takes away the cause of the malady from the parts affected." The like we may say of our magical effects, superstitious cure and such as are done by mountebanks and wizards. "As b wicked incredulity many men are hurt" (so saith Wierus of charms, spells, etc.), "we find in our experience, by the same means many are relieved." [1]   An empiric oftentimes, and a silly chirurgeon, doth more strange cures than a rational physician. Nymannus gives a reason, because the patient puts his confidence in him, which Avicenna prefers before art, precepts, and all remedies whatsoever.[2] 'Tis opinion alone (saith Cardan) that makes or mars physicians,[3] and he doth the best cures, according to Hippocrates, in whom most trust. So diversely doth this phantasy of ours affect, turn, and wind, so imperiously command our bodies, which "as another Proteus, or a chameleon, can take all shapes; and is of such force" (as Ficinus adds), "that it can work upon others as well as ourselves." [4] How can otherwise blear eyes in one man cause the like affection in another? Why doth one man's yawning make another yawn? [5] one man's pissing provoke a second many times to do the like? Why doth scraping of trenchers offend a third, or racking of files? Why doth a carcass bleed when the murderer is brought before it, some weeks after the murder hath been done? Why do witches and old women fascinate and bewitch children? but as Wierus, Paracelsus, Cardan, Mizaldus, Valeriola, Cæsar Vaninus, Campanella, and many philosophers think, the forcible imagination of the one party moves and alters the spirits of the other. Nay more, they can cause and cure not only diseases, maladies, and several infirmities by this means, as Avicenna, *de anim. lib.* 4, *sect.* 4, supposeth, in parties remote, but move bodies from their places, cause thunder, lightning, tempests, which opinion Alkindus, Paracelsus, and some others approve of. So that I may certainly conclude this strong conceit or imagination is *astrum hominis* [a man's guiding star], and the rudder of this our ship, which reason should steer, but, overborne by phantasy, cannot manage, and so suffers itself and this whole vessel of ours to be overruled, and often overturned. Read more of this in Wierus, *lib.* 3 *de lamiis, cap.* 8, 9, 10; Franciscus Valesius, *Med. controv, lib.* 5, *cont.* 6; Marcellus Donatus, *lib.* 2, *cap.* 1, *de hist. med. mirabil.*; Levinus Lemnius, *de occult. nat. mir. lib.* 1, *cap.* 12; Cardan, *lib.* 18 *de rerum var.*; Corn. Agrippa, *de occult. philos. cap.* 64, 65; Camerarius, *cent.* 1, *cap.* 54, *Horarum subcis.*; Nymannus, *in orat. de mag.*; Laurentius; and him that is *instar omnium* [the pick of the bunch], Fienus, a famous physician of Antwerp, that wrote three books *de viribus imaginationis* [on the force of imagination]. I have thus far digressed, because this imagination is

the *medium deferens* [instrument] of passions, by whose means
they work and produce many times prodigious effects: and
as the phantasy is more or less intended or remitted, and their
humours disposed, so do perturbations move, more or less, and
take deeper impression.

SUBSECT. III.—*Division of Perturbations*

Perturbations and passions which trouble the phantasy,
though they dwell between the confines of sense and reason,
yet they rather follow sense than reason, because they are
drowned in corporeal organs of sense. They are commonly
reduced into two inclinations, irascible and concupiscible.[1] The
Thomists subdivide them into eleven, six in the coveting, and
five in the invading. Aristotle reduceth all to pleasure and
pain, Plato to love and hatred, Vives[2] to good and bad. If
good, it is present, and then we absolutely joy and love; or to
come, and then we desire and hope for it. If evil, we absolutely
hate it; if present, it is sorrow; if to come, fear. These four
passions Bernard compares to the wheels of a chariot, by which
we are carried in this world.[3] All other passions are subordinate unto these four, or six, as some will: love, joy, desire,
hatred, sorrow, fear; the rest, as anger, envy, emulation, pride,
jealousy, anxiety, mercy, shame, discontent, despair, ambition,
avarice, etc., are reducible unto the first; and if they be immoderate, they consume the spirits, and melancholy is especially
caused by them.[4] Some few discreet men there are, that can
govern themselves, and curb in these inordinate affections, by
religion, philosophy, and such divine precepts, of meekness,
patience, and the like; but most part, for want of government,
out of indiscretion, ignorance, they suffer themselves wholly to
be led by sense, and are so far from repressing rebellious inclinations, that they give all encouragement unto them, leaving
the reins, and using all provocations to further them: bad by
nature, worse by art, discipline, custom, education, and a
perverse will of their own, they follow on, wheresoever their
unbridled affections will transport them, and do more out of
custom, self-will, than out of reason.[5] *Contumax voluntas*, as
Melancthon calls it, *malum facit:* this stubborn will of ours
perverts judgment, which sees and knows what should and
ought to be done, and yet will not do it. *Mancipia gulæ*, slaves
to their several lusts and appetite, they precipitate and plunge

themselves into a labyrinth of cares, blinded with lust, blinded with ambition;[1] "They seek that at God's hands which they may give unto themselves, if they could but refrain from those cares and perturbations wherewith they continually macerate their minds."[2] But giving way to these violent passions of fear, grief, shame, revenge, hatred, malice, etc., they are torn in pieces, as Actæon was with his dogs, and crucify their own souls.[3]

SUBSECT. IV.—*Sorrow a Cause of Melancholy*

In this catalogue of passions which so much torment the soul of man and cause this malady (for I will briefly speak of them all, and in their order), the first place in this irascible appetite may justly be challenged by sorrow; an inseparable companion, "the mother and daughter of melancholy, her epitome, symptom, and chief cause"; as Hippocrates hath it, they beget one another, and tread in a ring, for sorrow is both cause and symptom of this disease.[4] How it is a symptom shall be showed in his place. That it is a cause all the world acknowledgeth; *Dolor nonnullis insaniæ causa fuit, et aliorum morborum insanabilium,* saith Plutarch to Apollonius; a cause of madness, a cause of many other diseases, a sole cause of this mischief, Lemnius calls it.[5] So doth Rhasis, *Cont. lib.* 1, *tract.* 9; Guianerius, *tract.* 15, *cap.* 5. And if it take root once, it ends in despair, as Felix Plater observes,[6] and as in Cebes' Table,[7] may well be coupled with it. Chrysostom, in his seventeenth epistle to Olympia, describes it to be "a cruel torture of the soul, a most inexplicable grief, poisoned worm, consuming body and soul and gnawing the very heart, a perpetual executioner, continual night, profound darkness, a whirlwind, a tempest, an ague not appearing, heating worse than any fire, and a battle that hath no end. It crucifies worse than any tyrant; no torture, no strappado, no bodily punishment is like unto it."[8] 'Tis the eagle without question which the poets feigned to gnaw Prometheus' heart,[9] and "no heaviness is like unto the heaviness of the heart" (Ecclus. xxxviii, 18). "Every perturbation is a misery, but grief a cruel torment,"[10] a domineering passion: as in old Rome, when the Dictator was created, all inferior magistracies ceased; when grief appears, all other passions vanish. "It dries up the bones," saith Solomon (Prov. xvii), makes them hollow-eyed, pale, and lean, furrow-faced, to have dead looks, wrinkled brows, rivelled cheeks, dry bodies,

and quite perverts their temperature that are misaffected with
it. As Elenora, that exiled mournful duchess (in our English
Ovid[1]), laments to her noble husband, Humphrey, Duke of
Gloucester:

> Sawest thou those eyes in whose sweet cheerful look
> Duke Humphry once such joy and pleasure took,
> Sorrow hath so despoil'd me of all grace,
> Thou couldst not say, This was my El'nor's face.
> Like a foul Gorgon, etc.

It hinders concoction, refrigerates the heart, takes away
stomach, colour, and sleep;[2] thickens the blood (Fernelius
lib. 1, *cap.* 18, *de morb. causis*);[3] contaminates the spirits
(Piso);[4] overthrows the natural heat, perverts the good estate of
body and mind, and makes them weary of their lives, cry out,
howl and roar for the very anguish of their souls. David confessed as much, Psalm xxxviii, 8: "I have roared for the very
disquietness of my heart." And Psalm cxix, part 4, v. 4: "My
soul melteth away for very heaviness"; v. 38: "I am like a
bottle in the smoke." Antiochus complained that he could
not sleep, and that his heart fainted for grief; Christ Himself,
vir dolorum [a man of sorrows], out of an apprehension of
grief, did sweat blood;[5] Mark xiv: "His soul was heavy to the
death, and no sorrow was like unto his." Crato, *consil.* 21, *lib.* 2
gives instance in one that was so melancholy by reason of grief;
and Montanus, *consil.* 30, in a noble matron, "that had no other
cause of this mischief."[7] I. S. D., in Hildesheim, fully cured
a patient of his that was much troubled with melancholy, and
for many years, "but afterwards, by a little occasion of sorrow
he fell into his former fits, and was tormented as before."
Examples are common, how it causeth melancholy, desperation,
and sometimes death itself;[9] for (Ecclus. xxxviii, 18) "Of
heaviness comes death." "Worldly sorrow causeth death" (2 Cor.
vii, 10); Psalm xxxi, 10: "My life is wasted with heaviness, and
my years with mourning." Why was Hecuba said to be turned
to a dog? Niobe into a stone? but that for grief she was
senseless and stupid. Severus the emperor died for grief;
and how many myriads besides![11] *Tanta illi est feritas, tanta
est insania luctus* [such wildness, such madness, is there in
grief]. Melancthon gives a reason of it, "the gathering of much
melancholy blood about the heart, which collection extinguisheth
the good spirits, or at least dulleth them; sorrow strikes the
heart, makes it tremble and pine away, with great pain; and
the black blood drawn from the spleen, and diffused under the

ribs on the left side, makes those perilous hypochondriacal convulsions which happen to them that are troubled with sorrow." [1]

SUBSECT. V.—*Fear a Cause*

Cousin-german to sorrow is fear, or rather a sister, *fidus Achates* [trusty squire], and continual companion, an assistant and a principal agent in procuring of this mischief; a cause and symptom as the other. In a word, as Virgil of the Harpies,[2] I may justly say of them both:

> *Tristius haud illis monstrum, nec sævior ulla*
> *Pestis et ira deum Stygiis sese extulit undis.*

A sadder monster, or more cruel plague so fell,
Or vengeance of the gods, ne'er came from Styx or hell.

This foul fiend of fear was worshipped heretofore as a god by the Lacedæmonians, and most of those other torturing affections,[3] and so was sorrow amongst the rest, under the name of Angerona Dea; they stood in such awe of them, as Austin, *de Civitat. Dei, lib.* 4, *cap.* 8, noteth out of Varro. Fear was commonly adored and painted in their temples with a lion's head;[4] and as Macrobius records, 1, 10 *Saturnalium*: "In the calends of January, Angerona had her holy day, to whom in the temple of Volupia, or goddess of pleasure, their augurs and bishops did yearly sacrifice; that, being propitious to them, she might expel all cares, anguish, and vexation of the mind for the year following."[5] Many lamentable effects this fear causeth in men, as to be red, pale, tremble, sweat; it makes sudden cold and heat to come over all the body, palpitation of the heart, syncope, etc.[6] It amazeth many men that are to speak or show themselves in public assemblies, or before some great personages; as Tully confessed of himself, that he trembled still at the beginning of his speech; and Demosthenes, that great orator of Greece, before Philippus. It confounds voice and memory, as Lucian wittily brings in Jupiter Tragœdus[7] so much afraid of his auditory, when he was to make a speech to the rest of the gods, that he could not utter a ready word, but was compelled to use Mercury's help in prompting. Many men are so amazed and astonished with fear, they know not where they are, what they say, what they do,[8] and that which is worst, it tortures them many days before with continual affrights and suspicion. It hinders most honourable attempts, and makes

their hearts ache, sad and heavy. They that live in fear are
never free, resolute, secure, never merry, but in continual
pain:[1] that, as Vives truly said, *Nulla est miseria major quam
metus*, no greater misery, no rack, nor torture like unto it; ever
suspicious, anxious, solicitous, they are childishly drooping
without reason, without judgment, "especially if some terrible
object be offered," as Plutarch hath it.[2] It causeth oftentimes sudden madness, and almost all manner of diseases, as
I have sufficiently illustrated in my digression of the Force of
Imagination,[3] and shall do more at large in my section of
Terrors.[4] Fear makes our imagination conceive what it list,
invites the devil to come to us, as Agrippa and Cardan[5] avouch,
and tyrannizeth over our phantasy more than all other affections,
especially in the dark. We see this verified in most men, as
Lavater saith,[6] *Quæ metuunt, fingunt:* what they fear they
conceive, and feign unto themselves; they think they see
goblins, hags, devils, and many times become melancholy
thereby. Cardan, *Subtil. lib.* 18, hath an example of such an
one, so caused to be melancholy (by sight of a bugbear) all his
life after. Augustus Cæsar durst not sit in the dark; *Nisi aliquo
assidente*, saith Suetonius,[7] *nunquam tenebris evigilavit* [unless
someone was with him, he never sat up in the dark]. And 'tis
strange what women and children will conceive unto themselves,
if they go over a churchyard in the night, lie or be alone in a
dark room, how they sweat and tremble on a sudden. Many
men are troubled with future events, foreknowledge of their
fortunes, destinies, as Severus the Emperor, Hadrian, and Domitian, *quod sciret ultimum vitæ diem*, saith Suetonius, *valde
sollicitus*, much tortured in mind because he foreknew his end;
with many such, of which I shall speak more opportunely in
another place.[8] Anxiety, mercy, pity, indignation, etc., and
such fearful branches derived from these two stems of fear and
sorrow, I voluntarily omit; read more of them in Carolus
Pascalius,[9] Dandinus,[10] etc.

Subsect. VI.—*Shame and Disgrace, Causes*

Shame and disgrace cause most violent passions and bitter
pangs. *Ob pudorem et dedecus publicum, ob errorem commissum,
sæpe moventur generosi animi* (Felix Plater, *lib.* 3 *de alienat.
mentis*): generous minds are often moved with shame to despair
for some public disgrace. And "he," saith Philo, *lib.* 2 *de provid
Dei*, "that subjects himself to fear, grief, ambition, shame, is

not happy, but altogether miserable, tortured with continual
labour, care, and misery." [1] It is as forcible a batterer as any
of the rest. "Many men neglect the tumults of the world, and
care not for glory,[2] and yet they are afraid of infamy, repulse,
disgrace (Tully, *Offic. lib.* 1); they can severely contemn pleasure,
bear grief indifferently, but they are quite battered and broken
with reproach and obloquy" [3] (*siquidem vita et fama pari passu
ambulant* [seeing that life goes hand in hand with repute]),
and are so dejected many times for some public injury, disgrace,
as a box on the ear by their inferior, to be overcome of their
adversary, foiled in the field, to be out in a speech, some
foul fact committed or disclosed, etc., that they dare not
come abroad all their lives after, but melancholize in corners,
and keep in holes. The most generous spirits are most subject
to it; *Spiritus altos frangit et generosos* [it breaks noble and lofty
spirits] (Hieronymus). Aristotle, because he could not understand the motion of Euripus, for grief and shame drowned
himself (Cælius Rhodiginus, *Antiquar. lec. lib.* 29, *cap.* 8). *Homerus
pudore consumptus*, [Homer] was swallowed up with this passion of
shame "because he could not unfold the fisherman's riddle." [4]
Sophocles killed himself, "for that a tragedy of his was hissed
off the stage" [5] (Valer. Max., *lib.* 9, *cap.* 12). Lucretia stabbed
herself, and so did Cleopatra, "when she saw that she was
reserved for a triumph, to avoid the infamy." [6] Antonius the
Roman, "after he was overcome of his enemy, for three days'
space sat solitary in the fore-part of the ship, abstaining from
all company, even of Cleopatra herself, and afterwards for very
shame butchered himself" [7] (Plutarch, *vita ejus*). Apollonius
Rhodius "wilfully banished himself, forsaking his country, and
all his dear friends, because he was out in reciting his poems," [8]
(Plinius, *lib.* 7, *cap.* 23). Ajax ran mad, because his arms were
adjudged to Ulysses. In China 'tis an ordinary thing for such
as are excluded in those famous trials of theirs, or should take
degrees, for shame and grief to lose their wits (Mat. Riccius,
Expedit. ad Sinas, lib. 3, *cap.* 9).[9] Hostratus the friar took that book
which Reuchlin had writ against him, under the name of *Epist.
obscurorum virorum*, so to heart, that for shame and grief he
made away himself (Jovius, *in Elogiis*).[10] A grave and learned
minister, and an ordinary preacher at Alkmaar in Holland, was
(one day as he walked in the fields for his recreation) suddenly
taken with a lask or looseness, and thereupon compelled to retire
to the next ditch; but being surprised at unawares by some
gentlewomen of his parish wandering that way, was so abashed,

that he did never after show his head in public, or come into the
pulpit, but pined away with melancholy [1] (Pet. Forestus, *Med.
observat. lib.* 10, *observat.* 12).   So shame amongst other passions
can play his prize.

I know there be many base, impudent, brazen-faced rogues,
that will *nulla pallescere culpa* [2] [feel shame for no crime], be
moved with nothing, take no infamy or disgrace to heart, laugh
at all; let them be proved perjured, stigmatized, convict rogues,
thieves, traitors, lose their ears, be whipped, branded, carted,
pointed at, hissed, reviled, and derided with Ballio the bawd
in Plautus, [3] they rejoice at it: *Cantores probos!* [bravo!],
babæ! [whe-ew!] and *bombax!* [well, I never!], what care
they?   We have too many such in our times:

> *Exclamat Melicerta perisse*
> *Frontem de rebus.* [4]

[Men, cries Melicerta, have lost the power to blush.]

Yet a modest man, one that hath grace, a generous spirit, tender
of his reputation, will be deeply wounded, and so grievously
affected with it, that he had rather give myriads of crowns,
lose his life, than suffer the least defamation of honour or blot
in his good name.   And if so be that he cannot avoid it,
as a nightingale, *quæ cantando victa moritur* (saith Mizaldus [5]),
[which] dies for shame if another bird sing better, he languisheth
and pineth away in the anguish of his spirit.

SUBSECT. VII.—*Envy, Malice, Hatred, Causes*

Envy and malice are two links of this chain, and both, as
Guianerius, *tract.* 15, *cap.* 2, proves out of Galen, 3 *Aphorism.
com.* 22, "cause this malady by themselves, especially if their
bodies be otherwise disposed to melancholy." [6]   'Tis Valescus
de Taranta and Felix Plater's' observation, "Envy so gnaws
many men's hearts, that they become altogether melancholy." [7]
And therefore belike Solomon (Prov. xiv, 13) calls it "the rotting
of the bones"; Cyprian, *vulnus occultum* [a hidden wound]:

> *Siculi non invenere tyranni*
> *Majus tormentum,* [8]

the Sicilian tyrants never invented the like torment.   It
crucifies their souls, withers their bodies, makes them hollow-
eyed, pale, lean, and ghastly to behold [9] (Cyprian, *ser.* 2, *de zelo
et livore*).   "As a moth gnaws a garment, so," saith Chrysostom,

"doth envy consume a man"; [1] to be a living anatomy, a skeleton, to be "a lean and pale carcass,[2] quickened with a fiend"[3] (Hall, in Characters); for so often as an envious wretch sees another man prosper, to be enriched, to thrive, and be fortunate in the world, to get honours, offices, or the like, he repines and grieves.

> *Intabescitque videndo*
> *Successus hominum . . . suppliciumque suum est.*[4]

> [When he beholds another doing well,
> He wastes away, he suffers tortures fell.]

He tortures himself if his equal, friend, neighbour, be preferred, commended, do well; if he understand of it, it galls him afresh; and no greater pain can come to him than to hear of another man's well-doing; 'tis a dagger at his heart, every such object. He looks at him, as they that fell down in Lucian's rock of honour, with an envious eye, and will damage himself to do another a mischief: *Atque cadet subito, dum super hoste cadat* [ready to fall at once, so on a foe he fall]. As he did in Æsop, lose one eye willingly, that his fellow might lose both, or that rich man in Quintilian[5] that poisoned the flowers in his garden, because his neighbour's bees should get no more honey from them. His whole life is sorrow, and every word he speaks a satire: nothing fats him but other men's ruins. For to speak in a word, envy is naught else but *tristitia de bonis alienis*, sorrow for other men's good, be it present, past, or to come, *et gaudium de adversis*, and joy at their harms,[6] opposite to mercy, which grieves at other men's mischances, and misaffects the body in another kind;[7] so Damascene defines it, *lib. 2 de orthod. fid.*; Thomas, 2, 2, *quæst.* 36, *art.* 1; Aristotle, *lib. 2 Rhet. cap.* 4 *et* 10; Plato, *Philebo*; Tully, 3 *Tusc.*; Greg. Nic., *lib. de virt. animæ, cap.* 12; Basil *de Invidia*; Pindarus, *Od.* 1, *ser.* 5; and we find it true. 'Tis a common disease, and almost natural to us, as Tacitus holds,[8] to envy another man's prosperity. And 'tis in most men an incurable disease. "I have read," saith Marcus Aurelius, "Greek, Hebrew, Chaldee authors, I have consulted with many wise men for a remedy for envy; I could find none, but to renounce all happiness, and to be a wretch and miserable for ever."[9] 'Tis the beginning of hell in this life, and a passion not to be excused. "Every other sin hath some pleasure annexed to it, or will admit of an excuse; envy alone wants both. Other sins last but for a while; the gut may be satisfied, anger remits, hatred hath an end, envy never ceaseth"[10] (Cardan, *lib. 2 de sap.*). Divine and human examples are very familiar;

you may run and read them, as that of Saul and David, Cain
and Abel, *Angebat illum non proprium peccatum, sed fratris
prosperitas*, saith Theodoret, it was his brother's good fortune
galled him. Rachel envied her sister, being barren (Gen. xxx);
Joseph's brethren him (Gen. xxxvii); David had a touch of this
vice, as he confesseth[1] (Ps. lxxiii); Jeremy[2] and Habbakuk,[3]
they repined at others' good, but in the end they corrected themselves. Ps. lxxv: "Fret not thyself," etc. Domitian spited
Agricola for his worth, "that a private man should be so much
glorified."[4] Cæcina was envied of his fellow-citizens, because he
was more richly adorned.[5] But of all others, women are most
weak,[6] *Ob pulchritudinem invidæ sunt feminæ* [women are jealous
of other women's beauty] (Musæus); *Aut amat, aut odit, nihil
est tertium* (Granatensis): they love or hate, no medium amongst
them. *Implacabiles plerumque læsæ mulieres* [women as a rule
never forgive an injury]. Agrippina-like, "A woman, if she see
her neighbour more neat or elegant, richer in tires, jewels, or
apparel, is enraged, and like a lioness sets upon her husband,
rails at her, scoffs at her, and cannot abide her";[7] so the
Roman ladies in Tacitus did at Salonina, Cæcina's wife, "because
she had a better horse, and better furniture, as if she had hurt
them with it; they were much offended."[8] In like sort our
gentlewomen do at their usual meetings, one repines or scoffs
at another's bravery and happiness. Myrsine, an Attic wench,
was murdered of her fellows, "because she did excel the rest in
beauty"[9] (Constantine, *Agricult. lib.* ii, *cap.* 7). Every village
will yield such examples.

Subsect. VIII.—*Emulation, Hatred, Faction, Desire of Revenge, Causes*

Out of this root of envy spring those feral branches of faction,
hatred, livor, emulation,[10] which cause the like grievances, and
are *serræ animæ*, the saws of the soul, *consternationis pleni
affectus*,[11] affections full of desperate amazement; or as Cyprian
describes emulation, it is "a moth of the soul, a consumption,
to make another man's happiness his misery, to torture, crucify,
and execute himself, to eat his own heart. Meat and drink
can do such men no good, they do always grieve, sigh, and
groan, day and night without intermission, their breast is torn
asunder":[12] and a little after, "Whosoever he is whom thou
dost emulate and envy, he may avoid thee, but thou canst
neither avoid him nor thyself; wheresoever thou art, he is with

thee, thine enemy is ever in thy breast, thy destruction is within thee, thou art a captive, bound hand and foot, as long as thou art malicious and envious, and canst not be comforted. It was the devil's overthrow"; [1] and whensoever thou art throughly affected with this passion, it will be thine. Yet no perturbation so frequent, no passion so common.

> Καὶ κεραμεὺς κεραμεῖ κοτέει, καὶ τέκτονι τέκτων,
> Καὶ πτωχὸς πτωχῷ φθονέει, καὶ ἀοιδὸς ἀοιδῷ. [2]

> A potter emulates a potter;
>   One smith envies another:
> A beggar emulates a beggar;
>   A singing-man his brother.

Every society, corporation, and private family is full of it, it takes hold almost of all sorts of men, from the prince to the ploughman, even amongst gossips it is to be seen; scarce three in a company but there is siding, faction, emulation betwixt two of them, some *simultas*, jar, private grudge, heart-burning in the midst of them. Scarce two gentlemen dwell together in the country (if they be not near kin or linked in marriage), but there is emulation betwixt them and their servants, some quarrel or some grudge betwixt their wives or children, friends and followers, some contention about wealth, gentry, precedency, etc., by means of which, like the frog in Æsop, "that would swell till she was as big as an ox, burst herself at last," [3] they will stretch beyond their fortunes, callings, and strive so long that they consume their substance in lawsuits, or otherwise in hospitality, feasting, fine clothes, to get a few bombast titles, for *ambitiosa paupertate laboramus omnes* [though poor, we all kill ourselves to make a show]; to outbrave one another, they will tire their bodies, macerate their souls, and through contentions or mutual invitations beggar themselves. Scarce two great scholars in an age, but with bitter invectives they fall foul one on the other, and their adherents; Scotists, Thomists, Reals, Nominals, Plato and Aristotle, Galenists and Paracelsians, etc., it holds in all professions.

Honest emulation in studies, in all callings, is not to be disliked,[4] 'tis *ingeniorum cos*, as one calls it, the whetstone of wit, the nurse of wit and valour, and those noble Romans out of this spirit did brave exploits. There is a modest ambition, as Themistocles was roused up with the glory of Miltiades, Achilles' trophies moved Alexander.

> *Ambire semper stulta confidentia est,*
> *Ambire nunquam deses arrogantia est.*[5]

[With all in all things constantly to vie
  Shows foolish overweening confidence.
But for advancement never once to try
  Shows slothful self-conceit and arrogance.]

'Tis a sluggish humour not to emulate or to sue at all, to withdraw himself, neglect, refrain from such places, honours, offices,
through sloth, niggardliness, fear, bashfulness, or otherwise, to
which by his birth, place, fortunes, education, he is called, apt,
fit, and well able to undergo; but when it is immoderate, it is
a plague and a miserable pain. What a deal of money did
Henry VIII and Francis I, King of France, spend at that
famous interview![1] and how many vain courtiers, seeking
each to outbrave other, spent themselves, their livelihood and
fortunes, and died beggars! Hadrian the emperor was so galled
with it that he killed all his equals;[2] so did Nero. This passion
made Dionysius the tyrant banish Plato and Philoxenus the
poet, because they did excel and eclipse his glory, as he thought;[3]
the Romans exile Coriolanus, confine Camillus, murder Scipio;
the Greeks by ostracism to expel Aristides, Nicias, Alcibiades,
imprison Theseus, make away Phocion, etc. When Richard I
and Philip of France were fellow-soldiers together at the siege
of Acre in the Holy Land, and Richard had approved himself
to be the more valiant man, insomuch that all men's eyes were
upon him, it so galled Philip (*Francum urebat regis victoria*,
saith mine author,[4] *tam ægre ferebat Richardi gloriam, ut carpere
dicta, calumniari facta*), that he cavilled at all his proceedings,
and fell at length to open defiance; he could contain no longer,
but hasting home, invaded his territories and professed open
war. "Hatred stirs up contention" (Prov. x, 12), and they
break out at last into immortal enmity, into virulency, and
more than Vatinian hate[5] and rage; they persecute each other,
their friends, followers, and all their posterity, with bitter
taunts, hostile wars, scurrile invectives, libels, calumnies, fire,
sword, and the like, and will not be reconciled.[6] Witness that
Guelph and Ghibelline faction in Italy; that of the Adurni and
Fregosi in Genoa; that of Cnæus Papirius and Quintus Fabius
in Rome; Cæsar and Pompey; Orleans and Burgundy in France;
York and Lancaster in England: yea, this passion so rageth
many times, that it subverts not men only, and families, but
even populous cities; Carthage[7] and Corinth can witness as
much; nay, flourishing kingdoms are brought into a wilderness
by it.[8] This hatred, malice, faction, and desire of revenge,
invented first all those racks and wheels, strappadoes, brazen

bulls, feral engines, prisons, inquisitions, severe laws to macerate and torment one another. How happy might we be, and end our time with blessed days and sweet content, if we could contain ourselves, and, as we ought to do, put up injuries, learn humility, meekness, patience, forget and forgive, as in God's Word we are enjoined,[1] compose such small controversies amongst ourselves, moderate our passions in this kind, "and think better of others," as Paul would have us,[2] "than of ourselves: be of like affection one towards another, and not avenge ourselves, but have peace with all men." But being that we are so peevish and perverse, insolent and proud, so factious and seditious, so malicious and envious, we do *invicem angariare* [by turns constrain], maul and vex one another, torture, disquiet, and precipitate ourselves into that gulf of woes and cares, aggravate our misery and melancholy, heap upon us hell and eternal damnation.

SUBSECT. IX.—*Anger a Cause*

Anger, a perturbation, which carries the spirits outwards, preparing the body to melancholy, and madness itself: *Ira furor brevis est* [anger is temporary madness], and, as Piccolomineus accounts it,[3] one of the three most violent passions. Aretæus sets it down for an especial cause (so doth Seneca, *p.* 18, *lib.* 1) of this malady.[4] Magninus gives the reason, *Ex frequenti ira supra modum calefiunt*,[5] it overheats their bodies, and if it be too frequent, it breaks out into manifest madness, saith St. Ambrose. 'Tis a known saying, *Furor fit læsa sæpius patientia*, the most patient spirit that is, if he be often provoked, will be incensed to madness; it will make a devil of a saint: and therefore Basil (belike) in his homily *de Ira*, calls it *tenebras rationis, morbum animæ, et dæmonem pessimum*, the darkening of our understanding, and a bad angel. Lucian, *in Abdicato, tom.* 1,[6] will have this passion to work this effect, especially in old men and women. "Anger and calumny" saith he) "trouble them at first, and after a while break out into madness: many things cause fury in women, especially if they love or hate overmuch, or envy, be much grieved or angry; these things by little and little lead them on to this malady." From a disposition they proceed to an habit, for there is no difference between a madman and an angry man in the time of his fit; anger, as Lactantius describes it, *lib. de Ira Dei, ad Donatum, cap.* 5, is *sæva animi tempestas*, etc.,[7] a cruel tempest

of the mind, "making his eyes sparkle fire, and stare, teeth
gnash in his head, his tongue stutter, his face pale or red, and
what more filthy imitation can be of a madman?"

> *Ora tument ira, fervescunt sanguine venæ,*
> *Lumina Gorgonio sævius angue micant.*[1]

[Their faces swell, their blood boils up with ire,
Their eyes flash savagely with Gorgon fire.]

They are void of reason, inexorable, blind, like beasts and
monsters for the time, say and do they know not what, curse
swear, rail, fight, and what not?   How can a madman do
more? as he said in the comedy, *Iracundia non sum apud me,*
I am not mine own man [for anger]. If these fits be immoderate
continue long, or be frequent, without doubt they provoke mad
ness. Montanus, *consil.* 21, had a melancholy Jew to his patient; he
ascribes this for a principal cause: *Irascebatur levibus de causis*
he was easily moved to anger.   Ajax had no other beginning
of his madness; and Charles the Sixth, that lunatic French
king, fell into this misery, out of the extremity of his passion
desire of revenge and malice; incensed against the Duke of
Britain,[3] he could neither eat, drink, nor sleep for some day
together, and in the end, about the Calends of July, 1392, he
became mad upon his horseback, drawing his sword, striking
such as came near him promiscuously, and so continued all the
days of his life (Æmilius, *lib.* 10 *Gal. hist.*).   Hegesippus, *de excid
urbis Hieros. lib.* 1, *cap.* 37, hath such a story of Herod, that ou
of an angry fit became mad; leaping out of his bed, he killed
Josippus, and played many such bedlam pranks; the whole
court could not rule him for a long time after:[4] sometimes he wa
sorry and repented, much grieved for that he had done, *post
quam deferbuit ira* [when his rage had cooled down], by and
by outrageous again.   In hot choleric bodies, nothing so soon
causeth madness as this passion of anger, besides many other
diseases, as Pelezius observes, *cap.* 21, *lib.* 1, *de hum. affect. causis
Sanguinem imminuit, fel auget* [it diminishes blood, it increase
bile], and, as Valesius controverts, *Med. controv. lib.* 5, *contro.* 8,
many times kills them quite out.   If this were the worst of
this passion, it were more tolerable, "but it ruins and subvert
whole towns, cities,[6] families and kingdoms."[7] *Nulla pesti
humano generi pluris stetit*, saith Seneca, *de Ira, lib.* 1, n
plague hath done mankind so much harm.   Look into ou
histories, and you shall almost meet with no other subjec
but what a company of hare-brains have done in their rage.

Ve may do well therefore to put this in our procession amongst he rest: "From all blindness of heart, from pride, vainglory, nd hypocrisy, from envy, hatred, and malice, anger, and all uch pestiferous perturbations, good Lord, deliver us."

SUBSECT. X.—*Discontents, Cares, Miseries, etc., Causes*

Discontents, cares, crosses, miseries, or whatsoever it is that hall cause any molestation of spirits, grief, anguish, and per- lexity, may well be reduced to this head; preposterously placed ere in some men's judgments they may seem, yet in that ristotle in his Rhetoric[1] defines these cares, as he doth envy, mulation, etc., still by grief, I think I may well rank them in his irascible row; being that they are as the rest, both causes nd symptoms of this disease, producing the like inconveniences, nd are most part accompanied with anguish and pain. The ommon etymology will evince it, *cura quasi cor uro* [*cura* :are)=*cor uro* (I burn my heart)]; *dementes curæ, insomnes curæ, mnosæ curæ, tristes, mordaces, carnifices* etc., biting, eating, nawing, cruel, bitter, sick, sad, unquiet, pale, tetric, miserable, tolerable cares, as the poets call them,[2] worldly cares, and are s many in number as the sea sands. Galen,[3] Fernelius, Felix later, Valescus de Taranta, etc., reckon afflictions, miseries, ven all these contentions and vexations of the mind, as princi- al causes, in that they take away sleep, hinder concoction, dry p the body, and consume the substance of it. They are not) many in number, but their causes be as diverse, and not ne of a thousand free from them, or that can vindicate himself, hom that *Ate dea,*

> *Per hominum capita molliter ambulans,*
> *Plantas pedum teneras habens :* [4]

> Over men's heads walking aloft,
> With tender feet treading so soft:

omer's Goddess Ate, hath not involved into this discontented ink, or plagued with some misery or other.[5] Hyginus, *Fab.* 220,) this purpose hath a pleasant tale. Dame Cura [Care] by iance went over a brook, and taking up some of the irty slime, made an image of it; Jupiter, eftsoons coming by, it life to it, but Cura and Jupiter could not agree what ame to give him, or who should own him. The matter was eferred to Saturn as judge; he gave this arbitrament: His ame shall be *Homo* [Man], *ab humo* [from *humus* (earth)],

Cura eum possideat quamdiu vivat, Care shall have him whilst he lives, Jupiter his soul, and Tellus [Earth] his body when he dies. But to leave tales. A general cause, a continuate cause, an inseparable accident to all men, is discontent, care, misery; were there no other particular affliction (which who is free from?) to molest a man in this life, the very cogitation of that common misery were enough to macerate, and make him weary of his life; to think that he can never be secure, but still in danger, sorrow, grief, and persecution. For to begin at the hour of his birth, as Pliny doth elegantly describe it,[1] "he is born naked, and falls a-whining at the very first,[2] he is swaddled and bound up like a prisoner, cannot help himself, and so he continues to his life's end"; *cujusque feræ pabulum* [a prey to every wild beast], saith Seneca,[3] impatient of heat and cold, impatient of labour, impatient of idleness, exposed to fortune's contumelies. To a naked mariner Lucretius compares him, cast on shore by shipwreck, cold and comfortless in an unknown land. No estate, age, sex, can secure himself from this common misery.[4] "A man that is born of a woman is of short continuance, and full of trouble" (Job xiv, 1). "And while his flesh is upon him he shall be sorrowful, and while his soul is in him it shall mourn" (v. 22). "All his days are sorrow and his travails griefs: his heart also taketh not rest in the night" (Eccles. ii, 23); and (ii, 11), "All that is in it is sorrow and vexation of spirit." "Ingress, progress, regress, egress, much alike; blindness seizeth on us in the beginning, labour in the middle, grief in the end, error in all. What day ariseth to us without some grief, care, or anguish? Or what so secure and pleasing a morning have we seen, that hath not been overcast before evening?"[5] One is miserable, another ridiculous, a third odious. One complains of this grievance, another of that. *Aliquando nervi, aliquando pedes vexant* (Seneca), *nunc distillatio, nunc hepatis morbus; nunc deest, nunc superest sanguis* [sometimes his sinews, sometimes his feet trouble him; now it is a catarrh, now liver complaint; sometimes he has too much blood, sometimes too little]; now the head aches, then the feet, now the lungs, then the liver, etc. *Huic census exuberat, sed est pudor degener sanguis,* etc.; he is rich, but base-born; he is noble, but poor; a third hath means, but he wants health peradventure, or wit to manage his estate; children vex one, wife a second, etc. *Nemo facile cum conditione sua concordat,* no man is pleased with his fortune, a pound of sorrow is familiarly mixed with a dram of content, little or no joy, little comfort, but

everywhere danger, contention, anxiety, in all places; [1] go where
thou wilt, and thou shalt find discontents, cares, woes, complaints, sickness, diseases, encumbrances, exclamations. "If thou
look into the market, there" (saith Chrysostom [2]) "is brawling
and contention; if to the court, there knavery and flattery, etc.;
if to a private man's house, there's cark and care, heaviness,
etc." As he said of old, *Nil homine in terra spirat miserum
magis alma:* [3] no creature so miserable as man, so generally
molested, "in miseries of body, in miseries of mind, miseries
of heart, in miseries asleep, in miseries awake, in miseries wheresoever he turns," [4] as Bernard found. *Numquid tentatio est vita
humana super terram?* A mere temptation is our life (Austin,
Confess., lib. 10, *cap.* 28), *catena perpetuorum malorum* [a chain
of perpetual ills]; *et quis potet molestias et difficultates pati?*
who can endure the miseries of it? "In prosperity we are
insolent and intolerable, dejected in adversity, in all fortunes
foolish and miserable. [5] In adversity I wish for prosperity, and
in prosperity I am afraid of adversity. What mediocrity may
be found? Where is no temptation? What condition of life
is free?" [6] "Wisdom hath labour annexed to it, glory envy; riches
and cares, children and encumbrances, pleasure and diseases,
rest and beggary, go together: as if a man were therefore born
(as the Platonists hold) to be punished in this life for some
precedent sins." [7] Or that, as Pliny complains, "Nature may
be rather accounted a stepmother than a mother unto us, all
things considered: no creature's life so brittle, so full of fear,
so mad, so furious; only man is plagued with envy, discontent,
griefs, covetousness, ambition, superstition." [8] Our whole life
is an Irish Sea, wherein there is naught to be expected but
tempestuous storms and troublesome waves, and those infinite:

> *Tantum malorum pelagus aspicio,*
> *Ut non sit inde enatandi copia;* [9]

[I behold a sea of ills so vast that to swim clear seems
impossible;]

no halcyonian times, wherein a man can hold himself secure, or
free with his present estate; but, as Boethius infers, "There
is something in every one of us which before trial we seek, and
having tried abhor: [10] we earnestly wish, and eagerly covet,
and are eftsoons weary of it." [11] Thus betwixt hope and fear,
suspicions, angers, *Inter spemque metumque, timores inter et iras,* [12]
betwixt falling in, falling out, etc., we bangle away our best
days, befool out our times, we lead a contentious, discontent,

tumultuous, melancholy, miserable life; insomuch, that if w
could foretell what was to come, and it put to our choice, w
should rather refuse than accept of this painful life. In a word
the world itself is a maze, a labyrinth of errors, a desert,
wilderness, a den of thieves, cheaters, etc., full of filthy puddle
horrid rocks, precipitiums, an ocean of adversity, an heav
yoke, wherein infirmities and calamities overtake and follo
one another, as the sea-waves; and if we scape Scylla, we fa
foul on Charybdis, and so in perpetual fear, labour, anguish
we run from one plague, one mischief, one burden to anothe
duram servientes servitutem [undergoing a hard bondage], an
you may as soon separate weight from lead, heat from fir
moistness from water, brightness from the sun, as misery, di:
content, care, calamity, danger, from a man. Our towns an
cities are but so many dwellings of human misery, "in whic
grief and sorrow " (as he[1] right well observes out of Solon
"innumerable troubles, labours of mortal men, and all manne
of vices are included, as in so many pens." Our villages a:
like mole-hills, and men as so many emmets, busy, busy stil
going to and fro, in and out, and crossing one another's pr
jects, as the lines of several sea-cards cut each other in a glob
or map. "Now light and merry," but (as one follows it[2]) "b
and by sorrowful and heavy; now hoping, then distrusting; no
patient, to-morrow crying out; now pale, then red; runnin
sitting, sweating, trembling, halting," etc. Some few among
the rest, or perhaps one of a thousand, may be *pullus Jovis* :
the world's esteem, *gallinæ filius albæ*,[3] an happy and fortuna
man, *ad invidiam felix* [prosperous enough to be envied], b
cause rich, fair, well allied, in honour and office; yet pera
venture ask himself, and he will say that of all others he is mo
miserable and unhappy.[4] A fair shoe, *Hic soccus novus, elegar*
as he said,[5] *sed nescis ubi urat*, but thou knowest not whe
it pincheth. It is not another man's opinion can make r
happy but, as Seneca well hath it, "He is a miserable wret
that doth not account himself happy; though he be soverei:
lord of a world, he is not happy if he think himself not to
so; for what availeth it what thine estate is, or seem to othe:
if thou thyself dislike it?"[6] A common humour it is of all m
to think well of other men's fortunes, and dislike their own

Cui placet alterius, sua nimirum est odio sors;[7]

[When he beholds another doing well,
He wastes away, he suffers tortures fell;]

but *Qui fit, Mæcenas*, etc.,[1] how comes it to pass, what's the cause of it? Many men are of such a perverse nature, they are well pleased with nothing (saith Theodoret[2]), "neither with riches nor poverty, they complain when they are well and when they are sick, grumble at all fortunes, prosperity and adversity; they are troubled in a cheap year, in a barren; plenty or not plenty, nothing pleaseth them, war nor peace, with children nor without." This for the most part is the humour of us all, to be discontent, miserable, and most unhappy, as we think at least; and show me him that is not so, or that ever was otherwise. Quintus Metellus his felicity is infinitely admired amongst the Romans, insomuch that, as Paterculus mentioneth of him, you can scarce find of any nation, order, age, sex, one for happiness to be compared unto him:[3] he had, in a word, *bona animi, corporis, et fortunæ*, goods of mind, body, and fortune; so had P. Mutianus Crassus.[4] Lampito, that Lacædemonian lady, was such another in Pliny's conceit, a king's wife, a king's mother, a king's daughter:[5] and all the world esteemed as much of Polycrates of Samos. The Greeks brag of their Socrates, Phocion, Aristides; the Psophidians in particular of their Aglaus, *omni vita felix, ab omni periculo immunis* [fortunate throughout life, escaping every danger] (which by the way Pausanias held impossible); the Romans of their Cato,[6] Curius, Fabricius, for their composed fortunes and retired estates, government of passions and contempt of the world: yet none of all these were happy, or free from discontent, neither Metellus, Crassus, nor Polycrates, for he died a violent death, and so did Cato; and how much evil doth Lactantius and Theodoret speak of Socrates, a weak man, and so of the rest. There is no content in this life, but as he[7] said, "All is vanity and vexation of spirit"; lame and imperfect. Hadst thou Sampson's hair, Milo's strength, Scanderbeg's arm, Solomon's wisdom, Absalom's beauty, Crœsus his wealth, *Pasetis obolum* [the obol of Pases], Cæsar's valour, Alexander's spirit, Tully's or Demosthenes' eloquence, Gyges' ring, Perseus' Pegasus and Gorgon's head, Nestor's years to come, all this would not make thee absolute, give thee content and true happiness in this life, or so continue it. Even in the midst of all our mirth, jollity, and laughter, is sorrow and grief, or if there be true happiness amongst us, 'tis but for a time:

Desinit in piscem mulier formosa superne,[8]

[A handsome maid above ends in a fish below,]

a fair morning turns to a lowering afternoon. Brutus an
Cassius, once renowned, both eminently happy, yet you sha
scarce find two (saith Paterculus) *quos fortuna maturius destituerit*
whom fortune sooner forsook. Hannibal, a conqueror all hi
life, met with his match, and was subdued at last. *Occurrit forti
qui mage fortis erit* [the strong at length meets one even stronger]
One is brought in triumph, as Cæsar into Rome, Alcibiades int
Athens, *coronis aureis donatus*, crowned, honoured, admired
by and by his statues demolished, he hissed out, massacred
etc. Magnus Gonsalvo,[1] that famous Spaniard, was of the princ
and people at first honoured, approved; forthwith confined an
banished. *Admirandas actiones graves plerumque sequuntur in
vidiæ, et acres calumniæ:* 'tis Polybius his observation; grievou
enmities and bitter calumnies commonly follow renowned ac
tions. One is born rich, dies a beggar; sound to-day, sic
to-morrow; now in most flourishing estate, fortunate and happy
by and by deprived of his goods by foreign enemies, robbed b
thieves, spoiled, captivated, impoverished, as they of Rabba
"put under iron saws, and under iron harrows, and under axe
of iron, and cast into the tile-kiln."[2]

> *Quid me felicem toties jactastis, amici,*
> *Qui cecidit, stabili non erat ille gradu.*[3]

> [My friends, why have you so often extolled me as
> happy? He that has fallen was never secure.]

He that erst marched like Xerxes with innumerable armies, a
rich as Crœsus, now shifts for himself in a poor cock-boat,
bound in iron chains with Bajazet the Turk, and a footsto
with Aurelian, for a tyrannizing conqueror to trample on. S
many casualties there are, that, as Seneca said of a city co
sumed with fire, *Una dies interest inter maximam civitatem
nullam*, one day [lies] betwixt a great city and none: so mar
grievances from outward accidents, and from ourselves, o
own indiscretion, inordinate appetite, one day betwixt a ma
and no man. And which is worse, as if discontents and miseri
would not come fast enough upon us, *homo homini dæmon* [ma
is a devil to man]; we maul, persecute, and study how to stin
gall, and vex one another with mutual hatred, abuses, injurie
preying upon and devouring as so many ravenous birds;[4] a
as jugglers, panders, bawds, cozening one another; or raging
wolves, tigers, and devils, we take a delight to torment o
another;[5] men are evil, wicked, malicious, treacherous, a
naught, not loving one another, or loving themselves, n

hospitable, charitable, nor sociable as they ought to be, but counterfeit, dissemblers, ambidexters, all for their own ends, hard-hearted, merciless, pitiless, and, to benefit themselves, they care not what mischief they procure to others.[1] Praxinoe and Gorgo in the poet,[2] when they had got in to see those costly sights, they then cried *bene est* [we are all right], and would thrust out all the rest: when they are rich themselves, in honour, preferred, full, and have even that they would, they debar others of those pleasures which youth requires, and they formerly have enjoyed. He sits at table in a soft chair at ease, but he doth not remember in the meantime that a tired waiter stands behind him, "an hungry fellow ministers to him full; he is athirst that gives him drink" (saith Epictetus [3]), "and is silent whilst he speaks his pleasure; pensive, sad, when he laughs." *Pleno se proluit auro* [he drinks from a brimming golden goblet]; he feasts, revels, and profusely spends, hath variety of robes, sweet music, ease, and all the pleasure the world can afford, whilst many an hunger-starved poor creature pines in the street, wants clothes to cover him, labours hard all day long, runs, rides for a trifle, fights peradventure from sun to sun, sick and ill, weary, full of pain and grief, is in great distress and sorrow of heart. He loathes and scorns his inferior, hates or emulates his equal, envies his superior, insults over all such as are under him, as if he were of another species, a demi-god, not subject to any fall, or human infirmities. Generally they love not, are not beloved again: they tire out others' bodies with continual labour, they themselves living at ease, caring for none else, *sibi nati* [existing only for themselves]; and are so far many times from putting to their helping hand, that they seek all means to depress, even most worthy and well-deserving, better than themselves, those whom they are by the laws of nature bound to relieve and help as much as in them lies; they will let them caterwaul, starve, beg, and hang, before they will anyways (though it be in their power) assist or ease: so unnatural are they for the most part, so unregardful; so hardhearted, so churlish, proud, insolent, so dogged, of so bad a disposition.[4] And being so brutish, so devilishly bent one towards another, how is it possible but that we should be discontent of all sides, full of cares, woes, and miseries?

If this be not a sufficient proof of their discontent and misery, examine every condition and calling apart. Kings, princes, monarchs, and magistrates seem to be most happy, but look into their estate, you shall find them to be most encumbered with cares, in perpetual fear, agony, suspicion, jealousy:[1] that, as he said of a crown, if they knew but the discontents that accompany it, they would not stoop to take it up.[2] *Quem mihi regem dabis* (saith Chrysostom) *non curis plenum?* What king canst thou show me, not full of cares? "Look not on his crown, but consider his afflictions; attend not his number of servants, but multitude of crosses."[3] *Nihil aliud potestas culminis, quam tempestas mentis*, as Gregory seconds him; sovereignty is a tempest of the soul: Sylla-like, they have brave titles, but terrible fits: *splendorem titulo, cruciatum animo;* which made Demosthenes vow,[4] *si vel ad tribunal, vel ad interitum duceretur*, if to be a judge, or to be condemned, were put to his choice, he would be condemned. Rich men are in the same predicament; what their pains are, *stulti nesciunt, ipsi sentiunt*, they feel, fools perceive not, as I shall prove elsewhere, and their wealth is brittle, like children's rattles: they come and go, there is no certainty in them: those whom they elevate, they do as suddenly depress, and leave in a vale of misery. The middle sort of men are as so many asses to bear burdens; or if they be free, and live at ease, they spend themselves, and consume their bodies and fortunes with luxury and riot, contention, emulation, etc. The poor I reserve for another place, and their discontents.[5]

For particular professions, I hold as of the rest, there's no content or security in any. On what course will you pitch, how resolve? To be a divine, 'tis contemptible in the world's esteem; to be a lawyer, 'tis to be a wrangler; to be a physician, *pudet lotii*,[6] 'tis loathed; a philosopher, a madman; an alchymist, a beggar; a poet, *esurit*, an hungry jack; a musician, a player; a schoolmaster, a drudge; an husbandman, an emmet; a merchant, his gains are uncertain; a mechanician, base; a chirurgeon, fulsome; a tradesman, a liar;[7] a tailor, a thief; a serving-man, a slave; a soldier, a butcher; a smith, or a metalman, the pot's never from 's nose; a courtier, a parasite; as he could find no tree in the wood to hang himself, I can show no state of life to give content. The like you may say of all ages; children live in a perpetual slavery, still under that tyrannical government of masters; young men, and of riper years, subject to labour and a thousand cares of the world, to treachery, falsehood, and cozenage:

> *Incedit per ignes,*
> *Suppositos cineri doloso;*[8]

> [You incautious tread
> On fires with faithless embers overspread;]

old are full of aches in their bones,[1] cramps and convulsions,
silicernia [a funeral feast], dull of hearing, weak-sighted, hoary,
wrinkled, harsh, so much altered as that they cannot know
their own face in a glass, a burden to themselves and others;
after seventy years, "all is sorrow" (as David hath it), they do
not live, but linger. If they be sound, they fear diseases; if
sick, weary of their lives: *Non est vivere, sed valere vita* [life is
no life that is not lived in health]. One complains of want, a
second of servitude, another of a secret or incurable disease; [2]
of some deformity of body, of some loss, danger, death of friends,
shipwreck, persecution, imprisonment, disgrace, repulse, con-
tumely,[3] calumny, abuse, injury, contempt, ingratitude, un-
kindness, scoffs, flouts, unfortunate marriage, single life, too
many children, no children, false servants, unhappy children,
barrenness, banishment, oppression, frustrate hopes and
ill success, etc.

> *Talia de genere hoc adeo sunt multa, loquacem ut*
> *Delassare valent Fabium:* [4]

talking Fabius will be tired before he can tell half of them;
they are the subject of whole volumes, and shall (some of them)
be more opportunely dilated elsewhere. In the meantime thus
much I may say of them, that generally they crucify the soul of
man, attenuate our bodies,[5] dry them, wither them, rivel them
up like old apples, make them as so many anatomies (*Ossa
atque pellis est totus, ita curis macet* [6] [he is nothing but skin and
bone, he is so worn with care]), they cause *tempus fœdum et
squalidum,* cumbersome days, *ingrataque tempora,* slow, dull,
and heavy times: make us howl, roar, and tear our hairs, as
Sorrow did in Cebes' Table,[7] and groan for the very anguish of
our souls. Our hearts fail us as David's did (Ps. xl, 12), "for
innumerable troubles that compassed him"; and we are ready
to confess with Hezekiah (Is. xxxviii, 17), "Behold, for felicity I
had bitter grief"; to weep with Heraclitus, to curse the day of our
birth with Jeremy (xx, 14), and our stars with Job: to hold that
axiom of Silenus, "Better never to have been born, and the best
next of all, to die quickly": [8] or if we must live, to abandon
the world, as Timon did; creep into caves and holes, as our
anchorites; cast all into the sea, as Crates Thebanus; or as
Cleombrotus Ambraciotes' four hundred auditors, precipitate
ourselves to be rid of these miseries.

SUBSECT. XI.—*Concupiscible Appetite, as Desires, Ambition, Causes*

These concupiscible and irascible appetites are as the two twists of a rope, mutually mixed one with the other, and both twining about the heart: both good, as Austin holds, *lib.* 14, *cap.* 9, *de Civ. Dei*, "if they be moderate; both pernicious if they be exorbitant." [1] This concupiscible appetite, howsoever it may seem to carry with it a show of pleasure and delight, and our concupiscences most part affect us with content and a pleasing object, yet, if they be in extremes, they rack and wring us on the other side. A true saying it is, "Desire hath no rest," is infinite in itself, endless, and, as one [2] calls it, a perpetual rack, or horse-mill,[3] according to Austin, still going round as in a ring. They are not so continual as diverse; *Facilius atomos denumerare possem*, saith Bernard,[4] *quam motus cordis; nunc hæc, nunc illa cogito*, you may as well reckon up the motes in the sun as them. "It extends itself to everything," as Guianerius will have it, "that is superfluously sought after"; [5] or to any fervent desire,[6] as Fernelius interprets it; be it in what kind soever, it tortures if immoderate, and is (according to Plater [7] and others) an especial cause of melancholy. *Multuosis concupiscentiis dilaniantur cogitationes meæ*, Austin confessed,[8] that he was torn a-pieces with his manifold desires: and so doth Bernard complain that he could not rest for them a minute of an hour: "this I would have, and that, and then I desire to be such and such." [9] 'Tis a hard matter therefore to confine them, being they are so various and many, unpossible to apprehend all. I will only insist upon some few of the chief, and most noxious in their kind, as that exorbitant appetite and desire of honour, which we commonly call ambition; love of money, which is covetousness, and that greedy desire of gain; self-love, pride, and inordinate desire of vain glory or applause; love of study in excess; love of women (which will require a just volume of itself). Of the other I will briefly speak, and in their order.

Ambition, a proud covetousness, or a dry thirst of honour, a great torture of the mind, composed of envy, pride, and covetousness, a gallant madness, one defines it a pleasant poison; Ambrose, "a canker of the soul,[10] an hidden plague"; Bernard, "a secret poison, the father of livor, and mother of hypocrisy, the moth of holiness, and cause of madness, crucifying and disquieting all that it takes hold of." [11] Seneca [12] calls it *rem sollicitam, timidam, vanam, ventosam*, a windy thing, a vain, solicitous, and fearful thing. For commonly they that, like Sisyphus, roll this restless stone of ambition, are in a perpetual agony, still perplexed,[1] *semper taciti, tristesque recedunt* [they fall back continually, silent and sorrowful] (Lucretius), doubtful, timorous, suspicious, loath to offend in word or deed, still cogging and colloguing, embracing, capping, cringing, applauding, flattering, fleering, visiting, waiting at men's doors, with all affability, counterfeit honesty, and humility.[2] If that will not serve, if once this humour (as Cyprian describes it [3]) possess his thirsty soul, *ambitionis salsugo ubi bibulam animam possidet*, by hook and by crook he will obtain it, "and from his hole he will climb to all honours and offices, if it be possible for him to get up; flattering one, bribing another, he will leave no means unassayed to win all." It is a wonder to see how slavishly these kind of men subject themselves, when they are about a suit, to every inferior person;[4] what pains they will take, run, ride, cast, plot, countermine, protest and swear, vow, promise, what labours undergo, early up, down late; how obsequious and affable they are, how popular and courteous, how they grin and fleer upon every man they meet; with what feasting and inviting, how they spend themselves and their fortunes, in seeking that, many times, which they had much better be without; as Cineas the orator told Pyrrhus:[5] with what waking nights, painful hours, anxious thoughts, and bitterness of mind, *inter spemque metumque* [oscillating between hope and fear], distracted and tired, they consume the interim of their time. There can be no greater plague for the present. If they do obtain their suit, which with such cost and solicitude they have sought, they are not so freed, their anxiety is anew to begin, for they are never satisfied, *nihil aliud nisi imperium spirant*, their thoughts, actions, endeavours are all for sovereignty and honour, like Lues Sforza, that huffing Duke of Milan, "a man of singular wisdom, but profound ambition, born to his own, and to the destruction of Italy," [6] though it be to their own ruin, and friends' undoing, they will contend, they may not cease, but as a dog in a wheel, a bird in a cage, or a squirrel in a chain (so Budæus compares them [7]), they climb and climb still, with much labour, but never make an end, never at the top.[8] A knight would be a baronet, and then a lord, and then a viscount, and then an earl, etc.; a doctor, a dean, and then a bishop; from tribune to prætor, from bailiff to mayor; first this office, and then that; as Pyrrhus in Plutarch,[9] they will first have Greece, then Africa, and then

Asia, and swell with Æsop's frog so long, till in the end
they burst, or come down with Sejanus *ad Gemonias scalas*
[to the Gemonian steps][1] and break their own necks; or as
Evangelus, the piper in Lucian, that blew his pipe so long,
till he fell down dead. If he chance to miss, and have a
canvas, he is in a hell on the other side; so dejected, that he
is ready to hang himself, turn heretic, Turk, or traitor in an
instant. Enraged against his enemies, he rails, swears, fights,
slanders, detracts, envies, murders: and for his own part, *si
appetitum explere non potest, furor corripitur:* if he cannot
satisfy his desire (as Bodine writes [2]) he runs mad.[3] So that
both ways, hit or miss, he is distracted so long as his ambition
lasts, he can look for no other but anxiety and care, discontent
and grief in the meantime, madness itself or violent death in
the end.[4] The event of this is common to be seen in populous
cities, or in princes' courts, for a courtier's life (as Budæus
describes it) "is a gallimaufry of ambition, lust, fraud, impos-
ture, dissimulation, detraction, envy, pride; the court, a common conventicle of flatterers, time-servers, politicians, etc.";[5]
or, as Anthony Perez will, [6] "the suburbs of hell itself." If you
will see such discontented persons, there you shall likely find
them. And, which he observed of the markets of old Rome:[7]

> *Qui perjurum convenire vult hominem, mitto in Comitium ;*
> *Qui mendacem et gloriosum, apud Cluacinæ sacrum ;*
> *Dites, damnosos maritos, sub Basilica quærito,* etc.,

> [If any one wants to find a perjurer, I send him to
> the Comitium; a liar or a braggart, to the shrine of
> Cluacina; rich and prodigal husbands can be found
> under the Basilica,]

perjured knaves, knights of the post, liars, crackers, bad
husbands, etc., keep their several stations; they do still, and
always did in every commonwealth.

SUBSECT. XII.—Φιλαργυρία, *Covetousness, a Cause*

Plutarch, in his book whether the diseases of the body be
more grievous than those of the soul, is of opinion, "if you will
examine all the causes of our miseries in this life, you shall find
them most part to have had their beginning from stubborn
anger, that furious desire of contention, or some unjust or
immoderate affection, as covetousness," etc.[8] "From whence

are wars and contentions amongst you?" St. James asks.[1]
I will add usury, fraud, rapine, simony, oppression, lying,
swearing, bearing false witness, etc.; are they not from this
fountain of covetousness, that greediness in getting, tenacity in
keeping, sordidity in spending? that they are so wicked, "unjust
against God, their neighbour, themselves," [2] all comes hence.
"The desire of money is the root of all evil, and they that lust
after it, pierce themselves through with many sorrows" (1 Tim.
vi, 10). Hippocrates therefore, in his Epistle to Crateva, an
herbalist, gives him this good counsel, that if it were possible,
"amongst other herbs, he should cut up that weed of covetousness by the roots, that there be no remainder left; and then
know this for a certainty, that together with their bodies thou
mayest quickly cure all the diseases of their minds." [3] For it
is indeed the pattern, image, epitome of all melancholy, the
fountain of many miseries, much discontent, care and woe;
this "inordinate, or immoderate desire of gain, to get or keep
money," as Bonaventura defines it: [4] or, as Austin describes
it, a madness of the soul; Gregory, a torture; Chrysostom,
an insatiable drunkenness; Cyprian, blindness, *speciosum
supplicium* [a splendid torment], a plague subverting kingdoms, families, an incurable disease; [5] Budæus, an ill habit,
"yielding to no remedies": [6] neither Æsculapius nor Plutus
can cure them: a continual plague, saith Solomon, and vexation
of spirit, another hell. I know there be some of opinion that
covetous men are happy and wordly-wise, that there is more
pleasure in getting of wealth than in spending, and no delight
in the world like unto it. 'Twas Bias' problem of old: "With
what art thou not weary? with getting money. What is most
delectable? to gain." [7] What is it, trow you, that makes a
poor man labour all his lifetime, carry such great burdens, fare
so hardly, macerate himself, and endure so much misery, undergo
such base offices with so great patience, to rise up early, and lie
down late, if there were not an extraordinary delight in getting
and keeping of money? What makes a merchant that hath no
need, *satis superque domi* [enough and to spare at home], to
range all over the world, through all those intemperate zones
of heat and cold; [8] voluntarily to venture his life, and be content
with such miserable famine, nasty usage, in a stinking ship; if
there were not a pleasure and hope to get money, which doth
season the rest, and mitigate his indefatigable pains? What
makes them go into the bowels of the earth, an hundred fathom
deep, endangering their dearest lives, enduring damps and filthy

smells, when they have enough already if they could be content, and no such cause to labour, but an extraordinary delight they take in riches? This may seem plausible at first show, a popular and strong argument; but let him that so thinks consider better of it, and he shall soon perceive that it is far otherwise than he supposeth; it may be haply pleasing at the first, as most part all melancholy is. For such men likely have some *lucida intervalla* [lucid intervals], pleasant symptoms intermixed; but you must note that of Chrysostom, "'Tis one thing to be rich, another to be covetous": [1] generally they are all fools, dizzards, madmen, miserable wretches, living besides themselves, *sine arte fruendi* [having no notion of enjoyment], in perpetual slavery, fear, suspicion, sorrow, and discontent; [2] *plus aloes quam mellis habent* [they have more aloes than honey], and are indeed "rather possessed by their money, than possessors," as Cyprian hath it; [3] *mancipati pecuniis*, bound prentice to their goods, as Pliny; [4] or as Chrysostom, *servi divitiarum*, slaves and drudges to their substance; and we may conclude them all, as Valerius doth of Ptolemæus, King of Cyprus, "He was in title a king of that island, but in his mind a miserable drudge of money": [5]

> *potiore metallis*
> *Libertate carens,* [6]

wanting his liberty, which is better than gold.   Damasippus the Stoic, in Horace, proves that all mortal men dote by fits, some one way, some another, but that covetous men are madder than the rest; [7] and he that shall truly look into their estates, and examine their symptoms, shall find no better of them but that they are all fools, [8] as Nabal was, *re et nomine* [by name and nature] (1 Sam. xxv). For what greater folly can there be, or madness, than to macerate himself when he need not? [9] and when, as Cyprian notes, "he may be freed from his burden and eased of his pains, will go on still, his wealth increasing, when he hath enough, to get more, to live besides himself," [10] to starve his genius, keep back from his wife and children, neither letting them nor other friends use or enjoy that which is theirs by right, and which they much need perhaps (like a hog, or dog in the manger, he doth only keep it because it shall do nobody else good, hurting himself and others), and, for a little momentary pelf, damn his own soul? [11]   They are commonly sad and tetric by nature, as Ahab's spirit was because he could not get Naboth's vineyard (1 Kings xxii), and if he lay out his money at any time, though it be to necessary uses, to his own children'

good, he brawls and scolds, his heart is heavy, much disquieted
he is, and loath to part from it: *Miser abstinet ac timet uti* [the
wretch does not touch it and is afraid to use it] (Hor.). He is
of a wearish, dry, pale constitution, and cannot sleep for cares
and worldly business; his riches, saith Solomon, will not let him
sleep, and unnecessary business which he heapeth on himself;
or if he do sleep, 'tis a very unquiet, interrupt, unpleasing
sleep, with his bags in his arms:

> *Congestis undique saccis*
> *Indormit inhians.*

[He sleeps open-mouthed upon his money-bags.]

And though he be at a banquet, or at some merry feast, "he
sighs for grief of heart" (as Cyprian hath it[1]) "and cannot sleep
though it be upon a down bed"; his wearish body takes no rest,
"troubled in his abundance, and sorrowful in plenty, unhappy
for the present, and more unhappy in the life to come"[2] (Basil).
He is a perpetual drudge, restless in his thoughts, and never
satisfied,[3] a slave, a wretch, a dust-worm, *semper quod idolo suo
immolet, sedulus observat* (Cypr., *prolog. ad sermon.*), still seeking
what sacrifice he may offer to his golden god, *per fas et nefas*,
he cares not how, his trouble is endless, *crescunt divitiæ, tamen
curtæ nescio quid semper abest rei:*[4] his wealth increaseth, and
the more he hath, the more he wants:[5] like Pharaoh's lean
kine, which devoured the fat, and were not satisfied. Austin
therefore defines covetousness,[6] *quarumlibet rerum inhonestam
et insatiabilem cupiditatem*, a dishonest and insatiable desire of
gain; and in one of his epistles compares it to hell, "which
devours all, and yet never hath enough, a bottomless pit,"[7] an
endless misery; *in quem scopulum avaritiæ cadaverosi senes
ut plurimum impingunt* [avarice is the rock on which gaunt old
men mostly come to grief], and that which is their greatest
corrosive, they are in continual suspicion, fear, and distrust.
He thinks his own wife and children are so many thieves, and
go about to cozen him, his servants are all false:

> *Rem suam periisse, seque eradicarier,*
> *Et divum atque hominum clamat continuo fidem,*
> *De suo tigillo si qua exit foras.*

> If his doors creak, then out he cries anon,
> His goods are gone, and he is quite undone.

Timidus Plutus, an old proverb, "As fearful as Plutus": so doth
Aristophanes and Lucian bring him in fearful still, pale, anxious,

suspicious, and trusting no man. "They are afraid of tempests
for their corn: they are afraid of their friends lest they should
ask something of them, beg or borrow; they are afraid of their
enemies lest they hurt them, thieves lest they rob them; they
are afraid of war and afraid of peace, afraid of rich and afraid
of poor; afraid of all." [1] Last of all, they are afraid of want,
that they shall die beggars, which makes they lay up still, and
dare not use that they have: what if a dear year come, or dearth,
or some loss? and were it not that they are loath to lay out money
on a rope, they would be hanged forthwith,[2] and sometimes die
to save charges, and make away themselves, if their corn and
cattle miscarry; though they have abundance left, as A. Gellius
notes.[3] Valerius [4] makes mention of one that in a famine sold
a mouse for two hundred pence, and famished himself: such
are their cares, griefs, and perpetual fears.[5] These symptoms
are elegantly expressed by Theophrastus in his character of a
covetous man: "Lying in bed, he asked his wife whether she shut
the trunks and chests fast, the capcase be sealed, and whether
the hall door be bolted; and though she say all is well, he riseth
out of his bed in his shirt, barefoot and bare-legged, to see whether
it be so, with a dark lanthorn searching every corner, scarce
sleeping a wink all night." [6] Lucian, in that pleasant and
witty dialogue called *Gallus*, brings in Micyllus the cobbler
disputing with his cock, sometime Pythagoras; where after
much speech pro and con, to prove the happiness of a mean
estate and discontents of a rich man, Pythagoras' cock in the
end, to illustrate by examples that which he had said, brings
him to Gnipho the usurer's house at midnight, and after that
to Eucrates; whom they found both awake, casting up their
accounts, and telling of their money, lean, dry, pale, and anxious,[7]
still suspecting lest somebody should make a hole through the
wall, and so get in; or if a rat or mouse did but stir, starting
upon a sudden, and running to the door to see whether all were
fast. Plautus, in his *Aulularia*, makes old Euclio commanding
Staphyla his wife to shut the doors fast, and the fire to be put
out, lest anybody should make that an errand to come to his
house; [8] when he washed his hands, he was loath to fling away
the foul water; complaining that he was undone, because the
smoke got out of his roof.[9] And as he went from home, seeing
a crow scrat upon the muck-hill, returned in all haste, taking
it for *malum omen*, an ill sign, his money was digged up; with
many such. He that will but observe their actions shall find
these and many such passages not feigned for sport, but really

performed, verified indeed by such covetous and miserable
wretches, and that it is

manifesta phrenesis
Ut locuples moriaris egenti vivere fato,[1]

a mere madness, to live like a wretch, and die rich.

SUBSECT. XIII.—*Love of Gaming, etc., and Pleasures Immoderate, Causes*

It is a wonder to see, how many poor, distressed, miserable
wretches one shall meet almost in every path and street, begging
for an alms, that have been well descended, and sometime in
flourishing estate, now ragged, tattered, and ready to be starved,
lingering out a painful life, in discontent and grief of body and
mind, and all through immoderate lust, gaming, pleasure, and
riot. 'Tis the common end of all sensual epicures and brutish
prodigals, that are stupefied and carried away headlong with their
several pleasures and lusts. Cebes in his Table, St. Ambrose in
his second book of Abel and Cain, and amongst the rest, Lucian,
in his tract *de Mercede conductis*, hath excellent well deciphered
such men's proceedings in his picture of Opulentia, whom he
feigns to dwell on the top of a high mount, much sought after
by many suitors; at their first coming they are generally entertained by Pleasure and Dalliance, and have all the content that
possibly may be given, so long as their money lasts: but when
their means fail, they are contemptibly thrust out at a back-
door, headlong, and there left to Shame, Reproach, Despair.
And he at first that had so many attendants, parasites, and
followers, young and lusty, richly arrayed, and all the dainty
fare that might be had, with all kind of welcome and good
respect, is now upon a sudden stript of all, pale, naked, old,
diseased, and forsaken, cursing his stars, and ready to strangle
himself; having no other company but Repentance, Sorrow, Grief,
Derision, Beggary, and Contempt, which are his daily attendants
to his life's end.[2] As the prodigal son [3] had exquisite music,
merry company, dainty fare at first, but a sorrowful reckoning
in the end; so have all such vain delights and their followers.
Tristes voluptatum exitus, et quisquis voluptatum suarum reminisci
solet, intelliget [4] [pleasures bring sadness in their train, as any
one will perceive who recalls his own pleasures], as bitter as
gall and wormwood is their last; grief of mind, madness itself.
The ordinary rocks upon which such men do impinge and precipitate themselves, are cards, dice, hawks, and hounds (*insanum*
venandi studium [the mad craze for hunting], one calls it), *insanæ*

substructiones, their mad structures, disports, plays, etc., when
they are unseasonably used, imprudently handled, and beyond
their fortunes.   Some men are consumed by mad phantastical
buildings, by making galleries, cloisters, terraces, walks, orchards,
gardens, pools, rillets, bowers, and such-like places of pleasure;
inutiles domos [useless buildings], Xenophon calls them,[1] which,
howsoever they be delightsome things in themselves, and acceptable to all beholders, an ornament, and befitting some great men,
yet unprofitable to others, and the sole overthrow of their estates.
Forestus in his Observations hath an example of such a one that
became melancholy upon the like occasion, having consumed
his substance in an unprofitable building, which would afterward yield him no advantage.   Others, I say, are overthrown
by those mad sports of hawking and hunting;[2] honest recreations, and fit for some great men, but not for every base, inferior
person; whilst they will maintain their falconers, dogs, and
hunting nags, their wealth, saith Salmuth, "runs away with
hounds, and their fortunes fly away with hawks."[3]   They
persecute beasts so long, till in the end they themselves
degenerate into beasts, as Agrippa taxeth them,[4] Actæon-like,[5]
for as he was eaten to death by his own dogs, so do they devour
themselves and their patrimonies in such idle and unnecessary
disports, neglecting in the meantime their more necessary business, and to follow their vocations.   Over-mad, too, sometimes
are our great men in delighting and doting too much on it,
"when they drive poor husbandmen from their tillage,"[6] as
Sarisburiensis objects, *Polycrat., lib.* 1, *cap.* 4,[7] "fling down
country farms and whole towns, to make parks and forests,
starving men to feed beasts, and punishing in the meantime such
a man that shall molest their game, more severely than him that
is otherwise a common hacker, or a notorious thief."[8]   But great
men are some ways to be excused, the meaner sort have no
evasion why they should not be counted mad.   Poggius the
Florentine tells a merry story to this purpose, condemning the
folly and impertinent business of such kind of persons.   A
physician of Milan, saith he, that cured madmen, had a pit of
water in his house, in which he kept his patients, some up to
the knees, some to the girdle, some to the chin, *pro modo insaniæ*,
as they were more or less affected.   One of them by chance,
that was well recovered, stood in the door, and seeing a gallant
ride by with a hawk on his fist, well mounted, with his spaniels
after him, would needs know to what use all this preparation
served; he made answer, to kill certain fowls; the patient

demanded again, what his fowl might be worth which he killed
in a year; he replied, five or ten crowns; and when he urged him
farther what his dogs, horse, and hawks stood him in, he told
him four hundred crowns; with that the patient bade begone, as
he loved his life and welfare, "for if our master come and find
thee here, he will put thee in the pit amongst madmen up to
the chin": taxing the madness and folly of such vain men that
spend themselves in those idle sports, neglecting their business
and necessary affairs. Leo Decimus, that hunting pope, is
much discommended by Jovius in his life,[1] for his immoderate
desire of hawking and hunting,[2] insomuch that (as he saith) he
would sometimes live about Ostia weeks and months together,
leave suitors unrespected, bulls and pardons unsigned, to his
own prejudice and many private men's loss. "And if he had
been by chance crossed in his sport, or his game not so good,
he was so impatient, that he would revile and miscall many
times men of great worth with most bitter taunts, look so sour,
be so angry and waspish, so grieved and molested, that it is
incredible to relate it."[3] But if he had good sport, and been
well pleased on the other side, *incredibili munificentia*, with
unspeakable bounty and munificence he would reward all his
fellow-hunters, and deny nothing to any suitor when he was in
that mood. To say truth, 'tis the common humour of all
gamesters, as Galatæus observes; if they win, no men living are
so jovial and merry, but if they lose, though it be but a trifle,
two or three games at tables, or a dealing at cards for twopence
a game, they are so choleric and testy that no man may speak
with them, and break many times into violent passions, oaths,
imprecations, and unbeseeming speeches, little differing from
madmen for the time.[4] Generally of all gamesters and gaming,
if it be excessive, thus much we may conclude, that whether
they win or lose for the present, their winnings are not *munera
fortunæ, sed insidiæ*, as that wise Seneca determines, not fortune's gifts, but baits, the common catastrophe is beggary;[5]
Ut pestis vitam, sic adimit alea pecuniam,[6] as the plague takes
away life, doth gaming goods, for *omnes nudi, inopes et egeni*[7]
they are all stripped, penniless, and in want];

> *Alea Scylla vorax, species certissima furti,*
> *Non contenta bonis, animum quoque perfida mergit,*
> *Fœda, furax, infamis, iners, furiosa, ruina.*[8]
>
> [Gaming is a whirlpool, the surest form of robbery;
>   not content with one's goods, it crushes the mind
>   as well; it is foul, thievish, infamous, slothful,
>   mad, ruinous.]

For a little pleasure they take, and some small gains and gettings now and then, their wives and children are wringed in the meantime, and they themselves with loss of body and soul rue it in the end. I will say nothing of those prodigious prodigals, *perdendæ pecuniæ genitos* [people born to waste money], as he[1] taxed Anthony, *qui patrimonium sine ulla fori calumnia amittunt* [who squander their patrimony without any public disgrace], saith Cyprian,[2] and mad sybaritical spendthrifts,[3] *quique una comedunt patrimonia cœna*, that eat up all at a breakfast, at a supper, or amongst bawds, parasites, and players, consume themselves in an instant, as if they had flung it into Tiber,[4] with great wagers, vain and idle expenses, etc., not themselves only, but even all their friends; as a man desperately swimming drowns him that comes to help him, by suretyship and borrowing they will willingly undo all their associates and allies; *irati pecuniis*, as he saith,[5] angry with their money. What with "a wanton eye, a liquorish tongue, and a gamesome hand,"[6] when they have indiscreetly impoverished themselves, mortgaged their wits together with their lands, and entombed their ancestors' fair possessions in their bowels, they may lead the rest of their days in prison, as many times they do; they repent at leisure, and when all is gone begin to be thrifty: but *sera est in fundo parsimonia*, 'tis then too late to look about; their end is misery, sorrow, shame, and discontent.[7] And well they deserve to be infamous and discontent, *catomidiari in Amphitheatro*[8] [to be thrashed in the Amphitheatre], as by Hadrian the emperor's edict they were of old, *decoctores bonorum suorum*, so he calls them, prodigal fools, to be publicly shamed and hissed out of all societies, rather than to be pitied or relieved.[9] The Tuscans and Bœotians brought their bankrupts into the marketplace in a bier with an empty purse carried before them, all the boys following, where they sat all day *circumstante plebe* [in presence of the crowd], to be infamous and ridiculous. At Padua in Italy[10] they have a stone called the stone of turpitude, near the senate house, where spendthrifts, and such as disclaim nonpayment of debts, do sit with their hinder parts bare, that by that note of disgrace others may be terrified from all such vain expense, or borrowing more than they can tell how to pay. The civilians of old set guardians over such brain-sick prodigals,[11] as they did over madmen, to moderate their expenses, that they should not so loosely consume their fortunes, to the utter undoing of their families.

I may not here omit those two main plagues and common

dotages of human kind, wine and women, which have infatu-
ated and besotted myriads of people: they go commonly
together.

> *Qui vino indulget, quemque alea decoquit, ille*
> *In Venerem putris.*[1]

[Who wastes his health with drink, his wealth with play,
The same with womenfolk shall rot away.]

To whom is sorrow, saith Solomon (Prov. xxiii, 29), to whom
is woe, but to such a one as loves drink? it causeth torture
(*vino tortus et ira* [tortured with drunken rage]) and bitterness of
mind (Sirac. xxxiv, 29). *Vinum furoris*, Jeremy calls it (xxv, 15),
wine of madness, as well he may, for *insanire facit sanos*, it
makes sound men sick and sad, and wise men mad,[2] to say
and do they know not what. *Accidit hodie terribilis casus*
(saith St. Austin[3]), hear a miserable accident; Cyrillus' son this
day in his drink *matrem prægnantem nequiter oppressit, sororem
violare voluit, patrem occidit fere, et duas alias sorores ad mortem
vulneravit,* would have violated his sister, killed his father, etc.
A true saying it was of him, *vino dari lætitiam et dolorem,* drink
causeth mirth, and drink causeth sorrow, drink causeth "poverty
and want" (Prov. xxi), shame and disgrace. *Multi ignobiles
evasere ob vini potum, et* (Austin) *amissis honoribus profugi
aberrarunt:* many men have made shipwreck of their fortunes,
and go like rogues and beggars, having turned all their
substance into *aurum potabile* [potable gold], that otherwise might have lived in good worship and happy estate, and
for a few hours' pleasure (for their Hilary term's but short[4]), or
free madness, as Seneca calls it, purchase unto themselves
eternal tediousness and trouble.[5]

   That other madness is on women. *Apostatare facit cor* [it
maketh the heart go astray] saith the wise man, *atque homini
cerebrum minuit*[6] [and minishes the mind of man]. Pleasant
at first she is, like Dioscorides' rhododaphne, that fair plant to
the eye, but poison to the taste, the rest as bitter as wormwood in the end (Prov. v, 4), and sharp as a two-edged sword.
"Her house is the way to hell, and goes down to the chambers
of death" (Prov. vii, 27). What more sorrowful can be said?
they are miserable in this life, mad, beasts, led like "oxen to
the slaughter":[7] and that which is worse, whoremasters and
drunkards shall be judged; *Amittunt gratiam*, saith Austin, *per-
dunt gloriam, incurrunt damnationem æternam:* they lose grace
and glory:

Brevis illa voluptas
Abrogat æternum cæli decus; [1]

[That pleasure of a moment
Deprives him of eternal bliss above;]

they gain hell and eternal damnation.

Subsect. XIV.—*Philautia, or Self-love, Vainglory, Praise,
Honour, Immoderate Applause, Pride, overmuch Joy, etc.,
Causes*

Self-love, pride, and vainglory, *cæcus amor sui* [2] [blind love of
self], which Chrysostom calls one of the devil's three great nets;
Bernard, "an arrow which pierceth the soul through, and slays
it; a sly, insensible enemy, not perceived," [3] are main causes.
Where neither anger, lust, covetousness, fear, sorrow, etc., nor
any other perturbation can lay hold, this will slyly and insensibly
pervert us. *Quem non gula vicit, philautia superavit* (saith
Cyprian), whom surfeiting could not overtake, self-love hath
overcome. "He that hath scorned all money, bribes, gifts, upright
otherwise and sincere, hath inserted himself to no fond imagination, and sustained all those tyrannical concupiscences of the
body, hath lost all his honour, captivated by vainglory" [4]
(Chrysostom, *sup. Jo.*).

Tu sola animum mentemque peruris,
Gloria.

[By this one passion is my mind consumed,
By love of fame.]

A great assault and cause of our present malady, although we
do most part neglect, take no notice of it, yet this is a violent
batterer of our souls, causeth melancholy and dotage. This
pleasing humour, this soft and whispering popular air, *amabilis
insania*, this delectable frenzy, most irrefragable passion, *mentis
gratissimus error*, this acceptable disease, which so sweetly sets
upon us, ravisheth our senses, lulls our souls asleep, puffs up
our hearts as so many bladders, and that without all feeling
insomuch as "those that are misaffected with it never so much
as once perceive it, or think of any cure." [5] We commonly
love him best in this malady [6] that doth us most harm, and
are very willing to be hurt; *adulationibus nostris libentur favemus*
[we lend a willing ear to flattery] (saith Jerome [7]), we love him
we love him for it: *O Bonciari, suave, suave fuit a te tali hæ
tribui* [8] [ah, Bonciarius, 'twas sweet indeed to hear such prais

from such a man as thou]; 'twas sweet to hear it. And as
Pliny[1] doth ingenuously confess to his dear friend Augurinus,
"All thy writings are most acceptable, but those especially that
speak of us." Again, a little after to Maximus, "I cannot
express how pleasing it is to me to hear myself commended."[2]
Though we smile to ourselves, at least ironically, when parasites
bedaub us with false encomiums, as many princes cannot
choose but do, *quum tale quid nihil intra se repererint*, when they
know they come as far short as a mouse to an elephant of
any such virtues; yet it doth us good. Though we seem many
times to be angry, "and blush at our own praises, yet our souls
inwardly rejoice, it puffs us up";[3] 'tis *fallax suavitas, blandus
dæmon* [a deceptive sweetness, a tickling devil], "makes us
swell beyond our bounds, and forget ourselves." Her two
daughters are lightness of mind, immoderate joy and pride,
not excluding those other concomitant vices, which Jodocus
Lorichius[4] reckons up; bragging, hypocrisy, peevishness, and
curiosity.

Now the common cause of this mischief ariseth from ourselves
or others; we are active and passive.[5] It proceeds inwardly
from ourselves, as we are active causes, from an overweening
conceit we have of our good parts, own worth (which indeed is
no worth), our bounty, favour, grace, valour, strength, wealth,
patience, meekness, hospitality, beauty, temperance, gentry,
knowledge, wit, science, art, learning, our excellent gifts and
fortunes,[6] for which, Narcissus-like, we admire, flatter, and
applaud ourselves, and think all the world esteems so of us;
and as deformed women easily believe those that tell them they
be fair, we are too credulous of our own good parts and praises,
too well persuaded of ourselves. We brag and venditate our
own works,[7] and scorn all others in respect of us; *inflati scientia*
(saith Paul), [puffed up with] our wisdom, our learning; all
our geese are swans, and we as basely esteem and vilify other
men's, as we do over-highly prize and value our own.[8] We
will not suffer them to be *in secundis* [in the second rank],
no, not *in tertiis* [in the third rank]; what? *mecum confertur
Ulysses?* [is Ulysses to be compared with me?]; they are *mures,
muscæ, culices præ se*, nits and flies compared to his inexorable
and supercilious, eminent and arrogant worship: though indeed
they be far before him. Only wise, only rich, only fortunate,
valorous, and fair, puffed up with this tympany of self-conceit;
as that proud Pharisee,[9] they are "not" (as they suppose)
"like other men," of a purer and more precious metal:[10] *soli rei*

gerendi sunt efficaces [they alone are competent], which that wise Periander held of such: *meditantur omne qui prius negotium*, [who first think over every undertaking], etc. *Novi quendam*[1] (saith Erasmus[2]), I knew one so arrogant that he thought himself inferior to no man living, like Callisthenes the philosopher, that neither held Alexander's acts, or any other subject, worthy of his pen, such was his insolency;[3] or Seleucus, King of Syria, who thought none fit to contend with him but the Romans: *Eos solos dignos ratus quibuscum de imperio certaret.*[4] That which Tully writ to Atticus long since, is still in force: "There was never yet true poet nor orator, that thought any other better than himself."[5] And such for the most part are your princes, potentates, great philosophers, historiographers, authors of sects or heresies, and all our great scholars, as Hierome defines:[6] "A natural philosopher is glory's creature, and a very slave of rumour, fame, and popular opinion," and though they write *de contemptu gloriæ* [on the contempt of fame], yet, as he observes, they will put their names to their books. *Vobis et famæ me semper dedi*, saith Trebellius Pollio, I have wholly consecrated myself to you and fame. "'Tis all my desire, night and day, 'tis all my study to raise my name." Proud Pliny[7] seconds him: *Quamquam O!* etc.; and that vainglorious orator[8] is not ashamed to confess in an epistle of his to Marcus Lucceius, *Ardeo incredibili cupiditate*, etc., "I burn with an incredible desire to have my name registered in thy book."[9] Out of this fountain proceed all those cracks and brags: *Speramus carmina fingi Posse linenda cedro, et leni servanda cupresso*[10] [we cherish hopes of composing poems worthy to be preserved by cedar oil, and to be stored in cypress chests]. *Non usitata nec tenui ferar penna . . . nec in terra morabor longius* [I am borne on no common or slender wing. . . . I shall not tarry long upon earth]. *Nil parvum aut humili modo, nil mortale loquor* [no mean or humble strain is mine, nor soon to be forgot]. *Dicar qua violens obstrepit Aufidus* [where Aufidus rolls noisily my name shall be known]. *Exegi monumentum ære perennius* [I have carved a monument more durable than brass]. *Jamque opus exegi, quod nec Jovis ira, nec ignis, etc.*[11] [I have achieved a work which neither the wrath of heaven nor fire, etc.]. *Cum venit ille dies, etc.; Parte tamen meliore mei super alta perennis Astra ferar, nomenque erit indelebile nostrum.* (This of Ovid I have paraphrased in English:

> And when I am dead and gone,
> My corpse laid under a stone,

> My fame shall yet survive,
> And I shall be alive,
> In these my works for ever,
> My glory shall persever, etc.)

And that of Ennius,

> *Nemo me lacrimis decoret, neque funera fletu*
> *Faxit; cur? volito docta per ora virum.*

[Let none shed tears over me, or grace my grave with
weeping, because I am eternally in the mouths
of men;]

with many such proud strains, and foolish flashes too common
with writers. Not so much as Demochares on the Topics,[1] but
he will be immortal. Typotius *de fama* shall be famous, and
well he deserves, because he writ of fame; and every trivial poet
must be renowned: *Plausuque petit clarescere vulgi* [he seeks
the applause of the mob]. This puffing humour it is, that
hath produced so many great tomes, built such famous monuments, strong castles, and Mausolean tombs, to have their acts
eternized, *Digito monstrari, et dicier hic est* [to be pointed at
with the finger, and to have it said, "There he goes"]; to see
their names inscribed, as Phryne on the walls of Thebes, *Phryne
fecit*. This causeth so many bloody battles, *Et noctes cogit
vigilare serenas* [and forces us to watch during calm nights];
long journeys—*Magnum iter intendo, sed dat mihi gloria vires*
[I contemplate a monstrous journey, but the love of glory
strengthens me for it]; gaining honour, a little applause, pride,
self-love, vainglory. This is it which makes them take such
pains, and break out into those ridiculous strains, this high
conceit of themselves, to scorn all others;[2] *ridiculo fastu et
intolerando contemptu*, as Palæmon the grammarian contemned
Varro, *secum et natas et morituras literas jactans*[3] [boasting that
literature had been born with him and would die with him],
and brings them to that height of insolency, that they cannot
endure to be contradicted, "or hear of anything but their own
commendation,"[4] which Hierome notes of such kind of men;
and, as Austin well seconds him,[5] "'tis their sole study day and
night to be commended and applauded." Whenas indeed, in
all wise men's judgments, *quibus cor capit* [who are blessed
with sense], they are mad,[6] empty vessels, funges, beside themselves, derided, *et ut camelus in proverbio quærens cornua, etiam
quas habebat aures amisit* [and like the camel in the proverb,
who asked for horns and lost his ears], their works are toys, as
an almanac out of date, *Auctoris pereunt garrulitate sui*[7] [they

fall flat because their authors talk too much of them], they seek fame and immortality, but reap dishonour and infamy, they are a common obloquy, *insensati*, and come far short of that which they suppose or expect.

O puer, ut sis vitalis metuo.[1]

[O boy, I fear thou art short-lived.]

Of so many myriads of poets, rhetoricians, philosophers, sophisters, as Eusebius well observes,[2] which have written in former ages, scarce one of a thousand's works remains, *nomina et libri cum corporibus interierunt*, their books and bodies are perished together. It is not as they vainly think, they shall surely be admired and immortal; as one told Philip of Macedon, insulting after a victory, that his shadow was no longer than before, we may say to them:

Nos demiramur, sed non cum deside vulgo,
Sed velut Harpyas, Gorgonas, et Furias.

We marvel too, not as the vulgar we,
But as we Gorgons, Harpies, or Furies see.

Or if we do applaud, honour and admire, *quota pars*, how small a part, in respect of the whole world, never so much as hears our names! how few take notice of us! how slender a tract, as scant as Alcibiades his land in a map! And yet every many must and will be immortal, as he hopes, and extend his fame to our antipodes, whenas half, no, not a quarter, of his own province or city neither knows nor hears of him: but say they did, what's a city to a kingdom, a kingdom to Europe, Europe to the world, the world itself that must have an end, if compared to the least visible star in the firmament, eighteen times bigger than it? and then if those stars be infinite, and every star there be a sun, as some will, and, as this sun of ours, hath his planets about him, all inhabited, what proportion bear we to them, and where's our glory? *Orbem terrarum victor Romanus habebat*, as he cracked in Petronius, all the world was under Augustus; and so in Constantine's time, Eusebius brags he governed all the world, *universum mundum præclare admodum administravit, . . . et omnes orbis gentes imperatori subjecti* [he governed the whole world with great distinction, and all nations were subject to the emperor]: so of Alexander it is given out, the four monarchies, etc., whenas neither Greeks nor Romans ever had the fifteenth part of the now known world, nor half of that which was then described. What braggadocians are they and we then! *quam brevis hic de nobis sermo*, as he said,[1] *pudebit aucti nominis*,[2] how short a time, how little a while doth this fame of ours continue! Every private province, every small territory and city, when we have all done, will yield as generous spirits, as brave examples in all respects, as famous as ourselves; Cadwallader in Wales, Rollo in Normandy, Robin Hood and Little John are as much renowned in Sherwood, as Cæsar in Rome, Alexander in Greece, or his Hephæstion. *Omnis ætas omnisque populus in exemplum et admirationem veniet*[3] [every age, every people can furnish examples to excite our wonder], every town, city, book, is full of brave soldiers, senators, scholars; and though Brasidas[4] was a worthy captain, a good man, and, as they thought, not to be matched in Lacedæmon, yet, as his mother truly said, *plures habet Sparta Brasida meliores*, Sparta had many better men than ever he was; and howsoever thou admirest thyself, thy friend, many an obscure fellow the world never took notice of, had he been in place or action, would have done much better than he or he, or thou thyself.

Another kind of madmen there is opposite to these, that are insensibly mad, and know not of it, such as contemn all praise and glory, think themselves most free whenas indeed they are most mad: *calcant sed alio fastu* [these also trample upon others, but with another kind of pride]: a company of cynics, such as are monks, hermits, anachorites, that contemn the world, contemn themselves, contemn all titles, honours, offices, and yet in that contempt are more proud than any man living whatsoever. They are proud in humility, proud in that they are not proud; *sæpe homo de vanæ gloriæ contemptu vanius gloriatur* [a man can be most boastful in expressing his contempt of fame], as Austin hath it, *Confess. lib.* 10, *cap.* 38; like Diogenes, *intus gloriantur*, they brag inwardly, and feed themselves fat with a self-conceit of sanctity, which is no better than hypocrisy. They go in sheep's russet, many great men that might maintain themselves in cloth of gold, and seem to be dejected, humble by their outward carriage, whenas inwardly they are swollen full of pride, arrogancy, and self-conceit. And therefore Seneca adviseth his friend Lucilius,[5] "in his attire and gesture, outward actions, especially to avoid all such things as are more notable in themselves: as a rugged attire, hirsute head, horrid beard, contempt of money, coarse lodging, and whatsoever leads to fame that opposite way."

All this madness yet proceeds from ourselves, the main engine which batters us is from others, we are merely passive in this business: from a company of parasites and flatterers, that with immoderate praise and bombast epithets, glozing titles, false elogiums, so bedaub and applaud, gild over many a silly and undeserving man, that they clap him quite out of his wits. *Res imprimis violenta est*, as Hierome notes, this common applause is a most violent thing, *laudum placenta* [a cake of praises], a drum, fife, and trumpet cannot so animate; that fattens men, erects and dejects them in an instant. *Palma negata macrum, donata reducit opimum.*[1] It makes them fat and lean, as frost doth conies. "And who is that mortal man that can so contain himself, that, if he be immoderately commended and applauded, will not be moved?"[2] Let him be what he will, those parasites will overturn him: if he be a king, he is one of the Nine Worthies, more than a man, a god forthwith (*Edictum Domini Deique nostri*[3] [the edict of our Lord and God]), and they will sacrifice unto him:

Divinos si tu patiaris honores,
Ultro ipsi dabimus meritasque sacrabimus aras.[4]

[If you will accept divine honours, we will willingly pay them to you, and raise to you well-deserved altars.]

If he be a soldier, then Themistocles, Epaminondas, Hector, Achilles, *duo fulmina belli* [two thunderbolts of war], *triumviri terrarum* [the triumvirs of the universe[5]], etc., and the valour of both Scipios is too little for him, he is *invictissimus, serenissimus, multis trophæis ornatissimus, naturæ dominus* [invincible, most serene, adorned with numerous trophies, lord of nature], although he be *lepus galeatus* [a helmeted hare], indeed a very coward, a milksop, and as he[6] said of Xerxes, *postremus in pugna, primus in fuga* [last in fight, first in flight], and such a one as never durst look his enemy in the face. If he be a big man, then is he a Samson, another Hercules; if he pronounce a speech, another Tully or Demosthenes (as of Herod in the Acts, "the voice of God and not of man"); if he can make a verse, Homer, Virgil, etc. And then my silly weak patient takes all these elogiums to himself; if he be a scholar so commended for his much reading, excellent style, method, etc., he will eviscerate himself like a spider, study to death; *Laudatas ostendit avis Junonia pennas*, peacock-like he will display all his feathers. If he be a soldier, and so applauded, his valour extolled, though it be *impar congressus* [an unequal match], as that of Troilus and Achilles, *infelix puer* [luckless youth], he will combat with a giant, run first upon a breach;

as another Philippus,[1] he will ride into the thickest of his enemies. Commend his housekeeping, and he will beggar himself; commend his temperance, he will starve himself.

Laudataque virtus
Crescit, et immensum gloria calcar habet.

[Praise gives to virtue welcome nourishment,
And glory spurs it on to high intent.]

He is mad, mad, mad, no whoa with him;[2] *impatiens consortis erit* [he will be impatient of a colleague], he will over the Alps to be talked of, or to maintain his credit.[3] Commend an ambitious man, some proud prince or potentate, *si plus laudetur* (saith Erasmus) *cristas erigit, exuit hominem, Deum se putat*,[4] he sets up his crest, and will be no longer a man but a god.

Nihil est quod credere de se
Non audet quum laudatur dis æqua potestas.[5]

[For princes think, when lauded to the skies,
There is no height to which they cannot rise.]

How did this work with Alexander, that would needs be Jupiter's son, and go like Hercules in a lion's skin! Domitian a god (*Dominus Deus noster sic fieri jubet*[6] [the Master, our God, so orders]), like the Persian kings, whose image was adored by all that came into the city of Babylon.[7] Commodus the emperor was so gulled by his flattering parasites that he must be called Hercules. Antonius the Roman would be crowned with ivy, carried in a chariot, and adored for Bacchus.[8] Cotys, King of Thrace, was married to Minerva, and sent three several messengers, one after another, to see if she were come to his bed-chamber.[9] Such a one was Jupiter Menecrates,[10] Maximinus Jovianus, Dioclesianus Herculeus, Sapor the Persian king, brother of the sun and moon, and our modern Turks, that will be gods on earth, kings of kings, God's shadow, commanders of all that may be commanded, our kings of China and Tartary in this present age. Such a one was Xerxes, that would whip the sea, fetter Neptune, *stulta jactantia* [in his stupid pride], and send a challenge to Mount Athos; and such are many sottish princes, brought into a fool's paradise by their parasites. 'Tis a common humour, incident to all men, when they are in great places or come to the solstice of honour, have done or deserved well, to applaud and flatter themselves. *Stultitiam suam produnt* [they betray their folly], etc. (saith Platerus[11]); your very tradesmen, if they be excellent, will crack and brag, and

show their folly in excess. They have good parts, and they
know it, you need not tell them of it; out of a conceit of their
worth, they go smiling to themselves, a perpetual meditation
of their trophies and plaudits; they run at last quite mad, and
lose their wits.[1] Petrarch, *lib.* 1 *de contemptu mundi*, confessed
as much of himself, and Cardan, in his fifth book of Wisdom,
gives an instance in a smith of Milan, a fellow-citizen of his, one
Galeus de Rubeis, that being commended for refinding of an instrument of Archimedes, for joy ran mad.[2] Plutarch, in the life
of Artaxerxes, hath such a like story of one Carius, a soldier,
that wounded King Cyrus in battle, and "grew thereupon so
arrogant, that in a short space after he lost his wits."[3] So
many men, if any new honour, office, preferment, booty, treasure,
possession, or patrimony *ex insperato* [unexpectedly] fall unto
them, for immoderate joy, and continual meditation of it,
cannot sleep or tell what they say or do;[4] they are so ravished
on a sudden, and with vain conceits transported, there is no
rule with them. Epaminondas, therefore, the next day after
his Leuctrian victory, "came abroad all squalid and submiss,"[5]
and gave no other reason to his friends of so doing, than that
he perceived himself the day before, by reason of his good
fortune, to be too insolent, overmuch joyed. That wise and
virtuous lady, Queen Katherine, Dowager of England,[6] in
private talk upon like occasion, said that "she would not
willingly endure the extremity of either fortune; but if it were
so, that of necessity she must undergo the one, she would be
in adversity, because comfort was never wanting in it, but still
counsel and government were defective in the other":[7] they
could not moderate themselves.

SUBSECT. XV.—*Love of Learning, or overmuch Study. With a
Digression of the Misery of Scholars, and why the Muses are
Melancholy*

Leonartus Fuchsius, *Instit. lib.* 3, *sect.* 1, *cap.* 1; Felix
Plater, *lib.* 3 *de mentis alienat.*; Herc. de Saxonia, *tract. post
de melanch. cap.* 3, speak of a peculiar fury which comes by
overmuch study.[8] Fernelius, *lib.* 1, *cap.* 18, puts study, contemplation, and continual meditation as an especial cause of
madness:[9] and in his 86th *consul.* cites the same words. Jo.
Arculanus, *in lib.* 9 *Rhasis ad Almansorem, cap.* 16, amongst
other causes reckons up *studium vehemens* [passionate study];
so doth Levinus Lemnius, *lib. de occul. nat. mirac. lib.* 1, *cap.* 16.

"Many men" (saith he) "come to this malady by continual study,[1] and night-waking, and of all other men, scholars are most subject to it";[2] and such, Rhasis adds, "that have commonly the finest wits"[3] (*Cont. lib.* 1, *tract.* 9). Marsilius Ficinus, *de sanit. tuenda, lib.* 1, *cap.* 7, puts melancholy amongst one of those five principal plagues of students, 'tis a common moll unto them all, and almost in some measure an inseparable companion. Varro belike for that cause calls *tristes philosophos et severos* [philosophers sad and austere]; severe, sad, dry, tetric, are common epithets to scholars: and Patricius therefore,[4] in the institution of princes, would not have them to be great students. For (as Machiavel holds) study weakens their bodies, dulls the spirits, abates their strength and courage; and good scholars are never good soldiers, which a certain Goth well perceived, for when his countrymen came into Greece, and would have burned all their books, he cried out against it, by all means they should not do it; "Leave them that plague, which in time will consume all their vigour, and martial spirits."[5] The Turks abdicated Corcutus, the next heir, from the empire, because he was so much given to his book:[6] and 'tis the common tenent of the world, that learning dulls and diminisheth the spirits, and so *per consequens* produceth melancholy.

Two main reasons may be given of it, why students should be more subject to this malady than others. The one is, they live a sedentary, solitary life, *sibi et musis* [for themselves and their studies], free from bodily exercise, and those ordinary disports which other men use; and many times if discontent and idleness concur with it, which is too frequent, they are precipitated into this gulf on a sudden; but the common cause is overmuch study: "Too much learning" (as Festus told Paul[7]) "hath made thee mad"; 'tis that other extreme which effects it. So did Trincavellius, *lib.* 1, *consil.* 12 and 13, find by his experience, in two of his patients, a young baron and another, that contracted this malady by too vehement study. So Forestus, *Observat. lib.* 10, *observ.* 13, in a young divine in Louvain, that was mad, and said "he had a Bible in his head."[8] Marsilius Ficinus, *de sanit. tuend., lib.* 1, *cap.* 1, 3, 4, and *lib.* 2, *cap.* 16, gives many reasons "why students dote more often than others."[9] The first is their negligence: "Other men look to their tools; a painter will wash his pencils; a smith will look to his hammer, anvil, forge; a husbandman will mend his plough-irons, and grind his hatchet if it be dull; a falconer or huntsman will have an especial care of his hawks, hounds, horses, dogs, etc.; a musician will string and unstring his lute, etc.; only scholars neglect that instrument (their brain and spirits I mean) which they daily use, and by which they range over all the world, which by much study is consumed." [1] *Vide* (saith Lucian) *ne funiculum nimis intendendo, aliquando abrumpas:* "See thou twist not the rope so hard, till at length it break." [2] Facinus, in his fourth chap., gives some other reasons; Saturn and Mercury, the patrons of learning, are both dry planets: and Origanus [3] assigns the same cause why Mercurialists are so poor, and most part beggars; for that their president Mercury had no better fortune himself. The Destinies of old put poverty upon him as a punishment; since when, poetry and beggary are *gemelli*, twin-born brats, inseparable companions;

> And to this day is every scholar poor;
> Gross gold from them runs headlong to the boor: [4]

Mercury can help them to knowledge, but not to money. The second is contemplation, "which dries the brain and extinguisheth natural heat; for whilst the spirits are intent to meditation above in the head, the stomach and liver are left destitute, and thence come black blood and crudities by defect of concoction, and for want of exercise the superfluous vapours cannot exhale," [5] etc. The same reasons are repeated by Gomesius *lib.* 4, *cap.* 1, *de sale*; Nymannus, *orat. de Imag.*; [6] Jo. Voschius *lib.* 2, *cap.* 5, *de peste*; and something more they add, that hard students are commonly troubled with gouts, catarrhs, rheums, cachexia, bradypepsia, bad eyes, stone, and colic, crudities, oppilations, vertigo, winds, consumptions, and all such diseases as come by overmuch sitting; [7] they are most part lean, dry, ill-coloured, spend their fortunes, lose their wits, and many times their lives, and all through immoderate pains and extraordinary studies. If you will not believe the truth of this, look upon great Tostatus' and Thomas Aquinas' works, and tell me whether those men took pains? peruse Austin, Hierome, etc., and many thousands besides.

> *Qui cupit optatam cursu contingere metam,*
> *Multa tulit, fecitque puer, sudavit et alsit*

> He that desires this wished goal to gain,
> Must sweat and freeze before he can attain,

and labour hard for it. So did Seneca, by his own confession, *ep.* 8; "Not a day that I spend idle, part of the night I keep mine eyes open, tired with waking, and now slumbering to the continual task." [8] Hear Tully, *pro Archia Poeta*: "Whilst other

loitered, and took their pleasures, he was continually at his
book"; so they do that will be scholars, and that to the hazard
(I say) of their healths, fortunes, wits, and lives. How much
did Aristotle and Ptolemy spend? *unius regni pretium* they say,
more than a king's ransom; how many crowns per annum, to
perfect arts, the one about his History of Creatures, the other on
his Almagest? How much time did Thebet Benchorat employ,
to find out the motion of the eighth sphere? forty years and
more, some write. How many poor scholars have lost their wits,
or become dizzards, neglecting all worldly affairs and their own
health, *esse* and *bene esse* [being and well-being], to gain knowledge for which, after all their pains, in this world's esteem they
are accounted ridiculous and silly fools, idiots, asses, and (as oft
they are) rejected, contemned, derided, doting, and mad! Look
for examples in Hildesheim, *Spicil.* 2, *de mania et delirio*; read
Trincavellius, *lib.* 3, *consil.* 36, *et c.* 17; Montanus, *consil.* 233;
Garcæus, *de Judic. genit. cap.* 33; [1] Mercurialis, *consil.* 86, *cap.* 25;
Prosper Calenius in his book *de atra bile.* [2] Go to Bedlam and
ask. Or if they keep their wits, yet they are esteemed scrubs
and fools by reason of their carriage: "after seven years' study," [3]

> *statua taciturnius exit,*
> *Plerumque et risu populum quatit.*

> [Dumb as a statue, slow he stalks along,
> And shakes with laughter loud the gazing throng.]

Because they cannot ride an horse, which every clown can do;
salute and court a gentlewoman, carve at table, cringe and
make congees, which every common swasher can do, *his*
opulus ridet, [4] etc., they are laughed to scorn, and accounted
silly fools by our gallants. Yea, many times, such is their
misery, they deserve it: a mere scholar, a mere ass.

> *Obstipo capite, et figentes lumine terram,*
> *Murmura cum secum, et rabiosa silentia rodunt,*
> *Atque exporrecto trutinantur verba labello,*
> *Ægroti veteris meditantes somnia, gigni*
> *De nihilo nihilum ; in nihilum nil posse reverti.* [5]

> Who do lean awry
> Their heads, piercing the earth with a fixt eye;
> When, by themselves, they gnaw their murmuring,
> And furious silence, as 'twere balancing
> Each word upon their outstretched lip, and when
> They meditate the dreams of old sick men,
> As, "Out of nothing, nothing can be brought;
> And that which is, can ne'er be turn'd to nought." [6]

Thus they go commonly meditating unto themselves, thus they

sit, such is their action and gesture. Fulgosus, *lib.* 8, *cap.* 7, makes mention how Th. Aquinas, supping with King Louis of France, upon a sudden knocked his fist upon the table, and cried, *Conclusum est contra Manichæos* [This proves the Manichæans were wrong]; his wits were a-woolgathering, as they say, and his head busied about other matters; when he perceived his error, he wa much abashed.[1] Such a story there is of Archimedes in Vitruvius, that having found out the means to know how much gold was mingled with the silver in King Hiero's crown, ran naked forth of the bath and cried Εὕρηκα, I have found; "and was commonly so intent to his studies, that he never perceived what was done about him: when the city was taken, and the soldiers now ready to rifle his house, he took no notice of it." [2] St. Bernard rode all day long by the Lemnian lake,[3] and asked at last where he was (Marullus, *lib.* 2, *cap.* 4). It was Democritus' carriage alone that made the Abderites suppose him to have been mad, and send for Hippocrates to cure him: if he had been in any solemn company, he would upon all occasions fall a-laughing. Theophrastus saith as much of Heraclitus, for that he continually wept, and Laertius of Menedemus Lampsacus, because he ran like a madman, "saying he came from hell as a spy, to tell the devils what mortal men did." [4] Your greatest students are commonly no better, silly soft fellows in their outward behaviour, absurd, ridiculous to others, and no whit experienced in worldly business; they can measure the heavens, range over the world, teach others wisdom, and yet in bargains and contracts they are circumvented by every base tradesman. Are not these men fools? and how should they be otherwise, "but as so many sots in schools when" (as he well observed [5]) "they neither hear nor see such things as are commonly practised abroad"? how should they get experience, by what means? "I knew in my time many scholars," saith Æneas Sylvius (in an epistle of his to Gaspar Schlick, chancellor to the emperor), "excellent well learned, but so rude, so silly, that they had no common civility, nor knew how to manage their domestic or public affairs. Paglarensis was amazed, and said his farmer had surely cozened him, when he heard him tell that his sow had eleven pigs, and his ass had but one foal." [6] To say the best of this profession, I can give no other testimony of them in general, than that of Pliny of Isæus: "He is yet a scholar, than which kind of men there is nothing so simple, so sincere, none better"; [7] they are most part harmless, honest, upright, innocent, plain-dealing men.

Now because they are commonly subject to such hazards and inconveniences as dotage, madness, simplicity, etc., Jo. Voschius would have good scholars to be highly rewarded, and had in some extraordinary respect above other men, "to have greater privileges than the rest, that adventure themselves and abbreviate their lives for the public good." [1] But our patrons of learning are so far nowadays from respecting the Muses, and giving that honour to scholars, or reward, which they deserve and are allowed by those indulgent privileges of many noble princes, that after all their pains taken in the universities, cost and charge, expenses, irksome hours, laborious tasks, wearisome days, dangers, hazards (barred interim from all pleasures which other men have, mewed up like hawks all their lives), if they chance to wade through them, they shall in the end be rejected, contemned, and, which is their greatest misery, driven to their shifts, exposed to want, poverty, and beggary. Their familiar attendants are:

> *Pallentes morbi, luctus, curæque laborque,*
> *Et metus, et malesuada fames, et turpis egestas,*
> *Terribiles visu formæ.* [2]
>
> Grief, labour, care, pale sickness, miseries,
> Fear, filthy poverty, hunger that cries,
> Terrible monsters to be seen with eyes.

If there were nothing else to trouble them, the conceit of this alone were enough to make them all melancholy. Most other trades and professions, after some seven years' apprenticeship, are enabled by their craft to live of themselves. A merchant adventures his goods at sea, and though his hazard be great, yet if one ship return of four, he likely makes a saving voyage. An husbandman's gains are almost certain, *quibus ipse Jupiter nocere non potest* [whom Jove himself can't harm] ('tis Cato's hyperbole, a great husband himself [3]); only scholars methinks are most uncertain, unrespected, subject to all casualties, and hazards. For first, not one of a many proves to be a scholar, all are not capable and docile, *ex omni ligno non fit Mercurius* [4] a figure of Mercury is not made out of every log]: we can make mayors and officers every year, but not scholars: kings can invest knights and barons, as Sigismund the emperor confessed; universities can give degrees; and *Tu quod es, e populo quilibet esse potest* [what you are any one can be]; but he, nor they, nor all the world, can give learning, make philosophers, artists, orators, poets. We can soon say, as Seneca well notes, *O virum*

bonum! o divitem! point at a rich man, a good, a happy
man, a prosperous man, *sumptuose vestitum, calamistratum, bene
olentem* [a splendidly dressed man, a well-groomed man]; *magno
temporis impendio constat hæc laudatio, O virum literatum!*
but 'tis not so easily performed to find out a learned man.
Learning is not so quickly got; though they may be willing to
take pains, to that end sufficiently informed, and liberally
maintained by their patrons and parents, yet few can compass
it. Or if they be docile, yet all men's wills are not answerable
to their wits; they can apprehend, but will not take pains; they
are either seduced by bad companions, *vel in puellam impingunt,
vel in poculum* [or come to grief over women or wine], and so
spend their time to their friends' grief and their own undoings.
Or put case they be studious, industrious, of ripe wits, and
perhaps good capacities, then how many diseases of body and
mind must they encounter! No labour in the world like unto
study. It may be their temperature will not endure it, but
striving to be excellent, to know all, they lose health, wealth,
wit, life, and all. Let him yet happily escape all these hazards
æreis intestinis, with a body of brass, and is now consummate and
ripe, he hath profited in his studies, and proceeded with all
applause: after many expenses, he is fit for preferment; where
shall he have it? he is as far to seek it as he was (after twenty
years' standing) at the first day of his coming to the university.
For what course shall he take, being now capable and ready.
The most parable and easy, and about which many are employed, is to teach a school, turn lecturer or curate, and for that
he shall have falconer's wages, ten pound per annum and his
diet, or some small stipend, so long as he can please his patron
or the parish; if they approve him not (for usually they do but
a year or two, as inconstant as they that cried "Hosanna" one
day, and "Crucify Him" the other [1]), serving-man-like, he must
go look a new master; if they do, what is his reward?

> *Hoc quoque te manet ut pueros elementa docentem
> Occupet extremis in vicis balba senectus.* [2]
>
> [At last thy stammering age in suburb schools,
> Shall toil in teaching boys their grammar rules.]

Like an ass, he wears out his time for provender, and can show
a stump rod, *togam tritam et laceram,* saith Hædus, [3] an old torn
gown, an ensign of his infelicity; he hath his labour for his
pain, a modicum to keep him till he be decrepit, and that is all.
Grammaticus non est felix [the schoolmaster is not a happy

man], etc. If he be a trencher-chaplain in a gentleman's house, as it befell Euphormio,[1] after some seven years' service, he may perchance have a living to the halves, or some small rectory with the mother of the maids at length, a poor kinswoman, or a cracked chambermaid, to have and to hold during the time of his life. But if he offend his good patron, or displease his lady mistress in the meantime,

> *Ducetur planta velut ictus ab Hercule Cacus,*
> *Poneturque foras, si quid tentaverit unquam*
> *Hiscere,*[2]

as Hercules did by Cacus, he shall be dragged forth of doors by the heels, away with him! If he bend his forces to some other studies, with an intent to be *a secretis* [private secretary] to some nobleman, or in such a place with an ambassador, he shall find that these persons rise like prentices one under another, and in so many tradesmen's shops, when the master is dead, the foreman of the shop commonly steps in his place. Now for poets, rhetoricians, historians, philosophers, mathematicians, sophisters, etc.,[3] they are like grasshoppers, sing they must in summer, and pine in the winter, for there is no preferment for them. Even so they were at first, if you will believe that pleasant tale of Socrates, which he told fair Phædrus under a plane-tree, at the banks of the river Ilissus. About noon, when it was hot, and the grasshoppers made a noise, he took that sweet occasion to tell him a tale, how grasshoppers were once scholars, musicians, poets, etc., before the Muses were born, and lived without meat and drink, and for that cause were turned by Jupiter into grasshoppers. And may be turned again, *in Tithoni cicadas, aut Lyciorum ranas* [into the grasshoppers of Tithonus or the frogs of the Lycians], for any reward I see they are like to have: or else, in the meantime, I would they could live, as they did, without any viaticum, like so many *manucodiatæ*,[4] those Indian birds of paradise, as we commonly call them, those, I mean, that live with the air and dew of heaven, and need no other food; for being as they are, their "rhetoric only serves them to curse their bad fortunes,"[5] and many of them, for want of means, are driven to hard shifts; from grasshoppers they turn humble-bees and wasps, plain parasites, and make the Muses mules, to satisfy their hunger-starved paunches and get a meal's meat. To say truth, 'tis the common fortune of most scholars to be servile and poor, to complain pitifully, and lay open their wants to their respectless patrons, as Cardan doth,[1] as Xylander[2] and many others; and, which is too common in these dedicatory epistles, for hope of gain to lie, flatter, and with hyperbolical elogiums and commendations to magnify and extol an illiterate unworthy idiot for his excellent virtues, whom they should rather, as Machiavel observes, vilify and rail at downright for his most notorious villainies and vices.[3]   So they prostitute themselves, as fiddlers or mercenary tradesmen, to serve great men's turns for a small reward.   They are like Indians, they have store of gold, but know not the worth of it:[4] for I am of Synesius' opinion, "King Hiero got more by Simonides' acquaintance than Simonides did by his"; [5] they have their best education, good institution, sole qualification from us, and when they have done well, their honour and immortality from us; we are the living tombs, registers, and as so many trumpeters of their fames: what was Achilles without Homer? Alexander without Arrian and Curtius? who had known the Cæsars, but for Suetonius and Dion?

> *Vixerunt fortes ante Agamemnona*
> *Multi: sed omnes illacrimabiles*
> *Urgentur, ignotique longa*
> *Nocte, carent quia vate sacro.*[6]

> [Before great Agamemnon reign'd,
>   Reign'd kings as great as he, and brave,
> Whose huge ambition 's now contain'd
>   In the small compass of a grave:
> In endless night they sleep, unwept, unknown,
> No bard they had to make all time their own.]

They are more beholden to scholars, than scholars to them; but they undervalue themselves, and so by those great men are kept down.   Let them have that encyclopædian, all the learning in the world; they must keep it to themselves, "live in base esteem and starve, except they will submit," as Budæus well hath it "so many good parts, so many ensigns of arts, virtues, be slavishly obnoxious to some illiterate potentate, and live under his insolent worship, or honour, like parasites," [7] *qui tanquam mures alienum panem comedunt* [who like mice eat other persons bread].   For to say truth, *artes hæ non sunt lucrativæ,* a Guido Bonat, that great astrologer, could foresee, they be no gainful arts these, *sed esurientes et famelicæ,* but poor and hungry

> *Dat Galenus opes, dat Justinianus honores,*
>   *Sed genus et species cogitur ire pedes.*[8]

> The rich physician, honour'd lawyers ride,
>   Whilst the poor scholar foots it by their side.

Poverty is the Muses' patrimony, and as that poetical divinity teacheth us, when Jupiter's daughters were each of them married to the gods, the Muses alone were left solitary, Helicon forsaken of all suitors, and I believe it was because they had no portion.

> *Calliope longum cælebs cur vixit in ævum?*
> *Nempe nihil dotis, quod numeraret, erat.*

> Why did Calliope live so long a maid?
> Because she had no dowry to be paid.

Ever since all their followers are poor, forsaken, and left unto themselves; insomuch that, as Petronius argues, you shall likely know them by their clothes. "There came," saith he, "by chance into my company, a fellow not very spruce to look on, that I could perceive by that note alone he was a scholar, whom commonly rich men hate. I asked him what he was; he answered, a poet. I demanded again why he was so ragged; he told me this kind of learning never made any man rich." [1]

> *Qui pelago credit, magno se fænore tollit,*
> *Qui pugnas et rostra petit, præcingitur auro :*
> *Vilis adulator picto jacet ebrius ostro,*
> *Sola pruinosis horret facundia pannis.*

> A merchant's gain is great, that goes to sea;
>   A soldier embossed all in gold;
> A flatterer lies fox'd in brave array;
>   A scholar only ragged to behold.

All which our ordinary students, right well perceiving in the universities, how unprofitable these poetical, mathematical, and philosophical studies are, how little respected, how few patrons, apply themselves in all haste to those three commodious professions of law, physic, and divinity, sharing themselves between them, rejecting these arts in the meantime, history, philosophy, philology, or lightly passing them over, as pleasant toys fitting only table-talk, and to furnish them with discourse.[3] They are not so behoveful: he that can tell his money hath arithmetic enough: he is a true geometrician, can measure out a good fortune to himself; a perfect astrologer, that can cast the rise and fall of others, and mark their errant motions to his own use. The best optics are, to reflect the beams of some great men's favour and grace to shine upon him. He is a good engineer that alone can make an instrument to get preferment. This was the common tenent and practice of Poland, as Cromerus observed not long since, in the first book of his history; their

universities were generally base, not a philosopher, a mathematician, an antiquary, etc., to be found of any note amongst
them, because they had no set reward or stipend, but every man
betook himself to divinity, *hoc solum in votis habens, opimum
sacerdotium*, a good parsonage was their aim. This was the
practice of some of our near neighbours, as Lipsius inveighs;[1]
"they thrust their children to the study of law and divinity,
before they be informed aright, or capable of such studies."
*Scilicet omnibus artibus antistat spes lucri, et formosior est cumulus
auri, quam quicquid Græci Latinique delirantes scripserunt. Ex
hoc numero deinde veniunt ad gubernacula reipub., intersunt et
præsunt consiliis regum. O pater, o patria!* [The prospect of gain
outweighs all studies, and a heap of money is more attractive
than all the stuff written by the Greek and Latin authors.
From this class we draw the leaders of the State, the counsellors
and guides of kings. What a world!] So he complained, and so
may others. For even so we find, to serve a great man, to get
an office in some bishop's court (to practise in some good town),
or compass a benefice, is the mark we shoot at, as being so
advantageous, the highway to preferment.

Although many times, for aught I can see, these men fail as
often as the rest in their projects, and are as usually frustrate
of their hopes. For let him be a doctor of the law, an excellent
civilian of good worth, where shall he practise and expatiate?
Their fields are so scant, the civil law with us so contracted with
prohibitions, so few causes, by reason of those all-devouring
municipal laws, *quibus nihil illiteratius*, saith Erasmus,[2] an
illiterate and a barbarous study (for though they be never so
well learned in it, I can hardly vouchsafe them the name of
scholars, except they be otherwise qualified), and so few courts
are left to the profession, such slender offices, and those commonly to be compassed at such dear rates, that I know not
how an ingenuous man should thrive amongst them. Now for
physicians, there are in every village so many mountebanks,
empirics, quacksalvers, Paracelsians, as they call themselves,
causifici et sanicidæ [makers of pretexts and killers of healthy
people], so Clenard terms them,[3] wizards, alchemists, poor
vicars, cast apothecaries, physicians' men, barbers, and goodwives, professing great skill, that I make great doubt how they
shall be maintained, or who shall be their patients. Besides,
there are so many of both sorts, and some of them such harpies,
so covetous, so clamorous, so impudent; and as he said,[4]
litigious idiots,

Quibus loquacis affatim arrogantiæ est,
  Peritiæ parum aut nihil,
Nec ulla mica literarii salis,
  Crumenimulga natio :
Loquuteleia turba, litium strophæ,
  Maligna litigantium
Cohors, togati vultures,
  Lavernæ alumni, agyrtæ, etc.

Which have no skill but prating arrogance,
  No learning, such a purse-milking nation:
Gown'd vultures, thieves, and a litigious rout
  Of cozeners, that haunt this occupation, etc.

that they cannot well tell how to live one by another, but (as he jested in the comedy of clocks, they were so many), *major pars populi arida reptant fame,*[1] they are almost starved a great part of them, and ready to devour their fellows, *et noxia calliditate se corrupere*[2] [and become addicted to a mischievous cunning], such a multitude of pettifoggers and empirics, such impostors, that an honest man knows not in what sort to compose and behave himself in their society, to carry himself with credit in so vile a rout, *scientiæ nomen, tot sumptibus partum et vigiliis, profiteri dispudeat, postquam* [he is ashamed to lay claim to learning, which he has acquired with so much expense and trouble, now that], etc.

Last of all to come to our divines, the most noble profession and worthy of double honour, but of all others the most distressed and miserable. If you will not believe me, hear a brief of it, as it was not many years since publicly preached at Paul's Cross, by a grave minister then, and now a reverend bishop of this land:[3] "We that are bred up in learning, and destinated by our parents to this end, we suffer our childhood in the grammar-school, which Austin calls *magnum tyrannidem, et grave malum* [a great despotism, a terrible evil], and compares it to the torments of martyrdom; when we come to the university, if we live of the college allowance, as Phalaris objected to the Leontines, παντῶν ἐνδεεῖς πλὴν λιμοῦ καὶ φόβου, needy of all things but hunger and fear, or if we be maintained but partly by our parents' cost, do expend in unnecessary maintenance, books, and degrees, before we come to any perfection, five hundred pounds, or a thousand marks. If by this price of the expense of time, our bodies and spirits, our substance and patrimonies, we cannot purchase those small rewards which are ours by law, and the right of inheritance, a poor parsonage, or a vicarage of £50 per annum, but we must pay to the patron for the lease of a life (a spent and outworn life) either in annual pension, or above the rate of a copyhold, and that with the hazard and loss of our souls, by simony and perjury, and the forfeiture of all our spiritual preferments, in *esse* and *posse*, both present and to come. What father after a while will be so improvident to bring up his son, to his great charge, to this necessary beggary? What Christian will be so irreligious to bring up his son in that course of life, which by all probability and necessity *coget ad turpia*, enforcing to sin, will entangle him in simony and perjury, when, as the poet said, *Invitatus ad hæc aliquis de ponte negabit*: a beggar's brat taken from the bridge where he sits a-begging, if he knew the inconvenience, had cause to refuse it." This being thus, have not we fished fair all this while, that are initiate divines, to find no better fruits of our labours? *Hoc est cur palles? cur quis non prandeat hoc est?* [1] [Is it for this we have pale faces and do without our breakfasts?] Do we macerate ourselves for this? Is it for this we rise so early all the year long, "leaping" (as he saith) "out of our beds, when we hear the bell ring, as if we had heard a thunderclap?" [2] If this be all the respect, reward and honour we shall have, *Frange leves calamos, et scinde, Thalia, libellos* [3] [break your pens, Thalia, and tear up your books], let us give over our books, and betake ourselves to some other course of life. To what end should we study? *Quid me litterulas stulti docuere parentes?* [4] What did our parents mean to make us scholars, to be as far to seek of preferment after twenty years' study, as we were at first? Why do we take such pains? *Quid tantum insanis juvant impallescere chartis?* [Why lose the colour of our youthful age By constant bending o'er the stupid page?] If there be no more hope of reward, no better encouragement, I say again, *Frange leves calamos, et scinde, Thalia, libellos;* let's turn soldiers, sell our books and buy swords, guns, and pikes, or stop bottles with them, turn our philosophers' gowns, as Cleanthes once did, into millers' coats, leave all, and rather betake ourselves to any other course of life than to continue longer in this misery. *Præstat dentiscalpia radere, quam literariis monumentis magnatum favorem emendicare* [5] [it is better to sharpen toothpicks than to beg the favour of the great with literary productions].

Yea, but methinks I hear some man except at these words, that though this be true which I have said of the estate of scholars, and especially of divines, that it is miserable and distressed at this time, that the Church suffers shipwreck of

her goods, and that they have just cause to complain; there is
a fault, but whence proceeds it? If the cause were justly
examined, it would be retorted upon ourselves; if we were cited
at that tribunal of truth, we should be found guilty, and not
able to excuse it. That there is a fault among us, I confess,
and were there not a buyer, there would not be a seller: but to
him that will consider better of it, it will more than manifestly
appear that the fountain of these miseries proceeds from these
griping patrons. In accusing them, I do not altogether excuse
us; both are faulty, they and we: yet in my judgment, theirs
is the greater fault, more apparent causes, and much to be condemned. For my part, if it be not with me as I would, or as
it should, I do ascribe the cause, as Cardan did in the like case,[1]
meo infortunio potius quam illorum sceleri, to mine own infelicity
rather than their naughtiness:[2] although I have been baffled
in my time by some of them, and have as just cause to complain as another: or rather indeed to mine own negligence; for
I was ever like that Alexander in Plutarch,[3] Crassus his tutor
in philosophy, who, though he lived many years familiarly with
rich Crassus, was even as poor when from (which many wondered
at), as when he came first to him; he never asked, the other
never gave anything; when he travelled with Crassus he borrowed
a hat of him, at his return restored it again. I have had some
such noble friends' acquaintance, and scholars', but most part
(common courtesies and ordinary respects excepted), they and
I parted as we met, they gave me as much as I requested, and
that was—— And as Alexander ab Alexandro, *Genial. dier. lib.* 6,
cap. 16, made answer to Hieronymus Massianus, that wondered,
*quum plures ignavos et ignobiles ad dignitates et sacerdotia pro-
motos quotidie videret* [when he saw many indolent and unworthy persons daily promoted to high posts in the State and
the Church], when the other men rose, still he was in the same
state, *eodem tenore et fortuna, cui mercedem laborum studiorumque
deberi putaret*, whom he thought to deserve as well as the rest;
he made answer that he was content with his present estate,
was not ambitious, and although *objurgabundus suam segnitiem
accusaret, cum obscuræ sortis homines ad sacerdotia et pontificatus
evectos*, etc., he chid him for his backwardness, yet he was still
the same: and for my part, though I be not worthy perhaps to
carry Alexander's books, yet by some overweening and well-
wishing friends the like speeches have been used to me; but
I replied still with Alexander, that I had enough, and more
peradventure than I deserved; and with Libanius Sophista, that

rather chose (when honours and offices by the emperor were offered unto him) to be *talis sophista, quam talis magistratus* [such a sophist as he was than such a magistrate as others were], I had as lief be still Democritus Junior, and *privus privatus, si mihi jam daretur optio, quam talis fortasse doctor, talis dominus* [an obscure individual, if I had the choice, than a doctor of divinity or a bishop]. *Sed quorsum hæc?* [But why do I say all this?] For the rest 'tis on both sides *facinus detestandum* [a detestable crime] to buy and sell livings, to detain from the Church that which God's and men's laws have bestowed on it; but in them most, and that from the covetousness and ignorance of such as are interested in this business; I name covetousness in the first place, as the root of all these mischiefs, which, Achan-like, compels them to commit sacrilege, and to make simoniacal compacts (and what not), to their own ends, that kindles God's wrath,[1] brings a plague, vengeance, and an heavy visitation upon themselves and others. Some, out of that insatiable desire of filthy lucre, to be enriched, care not how they come by it, *per fas et nefas*, hook or crook, so they have it. And others, when they have with riot and prodigality embezzled their estates, to recover themselves, make a prey of the Church, robbing it, as Julian the Apostate did,[2] spoil parsons of their revenues (in keeping half back, as a great man amongst us observes[3]), "and that maintenance on which they should live": by means whereof, barbarism is increased, and a great decay of Christian professors: for who will apply himself to these divine studies, his son, or friend, when, after great pains taken, they shall have nothing whereupon to live? But with what event do they these things?

> *Opesque totis viribus venamini,*
> *At inde messis accidit miserrima.*[4]
>
> [You hunt for wealth with all your might, but reap a
> most wretched reward.]

They toil and moil, but what reap they? They are commonly unfortunate families that use it, accursed in their progeny, and, as common experience evinceth, accursed themselves in all their proceedings. "With what face" (as he[5] quotes out of Austin) "can they expect a blessing or inheritance from Christ in heaven, that defraud Christ of His inheritance here on earth?" I would all our simoniacal patrons, and such as detain tithes, would read those judicious tracts of Sir Henry Spelman and Sir James Sempill, knights; those late elaborate and learned treatises of

Dr. Tillesley, and Mr. Montague, which they have written of that subject. But though they should read, it would be to small purpose, *clames licet et mare cœlo confundas*; thunder, lighten, preach hell and damnation, tell them 'tis a sin, they will not believe it; denounce and terrify, "they have cauterized consciences,"[1] they do not attend; as the enchanted adder, they stop their ears. Call them base, irreligious, profane, barbarous, pagans, atheists, epicures (as some of them surely are), with the bawd in Plautus, *Euge! optime!* [Bravo! excellent!] they cry, and applaud themselves with that miser, *Simul ac nummos contemplor in arca*[2] [As soon as I see the money in the strongbox . . .]; say what you will, *quocunque modo rem* [however you get it, money]; as a dog barks at the moon, to no purpose are your sayings: take your heaven, let them have money. A base, profane, epicurean, hypocritical rout: for my part, let them pretend what zeal they will, counterfeit religion, blear the world's eyes, bombast themselves, and stuff out their greatness with church spoils, shine like so many peacocks; so cold is my charity, so defective in this behalf, that I shall never think better of them, than that they are rotten at core, their bones are full of epicurean hypocrisy, and atheistical marrow, they are worse than heathens. For, as Dionysius Halicarnasseus observes, *Antiq. Rom. lib. 7, Primum locum*, etc.,[3] "Greeks and barbarians observe all religious rites, and dare not break them for fear of offending their gods"; but our simoniacal contractors, our senseless Achans, our stupefied patrons, fear neither God nor devil, they have evasions for it, it is no sin, or not due *jure divino* [by divine law], or if a sin, no great sin, etc. And though they be daily punished for it, and they do manifestly perceive that, as he said, frost and fraud come to foul ends, yet, as Chrysostom[4] follows it, *Nulla ex pœna sit correctio, et quasi adversis malitia hominum provocetur, crescit quotidie quod puniatur* [correction brings no improvement, and, as if to spite the lawgiver, the crime which is punished becomes more common]: they are rather worse than better, *iram atque animos a crimine sumunt* [the very commission of the crime makes them more daring], and the more they are corrected, the more they offend: but let them take their course, *Rode, caper, vites*[5] [nibble away, goat, at the vines], go on still as they begin, 'tis no sin, let them rejoice secure, God's vengeance will overtake them in the end, and these ill-gotten goods, as an eagle's feathers, will consume the rest of their substance;[6] it is *aurum Tholosanum*[7] [gold of Toulouse (i.e. plundered)], and will produce no better effects. "Let them lay it up safe, and make their conveyances never so close, lock and shut door," saith Chrysostom, "yet fraud and covetousness, two most violent thieves, are still included, and a little gain evil-gotten will subvert the rest of their goods." [1] The eagle in Æsop, seeing a piece of flesh, now ready to be sacrificed, swept it away with her claws, and carried it to her nest; but there was a burning coal stuck to it by chance, which unawares consumed her young ones, nest, and all together. Let our simoniacal church-chopping patrons and sacrilegious harpies look for no better success.

A second cause is ignorance, and from thence contempt; *successit odium in literas ab ignorantia vulgi* [learning has become odious through the ignorance of the public], which Junius well perceived: [2] this hatred and contempt of learning proceeds out of ignorance; [3] as they are themselves barbarous, idiots, dull, illiterate, and proud, so they esteem of others. *Sint Mæcenates, non deerunt, Flacce, Marones:* let there be bountiful patrons, and there will be painful scholars in all sciences. But when they contemn learning, and think themselves sufficiently qualified, if they can write and read, scramble at a piece of evidence, or have so much Latin as that emperor [4] had: *Qui nescit dissimulare, nescit vivere* [he who cannot dissemble cannot live], they are unfit to do their country service, to perform or undertake any action or employment which may tend to the good of a commonwealth, except it be to fight, or to do country justice with common sense, which every yeoman can likewise do. And so they bring up their children, rude as they are themselves, unqualified, untaught, uncivil most part. *Quis e nostra juventute legitime instituitur literis? Quis oratores aut philosophos tangit? Quis historiam legit, illam rerum agendarum quasi animam? Præcipitant parentes vota sua* [5] [Which of our youths is properly trained in literature? Which of them knows anything of the orators or philosophers? Who reads history, the inspiration of public activity? Parents are in too great a hurry], etc., 'twas Lipsius' complaint to his illiterate countrymen, it may be ours. Now shall these men judge of a scholar's worth, that have no worth, that know not what belongs to a student's labours, that cannot distinguish between a true scholar and a drone? or him that by reason of a voluble tongue, a strong voice, a pleasing tone, and some trivantly polyanthean helps, steals and gleans a few notes from other men's harvests, and so makes a fairer show than he that is truly learned indeed: that thinks it no more to preach than to speak, "or to run away

with an empty cart," as a grave man said: [1] and thereupon vilify
us and our pains; scorn us and all learning. Because they
are rich, and have other means to live, they think it concerns
them not to know, or to trouble themselves with it; [2] a fitter
task for younger brothers, or poor men's sons, to be pen and
inkhorn men, pedantical slaves, and no whit beseeming the
calling of a gentleman; as Frenchmen and Germans commonly
do, neglect therefore all human learning, what have they to do
with it? Let mariners learn astronomy; merchants' factors
study arithmetic; surveyors get them geometry; spectacle-
makers optic; landleapers geography; town-clerks rhetoric;
what should he do with a spade, that hath no ground to dig;
or they with learning, that have no use of it? Thus they reason,
and are not ashamed to let mariners, prentices, and the
basest servants be better qualified than themselves. In former
times, kings, princes, and emperors were the only scholars,
excellent in all faculties.

Julius Cæsar mended the year, and writ his own Commentaries:

Media inter prælia semper,
Stellarum cœlique plagis, superisque vacavit.[3]

[In the midst of warfare he found time to study the
stars, the heavens, and the upper world.]

Antonius, Hadrian, Nero, Severus, Julian, etc.,[4] Michael the
emperor, and Isacius [5] were so much given to their studies that no
base fellow would take so much pains; Orion, Perseus, Alphonsus,
Ptolemæus, famous astronomers; Sabor, Mithridates, Lysimachus,
admired physicians; Plato's kings all; Evax, that Arabian
prince, a most expert jeweller and an exquisite philosopher;
the kings of Egypt were priests of old, and chosen from thence
—*Idem rex hominum Phœbique sacerdos* [both king he was of
men and priest to Phœbus]; but those heroical times are past;
the Muses are now banished in this bastard age *ad sordida
tuguriola* [to mean hovels], to meaner persons, and confined
alone almost to universities. In those days, scholars were
highly beloved, honoured,[6] esteemed; as old Ennius by Scipio
Africanus, Virgil by Augustus, Horace by Mæcenas: princes'
companions; dear to them, as Anacreon to Polycrates, Philoxenus to Dionysius, and highly rewarded. Alexander sent Xenocrates the philosopher fifty talents, because he was poor; *visu
rerum, aut eruditione præstantes viri, mensis olim regum adhibiti*
[men notable for foresight or learning formerly sat at table
with kings], as Philostratus relates of Hadrian and Lampridius

of Alexander Severus: famous clerks came to these princes'
courts, *velut in Lyceum*, as to an university, and were admitted
to their tables, *quasi divum epulis accumbentes* [as though being
entertained at feasts of the gods]; Archelaus, that Macedonian
king, would not willingly sup without Euripides (amongst the
rest he drank to him at supper one night and gave him a cup
of gold for his pains), *delectatus poetæ suavi sermone* [charmed
with the poet's delightful conversation]; and it was fit it should
be so, because, as Plato in his *Protagoras* well saith, a good
philosopher as much excels other men as a great king doth the
commons of his country;[1] and again, *quoniam illis nihil deest,
et minime egere solent, et disciplinas quas profitentur, soli a contemptu vindicare possunt*[2] [since they lack nothing and have
few wants, and alone are able to inspire respect for the arts
which they profess], they needed not to beg so basely, as they
compel scholars in our times to complain of poverty,[3] or crouch
to a rich chuff for a meal's meat, but could vindicate themselves, and those arts which they professed. Now they would
and cannot: for it is held by some of them as an axiom, that
to keep them poor will make them study; they must be dieted,
as horses to a race, not pampered, *alendos volunt, non saginandos,
ne melioris mentis flammula extinguatur*[4] [they want them to
be fed, not stuffed, lest the spark of genius in them should be
extinguished]; a fat bird will not sing, a fat dog cannot hunt,
and so by this depression of theirs, some want means,[5] others
will, all want encouragement,[6] as being forsaken almost; and
generally contemned. 'Tis an old saying, *Sint Mæcenates, non
deerunt, Flacce, Marones* [let there be patrons like Mæcenas,
there will be poets like Virgil], and 'tis a true saying still.
Yet oftentimes, I may not deny it, the main fault is in ourselves. Our academics too frequently offend in neglecting
patrons, as Erasmus well taxeth,[7] or making ill choice of them;
negligimus oblatos aut amplectimur parum aptos [we neglect
them when they offer themselves, or we cling to those that
are unsuitable], or if we get a good one, *non studemus mutuis
officiis favorem ejus alere*, we do not ply and follow him as we
should. *Idem mihi accidit adolescenti* [this happened to me
when I was a young man] (saith Erasmus, acknowledging his
fault), *et gravissime peccavi*, and I made a very serious mistake,
and so may I say myself,[8] I have offended in this, and so
peradventure have many others. We did not *respondere magnatum favoribus, qui cœperunt nos amplecti* [respond to the
favours of the great, who began to take us up], apply ourselves

with that readiness we should: idleness, love of liberty (*Immo-
dicus amor libertatis effecit ut diu cum perfidis amicis*, as he confesseth, *et pertinaci paupertate colluctarer* [through an excessive
love of liberty, I had for a long time to struggle with false
friends and poverty]), bashfulness, melancholy, timorousness,
cause many of us to be too backward and remiss. So some
offend in one extreme, but too many on the other, we are most
part too forward, too solicitous, too ambitious, too impudent;
we commonly complain *deesse Mæcenates*, of want of encouragement, want of means, whenas the true defect is in our want of
worth, our insufficiency. Did Mæcenas take notice of Horace or
Virgil till they had shown themselves first? or had Bavius and
Mævius any patrons? *Egregium specimen dent*, saith Erasmus,
let them approve themselves worthy first, sufficiently qualified
for learning and manners, before they presume or impudently
intrude and put themselves on great men as too many do; with
such base flattery, parasitical colloguing, such hyperbolical
elogies they do usually insinuate, that it is a shame to hear and
see. *Immodicæ laudes conciliant invidiam, potius quam laudem*
[excessive praise brings envy rather than fame], and vain commendations derogate from truth, and we think in conclusion
non melius de laudato, pejus de laudante, ill of both, the com-
mender and commended. So we offend, but the main fault is
in their harshness, defect of patrons. How beloved of old, and
how much respected was Plato to Dionysius! How dear to
Alexander was Aristotle, Demaratus to Philip, Solon to Crœsus,
Anaxarchus and Trebatius to Augustus, Cassius to Vespasian,
Plutarch to Trajan, Seneca to Nero, Simonides to Hiero! how
honoured!

> *Sed hæc prius fuere, nunc recondita*
> *Senent quiete,*[1]

[But all this was in the past, now it is gone and forgotten,]

those days are gone;

> *Et spes et ratio studiorum in Cæsare tantum:*[2]

> [Nor hope have we or any cause to study,
> Save in great Cæsar:]

as he said of old, we may truly say now; he is our
amulet, our sun,[3] our sole comfort and refuge, our Ptolemy,
our common Mæcenas, *Jacobus munificus, Jacobus pacificus,
mysta Musarum, rex Platonicus* [James the munificent, James the
pacific, the votary of the Muses, the Platonic king], *Grande decus,
columenque nostrum* [our great and crowning glory], a famous

scholar himself, and the sole patron, pillar, and sustainer of
learning: but his worth in this kind is so well known, that as
Paterculus of Cato, *Jam ipsum laudare nefas sit* [praise itself
would be impiety]: and which Pliny to Trajan,[1] *Seria te carmina,
honorque æternus annalium, non hæc brevis et pudenda prædicatio
colet* [Your glory will be enshrined in solemn epics and immortal
histories, not in this fleeting and worthless oration]. But he
is now gone, the sun of ours set, and yet no night follows, *Sol
occubuit, nox nulla secuta est.* We have such another in his
room, *aureus alter. Avulsus, simili frondescit virga metallo* [2]
[when the first is plucked, another bough appears likewise
of gold], and long may he reign and flourish amongst us.

 Let me not be malicious, and lie against my genius; I may
not deny but that we have a sprinkling of our gentry, here and
there one, excellently well learned, like those Fuggeri in Germany; Du Bartas, Du Plessis, Sadael, in France; Picus Mirandula,
Schottus, Barocius, in Italy; *Apparent rari nantes in gurgite vasto*
[Some scattered swimmers in the vasty deep]. But they are
but few in respect of the multitude, the major part (and some
again excepted, that are indifferent) are wholly bent for hawks
and hounds, and carried away many times with intemperate
lust, gaming, and drinking. If they read a book at any time
(*si quod est interim otii a venatu, poculis, alea, scortis* [if there is
any time which they can spare from hunting, drinking, gambling,
and women]) 'tis an English Chronicle, Sir Huon of Bordeaux,
Amadis de Gaul, etc., a play-book, or some pamphlet of news,
and that at such seasons only, when they cannot stir abroad, to
drive away time, their sole discourse is dogs, hawks, horses, and
what news? [3] If someone have been a traveller in Italy, or
as far as the emperor's court, wintered in Orleans, and can
court his mistress in broken French, wear his clothes neatly in
the newest fashion, sing some choice outlandish tunes, discourse
of lords, ladies, towns, palaces, and cities, he is complete and to
be admired: otherwise he and they are much at one; [4] no
difference between the master and the man, but worshipful
titles: wink and choose betwixt him that sits down (clothes
excepted) and him that holds the trencher behind him,
yet these men must be our patrons, our governors too sometimes, statesmen, magistrates, noble, great, and wise by
inheritance.

 Mistake me not (I say again), *Vos, o patricius sanguis*, you
that are worthy senators, gentlemen, I honour your names and
persons, and with all submissiveness prostrate myself to your

censure and service.   There are amongst you, I do ingenuously
confess, many well-deserving patrons and true patriots of my
knowledge, besides many hundreds which I never saw, no
doubt, or heard of, pillars of our commonwealth, whose worth,
bounty, learning, forwardness, true zeal in religion, and good
esteem of all scholars ought to be consecrated to all posterity; [1]
but of your rank, there are a debauched, corrupt, covetous,
illiterate crew again, no better than stocks, *merum pecus (testor
Deum, non mihi videri dignos ingenui hominis appellatione)*
[mere animals (as God lives, I do not think them worthy to
be called real human beings)], barbarous Thracians, *et quis ille
Thrax qui hoc neget?* [and what Thracian would deny this?],
a sordid, profane, pernicious company, irreligious, impudent,
and stupid, I know not what epithets to give them, enemies to
learning, confounders of the Church, and the ruin of a commonwealth; patrons they are by right of inheritance, and put in
trust freely to dispose of such livings to the Church's good; but
(hard taskmasters they prove) they take away their straw, and
compel them to make their number of brick; they commonly
respect their own ends, commodity is the steer of all their
actions, and him they present in conclusion as a man of greatest
gifts, that will give most; no penny, no paternoster,[2] as the
saying is.   *Nisi preces auro fulcias, amplius irritas* [unless you
support your suit with gold, you merely vex them]; *ut Cerberus
offa*, their attendants and officers must be bribed, fee'd, and
made, as Cerberus is with a sop by him that goes to hell.   It
was an old saying, *Omnia Romæ venalia* [all things are for sale at
Rome], 'tis a rag of Popery, which will never be rooted out,
there is no hope, no good to be done without money.   A clerk
may offer himself, approve his worth, learning, honesty, religion,
zeal,[3] they will commend him for it; but *probitas laudatur et
alget*[4] [virtue is praised and left to freeze].   If he be a man of
extraordinary parts, they will flock afar off to hear him, as they
did in Apuleius, to see Psyche: *Multi mortales confluebant ad
videndum sæculi decus, speculum gloriosum; laudatur ab omnibus,
spectatur ob omnibus, nec quisquam non rex, non regius, cupidus
ejus nuptiarum, petitor accedit; mirantur quidem divinam formam
omnes, sed ut similacrum fabre politum mirantur:* many mortal
men came to see fair Psyche, the glory of her age, they did admire
her, commend, desire her for her divine beauty, and gaze upon
her; but as on a picture; none would marry her, *quod indotata*
[because she had no dowry]; fair Psyche had no money.   So
they do by learning: [5]

Didicit jam dives avarus
Tantum admirari, tantum laudare disertos,
Ut pueri Junonis avem [1]

Your rich men have now learn'd of latter days
    T' admire, commend, and come together
To hear and see a worthy scholar speak,
    As children do a peacock's feather.

He shall have all the good words that may be given, "a proper
man, and 'tis pity he hath no preferment," [2] all good wishes, but
inexorable, indurate as he is, he will not prefer him, though it be
in his power, because he is *indotatus*, he hath no money. Or if
he do give him entertainment, let him be never so well qualified,
plead affinity, consanguinity, sufficiency, he shall serve seven
years, as Jacob did for Rachel, before he shall have it. If he
will enter at first, he must yet in at that simoniacal gate, come
off soundly, and put in good security to perform all covenants,
else he will not deal with, or admit him. [3] But if some poor
scholar, some parson chaff, will offer himself; some trencher-
chaplain, that will take it to the halves, thirds, or accept of
what he will give, he is welcome; be conformable, preach as he
will have him, he likes him before a million of others; for the best
is always best cheap: and then, as Hierome said to Chromatius,
patella dignum operculum [the lid is worthy of the pan], such
a patron, such a clerk; the cure is well supplied, and all parties
pleased. So that is still verified in our age, which Chrysostom
complained of in his time: *Qui opulentiores sunt, in ordinem*
parasitorum cogunt eos, et ipsos tanquam canes ad mensas sua
enutriunt, corumque impudentes ventres iniquarum cœnarum
reliquiis differciunt, iisdem pro arbitrio abutentes: [4] rich men
keep these lecturers and fawning parasites like so many dogs
at their tables, and filling their hungry guts with the offals of
their meat, they abuse tham at their pleasure, and make them
say what they propose. "As children do by a bird or a butterfly
in a string, pull in and let him out as they list, do they by their
trencher-chaplains, prescribe, command their wits, let in and
out as to them it seems best." [5] If the patron be precise, so
must his chaplain be; if he be papistical, his clerk must be
so, or else be turned out. These are those clerks which serve
the turn, whom they commonly entertain and present to
church livings, whilst in the meantime we that are university
men, like so many hide-bound calves in a pasture, tarry out our
time, wither away as a flower ungathered in a garden, and are
never used; or, as so many candles, illuminate ourselves alone,

obscuring one another's light, and are not discerned here at all, the least of which, translated to a dark room, or to some country benefice, where it might shine apart, would give a fair light and be seen over all. Whilst we lie waiting here, as those sick men did at the Pool of Bethesda,[1] till the angel stirred the water, expecting a good hour, they step between, and beguile us of our preferment. I have not yet said. If after long expectation, much expense, travel, earnest suit of ourselves and friends, we obtain a small benefice at last, our misery begins afresh; we are suddenly encountered with the flesh, world, and devil, with a new onset; we change a quiet life for an ocean of troubles, we come to a ruinous house, which, before it be habitable, must be necessarily to our great damage repaired; we are compelled to sue for dilapidations, or else sued ourselves, and scarce yet settled, we are called upon for our predecessors' arrearages; first-fruits, tenths, subsidies, are instantly to be paid, benevolence, procurations, etc., and, which is most to be feared, we light upon a cracked title, as it befell Clenard of Brabant, for his rectory and charge of his Beginæ; he was no sooner inducted, but instantly sued, *cœpimusque* (saith he [2]) *strenue litigare, et implacabili bello confligere* [we were at once involved in a tough lawsuit, and had to fight tooth and nail]; at length, after ten years' suit, as long as Troy's siege, when he had tired himself and spent his money, he was fain to leave all for quietness' sake, and give it up to his adversary. Or else we are insulted over and trampled on by domineering officers, fleeced by those greedy harpies to get more fees; we stand in fear of some precedent lapse; we fall amongst refractory, seditious sectaries, peevish puritans, perverse papists, a lascivious rout of atheistical epicures, that will not be reformed, or some litigious people (those wild beasts of Ephesus must be fought with) that will not pay their dues without much repining, or compelled by long suit; or *Laici clericis oppido infesti* [the laity hate the clergy], an old axiom; all they think well gotten that is had from the Church, and by such uncivil, harsh dealings they make their poor minister weary of his place, if not his life; and put case they be quiet, honest men, make the best of it, as often it falls out, from a polite and terse academic he must turn rustic, rude, melancholize alone, learn to forget, or else, as many do, become maltsters, graziers, chapmen, etc. (now banished from the academy, all commerce of the Muses, and confined to a country village, as Ovid was from Rome to Pontus), and daily converse with a company of idiots and clowns.

Nos interim quod attinet (nec enim immunes ab hac noxa sumus) idem reatus manet, idem nobis, et si non multo gravius, crimen objici potest: nostra enim culpa sit, nostra incuria, nostra avaritia, quod tam frequentes fœdæque fiant in Ecclesia nundinationes (templum est venale, deusque), *tot sordes invehantur, tanta grassetur impietas, tanta nequitia, tam insanus miseriarum euripus, et turbarum æstuarium, nostro, inquam, omnium (academicorum imprimis) vitio sit. Quod tot respublica malis afficiatur, a nobis seminarium; ultro malum hoc accersimus, et quavis contumelia, quavis interim miseria digni, qui pro virili non occurrimus. Quid enim fieri posse speramus, quum tot indies sine delectu pauperes alumni, terræ filii, et cujuscunque ordinis homunciones, ad gradus certatim admittantur? qui si definitionem, distinctionemque unam aut alteram memoriter edidicerint, et pro more tot annos in dialectica posuerint, non refert quo profectu, quales demum sint, idiotæ, nugatores, otiatores, aleatores, compotores, indigni, libidinis voluptatumque administri,* Sponsi Penelopes, nebulones, Alcinoique, *modo tot annos in academia insumpserint, et se pro togatis venditarint; lucri causa, et amicorum intercessu præsentantur: addo etiam et magnificis nonnunquam elogiis morum et scientiæ; et jam valedicturi testimonialibus hisce literis, amplissime conscriptis in eorum gratiam honorantur, ab iis qui fidei suæ et existimationis jacturam proculdubio faciunt.* Doctores enim et professores (*quod ait ille* [1]) id unum curant, ut ex professionibus frequentibus, et tumultuariis potius quam legitimis, commoda sua promoveant, et ex dispendio publico suum faciant incrementum. *Id solum in votis habent annuu plerumque magistratus, ut ab incipientium numero pecunias emungant,* [2] *nec multum interest qui sint, literatores an literati modo pingues, nitidi, ad aspectum speciosi, et quod verbo dicam pecuniosi sint. Philosophastri licentiantur in artibus, artem qu non habent,* [3] eosque sapientes esse jubent, qui nulla prædit sunt sapientia, et nihil ad gradum præterquam velle adferunt. *Theologastri (solvant modo), satis superque docti, per omne honorum gradus evehuntur et ascendunt. Atque hinc fit quod ta viles scurræ, tot passim idiotæ, literarum crepusculo positi, larvæ pastorum, circumforanei, vagi, barbi, fungi, crassi, asini, merur pecus, in sacrosanctos theologiæ aditus illotis pedibus irrumpant præter inverecundam frontem adferentes nihil, vulgares quasdar quisquilias, et scholarium quædam nugamenta, indigna quæ ve recipiantur in triviis. Hoc illud indignum genus hominum famelicum, indigum, vagum, ventris mancipium, ad stivam potiu relegandum, ad haras aptius quam ad aras, quod divinas hasc*

*literas turpiter prostituit; hi sunt qui pulpita complent, in ædes
nobilium irrepunt, et quum reliquis vitæ destituantur subsidiis,
ob corporis et animi egestatem, aliarum in repub. partium minime
capaces sint; ad sacram hanc ancoram confugiunt, sacerdotium
quovismodo captantes, non ex sinceritate, quod Paulus ait,*[1] sed
cauponantes verbum Dei. *Ne quis interim viris bonis detractum
quid putet, quos habet Ecclesia Anglicana quamplurimos, egregie
doctos, illustres, intactæ famæ homines, et plures forsan quam
quævis Europæ provincia; ne quis a florentissimis Academiis,
quæ viros undiquaque doctissimos, omni virtutum genere suspi-
ciendos, abunde producunt. Et multo plures utraque habitura,
multo splendidior futura, si non hæ sordes splendidum lumen
ejus obfuscarent, obstaret corruptio, et cauponantes quædam
harpyæ proletariique bonum hoc nobis non inviderent. Nemo
enim tam cæca mente, qui non hoc ipsum videat: nemo tam stolido
ingenio, qui non intelligat, tam pertinaci judicio, qui non agnoscat, ab his idiotis circumforaneis sacram pollui Theologiam,
ac cœlestes Musas quasi profanum quiddam prostitui.* Viles
animæ et effrontes (*sic enim Lutherus alicubi vocat*[2]) lucelli
causa, ut muscæ ad mulctra, ad nobilium et heroum mensas
advolant, in spem sacerdotii, *cujuslibet honoris, officii, in quamvis
aulam, urbem se ingerunt, ad quodvis se ministerium componunt:*

> *Ut nervis alienis mobile lignum
> Ducitur,*

offam sequentes, psittacorum more, in prædæ spem quidvis effu-
tiunt:[3] *obsecundantes parasiti* (*Erasmus ait*[4]) quidvis docent,
dicunt, scribunt, suadent, et contra conscientiam probant, non
ut salutarem reddant gregem, sed ut magnificam sibi parent
fortunam. Opiniones quasvis et decreta contra verbum Dei
astruunt, ne non offendant patronum, sed ut retineant favorem
procerum, et populi plausum, sibique ipsis opes accumulent.[5]
*Eo etenim plerumque animo ad Theologiam accedunt, non ut rem
divinam, sed ut suam faciant; non ad Ecclesiæ bonum promovendum,
sed expilandum; quærentes, quod Paulus ait,* non quæ Jesu
Christi, sed quæ sua, *non Domini thesaurum, sed ut sibi, suisque
thesaurizent. Nec tantum iis, qui vilioris fortunæ, et abjectæ
sortis sunt, hoc in usu est: sed et medios, summos, elatos, ne dicam
episcopos, hoc malum invasit.* Dicite, pontifices, in sacris quid
facit aurum?[6] Summos sæpe viros transversos agit avaritia,[7]
*et qui reliquis morum probitate prælucerent; hi facem præferunt ad
simoniam, et in corruptionis hunc scopulum impingentes, non
tondent pecus, sed deglubunt, et quocunque se conferunt, expilant,
exhauriunt, abradunt, magnum famæ suæ, si non animæ, nau-*

fragium facientes; ut non ab infimis ad summos, sed a summis ad infimos malum promanasse videatur, et illud verum sit quod ille olim lusit, Emerat ille prius, vendere jure potest. Simoniacus enim *(quod cum Leone dicam)* gratiam non accepit; si non accipit, non habet, et si non habet, nec gratus potest esse. *Tantum enim absunt istorum nonnulli, qui ad clavum sedent a promovendo reliquos, ut penitus impediant, probe sibi conscii, quibus artibus illic pervenerint.* Nam qui ob literas emersisse illos credat, desipit; qui vero ingenii, eruditionis, experientiæ, probitatis, pietatis, et Musarum id esse pretium putat *(quod olim revera fuit, hodie promittitur),* planissime insanit.[1] *Utcunque vel undecunque malum hoc originem ducat, non ultra quæram, ex his primordiis cœpit vitiorum colluvies, omnis calamitas, omne miseriarum agmen in Ecclesiam invehitur. Hinc tam frequens simonia, hinc ortæ querelæ, fraudes, imposturæ, ab hoc fonte se derivarunt omnes nequitiæ. Ne quid obiter dicam de ambitione, adulatione plusquam aulica, ne tristi domicœnio laborent, de luxu, de fœdo nonnunquam vitæ exemplo, quo nonnullos offendunt, de compotatione Sybaritica, etc. Hinc ille squalor academicus,* tristes hac tempestate Camenæ, *quum quivis homunculus artium ignarus, his artibus assurgat, hunc in modum promoveatur et ditescat, ambitiosis appellationibus insignis, et multis dignitatibus augustus, vulgi oculos perstringat, bene se habeat, et grandia gradiens majestatem quandam ac amplitudinem præ se ferens, miramque sollicitudinem, barba reverendus, toga nitidus, purpura coruscus, supellectilis splendore et famulorum numero maxime conspicuus.* Quales statuæ *(quod ait ille* [2]*)* quæ sacris in ædibus columnis imponuntur, velut oneri cedentes videntur, ac si insudarent, quum revera sensu sint carentes, et nihil saxeam adjuvent firmitatem: *Atlantes videri volunt, quum sint statuæ lapideæ, umbratiles revera homunciones, fungi forsan et bardi, nihil a saxo differentes. Quum interim docti viti, et vitæ sanctioris ornamentis præditi, qui æstum diei sustinent, his iniqua sorte serviant, minimo forsan salario contenti, puris nominibus nuncupati, humiles, obscuri, multoque digniores licet, egentes, inhonorati vitam privam privatam agant, tenuique sepulti sacerdotio, vel in collegiis suis in æternum incarcerati, inglorie delitescant. Sed nolo diutius hanc movere sentinam. Hinc illæ lacrimæ, lugubris Musarum habitus, hinc ipsa religio (quod cum Sesellio dicam)* in ludibrium et contemptum adducitur,[3] *abjectum sacerdotium (atque hæc ubi fiunt, ausim dicere, et putidum putidi dicterium de clero* [4] *usurpare)* putidum vulgus, *inops, rude, sordidum, melancholicum, miserum, despicabile, contemnendum.*

[As for ourselves (for we also are tarred with this brush), the same reproach applies to us, and the same charge can be brought against us even more forcibly. It is through our fault, our laxity, our greed, that there is so much disgraceful trafficking in the Church ("The temple is for sale, and eke its god"), that corruption, impiety, and wickedness are rampant in it, that it is a mad welter of misery, a seething mass of trouble. I say this is the fault of all of us, and especially those of us who belong to a university. It is we who are the ultimate cause of the evils under which the State is labouring. We have actually introduced these evils ourselves, though there is no reproach and no suffering we do not deserve for not having used all our might to oppose them. What can we expect when we vie with one another every day in admitting to degrees any and every impecunious student drawn from the dregs of the people who applies for one? They need only to have learnt by heart one or two definitions and distinctions, and to have spent the usual number of years in chopping logic—it matters not what progress they have made or of what character they are; they can be idiots, wasters, idlers, gamesters, boon companions, utterly worthless and abandoned, squanderers and profligates; let them only have spent so many years at the university in the capacity, real or supposed, of gownsmen, and they will find those who for the sake of profit or friendship will get them presented, and, what is more, in many cases with splendid testimonials to their character and learning. These they procure on leaving from persons who unquestionably jeopardize their own reputation by writing them. For (as one saith) doctors and professors think of nothing save how from their various professions, and especially those which are irregular, they may further their own advantage, and benefit themselves at the expense of the State. Our annual university heads as a rule pray only for the greatest possible number of freshmen to squeeze money from, and do not care whether they are educated or not, provided they are sleek, well groomed, and good-looking, and in one word, men of means. Philophasters innocent of the arts become Masters of Arts, and those are made wise by order who are endowed with no wisdom, and have no qualifications for a degree save a desire for it. Theologasters, if they can but pay, have enough learning and to spare, and proceed to the very highest degrees. Hence it comes that such a pack of vile buffoons, ignoramuses wandering in the twilight of learning, ghosts of clergymen, itinerant quacks, dolts, clods, asses, mere cattle, intrude with unwashed feet upon the sacred precincts of Theology, bringing with them nothing save brazen impudence, and some hackneyed quillets and scholastic trifles not good enough for a crowd at a street corner. This is that base and starveling class, needy, vagabond, slaves of their bellies, worthy to be sent back to the plough-tail, fitter for the pigsty than the altar, which has basely prostituted the study of divinity. These it is who fill the pulpits and creep into noblemen's houses. Having no other means of livelihood, and being incapable both mentally and physically of filling any other post, they find here an anchorage, and clutch at the priesthood, not from religious motives, but, as Paul says, "huckstering the word of God."

Let no one, however, think that I intend any disparagement of the many excellent men who are to be found in the Church of England, men eminent for their learning and of spotless reputation, of whom perhaps we can show more than any country in Europe; nor of our noble universities, which send out in abundance men of the highest learning and endowed with every virtue. Yet each of them would have many more such and would rise to much greater eminence, were its lustre not dimmed by these blots, and its purity corrupted by these huckstering harpies and beggars who envy it this boon. No one can be so blind as not to see, so stupid as not to perceive, so obstinate as not to admit that sacred Theology is defiled and the heavenly Muses prostituted by these ignorant mountebanks. Vile and shameless souls (as Luther calls them somewhere), in search of gain they fly to the tables of the nobility like flies to the milk-pail, in the hope of getting a church living or any other post or honour, they betake themselves to any hall or town, they will accept any employment, like marionettes pulled by strings, always on the scent, and like parrots babbling anything for the sake of a morsel: complaisant parasites (as Erasmus calls them), who will teach, write, say, recommend, approve anything, even against their own consciences, not to edify their flocks, but to improve their own fortunes. They subscribe to any opinions and tenets contrary to the word of God, only so as not to offend their patrons and to retain the favour of the nobles and the applause of the masses, and thereby acquire riches for themselves. Their object in taking up theology is to serve not God but themselves, not to promote the interests of the Church, but to plunder it, "seeking," as Paul says, "not the things of Jesus Christ but their own things"; not the treasure of the Lord, but the enrichment of themselves and their families. Nor is this

the practice only of those of meaner fortune and humbler
station, but also of the middle and higher ranks, even of the
bishops. "Tell us, ye pontiffs, what doth gold among the
sacraments?" Avarice often leads astray men of the highest
position, and those who ought to outshine all others in virtue.
These show the way to simony, and, falling foul of this stumbling-
block, do not merely shear but fleece the flock, and wherever
they turn they plunder, drain, and fleece, making shipwreck of
their reputations, if not of their souls, so that the evil seems to
proceed not from the bottom to the top, but from the top to
the bottom. They provide an illustration of the old gibe,
"What he had purchased he could rightly sell." For the
simoniac (to use the words of Leo) has not received a favour; if
he has not received it, he has it not; if he has it not, he cannot
confer it. Indeed, some of those who sit at the helm are so far
from promoting others that they do their best to hinder them,
being conscious of the arts by which they themselves attained
to their positions. For he who imagines that they rose to
eminence on account of their learning is no more than a simple-
ton; and any one who thinks that their position has been the
reward of talent, erudition, experience, virtue, piety, and love
of letters (once this was actually the case, but nowadays only
promises are secured by these means) is absolutely mad. How
or where this evil originated, I shall not further inquire; these,
however, are the beginnings of the foul stream of vice and the
host of miseries that have invaded the Church. Hence the
frequency of simony; here is the fount of complaints, frauds,
impostures, and all villainies. I say nothing of their ambition,
their flattery, grosser than that of the Court, whereby they seek
to escape cheerless fare at home, their luxury, the scandal given
by the bad example of their lives, their sybaritic drinking-bouts.
Hence the degradation of the universities, "the sadness of the
Muses in these times," when any contemptible ignoramus can
rise by these arts, obtain promotion and wealth by these methods,
with imposing titles and distinctions, in virtue of which he can
dazzle the eyes of the multitude, give himself airs, and strut
about with great pomp and dignity, paying great attention to
his person, cultivating a flowing beard, wearing a robe glittering
with purple, and further attracting attention by the splendour of
his furniture and the number of his servants. Just as the
statues (as he says) which are set on pillars in sacred buildings
seem to be giving way under their load, and almost to sweat,
though they are devoid of feeling and add nothing to the strength

of the building; so these people wish to be thought Atlases, though they are merely stone statues, effeminate manikins, perhaps dizzards and dolts, differing in no way from stone. Meanwhile learned men, graced with all the distinctions of a holy life, and who bear the heat of the day, are condemned by a hard fate to serve these men, content perhaps with a scanty salary, without any titles to their names, humble and obscure, though eminently worthy, and so, needy and unhonoured, they lead a retired life, buried in some poor benefice or imprisoned for ever in their college chambers, where they languish in obscurity. But I will stir up these foul waters no more. Hence our tears, hence it is that the Muses are in mourning, and that religion itself, as Sesellius says, is brought into ridicule and contempt, and the clerical calling is rendered vile. And in view of these facts, I venture to repeat the abusive expressions which some vulgar fellow has applied to the clergy, that they are a rotten crowd, beggarly, uncouth, filthy, melancholy, miserable, despicable, and contemptible.]

MEMB. IV.

Subsect. I.—*Non-necessary, remote, outward, adventitious, or accidental Causes: as first from the Nurse*

Of those remote, outward, ambient, necessary causes, I have sufficiently discoursed in the precedent member. The non-necessary follow; of which, saith Fuchsius, no art can be made, by reason of their uncertainty, casualty, and multitude;[1] so called "not necessary" because, according to Fernelius, "they may be avoided, and used without necessity."[2] Many of these accidental causes, which I shall entreat of here, might have well been reduced to the former, because they cannot be avoided, but fatally happen to us, though accidentally and unawares, at some time or other: the rest are contingent and inevitable, and more properly inserted in this rank of causes. To reckon up all is a thing unpossible; of some, therefore, most remarkable of these contingent causes which produce melancholy, I will briefly speak, and in their order.

From a child's nativity, the first ill accident that can likely befall him in this kind is a bad nurse, by whose means alone he

may be tainted with this malady from his cradle.[1] Aulus
Gellius, *lib.* 12, *cap.* 1, brings in Favorinus, that eloquent philosopher, proving this at large, "that there is the same virtue
and property in the milk as in the seed, and not in men alone,
but in all other creatures." He gives instance in a kid and lamb:
"if either of them suck of the other's milk, the lamb of the
goat's, or the kid of the ewe's, the wool of the one will be hard,
and the hair of the other soft." [2] Giraldus Cambrensis, *Itinerar.
Cambriæ, lib.* 1, *cap.* 2, confirms this by a notable example which
happened in his time. A sow-pig by chance sucked a brach,
and when she was grown, "would miraculously hunt all manner of
deer, and that as well, or rather better than any ordinary
hound." [3] His conclusion is, "that men and beasts participate
of her nature and conditions by whose milk they are fed." [4]
Favorinus urgeth it farther, and demonstrates it more evidently,
that if a nurse be "misshapen, unchaste, unhonest, impudent,
drunk," [5] cruel,[6] or the like, the child that sucks upon her breast
will be so too"; all other affections of the mind and diseases are
almost engrafted, as it were, and imprinted into the temperature
of the infant, by the nurse's milk, as pox, leprosy, melancholy, etc.
Cato for some such reason would make his servants' children
suck upon his wife's breast, because by that means they would
love him and his the better, and in all likelihood agree with
them. A more evident example that the minds are altered by
milk cannot be given, than that of Dion, which he relates of
Caligula's cruelty; [7] it could neither be imputed to father nor
mother, but to his cruel nurse alone, that anointed her paps
with blood still when he sucked, which made him such a murderer, and to express her cruelty to a hair: and that of Tiberius,
who was a common drunkard, because his nurse was such a
one. *Et si delira fuerit* (one observes [8]), *infantulum delirum
faciet*, if she be a fool or dolt, the child she nurseth will take
after her, or otherwise be misaffected; which Franciscus Barbarus, *lib.* 2, *cap. ult.de re uxoria*, proves at full, and Ant. Guevara,
lib. 2, *de Marco Aurelio*: the child will surely participate. For
bodily sickness there is no doubt to be made. Titus, Vespasian's son, was therefore sickly, because the nurse was so
(Lampridius). And if we may believe physicians, many times
children catch the pox from a bad nurse (Botaldus, *cap.* 61 *de
lue vener.*). Besides evil attendance, negligence, and many gross
inconveniences which are incident to nurses, much danger may
so come to the child. For these causes [9] Aristotle, *Polit. lib.* 7,
cap. 17, Favorinus, and Marcus Aurelius would not have a

child put to nurse at all, but every mother to bring up her own, of what condition soever she be; for a sound and able mother to put out her child to nurse, is *naturæ intemperies* [an outrage on Nature], so Guazzo calls it,[1] 'tis fit therefore she should be nurse herself; the mother will be more careful, loving, and attendant, than any servile woman, or such hired creatures; this all the world acknowledgeth; *convenientissimum est* (as Rod. à Castro, *de nat. mulierum, lib.* 4, *cap.* 12, in many words confesseth) *matrem ipsam lactare infantem* [it is most fit that the mother should suckle her own infant]—who denies that it should be so?—and which some women most curiously observe; amongst the rest, that Queen of France, a Spaniard by birth, that was so precise and zealous in this behalf, that when in her absence a strange nurse had suckled her child, she was never quiet till she had made the infant vomit it up again.[2] But she was too jealous. If it be so, as many times it is, they must be put forth, the mother be not fit or well able to be a nurse, I would then advise such mothers (as Plutarch doth in his book *de liberis educandis*,[3] and St. Hierome, *lib.* 2, *epist.* 27, *Lætæ de institut. fil.*, Magninus, *part.* 2 *Reg. sanit. cap.* 7,[4] and the said Rodericus), that they make choice of a sound woman, of a good complexion, honest, free from bodily diseases, if it be possible, all passions and perturbations of the mind, as sorrow, fear, grief, folly,[5] melancholy. For such passions corrupt the milk, and alter the temperature of the child, which now being *udum et molle lutum*[6] [moist and soft clay], is easily seasoned and perverted. And if such a nurse may be found out, that will be diligent and careful withal, let Favorinus and M. Aurelius plead how they can against it, I had rather accept of her in some cases than the mother herself, and which Bonaciolus the physician, Nic. Biesius the politician, *lib.* 4 *de repub. cap.* 8, approves, "some nurses are much to be preferred to some mothers."[7] For why may not the mother be naught, a peevish, drunken flirt, a waspish, choleric slut, a crazed piece, a fool (as many mothers are), unsound, as soon as the nurse? There is more choice of nurses than mothers; and therefore, except the mother be most virtuous, staid, a woman of excellent good parts, and of a sound complexion, I would have all children in such cases committed to discreet strangers. And 'tis the only way; as by marriage they are engrafted to other families to alter the breed, or if anything be amiss in the mother, as Lodovicus Mercatus contends, *tom.* 2, *lib. de morb. hæred.*, to prevent diseases and future maladies, to correct and qualify the child's ill-disposed temperature, which he had from his parents. This is an excellent remedy, if good choice be made of such a nurse.

SUBSECT. II.—*Education a Cause of Melancholy*

Education, of these accidental causes of melancholy, may justly challenge the next place, for if a man escape a bad nurse, he may be undone by evil bringing up. Jason Pratensis [1] puts this of education for a principal cause; bad parents, stepmothers, tutors, masters, teachers, too rigorous, too severe, too remiss or indulgent on the other side, are often fountains and furtherers of this disease. Parents, and such as have the tuition and oversight of children, offend many times in that they are too stern, always threatening, chiding, brawling, whipping, or striking; by means of which their poor children are so disheartened and cowed, that they never after have any courage, a merry hour in their lives, or take pleasure in anything. There is a great moderation to be had in such things, as matters of so great moment to the making or marring of a child. Some fright their children with beggars, bugbears, and hobgoblins, if they cry, or be otherwise unruly; but they are much to blame in it, many times, saith Lavater, *de spectris, part.* 1, *cap.* 5, *ex metu in morbos graves incidunt et noctu dormientes clamant*, for fear they fall into many diseases, and cry out in their sleep, and are much the worse for it all their lives: these things ought not at all, or to be sparingly done, and upon just occasion. Tyrannical, impatient, hair-brain schoolmasters, *aridi magistri* [dry masters], as Fabius terms them,[2] *Ajaces flagelliferi* [flogging bullies], are in this kind as bad as hangmen and executioners; they make many children endure a martyrdom all the while they are at school; with bad diet, if they board in their houses, too much severity and ill-usage, they quite pervert their temperature of body and mind: still chiding, railing, frowning, lashing, tasking, keeping, that they are *fracti animis*, moped many times, weary of their lives, *nimia severitate deficiunt et desperant* [3] [through harsh treatment they become dull and dispirited], and think no slavery in the world (as once I did myself) like to that of a grammar scholar. *Præceptorum ineptiis discruciantur ingenia puerorum* [the teachers through their stupidities make the pupils suffer agonies of mind], saith Erasmus, they tremble at his voice, looks, coming in. St. Austin, in the first book of his Confessions and 9th *cap.*, calls this schooling *meticulosam necessitatem* [a dreadful compulsion], and elsewhere a martyrdom, and confesseth of

himself, how cruelly he was tortured in mind for learning Greek:
Nulla verba noveram, et sævis terroribus et pænis, ut nossem
instabatur mihi vehementer, I knew nothing, and with cruel
terrors and punishment I was daily compelled. Beza[1] complains in like case of a rigorous schoolmaster in Paris, that made
him by his continual thunder and threats once in a mind to
drown himself, had he not met by the way with an uncle of his
that vindicated him from that misery for the time, by taking
him to his house. Trincavellius, *lib.* 1, *consil.* 16, had a patient
nineteen years of age, extremely melancholy, *ob nimium studium*
Tarvitii et præceptoris minas, by reason of overmuch study, and
his tutor's threats.[2] Many masters are hard-hearted, and
bitter to their servants, and by that means do so deject, with
terrible speeches and hard usage so crucify them, that they
become desperate, and can never be recalled.

Others again, in that opposite extreme, do as great harm by
their too much remissness; they give them no bringing up, no
calling to busy themselves about, or to live in, teach them no
trade, or set them in any good course; by means of which their
servants, children, scholars, are carried away with that stream
of drunkenness, idleness, gaming, and many such irregular
courses, that in the end they rue it, curse their parents, and
mischief themselves. Too much indulgence causeth the like
inepta patris lenitas et facilitas prava[3] [the father's gentleness
can be misplaced and his indulgence corrupting], whenas,
Micio-like, with too much liberty and too great allowance, they
feed their children's humours, let them revel, wench, riot,
swagger, and do what they will themselves, and then punish
them with a noise of musicians.

> *Obsonet, potet, oleat unguenta de meo;*
> *Amat? dabitur a me argentum ubi erit commodum.*
> *Fores effregit? restituentur; discidit*
> *Vestem? resarcietur. . . . Faciat quod lubet,*
> *Sumat, consumat, perdat, decretum est pati.*[4]

He wants to eat, drink, perfume? I will pay.
Money for his sweetheart? He shall have it.
He has broken doors? Rebuild them. Torn his coat?
Repair it. Let him do just what he likes.
He 's free to take, to spend, to waste my all.
I will not murmur.

But, as Demea told him, *Tu illum corrumpi sinis,* your lenity will
be his undoing, *prævidere videor jam diem illum, quum hic egens*
profugiet aliquo militatum [methinks I foresee the day when he
will run away and join the army], I foresee his ruin. So parents

often err, many fond mothers especially, doat so much upon their children, like Æsop's ape,[1] till in the end they crush them to death, *Corporum nutrices animarum novercæ*, pampering up their bodies to the undoing of their souls: they will not let them be corrected or controlled,[2] but still soothed up in everything they do, that in conclusion "they bring sorrow, shame, heaviness to their parents" (Eccles. xxx, 8, 9), "become wanton, stubborn, wilful, and disobedient"; rude, untaught, headstrong, incorrigible, and graceless. "They love them so foolishly," saith Cardan, "that they rather seem to hate them, bringing them not up to virtue but injury, not to learning but to riot, not to sober life and conversation but to all pleasure and licentious behaviour."[3] Who is he of so little experience that knows not this of Fabius to be true? "Education is another nature, altering the mind and will, and I would to God" (saith he) "we ourselves did not spoil our children's manners by our overmuch cockering and nice education, and weaken the strength of their bodies and minds; that causeth custom, custom nature,"[4] etc. For these causes Plutarch, in his book *de lib. educ.*, and Hierome, *Epist. lib. i, epist.* 17, to Læta, *de institut. filiæ*, gives a most especial charge to all parents, and many good cautions about bringing up of children, that they be not committed to undiscreet, passionate, bedlam tutors, light, giddy-headed, or covetous persons, and spare for no cost, that they may be well nurtured and taught, it being a matter of so great consequence. For such parents as do otherwise, Plutarch esteems of them "that [they] are more careful of their shoes than of their feet,"[5] that rate their wealth above their children. And he, saith Cardan, "that leaves his son to a covetous schoolmaster to be informed, or to a close abbey to fast and learn wisdom together, doth no other, than that he be a learned fool, or a sickly wise man."[6]

SUBSECT. III.—*Terrors and Affrights, Causes of Melancholy*

Tully, in the fourth of his Tusculans, distinguishes these errors which arise from the apprehension of some terrible object heard or seen, from other fears, and so doth Patricius, *lib.* 5, *tit.* 4, *de regis institut.* Of all fears they are most pernicious and violent, and so suddenly alter the whole temperature of the body, move the soul and spirits, strike such a deep impression, that the parties can never be recovered, causing more grievous and fiercer melancholy, as Felix Plater, *cap.* 3 *de mentis lienat.*, speaks out of his experience, than any inward cause

whatsoever; "and imprints itself so forcibly in the spirits, brain,
humours, that if all the mass of blood were let out of the body,
it could hardly be extracted. This horrible kind of melancholy"
(for so he terms it) "had been often brought before him, and
troubles and affrights commonly men and women, young and
old of all sorts."[1] Hercules de Saxonia calls this kind of
melancholy (*ab agitatione spirituum*) by a peculiar name; it
comes from the agitation, motion, contraction, dilatation of
spirits,[2] not from any distemperature of humours, and produceth strong effects. This terror is most usually caused, as
Plutarch will have, "from some imminent danger, when a
terrible object is at hand,"[3] heard, seen, or conceived, "truly
appearing,[4] or in a dream":[5] and many times the more sudden
the accident, it is the more violent.

> *Stat terror animis, et cor attonitum salit,*
> *Pavidumque trepidis palpitat venis jecur.*[6]

> Their soul's affright, their heart amazed quakes,
> The trembling liver pants i' th' veins, and aches.

Artemidorus the grammarian lost his wits by the unexpected
sight of a crocodile (Laurentius, 7 *de melan.*). The massacre at
Lyons, 1572, in the reign of Charles IX, was so terrible and
fearful, that many ran mad, some died, great-bellied women
were brought to bed before their time, generally all affrighted
and aghast.[7] Many lose their wits "by the sudden sight of some
spectrum or devil, a thing very common in all ages,"[8] saith
Lavater, *part.* 1, *cap.* 9, as Orestes did at the sight of the Furies
which appeared to him in black (as Pausanias records[9]). The
Greeks call them μορμολυκεῖα [bogies], which so terrify their
souls, or if they be but affrighted by some counterfeit devils
in jest,

> *Ut pueri trepidant, atque omina cæcis*
> *In tenebris metuunt,*[10]

as children in the dark conceive hobgoblins, and are so afraid
they are the worse for all their lives; some by sudden fires,
earthquakes, inundations, or any such dismal objects—Themison
the physician fell into an hydrophobia, by seeing one sick of that
disease (Diosorides, *lib.* 6, *cap.* 33)—or by the sight of a monster, a
carcass, they are disquieted many months following, and canno
endure the room where a corse hath been, for a world would
not be alone with a dead man, or lie in that bed many year
after in which a man hath died. At Basil many little children
in the springtime went to gather flowers in a meadow at the

town's end, where a malefactor hung in gibbets; all gazing at it, one by chance flung a stone, and made it stir, by which accident the children affrighted ran away; one slower than the rest, looking back, and seeing the stirred carcass wag towards her, cried out it came after, and was so terribly affrighted that for many days she could not rest, eat, or sleep, she could not be pacified, but melancholy, died.[1] In the same town another child, beyond the Rhine, saw a grave opened, and upon the sight of a carcass, was so troubled in mind that she could not be comforted, but a little after departed, and was buried by it[2] (Platerus, *Observat. lib.* 1). A gentlewoman of the same city saw a fat hog cut up; when the entrails were opened, and a noisome savour offended her nose, she much misliked, and would not longer abide; a physician in presence told her, as that hog, so was she, full of filthy excrements, and aggravated the matter by some other loathsome instances, insomuch this nice gentlewoman apprehended it so deeply that she fell forthwith a-vomiting, was so mightily distempered in mind and body, that with all his art and persuasions, for some months after, he could not restore her to herself again; she could not forget it, or remove the object out of her sight (*Idem*). Many cannot endure to see a wound opened, but they are offended: a man executed, or labour of any fearful disease, as possession, apoplexies, one bewitched; or if they read by chance of some terrible thing,[3] the symptoms alone of such a disease, or that which they dislike, they are instantly troubled in mind, aghast, ready to apply it to themselves, they are as much disquieted as if they had seen it, or were so affected themselves. *Hecatas sibi videntur somniare*, they dream and continually think of it. As lamentable effects are caused by such terrible objects heard, read, or seen; *auditus maximos motus in corpore facit* [the body is greatly affected through the sense of hearing], as Plutarch holds,[4] no sense makes greater alteration of body and mind: sudden speech sometimes, unexpected news, be they good or bad, *prævisa minus oratio*, will move as much, *animum obruere, et de sede sua dejicere*, as a philosopher observes,[5] will take away our sleep and appetite, disturb and quite overturn us. Let them bear witness that have heard those tragical alarums, outcries, hideous noises, which are many times suddenly heard in the dead of night by irruption of enemies and accidental fires, etc., those panic fears,[6] which often drive men out of their wits, bereave them of sense, understanding, and all, some for a time, some for their whole lives, they never recover it.

The Midianites were so affrighted by Gideon's soldiers, they breaking but every one a pitcher;[1] and Hannibal's army by such a panic fear was discomfited at the walls of Rome.[2] Augusta Livia, hearing a few tragical verses recited out of Virgil, *Tu Marcellus eris*, etc., fell down dead in a swoon. Edinus, King of Denmark, by a sudden sound which he heard, "was turned into fury with all his men"[3] (Cranzius, *lib.* 5 *Dan. hist.* and Alexander ab Alexandro, *lib.* 3, *cap.* 5). Amatus Lusitanus had a patient, that by reason of bad tidings became *epilepticus* (*cen.* 2, *cura* 90). Cardan, *Subtil. lib.* 18, saw one that lost his wits by mistaking of an echo. If one sense alone can cause such violent commotions of the mind, what may we think when hearing, sight, and those other senses are all troubled at once, as by some earthquakes, thunder, lightning, tempests, etc.? At Bologna in Italy, *anno* 1504, there was such a fearful earthquake about eleven o'clock in the night (as Beroaldus, in his book *de terræ motu*, hath commended to posterity[4]) that all the city trembled, the people thought the world was at an end, *actum de mortalibus*; such a fearful noise it made, such a detestable smell, the inhabitants were infinitely affrighted, and some ran mad. *Audi rem atrocem, et annalibus memorandum* (mine author adds), hear a strange story, and worthy to be chronicled; I had a servant at the same time called Fulco Argelanus, a bold and proper man, so grievously terrified with it, that he was first melancholy, after doted, at last mad, and made away himself. At Fuscinum in Japan "there was such an earthquake, and darkness on a sudden, that many men were offended with headache, many overwhelmed with sorrow and melancholy. At Meacum whole streets and goodly palaces were overturned at the same time, and there was such a hideous noise withal, like thunder, and filthy smell, that their hair stared for fear, and their hearts quaked, men and beasts were incredibly terrified. In Sacai, another city, the same earthquake was so terrible unto them, that many were bereft of their senses; and others by that horrible spectacle so much amazed, that they knew not what they did."[6] Blasius, a Christian, the reporter of the news, was so affrighted for his part, that, though it were two months after, he was scarce his own man, neither could he drive the remembrance of it out of his mind. Many times some years following, they will tremble afresh at the remembrance or conceit of such a terrible object,[7] even all their lives long, if mention be made of it. Cornelius Agrippa relates, or of Gulielmus Parisiensis, a story of one that, after a distasteful purge which a physician had prescribed unto him, was so much moved, "that at the very sight of physic he would be distempered";[1] though he never so much as smelled to it, the box of physic long after would give him a purge; nay, the very remembrance of it did effect it; "like travellers and seamen," saith Plutarch, "that when they have been sanded, or dashed on a rock, for ever after fear not that mischance only, but all such dangers whatsoever."[2]

SUBSECT. IV.—*Scoffs, Calumnies, bitter Jests, how they cause Melancholy*

It is an old saying, "A blow with a word strikes deeper than a blow with a sword";[3] and many men are as much galled with a calumny, a scurrile and bitter jest, a libel, a pasquil, satire, apologue, epigram, stage-plays, or the like, as with any misfortune whatsoever. Princes and potentates, that are otherwise happy and have all at command, secure and free, *quibus potentia sceleris impunitatem fecit* [who are able to commit crimes with impunity], are grievously vexed with these pasquilling libels and satires; they fear a railing Aretine more than an enemy in the field,[4] which made most princes of his time (as some relate) "allow him a liberal pension, that he should not tax them in his satires."[5] The gods had their Momus, Homer his Zoilus, Achilles his Thersites, Philip his Demades: the Cæsars themselves in Rome were commonly taunted. There was never wanting a Petronius, a Lucian in those times, nor will be a Rabelais, an Euphormio, a Boccalinus in ours. Adrian the sixth Pope[6] was so highly offended, and grievously vexed with pasquillers at Rome, he gave command that statue[7] should be demolished and burned, the ashes flung into the River Tiber, and had done it forthwith, had not Lodovicus Suessanus, a facete companion, dissuaded him to the contrary, by telling him that Pasquil's ashes would turn to frogs in the bottom of the river, and croak worse and louder than before.[8] *Genus irritabile vatum* [poets are a quick-tempered tribe], and therefore Socrates in Plato adviseth all his friends, "that respect their credits, to stand in awe of poets, for they are terrible fellows, can praise and dispraise as they see cause."[9] *Hinc quam sit calamus sævior ense patet* [Hence you may see, the written word can be more cruel than the sword]. The prophet David complains (Ps. cxxiii, 4), "that his soul was full of the mocking of the wealthy, and of the despitefulness of the proud," and

(Ps. lv, 3, 4) "for the voice of the wicked, etc., and their hate; his heart trembled within him, and the terrors of death came upon him; fear and horrible fear," etc., and (Ps. lxix, 20) "Rebuke hath broken my heart, and I am full of heaviness." Who hath not like cause to complain, and is not so troubled, that shall fall into the mouths of such men? for many are of so petulant a spleen,[1] and have that figure *sarcasmus* so often in their mouths, so bitter, so foolish, as Balthasar Castilio notes of them, that "they cannot speak, but they must bite";[2] they had rather lose a friend than a jest; and what company soever they come in, they will be scoffing, insulting over their inferiors, especially over such as anyway depend upon them, humouring, misusing, or putting gulleries on some or other till they have made by their humouring or gulling *ex stulto insanum*[3] [a fool into a madman] a mope or a noddy, and all to make themselves merry:

> *Dummodo risum*
> *Excutiat sibi, non hic cuiquam parcit amico.*[4]

[To raise a laugh he will not spare a friend.]

Friends, neuters, enemies, all are as one, to make a fool a madman is their sport, and they have no greater felicity than to scoff and deride others; they must sacrifice to the god of laughter, with them in Apuleius,[5] once a day, or else they shall be melancholy themselves; they care not how they grind and misuse others, so they may exhilarate their own persons. Their wits indeed serve them to that sole purpose, to make sport, to break a scurrile jest, which is *levissimus ingenii fructus*, the froth of wit, as Tully holds,[6] and for this they are often applauded; in all other discourse, dry, barren, stramineous, dull and heavy, here lies their genius, in this they alone excel, please themselves and others. Leo Decimus, that scoffing pope, as Jovius hath registered in the fourth book of his life, took an extraordinary delight in humouring of silly fellows, and to put gulleries upon them; by commending some, persuading others to this or that,[7] he made *ex stolidis stultissimos et maxime ridiculos, ex stultis insanos*, soft fellows stark noddies, and such as were foolish quite mad before he left them. One memorable example he recites there, of Tarascomus of Parma, a musician that was so humoured by Leo Decimus and Bibbiena his second in this business, that he thought himself to be a man of most excellent skill (who was indeed a ninny); they "made him so foolish songs, and invent new ridiculous precepts, which they did highly commend,"[8] as to tie his arm that played on the

lute, to make him strike a sweeter stroke, "and to pull down
the arras hangings, because the voice would be clearer, by
reason of the reverberation of the wall." [1]   In the like manner
they persuaded one Baraballius, of Caieta, that he was as good
a poet as Petrarch; would have him to be made a laureate
poet, and invite all his friends to his instalment; and had so
possessed the poor man with a conceit of his excellent poetry,
that, when some of his more discreet friends told him of his
folly, he was very angry with them, and said "they envied his
honour, and prosperity": [2] it was strange (saith Jovius) to see
an old man of sixty years, a venerable and grave old man, so
gulled.   But what cannot such scoffers do, especially if they
find a soft creature on whom they may work? Nay, to say
truth, who is so wise, or so discreet, that may not be humoured
in this kind, especially if some excellent wits shall set upon
him. He that mads others, if he were so humoured, would be as
mad himself, as much grieved and tormented; he might cry
with him in the comedy, *Pro Jupiter, tu homo me adigis ad
insaniam* [Man alive, you are driving me mad]. For all is in
these things as they are taken; if he be a silly soul, and do
not perceive it, 'tis well, he may haply make others sport, and
be no whit troubled himself; but if he be apprehensive of his
folly, and take it to heart, then it torments him worse than
any lash. A bitter jest, a slander, a calumny, pierceth deeper
than any loss, danger, bodily pain, or injury whatsoever; *leviter
enim volat* [it flies swiftly], as Bernard of an arrow, *sed graviter
vulnerat* [but wounds deeply], especially if it shall proceed from
a virulent tongue, "it cuts" (saith David) "like a two-edged sword.
They shoot bitter words as arrows" (Ps. lxiv, 3); "And they
smote with their tongues" (Jer. xviii, 18), and that so hard,
that they leave an incurable wound behind them Many men
are undone by this means, moped, and so dejected, that they
are never to be recovered; and of all other men living, those
which are actually melancholy, or inclined to it, are most
sensible (as being suspicious, choleric, apt to mistake) and
impatient of an injury in that kind: they aggravate, and so
meditate continually of it, that it is a perpetual corrosive, not
to be removed till time wear it out.   Although they peradventure that so scoff do it alone in mirth and merriment, and
hold it *optimum aliena frui insania*, an excellent thing to enjoy
another man's madness; yet they must know that it is a mortal
sin (as Thomas holds [3]) and, as the prophet David denounceth,
"they that use it shall never dwell in God's tabernacle." [4]

Such scurrile jests, flouts, and sarcasms, therefore, ought not at all to be used; especially to our betters, to those that are in misery, or anyway distressed: for to such *ærumnarum incrementa sunt*, they multiply grief, and as he perceived,[1] *In multis pudor, in multis iracundia*, etc., many are ashamed, many vexed, angered, and there is no greater cause or furtherer of melancholy. Martin Cromerus, in the sixth book of his history, hath a pretty story to this purpose, of Uladislaus the Second, King of Poland, and Peter Dunnius, Earl of Shrine; they had been hunting late, and were enforced to lodge in a poor cottage. When they went to bed, Uladislaus told the earl in jest, that his wife lay softer with the Abbot of Shrine; he, not able to contain, replied, *Et tua cum Dabesso*, And yours with Dabessus, a gallant young gentleman in the court, whom Christina the queen loved. *Tetigit id dictum principis animum*, these words of his so galled the prince, that he was long after *tristis et cogitabundus*, very sad and melancholy for many months; but they were the earl's utter undoing: for when Christina heard of it, she persecuted him to death. Sophia the empress, Justinian's wife, broke a bitter jest upon Narses the eunuch, a famous captain, then disquieted for an overthrow which he lately had: that he was fitter for a distaff, and to keep women company, than to wield a sword, or to be general of an army; but it cost her dear, for he so far distasted it, that he went forthwith to the adverse part, much troubled in his thoughts, caused the Lombards to rebel, and thence procured many miseries to the commonwealth. Tiberius the emperor withheld a legacy from the people of Rome, which his predecessor Augustus had lately given, and perceiving a fellow round a dead corse in the ear, would needs know wherefore he did so; the fellow replied, that he wished the departed soul to signify to Augustus, the commons of Rome were yet unpaid: for this bitter jest the emperor caused him forthwith to be slain, and carry the news himself. For this reason, all those that otherwise approve of jests in some cases, and facete companions (as who doth not?), let them laugh and be merry, *rumpantur et ilia Codro* [though Codrus should burst], 'tis laudable and fit; those yet will by no means admit them in their companies, that are anyway inclined to this malady; *non jocandum cum iis qui miseri sunt et ærumnosi*, no jesting with a discontented person: 'tis Castilio's caveat, Jo. Pontanus',[2] and Galateus',[3] and every good man's.

> Play with me, but hurt me not:
> Jest with me, but shame me not.

Comitas is a virtue between rusticity and scurrility, two extremes; as affability is between flattery and contention, it must not exceed, but be still accompanied with that ἀβλάβεια [1] or innocency, *quæ nemini nocet, omnem injuriæ oblationem abhorrens,* [which] hurts no man, abhors all offer of injury. Though a man be liable to such a jest or obloquy, have been overseen, or committed a foul fact, yet it is no good manners or humanity to upbraid, to hit him in the teeth with his offence, or to scoff at such a one; 'tis an old axiom, *turpis in reum omnis exprobratio* [it is unseemly to upbraid a prisoner with his crime]. I speak not of such as generally tax vice, Barclay, Gentilis, Erasmus, Agrippa, Fischartus, etc., the Varronists and Lucians of our time, satirists, epigrammatists, comedians, apologists, etc., but such as personate, rail, scoff, calumniate, perstringe by name, or in presence offend.

> *Ludit qui stolida procacitate,*
> *Non est Sestius ille, sed caballus.* [2]

[He who goes jesting with stupid talkativeness is not Sestius but a horse.]

'Tis horse-play this, and those jests (as he saith [2]) "are no better than injuries," biting jests, *mordentes et aculeati*, they are poisoned jests, leave a sting behind them, and ought not to be used.

> Set not thy foot to make the blind to fall;
> Nor wilfully offend thy weaker brother:
> Nor wound the dead with thy tongue's bitter gall,
> Neither rejoice thou in the fall of other. [4]

If these rules could be kept, we should have much more ease and quietness than we have, less melancholy: whereas, on the contrary, we study to misuse each other, how to sting and gall, like two fighting boars, bending all our force and wit, friends, fortune, to crucify one another's souls; [5] by means of which here is little content and charity, much virulency, hatred, malice, and disquietness among us.

SUBSECT. V.—*Loss of Liberty, Servitude, Imprisonment, how they cause Melancholy*

To this catalogue of causes I may well annex loss of liberty, servitude, or imprisonment, which to some persons is as great a torture as any of the rest. Though they have all things convenient, sumptuous houses to their use, fair walks and gardens, delicious bowers, galleries, good fare and diet, and all things correspondent, yet they are not content, because they are confined, may not come and go at their pleasure, have and do what they will, but live *aliena quadra*,[1] at another man's table and command. As it is in meats, so it is in all other things,[2] places, societies, sports; let them be never so pleasant, commodious, wholesome, so good; yet *omnium rerum est satietas*, there is a loathing satiety of all things. The children of Israel were tired with manna; it is irksome to them so to live, as to a bird in a cage, or a dog in his kennel, they are weary of it. They are happy, it is true, and have all things, to another man's judgment, that heart can wish, or that they themselves can desire, *bona si sua norint* [did they but know the blessings they enjoy]; yet they loathe it, and are tired with the present. *Est natura hominum novitatis avida;* men's nature is still desirous of news, variety, delights; and our wandering affections are so irregular in this kind, that they must change, though it must be to the worst. Bachelors must be married, and married men would be bachelors; they do not love their own wives, though otherwise fair, wise, virtuous, and well qualified, because they are theirs; our present estate is still the worst, we cannot endure one course of life long, *et quod modo voverat, odit* [he hates what he just now prayed for]; one calling long, *esse in honore juvat, mox displicet* [honour at first delights him, in a while it likes him not]; one place long, *Romæ Tibur amo, ventosus Tibure Romam*[3] [As changeful as the wind, nowhere at home; At Rome I Tibur miss, at Tibur Rome]; that which we earnestly sought, we now contemn. *Hoc quosdam agit ad mortem* (saith Seneca[4]) *quod proposita sæpe mutando in eadem revolvuntur, et non relinquunt novitati locum. Fastidio cœpit esse vita, et ipse mundus, et subit illud rapidissimarum deliciarum, Quousque eadem?* This alone kills many a man, that they are tied to the same still; as a horse in a mill, a dog in a wheel, they run round, without alteration or news; their life groweth odious, the world loathsome, and that which crosseth their furious delights, "What? still the same?" Marcus Aurelius and Solomon, that had experience of all worldly delights and pleasure, confessed as much of themselves; what they most desired was tedious at last, and that their lust could never be satisfied, all was vanity and affliction of mind.

Now if it be death itself, another hell, to be glutted with one kind of sport, dieted with one dish, tied to one place; though they have all things otherwise as they can desire, and are in heaven to another man's opinion, what misery and discontent shall they have, that live in slavery, or in prison itself! *Quod tristius morte, in servitute vivendum*, as Hermolaus told Alexander in Curtius,[1] worse than death is bondage: *hoc animo scito omnes fortes, ut mortem servituti anteponant*,[2] all brave men at arms (Tully holds) are so affected. *Equidem ego is sum, qui servitutem extremum omnium malorum esse arbitror*:[3] I am he (saith Boterus) that account servitude the extremity of misery. And what calamity do they endure, that live with those hard taskmasters, in gold mines (like those 30,000 Indian slaves at Potosi,[4] in Peru), tin-mines, lead-mines, stone-quarries, coal-pits, like so many mouldwarps underground, condemned to the galleys, to perpetual drudgery, hunger, thirst, and stripes, without all hope of delivery! How are those women in Turkey affected, that most part of the year come not abroad; those Italian and Spanish dames, that are mewed up like hawks, and locked up by their jealous husbands! how tedious is it to them that live in stones and caves half a year together! as in Iceland, Muscovy, or under the Pole itself,[5] where they have six months' perpetual night. Nay, what misery and discontent do they endure, that are in prison! They want all those six non-natural things at once, good air, good diet, exercise, company, sleep, rest, ease, etc., that are bound in chains all day long, suffer hunger, and (as Lucian describes it[6]) "must abide that filthy stink, and rattling of chains, howlings, pitiful outcries, that prisoners usually make; these things are not only troublesome, but intolerable." They lie nastily among toads and frogs in a dark dungeon, in their own dung, in pain of body, in pain of soul, as Joseph did (Ps. cv. 18): "They hurt his feet in his stocks, the iron entered his soul." They live solitary, alone, sequestered from all company but heart-eating melancholy; and, for want of meat, must eat that bread of affliction, prey upon themselves. Well might Arculanus put long imprisonment for a cause,[7] especially to such as have lived jovially, in all sensuality and lust, upon a sudden are estranged and debarred from all manner of pleasures: as were Huniades, Edward and Richard II, Valerian the Emperor, Bajazet the Turk. If it be irksome to miss our ordinary companions and repast for once a day, or an hour, what shall it be to lose them for ever? If it be so great a delight to live at liberty, and to enjoy that variety of objects the world affords, what misery and discontent must it needs bring to him, that shall now be cast headlong into that Spanish Inquisition, to fall from heaven

to hell, to be cubbed up upon a sudden, how shall he be perplexed, what shall become of him? Robert, Duke of Normandy,[1] being imprisoned by his youngest brother Henry I,
ab illo die inconsolabili dolore in carcere contabuit, saith Matthew
Paris, from that day forward pined away with grief. Jugurtha,[2]
that generous captain, "brought to Rome in triumph, and after
imprisoned, through anguish of his soul and melancholy, died."
Roger, Bishop of Salisbury,[3] the second man from King Stephen
(he that built that famous castle of Devizes [4] in Wiltshire), was
so tortured in prison with hunger, and all those calamities
accompanying such men, *ut vivere noluerit, mori nescierit*,[5] he
would not live and could not die, betwixt fear of death and
torments of life. Francis, King of France, was taken prisoner
by Charles V, *ad mortem fere melancholicus*, saith Guicciardine,
melancholy almost to death, and that in an instant. But this
is as clear as the sun, and needs no further illustration.

SUBSECT. VI.—*Poverty and Want, Causes of Melancholy*

Poverty and want are so violent oppugners, so unwelcome
guests, so much abhorred of all men, that I may not omit to
speak of them apart. Poverty, although (if considered aright,
to a wise, understanding, truly regenerate, and contented man)
it be *donum Dei* [a gift of God], a blessed estate, the way to
heaven, as Chrysostom calls it,[6] God's gift, the mother of
modesty, and much to be preferred before riches (as shall be
showed in his place [7]), yet as it is esteemed in the world's censure,
it is a most odious calling, vile and base, a severe torture,
summum scelus, a most intolerable burden; we shun it all,[8]
cane pejus et angue [worse than a dog or a snake], we abhor
the name of it — *Paupertas fugitur, totoque arcessitur orbe* [9]
[poverty is shunned and barred from all the world]—as being
the fountain of all other miseries, cares, woes, labours, and
grievances whatsoever. To avoid which, we will take any pains
—*extremos currit mercator ad Indos* [the merchant dashes to the
farthest Ind]—we will leave no haven, no coast, no creek of the
world unsearched, though it be to the hazard of our lives; we
will dive to the bottom of the sea, to the bowels of the earth,
five, six, seven, eight, nine hundred fathom deep,[10] through all
five zones, and both extremes of heat and cold; we will turn
parasites and slaves, prostitute ourselves, swear and lie, damn
our bodies and souls, forsake God, abjure religion, steal, rob

murder, rather than endure this unsufferable yoke of poverty,
which doth so tyrannize, crucify, and generally depress us.

For look into the world, and you shall see men most part
esteemed according to their means, and happy as they are
rich: *Ubique tanti quisque quantum habuit fuit* [1] [everywhere a
man is worth as much as he has]. If he be likely to thrive,
and in the way of preferment, who but he? In the vulgar
opinion, if a man be wealthy, no matter how he gets it, of what
parentage, how qualified, how virtuously endowed or villain-
ously inclined; let him be a bawd, a gripe, an usurer, a villain,
a pagan, a barbarian, a wretch, Lucian's tyrant,[2] "on whom
you may look with less security than on the sun"; so that he
be rich (and liberal withal) he shall be honoured, admired,
adored, reverenced, and highly magnified.[3] "The rich is had
in reputation because of his goods" (Ecclus. x, 30). He shall
be befriended, "for riches gather many friends" (Prov. xix, 4);
multos numerabit amicos, all happiness ebbs and flows
with his money.[4] He shall be accounted a gracious lord, a
Mæcenas, a benefactor, a wise, discreet, a proper, a valiant, a
fortunate man, of a generous spirit, *pullus Jovis, et gallinæ
filius albæ* [Jove's offspring, a chick of a white hen], a hopeful,
a good man, a virtuous, honest man. *Quando ego te Junonium
puerum, et matris partum vere aureum?* [When shall I see you,
my Junonian youth, your mother's golden boy?] as Tully [5]
said of Octavianus; while he was adopted Cæsar, and an heir
apparent of so great a monarchy, he was a golden child.[6] All
honour,[7] offices, applause, grand titles, and turgent epithets
are put upon him, *omnes omnia bona dicere* [all praises from all
men]; all men's eyes are upon him, God bless his good worship,
his honour! every man speaks well of him,[8] every man presents
him, seeks and sues to him for his love, favour, and protection,
to serve him, belong unto him; every man riseth to him, as to
Themistocles in the Olympics; if he speak, as of Herod, *Vox
Dei, non hominis,* [it is] the voice of God, not of man. All the
graces, veneres, pleasures, elegances attend him, golden Fortune
accompanies and lodgeth with him, and, as to those Roman
emperors, is placed in his chamber.[9]

*Secura naviget aura,
Fortunamque suo temperet arbitrio:* [10]

he may sail as he will himself, and temper his estate at his
pleasure; jovial days, splendour and magnificence, sweet music,
dainty fare, the good things and fat of the land, fine clothes,

rich attires, soft beds, down pillows are at his command; all
the world labours for him, thousands of artificers are his slaves
to drudge for him, run, ride, and post for him; divines (for
Pythia Philippizat [the oracle is on the side of Philip]), lawyers,
physicians, philosophers, scholars are his, wholly devote to his
service.[1] Every man seeks his acquaintance,[2] his kindred, to
match with him, though he be an oaf, a ninny, a monster, a
goosecap, *uxorem ducat Danaen,* [he may have Danae for wife],
when and whom he will, *hunc optant generum rex et regina*
[the lord and lady want him for a son-in-law], he is an excellent
match for my son, my daughter, my niece, etc.[3] *Quicquid
calcaverit hic, rosa fiet* [the ground shall become roses under
his feet], let him go whither he will, trumpets sound, bells ring,
etc., all happiness attends him, every man is willing to entertain him, he sups in Apollo[4] wheresoever he comes; what
preparation is made for his entertainment![5] fish and fowl,
spices and perfumes, all that sea and land affords. What
cookery, masking, mirth to exhilarate his person!

> *Da Trebio, pone ad Trebium. Vis, frater, ab illis
> Ilibus?*[6]

[Give Trebius some, pass to Trebius. Would you like
some of the flank, brother?]

What dish will your good worship eat of?

> *Dulcia poma,
> Et quoscunque feret cultus tibi fundus honores,
> Ante Larem, gustet venerabilior Lare dives.*[7]

Sweet apples, and whate'er thy fields afford,
Before thy gods be serv'd, let serve thy lord.

What sport will your honour have? hawking, hunting, fishing,
fowling, bulls, bears, cards, dice, cocks, players, tumblers,
fiddlers, jesters, etc., they are at your good worship's command.
Fair houses, gardens, orchards, terraces, galleries, cabinets,
pleasant walks, delightsome places, they are at hand; *in aureis
lac, vinum in argenteis, adolescentulæ ad nutum speciosæ*[8] [milk
in gold cups, wine in silver, beautiful maidens at his beck],
wine, wenches, etc., a Turkey paradise, an heaven upon earth.
Though he be a silly soft fellow, and scarce have common
sense, yet if he be born to fortunes (as I have said) *jure hæreditario sapere jubetur*[9] [he is bidden to be wise by hereditary
right], he must have honour and office in his course: *Nemo nisi
dives honore dignus*[10] (Ambros. *Offic.* 21) none so worthy as
himself: he shall have it, *atque esto quicquid Servius aut Labeo*

[let him be whatever Servius or Labeo was]. Get money
enough and command kingdoms,[1] provinces, armies, hearts,
hands, and affections; thou shalt have popes, patriarchs to be
thy chaplains and parasites: thou shalt have (Tamerlane-like)
kings to draw thy coach, queens to be thy laundresses, emperors thy footstools, build more towns and cities than great
Alexander, Babel towers, pyramids and mausolean tombs, etc.,
command heaven and earth, and tell the world it is thy vassal;
*auro emitur diadema, argento cœlum panditur, denarius philo-
sophum conducit, nummus jus cogit, obolus literatum pascit,
metallum sanitatem conciliat, æs amicos conglutinat* [a diadem
is bought for gold, the gates of heaven are opened to silver, a
penny buys the philosopher, money controls the course of
justice, a farthing feeds the man of letters, cash procures health,
wealth attaches friends]. And therefore not without good
cause, John Medices, that rich Florentine, when he lay upon
his death-bed, calling his sons, Cosmus and Laurence, before
him, amongst other sober saying, repeated this, *Animo quieto
digredior, quod vos sanos et divites post me delinquam,* "It doth
me good to think yet, though I be dying, that I shall leave you,
my children, sound and rich"; for wealth sways all. It is not
with us, as amongst those Lacedæmonian senators of Lycurgus
in Plutarch, "he preferred that deserved best, was most virtuous
and worthy of the place; not swiftness, or strength, or wealth,
or friends carried it in those days"; [2] but *inter optimos optimus,
inter temperantes temperantissimus,* the most temperate and best.
We have no aristocracies but in contemplation, all oligarchies,
wherein a few rich men domineer, do what they list, and are
privileged by their greatness. They may freely trespass,[3] and
do as they please, no man dare accuse them, no, not so much as
mutter against them, there is no notice taken of it, they may
securely do it, live after their own laws, and for their money
get pardons, indulgences, redeem their souls from purgatory
and hell itself; *clausum possidet arca Jovem* [Jupiter is shut
up in the money-box]. Let them be epicures, or atheists,
libertines, Machiavellians (as they often are), *Et quamvis
perjurus erit, sine gente, cruentus* [4] [though perjured, base-
born, blood-stained], they may go to heaven through the eye
of a needle, if they will themselves, they may be canonized for
saints, they shall be honourably interred in mausolean tombs,[5]
commended by poets, registered in histories, have temples and
statues erected to their names: *E manibus illis . . . nascentur
violæ* [from his remains violets shall spring]. If he be

bountiful in his life and liberal at his death, he shall have one
to swear, as he did by Claudius the emperor in Tacitus, he saw
his soul go to heaven, and be miserably lamented at his funeral.
Ambubaiarum collegia, etc.[1]   *Trimalchionis tapanta* [Trimalchio's
all-in-all (i.e. his wife Fortunata)] in Petronius *recta in
cælum abiit*, went right to heaven: a base quean, "thou
wouldst have scorned once in thy misery to have a penny
from her";[2] and why? *modio nummos metiit*, she measured
her money by the bushel.   These prerogatives do not usually
belong to rich men, but to such as are most part seeming rich;
let him have but a good outside,[3] he carries it, and shall be
adored for a god, as Cyrus was amongst the Persians,[4] *ob
splendidum apparatum*, for his gay tires; now most men are
esteemed according to their clothes.   In our gullish times, whom
you peradventure in modesty would give place to, as being
deceived by his habit, and presuming him some great worshipful
man, believe it, if you shall examine his estate, he will likely
be proved a serving-man of no great note, my lady's tailor, his
lordship's barber, or some such gull, a Fastidious Brisk, Sir
Petronel Flash,[5] a mere outside.   Only this respect is given
him, that wheresoever he comes, he may call for what he will,
and take place by reason of his outward habit.

But on the contrary, if he be poor (Prov. xv, 15), "all his
days are miserable," he is under hatches, dejected, rejected, and
forsaken, poor in purse, poor in spirit; *prout res nobis fluit, ita
et animus se habet;*[6] money gives life and soul.[7]   Though he
be honest, wise, learned, well-deserving, noble by birth, and of
excellent good parts; yet, in that he is poor, unlikely to rise,
come to honour, office, or good means, he is contemned, neglected, *frustra sapit, inter literas esurit, amicus molestus* [his
wisdom is worthless, he starves for all his learning, he is a
troublesome friend].   "If he speak, what babbler is this?"[8]
(Ecclus.), his nobility without wealth is *projecta vilior alga*[9]
[more worthless than the seaweed on the beach], and he not
esteemed.   *Nos viles pulli nati infelicibus ovis* [we are worthless
chicks of luckless fowls], if once poor, we are metamorphosed
in an instant, base slaves, villains, and vile drudges; for to be
poor is to be a knave, a fool, a wretch, a wicked, an odious
fellow, a common eye-sore, say poor and say all:[10] they are born
to labour, to misery, to carry burdens like juments, *pistum
stercus comedere* [to eat dung] with Ulysses' companions, and
as Chremylus objected in Aristophanes, *salem lingere*,[11] [to] lick
salt, to empty jakes, fay channels, carry out dirt and dunghills,

sweep chimneys, rub horse-heels, etc.[1]   (I say nothing of Turks'
galley-slaves, which are bought and sold like juments,[2] or those
African negroes, or poor Indian drudges,[3] *qui indies hinc inde
deferendis oneribus occumbunt, nam quod apud nos boves et asini
vehunt, trahunt* [who daily succumb on the roadside under their
burdens, for they do the work of oxen and asses among us], etc.
Id omne misellis Indis, etc.).   They are ugly to behold, and though
erst spruce, now rusty and squalid, because poor, *immundas
fortunas æquum est squalorem sequi* [4] [dirty luck naturally brings
on dirty living], it is ordinarily so.   "Others eat to live, but
they live to drudge," [5] *servilis et misera gens nihil recusare audet,*[6]
a servile generation, that dare refuse no task.   *Heus tu,
Dromo, cape hoc flabellum, ventulum hinc facito dum lavamur,*[7]
Sirrah, blow wind upon us while we wash, and bid your fellow
get him up betimes in the morning; be it fair or foul, he shall
run fifty miles afoot to-morrow, to carry me a letter to my
mistress; *Sosia ad pistrinam,* Sosia shall tarry at home and
grind malt all day long, Tristan thresh.   Thus are they commanded, being indeed some of them as so many footstools for
rich men to tread on, blocks for them to get on horseback, or
as "walls for them to piss on." [8]   They are commonly such
people, rude, silly, superstitious idiots, nasty, unclean, lousy,
poor, dejected, slavishly humble, and, as Leo Afer observes of
the commonalty of Africa,[9] *natura viliores sunt, nec apud suos
duces majore in pretio quam si canes assent:* base by nature,
and no more esteemed than dogs,[10] *miseram, laboriosam, cala-
mitosam vitam agunt, et inopem, infelicem, rudiores asinis, ut e
brutis plane natos dicas* [their life is full of misery, toil and
suffering, want and misfortune; they are more ignorant than
asses, and you would say they were the offspring of brutes]: no
learning, no knowledge, no civility, scarce common sense,
naught but barbarism amongst them; *belluino more vivunt,
neque calceos gestant, neque vestes,* like rogues and vagabonds,
they go barefooted and barelegged, the soles of their feet being
as hard as horse-hoofs, as Radzivilius observed at Damietta in
Egypt,[11] leading a laborious, miserable, wretched, unhappy life,
"like beasts and juments, if not worse" [12] (for a Spaniard in
Yucatan [13] sold three Indian boys for a cheese, and an hundred
negro slaves for a horse); their discourse is scurrility, their
summum bonum a pot of ale.   There is not any slavery which
these villains will not undergo, *inter illos plerique latrinas evacu-
ant, alii culinariam curant, alii stabularios agunt, urinatores, et
id genus similia exercent,* etc., like those people that dwell in the

Alps,[1] "chimney-sweepers, jakes-farmers, dirt-daubers, vagrant rogues," they labour hard, some, and yet cannot get clothes to put on, or bread to eat. For what can filthy poverty give else, but beggary, fulsome nastiness, squalor, contempt, drudgery, labour, ugliness, hunger and thirst,[2] *pediculorum et pulicum numerum*, as he[3] well followed it in Aristophanes, fleas and lice, *pro pallio vestem laceram, et pro pulvinari lapidem bene magnum ad caput*, rags for his raiment, and a stone for his pillow, *pro cathedra ruptæ caput urnæ*, he sits in a broken pitcher, or on a block for a chair, *et malvæ ramos pro panibus comedit*, he drinks water, and lives on wort-leaves, pulse, like a hog, or scraps like a dog; *ut nunc nobis vita afficitur, quis non putabit insaniam esse, infelicitatemque?* as Chremylus concludes his speech, as we poor men live nowadays, who will not take our life to be infelicity, misery, and madness?[4]

If they be of [a] little better condition than those base villains, hunger - starved beggars, wandering rogues, those ordinary slaves and day-labouring drudges, yet they are commonly so preyed upon by polling officers for breaking the laws,[5] by their tyrannizing landlords, so flayed and fleeced by perpetual exactions,[6] that though they do drudge, fare hard, and starve their genius, they cannot live in some countries;[7] but what they have is instantly taken from them; the very care they take to live, to be drudges, to maintain their poor families, their trouble and anxiety, "takes away their sleep" (Sirac. xxxi, 1), it makes them weary of their lives: when they have taken all pains, done their utmost and honest endeavours, if they be cast behind by sickness, or overtaken with years, no man pities them; hard-hearted and merciless, uncharitable as they are, they leave them so distressed, to beg, steal, murmur, and rebel, or else starve.[8] The feeling and fear of this misery compelled those old Romans, whom Menenius Agrippa pacified, to resist their governors; outlaws and rebels in most places, to take up seditious arms; and in all ages hath caused uproars, murmurings, seditions, rebellions, thefts, mutinies, jars and contentions in every commonwealth: grudging, repining, complaining, discontent in each private family, because they want means to live according to their callings, bring up their children; it breaks their hearts, they cannot do as they would. No greater misery than for a lord to have a knight's living, a gentleman a yeoman's, not to be able to live as his birth and place require. Poverty and want are generally corsives to all kind of men, especially to such as have been in good and flourishing estate, are suddenly

distressed, nobly born, liberally brought up, and by some
disaster and casualty miserably dejected.[1] For the rest, as they
have base fortunes, so have they base minds correspondent,
like beetles, *e stercore orti, e stercore victus, in stercore delicium*,
as they were obscurely[2] born and bred, so they delight in
obscenity; they are not so throughly touched with it. *Angustas
animas angusto in pectore versant* [narrow in soul, narrow in
spirit]. Yea, that which is no small cause of their torments,
if once they come to be in distress, they are forsaken of their
fellows, most part neglected, and left unto themselves; as poor
Terence[3] in Rome was by Scipio, Lælius, and Furius, his
great and noble friends.

> *Nil Publius Scipio profuit, nil ei Lælius, nil Furius,*
> *Tres per idem tempus qui agitabant nobiles facillime,*
> *Horum ille opera ne domum quidem habuit conductitiam.*

> [They were of so little use to him that he had not even
> money to pay for a lodging.]

'Tis generally so, *Tempora si fuerint nubila, solus eris* [should
the sky of your fortunes be overcast, you will be alone], he is
left cold and comfortless, *nullus ad amissas ibit amicus opes*
[to him that has lost his wealth no friend will go], all flee from
him as from a rotten wall, now ready to fall on their heads.
Prov. xix, 4: "Poverty separates them from their neighbours."[4]

> *Dum fortuna favet, vultum servatis, amici,*
> *Cum cecidit, turpi vertitis ora fuga.*[5]

> Whilst fortune favour'd, friends, you smil'd on me,
> But when she fled, a friend I could not see.

Which is worse yet, if he be poor every man contemns him,[6]
insults over him, oppresseth him, scoffs at, aggravates his
misery.

> *Quum cœpit quassata domus subsidere, partes*
> *In proclinatas omne recumbit onus.*[7]

> When once the tottering house begins to shrink,
> Thither comes all the weight by an instinct.

Nay, they are odious to their own brethren and dearest friends.
Prov. xix, 7: "His brethren hate him if he be poor"; *omnes
vicini oderunt*,[8] "his neighbours hate him" (Prov. xiv, 20);
Omnes me noti ac ignoti deserunt,[9] as he complained in the
comedy, Friends and strangers, all forsake me. Which is most
grievous, poverty makes men ridiculous, *Nil habet infelix*

paupertas durius in se, Quam quod ridiculos homines facit, they must endure jests,[1] taunts, flouts, blows of their betters, and take all in good part to get a meal's meat: *Magnum pauperies opprobrium, jubet quidvis et facere et pati* [2] [poverty is a great source of shame; it makes a man do and suffer anything]. He must turn parasite, jester, fool (*cum desipientibus desipere* [play the fool when others do so], saith Euripides [3]), slave, villain, drudge to get a poor living, apply himself to each man's humours, to win and please, etc., and be buffeted when he hath all done, as Ulysses was by Melanthius in Homer,[4] be reviled, baffled, insulted over, for *potentiorum stultitia perferenda est* [5] [the folly of the great has to be endured], and may not so much as mutter against it. He must turn rogue and villain; for, as the saying is, *Necessitas cogit ad turpia,* poverty alone makes men thieves, rebels, murderers, traitors, assassinates ("because of poverty we have sinned," Ecclus. xxvii, 1), swear and forswear, bear false witness, lie, dissemble, anything, as I say, to advantage themselves and to relieve their necessities; *culpæ scelerisque magistra est* [6] [it teaches guilt and crime]; when a man is driven to his shifts, what will he not do?

> *Si miserum fortuna Sinonem*
> *Finxit, vanum etiam mendacemque improba finget;*
>
> [The fate that brought Sinon to poverty
> A lying knave will make him eke to be;]

he will betray his father, prince, and country, turn Turk, forsake religion, abjure God and all; *nulla tam horrenda proditio, quam illi lucri causa* (saith Leo Afer [7]) *perpetrare nolint* [there is no reason so abominable that they will not commit it for the sake of gain]. Plato therefore calls poverty "thievish, sacrilegious, filthy, wicked, and mischievous"; [8] and well he might. For it makes many an upright man otherwise, had he not been in want, to take bribes, to be corrupt, to do against his conscience, to sell his tongue, heart, hand, etc., to be churlish, hard, unmerciful, uncivil, to use indirect means to help his present estate. It makes princes to exact upon their subjects, great men tyrannize, landlords oppress, justice mercenary, lawyers vultures, physicians harpies, friends importunate, tradesmen liars, honest men thieves, devout assassinates, great men to prostitute their wives, daughters, and themselves, middle sort to repine, commons to mutiny, all to grudge, murmur, and complain. A great temptation to all mischief, it compels some miserable wretches to counterfeit several diseases

to dismember, make themselves blind, lame, to have a more
plausible cause to beg, and lose their limbs to recover their
present wants. Jodocus Damhoderius, a lawyer of Bruges,
Praxi rerum criminal. cap. 112, hath some notable examples of
such counterfeit cranks, and every village almost will yield
abundant testimonies amongst us; we have dummerers, Abra-
ham-men, etc. And, that which is the extent of misery, it
enforceth them, through anguish and wearisomeness of their
lives, to make away themselves: they had rather be hanged,
drowned, etc., than to live without means.

> *In mare cetiferum, ne te premat aspera egestas,*
> *Desili, et a celsis corrue, Cyrne, jugis.*[1]

> Much better 'tis to break thy neck,
>   Or drown thyself i' th' sea,
> Than suffer irksome poverty;
>   Go make thyself away.

A Sybarite of old, as I find it registered in Athenæus,[2] supping
in *†hiditiis* [at the public tables] in Sparta, and observing their
hard fare, said it was no marvel if the Lacedæmonians were
valiant men; "for his part, he would rather run upon a
sword-point (and so would any man in his wits), than live
with such base diet, or lead so wretched a life." In Japonia[3]
'tis a common thing to stifle their children if they be
poor, or to make an abort, which Aristotle commends. In
that civil commonwealth of China, the mother strangles her
child, if she be not able to bring it up, and had rather
lose than sell it, or have it endure such misery as poor
men do.[4] Arnobius, *lib.* 7 *adversus gentes*, Lactantius,
lib. 5, *cap.* 9, objects as much to those ancient Greeks and
Romans; "they did expose their children to wild beasts, strangle,
or knock out their brains against a stone[5] in such cases." If
we may give credit to Munster,[6] amongst us Christians in
Lithuania they voluntarily mancipate and sell themselves, their
wives and children to rich men, to avoid hunger and beggary;
many make away themselves in this extremity.[7] Apicius the
Roman, when he cast up his accounts and found but 100,000
crowns left, murdered himself for fear he should be famished to
death. P. Forestus, in his Medicinal Observations, hath a
memorable example of two brothers of Louvain that, being
destitute of means, became both melancholy, and in a discontented humour massacred themselves; another of a merchant, learned, wise otherwise and discreet, but, out of a deep

apprehension he had of a loss at seas, would not be persuaded but, as Ummidius in the poet,[1] he should die a beggar. In a word, thus much I may conclude of poor men, that though they have good parts they cannot show or make use of them:[2] *ab inopia ad virtutem obsepta est via*[3] [poverty bars the way to the advance of merit], 'tis hard for a poor man to rise:

> *Haud facile emergunt, quorum virtutibus obstat*
> *Res angusta domi.*[4]
>
> ['Tis hard to rise to eminence for one
> Who by his poverty is still undone.]

"The wisdom of the poor is despised, and his words are not heard" (Eccles. ix, 16). His works are rejected, contemned, for the baseness and obscurity of the author; though laudable and good in themselves, they will not likely take.

> *Nulla placere diu, neque vivere carmina possunt,*
> *Quæ scribuntur aquæ potoribus.*
>
> [No verses can please or live long that are
> written by water-drinkers.]

Poor men cannot please, their actions, counsels, consultations, projects, are vilified in the world's esteem, *amittunt consilium in re* [their counsel perishes with their money], which Gnatho long since observed. *Sapiens crepidas sibi nunquam nec soleas fecit*, a wise man never cobbled shoes, as he[5] said of old, but how doth he prove it? I am sure we find it otherwise in our days, *pruinosis horret facundia pannis*[6] [eloquence shivers in miserable rags]. Homer himself must beg if he want means, and, as by report sometimes he did, "go from door to door, and sing ballads, with a company of boys about him."[7] This common misery of theirs must needs distract, make them discontent and melancholy, as ordinarily they are, wayward, peevish, like a weary traveller for *Fames et mora bilem in nares conciunt* [hunger and waiting cause terrible impatience], still murmuring and repining. *Ob inopiam morosi sunt, quibus est male* [want makes people illtempered], as Plutarch quotes out of Euripides, and that comical poet well seconds:

> *Omnes quibus res sunt minus secundæ, nescio quomodo*
> *Suspiciosi, ad contumeliam omnia accipiunt magis,*
> *Propter suam impotentiam se credunt negligi;*[8]

if they be in adversity, they are more suspicious and apt to mistake: they think themselves scorned by reason of their misery; and therefore many generous spirits in such cases withdraw themselves from all company, as that comedian Terence [1] is said to have done; when he perceived himself to be forsaken and poor, he voluntarily banished himself to Stymphalus, a base town in Arcadia, and there miserably died.

Ad summam inopiam redactus,
Itaque e conspectu omnium abiit Græciæ in terram ultimam.

[Being reduced to poverty, he withdrew out of sight of
all men to the extreme confines of Greece.]

Neither is it without cause, for we see men commonly respected according to their means (*an dives sit omnes quærunt, nemo an bonus* [2] [every one asks if a man is rich, no one if he is good]), and vilified if they be in bad clothes. Philopœmen the orator was set to cut wood, because he was so homely attired.[3] Terentius was placed at the lower end of Cæcilius' table, because of his homely outside.[4] Dante, that famous Italian poet, by reason his clothes were but mean, could not be admitted to sit down at a feast.[5] Gnatho scorned his old familiar friend because of his apparel: *Hominem video pannis annisque obsitum, hic ego illum contempsi præ me.*[6] King Persius, overcome, sent a letter to Paulus Æmilius, the Roman general: *Perseus P. Consuli S.* [Perseus to the Consul Publius, greeting]; but he scorned him any answer, *tacite exprobrans fortunam suam* (saith mine author) [silently] upbraiding him with his present fortune.[7] Carolus Pugnax, that great Duke of Burgundy, made H. Holland, late Duke of Exeter, exiled, run after his horse like a lackey, and would take no notice of him:[8] 'tis the common fashion of the world.[9] So that such men as are poor may justly be discontent, melancholy, and complain of their present misery, and all may pray with Solomon,[10] "Give me, O Lord, neither riches nor poverty; feed me with food convenient for me."

SUBSECT. VII.—*An heap of other Accidents causing Melancholy,
Death of Friends, Losses, etc.*

In this labyrinth of accidental causes, the farther I wander, the more intricate I find the passage; *multæ ambages* [there are many windings], and new causes as so many by-paths offer themselves to be discussed. To search out all, were an Herculean work, and fitter for Theseus; I will follow mine intended thread, and point only at some few of the chiefest.

Amongst which, loss and death of friends may challenge a

first place. *Multi tristantur*, as Vives [1] well observes, *post delicias, convivia, dies festos*, many are melancholy after a feast, holiday, merry meeting, or some pleasing sport, if they be solitary by chance, left alone to themselves, without employment, sport, or want their ordinary companions; some at the departure of friends only whom they shall shortly see again, weep and howl, and look after them as a cow lows after her calf, or a child takes on that goes to school after holidays. *Ut me levarat tuus adventus, sic discessus afflixit* (which Tully [2] writ to Atticus), "Thy coming was not so welcome to me as thy departure was harsh." Montanus, *consil.* 132, makes mention of a country-woman that, parting with her friends and native place, became grievously melancholy for many years; and Trallianus of another, so caused for the absence of her husband: which is an ordinary passion amongst our goodwives; if their husband tarry out a day longer than his appointed time, or break his hour, they take on presently with sighs and tears, "he is either robbed, or dead, some mischance or other is surely befallen him," they cannot eat, drink, sleep, or be quiet in mind till they see him again. If parting of friends, absence alone, can work such violent effects, what shall death do, when they must eternally be separated, never in this world to meet again? This is so grievous a torment for the time, that it takes away their appetite, desire of life, extinguisheth all delights, it causeth deep sighs and groans, tears, exclamations:

> *O dulce germen matris! o sanguis meus!*
> *Eheu! tepentes*, etc. . . . *o flos tener!*

[O sweet offspring of mine! my very blood! O tender flower!]

howling, roaring, many bitter pangs (*Lamentis gemituque et femineo ululatu Tecta fremunt* [3] [With groans and female lamentation loud The house resounds]), and by frequent medita-tion extends so far sometimes, "they think they see their dead friends continually in their eyes," [4] *observantes imagines* [per-ceiving their images], as Conciliator confesseth he saw his mother's ghost presenting herself still before him. *Quod nimis miseri volunt, hoc facile credunt* [in the excess of their misery, they easily believe what they wish]; still, still, still, that good father, that good son, that good wife, that dear friend runs in their minds; *totus animus hac una cogitatione defixus est* [their mind is absorbed by this one thought], all the year long, as Pliny complains to Romanus,[5] "Methinks I see Virginius, I hear Virginius, I talk with Virginius," etc.

Te sine, væ misero mihi, lilia nigra videntur,
Pallentesque rosæ, nec dulce rubens hyacinthus,
Nullos nec myrtus, nec laurus spirat odores.[1]

[Without thee, alas, the lilies seem black, the roses pale,
the hyacinth forgets to blush, the myrtle and the
laurel lose their scent.]

They that are most staid and patient are so furiously carried
headlong by the passion of sorrow in this case, that brave
discreet men otherwise oftentimes forget themselves, and weep
like children many months together, "as if that they to water
would,"[2] and will not be comforted. They are gone, they are
gone!

Abstulit atra dies et funere mersit acerbo.

[In an ill-omened hour bitter death has overwhelmed them.]

What shall I do?

Quis dabit in lacrimas fontem mihi? quis satis altos
Accendet gemitus, et acerbo verba dolori?
Exhaurit pietas oculos, et hiantia frangit
Pectora, nec plenos avido sinit edere questus,
Magna adeo jactura premit, etc.

Fountains of tears who gives? who lends me groans,
Deep sighs sufficient to express my moans?
Mine eyes are dry, my breast in pieces torn,
My loss so great, I cannot enough mourn.

So Stroza *filius* [the younger], that elegant Italian poet, in his
Epicedium bewails his father's death; he could moderate his
passions in other matters (as he confesseth), but not in this,
he yields wholly to sorrow:

Nunc fateor do terga malis, mens illa fatiscit,
Indomitus quondam vigor et constantia mentis.

[No more can I bear up, my spirit quails,
My strength of mind is gone, my courage fails.]

How doth Quintilian[3] complain for the loss of his son, to
despair almost! Cardan lament his only child in his book *de
libris propriis,* and elsewhere in many other of his tracts! St.
Ambrose his brother's death![4] (*An ego possum non cogitare de te,
aut sine lacrimis cogitare? O amari dies! o flebiles noctes!* [Can
I ever cease to think of thee, or to think of thee without tears?
O bitter days! O nights of sorrow!] etc.); Gregory Nazianzen
that noble Pulcheria! (*O decorem, etc., flos recens, pullulans*
[How beauteous, like a new blossoming flower], etc.). Alexander,
a man of most invincible courage, after Hephæstion's death, as

Curtius relates, *triduum jacuit ad moriendum obstinatus*, lay three days together upon the ground, obstinate to die with him, and would neither eat, drink, nor sleep. The woman that communed with Esdras (*lib. 2, cap.* 10), when her son fell down dead, "fled into the field, and would not return into the city, but there resolved to remain, neither to eat nor drink, but mourn and fast until she died." "Rachel wept for her children, and would not be comforted because they were not" (Matt. ii, 18). So did Hadrian the emperor bewail his Antinous; Hercules, Hylas; Orpheus, Eurydice; David, Absalom (O my dear son Absalom!); Austin his mother Monica, Niobe her children, insomuch that the poets feigned her to be turned into a stone, as being stupefied through the extremity of grief.[1] Ægeus, *signo lugubri filii consternatus, in mare se præcipitem dedit*,[2] impatient of sorrow for his son's death, drowned himself. Our late physicians are full of such examples. Montanus, *consil.* 242, had a patient troubled with this infirmity, by reason of her husband's death, many years together.[3] Trincavellius, *lib.* 1, *cap.* 14, hath such another, almost in despair, after his mother's departure,[4] *ut se ferme præcipitem daret*, and ready through distraction to make away himself; and, in his fifteenth counsel, tells a story of one fifty years of age, "that grew desperate upon his mother's death"; and, cured by Fallopius, fell many years after into a relapse, by the sudden death of a daughter which he had, and could never after be recovered. The fury of this passion is so violent sometimes, that it daunts whole kingdoms and cities. Vespasian's death was pitifully lamented all over the Roman Empire, *totus orbis lugebat*, saith Aurelius Victor. Alexander commanded the battlements of houses to be pulled down, mules and horses to have their manes shorn off, and many common soldiers to be slain, to accompany his dear Hephæstion's death; which is now practised amongst the Tartars, when a great Cham dieth,[5] ten or twelve thousand must be slain, men and horses, all they meet; and among those pagan Indians, their wives and servants voluntarily die with them.[6] Leo Decimus was so much bewailed in Rome after his departure, that, as Jovius gives out,[7] *communis salus, publica hilaritas*, the common safety, all good fellowship, peace, mirth, and plenty died with him, *tanquam eodem sepulchro cum Leone condita lugebantur* [as though buried in the same grave with Leo]; for it was a golden age whilst he lived, but after his decease an iron season succeeded,[8] *barbara vis et fœda vastitas, et dira malorum omnium incommoda*, wars, plagues, vastity, discontent. When Augustus Cæsar died, saith Paterculus, *orbis ruinam timueramus*, we were all afraid, as if heaven had fallen upon our heads. Budæus records [1] how that, at Louis the Twelfth his death, *tam subita mutatio, ut qui prius digito cælum attingere videbantur, nunc humi derepente serpere, sideratos esse diceres*, they that were erst in heaven, upon a sudden, as if they had been planet-strucken, lay grovelling on the ground:

> *Concussis cecidere animis, ceu frondibus ingens*
> *Silva dolet lapsis;* [2]
>
> [Nerveless they crashed, as when the forest moans
> Its fallen leaves;]

they looked like cropped trees. At Nancy in Lorraine, when Claudia Valesia, Henry the second French king's sister and the duke's wife, deceased, the temples for forty days were all shut up, no prayers nor masses but in that room where she was; the senators all seen in black, "and for a twelvemonth's space throughout the city they were forbid to sing or dance." [3]

> *Non ulli pastos illis egere diebus*
> *Frigida, Daphni, boves ad flumina, nulla nec amnem*
> *Libavit quadrupes, nec graminis attigit herbam.* [4]
>
> [The swains forgot their sheep, nor near the brink
> Of running waters brought their herds to drink;
> The thirsty cattle, of themselves, abstained
> From water, and their grassy fare disdained.]

How were we affected here in England for our Titus, *deliciæ humani generis* [the darling of the human race], Prince Henry's immature death, as if all our dearest friends' lives had exhaled with his! Scanderbeg's death was not so much lamented in Epirus. [5] In a word, as he [6] saith of Edward the First at the news of Edward of Carnarvon his son's birth, *immortaliter gavisus*, he was immortally glad, may we say on the contrary of friends' deaths, *immortaliter gementes*, we are divers of us, as so many turtles, eternally dejected with it.

There is another sorrow, which arises from the loss of temporal goods and fortunes, which equally afflicts, and may go hand in hand with the precedent; loss of time, loss of honour, office, of good name, of labour, frustrate hopes, will much torment; but in my judgment, there is no torture like unto it, or that sooner procureth this malady and mischief:

> *Ploratur lacrimis amissa pecunia veris:* [7]
>
> [Lost money is bewailed with grief sincere:]

It wrings true tears from our eyes, many sighs, much sorrow

from our hearts, and often causes habitual melancholy itself.
Guianerius, *tract.* 15, 5, repeats this for an especial cause: "Loss
of friends, and loss of goods, make many men melancholy, as
I have often seen by continual meditation of such things." [1]
The same causes Arnoldus Villanovanus inculcates, *Breviar. lib.* 1,
cap. 18, *ex rerum amissione, damno, amicorum morte* [from loss of
property, damage, death of friends], etc.   Want alone will make
a man mad, to be *sans argent* will cause a deep and grievous
melancholy.   Many persons are affected like Irishmen [2] in this
behalf, who if they have a good scimitar, had rather have a
blow on their arm than their weapon hurt: they will sooner
lose their life than their goods: and the grief that cometh
hence continueth long (saith Plater [3]) "and out of many dispositions, procureth an habit."   Montanus [4] and Frisimelica
cured a young man of twenty-two years of age, that so became
melancholy, *ob amissam pecuniam*, for a sum of money which
he had unhappily lost.   Sckenkius hath such another story of
one melancholy, because he overshot himself and spent his
stock in unnecessary building.   Roger, that rich Bishop of
Salisbury,[5] *exutus opibus et castris a Rege Stephano*, spoiled of
his goods by King Stephen, *vi doloris absorptus, atque in amen-
tiam versus, indecentia fecit*, through grief ran mad, spoke and
did he knew not what.   Nothing so familiar as for men in such
cases through anguish of mind to make away themselves.   A
poor fellow went to hang himself (which Ausonius hath elegantly
expressed in a neat epigram [6]), but finding by chance a pot of
money, flung away the rope and went merrily home; but he
that hid the gold, when he missed it, hanged himself with that
rope which the other man had left, in a discontented humour.

> *At qui condiderat, postquam non repperit aurum,*
> *Aptavit collo, quem reperit laqueum.*

Such feral accidents can want and penury produce.   Be it by
suretyship, shipwreck, fire, spoil and pillage of soldiers, or what
loss soever, it boots not, it will work the like effect, the same
desolation in provinces and cities, as well as private persons.
The Romans were miserably dejected after the battle of Cannæ,
the men amazed for fear, the stupid women tore their hair and
cried.   The Hungarians, when their King Ladislaus and bravest
soldiers were slain by the Turks, *Luctus publicus* [a public
mourning], etc.   The Venetians, when their forces were overcome by the French king Louis, the French and Spanish kings,
pope, emperor, all conspired against them at Cambrai, the

French herald denounced open war in the senate: *Lauredane,
Venetorum dux* [Loredano, Doge of Venice], etc., and they
had lost Padua, Brixia, Verona, Forum Julii, their territories
in the continent, and had now nothing left, but the city
of Venice itself, *et urbi quoque ipsi* (saith Bembus[1]) *timendum
putarent,* and the loss of that was likewise to be feared, *tantus
repente dolor omnes tenuit, ut nunquam alias,* etc., they were
pitifully plunged, never before in such lamentable distress.
Anno 1527, when Rome was sacked by Burbonius,[2] the common
soldiers made such spoil, that fair churches were turned to
stables, old monuments and books made horse-litter, or burned
like straw; relics, costly pictures defaced; altars demolished,
rich hangings, carpets, etc., trampled in the dirt;[3] their wives
and loveliest daughters constuprated by every base cullion,[4] as
Sejanus' daughter was by the hangman in public, before their
fathers' and husbands' faces; noblemen's children, and of the
wealthiest citizens, reserved for princes' beds, were prostitute
to every common soldier, and kept for concubines; senators and
cardinals themselves dragged along the streets, and put to
exquisite torments, to confess where their money was hid; the
rest, murdered on heaps, lay stinking in the streets; infants'
brains dashed out before their mothers' eyes. A lamentable
sight it was to see a goodly a city so suddenly defaced, rich
citizens sent a-begging to Venice, Naples, Ancona, etc., that
erst lived in all manner of delights. "Those proud palaces,
that even now vaunted their tops up to heaven, were dejected
as low as hell in an instant."[5] Whom will not such misery
make discontent? Terence the poet drowned himself (some
say) for the loss of his comedies, which suffered shipwreck.
When a poor man hath made many hungry meals, got together
a small sum, which he loseth in an instant; a scholar spent many
an hour's study to no purpose, his labours lost, etc., how should
it otherwise be? I may conclude with Gregory, *Temporalium
amor, quantum afficit, cum hæret possessio, tantum, quum sub-
trahitur, urit dolor;* riches do not so much exhilarate us with
their possession, as they torment us with their loss.

Next to sorrow still I may annex such accidents as procure
fear; for besides those terrors which I have before touched,[6]
and many other fears (which are infinite), there is a superstitious
fear, one of the three great causes of fear in Aristotle, commonly
caused by prodigies and dismal accidents, which much trouble
many of us. (*Nescio quid animus mihi præsagit mali* [my mind
has a presentiment of some evil]). As if a hare cross the way

at our going forth, or a mouse gnaw our clothes; if they bleed three drops at nose, the salt falls towards them, a black spot appear in their nails, etc., with many such, which Delrio, *tom. 2, lib. 3, sect.* 4; Austin Niphus in his book *de auguriis;* Polydore Virgil, *lib. 3 de prodigiis;* Sarisburiensis, *Polycrat. lib.* 1, *cap.* 13, discuss at large. They are so much affected that, with the very strength of imagination, fear, and the devil's craft, "they pull those misfortunes they suspect upon their own heads, and that which they fear shall come upon them," [1] as Solomon foretelleth (Prov. x, 24) and Isaiah denounceth (lxvi, 4), which, "if they could neglect and contemn, would not come to pass." [2] *Eorum vires nostra resident opinione, ut morbi gravitas ægrotantium cogitatione* [their force lies in our own fancy, as the virulence of a disease depends on the mind of the patient], they are intended and remitted as our opinion is fixed, more or less. *N. N. dat pœnas*, saith Crato of such a one,[3] *utinam non attraheret !* he is punished, and is the cause of it himself.[4] *Dum fata fugimus fata stulti incurrimus* [5] [in fleeing from our destiny we run into its arms]. "The thing that I feared," saith Job, "is fallen upon me."

As much we may say of them that are troubled with their fortunes, or ill destinies foreseen; *multos angit præscientia malorum:* the foreknowledge of what shall come to pass crucifies many men: foretold by astrologers, or wizards, *iratum ob cœlum* [because of the anger of the heavens], be it ill accident, or death itself: which often falls out by God's permission; *Quia dæmonem timent* (saith Chrysostom), *Deus ideo permittit accidere* [because they fear the devil, therefore God suffers it to happen]. Severus, Hadrian, Domitian, can testify as much, of whose fear and suspicion Suetonius, Herodian, and the rest of those writers tell strange stories in this behalf. Montanus, *consil.* 31, hath one example of a young man, exceeding melancholy upon this occasion.[6] Such fears have still tormented mortal men in all ages, by reason of those lying oracles and juggling priests. There was a fountain in Greece, near Ceres temple in Achaia, where the event of such diseases was to be known. "A glass let down by a thread," etc.[7] Amongst those Cyanean rocks at the springs of Lycia, was the oracle of Thryxeus Apollo, "where all fortunes were foretold, sickness, health, or what they would besides": so common people have been always deluded with future events. At this day, *metu futurorum maxime torquet Sinas*, this foolish fear mightily crucifies them in China; as Matthew Riccius the Jesuit in formeth us, in his commentaries of those countries,[1] of all nations they are most superstitious, and much tormented in this kind, attributing so much to their divinators, *ut ipse metus fidem faciat*, that fear itself and conceit cause it to fall out;[2] if he foretell sickness such a day, that very time they will be sick, *vi metus afflicti in ægritudinem cadunt*, and many times die as it is foretold. A true saying, *Timor mortis, morte pejor*, the fear of death is worse than death itself, and the memory of that sad hour, to some fortunate and rich men, "is as bitter as gall" (Ecclus. xli, 1). *Inquietam nobis vitam facit mortis metus* [the fear of death disturbs our life]; a worse plague cannot happen to a man than to be so troubled in his mind; 'tis *triste divortium*, a heavy separation, to leave their goods, with so much labour got, pleasures of the world which they have so deliciously enjoyed, friends and companions whom they so dearly loved, all at once. Axiochus the philosopher was bold and courageous all his life, and gave good precepts *de contemnenda morte* [for contemning death], and against the vanity of the world, to others; but being now ready to die himself he was mightily dejected: *Hac luce privabor? his orbabor bonis?* [Am I to be banished from light, to be deprived of so many good things?] he lamented like a child, etc. And though Socrates himself was there to comfort him: *Ubi pristina virtutum jactatio, o Axioche?* [Where is all your boasted virtue now, my friend?] yet he was very timorous and impatient of death, much troubled in his mind, *imbellis pavor et impatientia* [craven fear and weakness], etc. "O Clotho," Megapenthes, the tyrant in Lucian, exclaims, now ready to depart, "let me live awhile longer. I will give thee a thousand talents of gold, and two bowls besides, which I took from Cleocritus, worth an hundred talents apiece."[3] "Woe's me!" saith another,[4] "what goodly manors shall I leave! what fertile fields! what a fine house! what pretty children! how many servants! who shall gather my grapes, my corn? Must I now die so well settled? leave all, so richly and well provided? Woe's me, what shall I do?" *Animula vagula, blandula, quæ nunc abibis in loca?*[5] [Poor fluttering, coaxing soul of mine, What new abode shall now be thine?]

To these tortures of fear and sorrow may well be annexed curiosity, that irksome, that tyrannizing care, *nimia sollicitudo*, superfluous industry about unprofitable things and their qualities,"[6] as Thomas defines it: an itching humour or a kind of longing to see that which is not to be seen, to do that

which ought not to be done, to know that secret which should
not be known, to eat of the forbidden fruit.[1] We commonly
molest and tire ourselves about things unfit and unnecessary,
as Martha troubled herself to little purpose. Be it in religion,
humanity, magic, philosophy, policy, any action or study, 'tis
a needless trouble, a mere torment. For what else is school
divinity? How many doth it puzzle! what fruitless questions
about the Trinity, resurrection, election, predestination, repro-
bation, hell-fire, etc., how many shall be saved, damned! What
else is all superstition, but an endless observation of idle ceremonies, traditions? What is most of our philosophy but a
labyrinth of opinions, idle questions, propositions, metaphysical
terms? Socrates therefore held all philosophers cavillers and
madmen, *circa subtilia cavillatores pro insanis habuit, palam
eos arguens,* saith Eusebius,[2] because they commonly sought
after such things *quæ nec percipi a nobis neque comprehendi
possent* [which can be neither perceived nor understood by us]
or put case they did understand, yet they were altogether
unprofitable. For what matter is it for us to know how high
the Pleiades are, how far distant Perseus and Cassiopea from
us, how deep the sea, etc.? We are neither wiser, as he follows
it, nor modester, nor better, nor richer, nor stronger for the
knowledge of it. *Quod supra nos nihil ad nos* [what is above
us does not concern us]. I may say the same of those geneth-
liacal studies: what is astrology but vain elections, predictions?
all magic, but a troublesome error, a pernicious foppery?
physic, but intricate rules and prescriptions? philology, but
vain criticisms? logic, needless sophisms? metaphysics themselves, but intricate subtleties and fruitless abstractions?
alchemy, but a bundle of errors? To what end are such great
tomes? why do we spend so many years in their studies?
Much better to know nothing at all, as those barbarous Indians
are wholly ignorant, than, as some of us, to be so sore vexed
about unprofitable toys: *stultus labor est ineptiarum* [it is foolish
to labour at trifles], to build a house without pins, make a rope
of sand, to what end? *cui bono?* He studies on, but, as the boy
told St. Austin, when I have laved the sea dry, thou shalt
understand the mystery of the Trinity. He makes observations, keeps times and seasons; and as Conradus the emperor
would not touch his new bride till an astrologer had told him
a masculine hour;[3] but with what success? He travels into
Europe, Africa, Asia, searcheth every creek, sea, city, mountain,
gulf, to what end? See one promontory (said Socrates of old)

one mountain, one sea, one river, and see all. An alchemist spends his fortunes to find out the philosopher's stone forsooth, cure all diseases, make men long-lived, victorious, fortunate, invisible, and beggars himself, misled by those seducing impostors, (which he shall never attain) to make gold; an antiquary consumes his treasure and time to scrape up a company of old coins, statues, rolls, edicts, manuscripts, etc.; he must know what was done of old in Athens, Rome, what lodging, diet, houses they had, and have all the present news at first, though never so remote, before all others, what projects, counsels, consultations, etc., *quid Juno in aurem insusurraret Jovi* [what Juno whispered in Jupiter's ear], what's now decreed in France, what in Italy: who was he, whence comes he, which way, whither goes he, etc. Aristotle must find out the motion of Euripus; Pliny must needs see Vesuvius; but how sped they? One loseth goods, another his life. Pyrrhus will conquer Africa first, and then Asia. He will be a sole monarch, a second immortal, a third rich, a fourth commands. *Turbine magno spes sollicitæ in urbibus errant*[1] [one finds in cities a great turmoil of anxious hopes]; we run, ride, take indefatigable pains, all up early, down late, striving to get that which we had better be without (Ardelios,[2] busybodies as we are), it were much fitter for us to be quiet, sit still, and take our ease. His sole study is for words, that they be *lepide lexeis compostæ ut tesserulæ omnes* [elegant expressions put together like a mosaic], not a syllable misplaced, to set out a stramineous subject; as thine is about apparel, to follow the fashion, to be terse and polite, 'tis thy sole business; both with like profit. His only delight is building, he spends himself to get curious pictures, intricate models and plots; another is wholly ceremonious about titles, degrees, inscriptions; a third is over-solicitous about his diet, he must have such and such exquisite sauces, meat so dressed, so far-fetched, *peregrini aeris volucres* [birds from a foreign clime], so cooked, etc., something to provoke thirst, something anon to quench his thirst. Thus he redeems his appetite with extraordinary charge to his purse, is seldom pleased with any meal, whilst a trivial stomach useth all with delight and is never offended. Another must have roses in winter, *alieni temporis flores* [flowers out of season] snow-water in summer, fruits before they can be or are usually ripe, artificial gardens and fish-ponds on the tops of houses, all things opposite to the vulgar sort, intricate and rare, or else they are nothing worth. So busy, nice, curious wits make that unsupportable in all vocations, trades, actions, employments, which to duller apprehensions is not offensive, earnestly seeking that which others as scornfully neglect. Thus through our foolish curiosity do we macerate ourselves, tire our souls, and run headlong, through our indiscretion, perverse will, and want of government, into many needless cares and troubles, vain expenses, tedious journeys, painful hours; and when all is done, *quorsum hæc? cui bono?* to what end?

> *Nescire velle quæ Magister maximus*
> *Docere non vult, erudita inscitia est.*[1]

> [Humbly to be contented not to know
> What the Great Master hath not deigned to show,
> Though ignorance, is learning quite enow.]

Amongst these passions and irksome accidents, unfortunate marriage may be ranked: a condition of life appointed by God Himself in Paradise, an honourable and happy estate, and as great a felicity as can befall a man in this world, if the parties can agree as they ought,[2] and live as Seneca lived with his Paulina;[3] but if they be unequally matched, or at discord, a greater misery cannot be expected, to have a scold, a slut, an harlot, a fool, a fury or a fiend, there can be no such plague. "He that hath her is as if he held a scorpion," etc. (Ecclus xxvi, 14), and "a wicked wife makes a sorry countenance, an heavy heart, and he had rather dwell with a lion than keep house with such a wife" (xxv, 23, 16). Her properties Jovianus Pontanus hath described at large, *Ant. dial. tom. 2*, under the name of Euphorbia.[4] Or if they be not equal in years, the like mischief happens; Cæcilius, in A. Gellius, *lib. 2, cap. 23*, complains much of an old wife: *Dum ejus morti inhio, egomet mortuus vivo inter vivos*, Whilst I gape after her death, I live a dead man amongst the living; or if they dislike upon any occasion:

> Judge who that are unfortunately wed
> What 'tis to come into a loathed bed.[5]

The same inconvenience befalls women.

> *At vos, o duri, miseram lugete parentes,*
> *Si ferro aut laqueo læva hac me exsolvere sorte*
> *Sustineo:*[6]

> Hard-hearted parents, both lament my fate,
> If self I kill or hang, to ease my state.

A young gentlewoman in Basil was married,[7] saith Felix Plater, *Observat. lib. 1*, to an ancient man against her will, whom she could not affect; she was continually melancholy, and pined away for grief; and though her husband did all he could possibly to give her content, in a discontented humour at length she hanged herself. Many other stories he relates in this kind. Thus men are plagued with women, they again with men, when they are of diverse humours and conditions; he a spendthrift, she sparing; one honest, the other dishonest, etc. Parents many times disquiet their children, and they their parents. "A foolish son is an heaviness to his mother." [1] *Injusta noverca:* a stepmother often vexeth a whole family, is matter of repentance, exercise of patience, fuel of dissension, which made Cato's son expostulate with his father, why he should offer to marry his client Salonius' daughter, a young wench, *cujus causa novercam induceret?* what offence had he done, that he should marry again?

Unkind, unnatural friends, evil neighbours, bad servants, debts and debates, etc.; 'twas Chilo's sentence, *comes æris alieni et litis est miseria,* misery and usury do commonly together; suretyship is the bane of many families, *Sponde, præsto noxa est* [go surety, and ruin is near at hand]: "he shall be sore vexed that is surety for a stranger" (Prov. xi, 15), "and he that hateth suretyship is sure." Contention, brawling, lawsuits, falling out of neighbours and friends, *discordia demens* [frantic discord] (Virg. *Æn.* 6), are equal to the first, grieve many a man, and vex his soul. *Nihil sane miserabilius eorum mentibus* (as Boter holds [2]) "nothing so miserable as such men, full of cares, griefs, anxieties, as if they were stabbed with a sharp sword; fear, suspicion, desperation, sorrow, are their ordinary companions." Our Welshmen are noted by some of their own writers,[3] to consume one another in this kind; but whosoever they are that use it, these are their common symptoms, especially if they be convict or overcome, cast in a suit. Arius, put out of a bishopric by Eustathius, turned heretic, and lived after discontented all his life. Every repulse is of like nature;[4] *Heu quanta de spe decidi!* [Alas, what prospects have I lost!]. Disgrace, infamy, detraction, will almost effect as much, and that a long time after. Hipponax, a satirical poet, so vilified and lashed two painters in his iambics, *ut ambo laqueo se suffocarent,* Pliny saith,[5] both hanged themselves. All oppositions, dangers, perplexities, discontents, to live in any suspense, are of the same rank:[6] *Potes hoc sub casu ducere somnos?* Can you sleep with such trouble impending?] Who can be secure in such cases? Ill-bestowed benefits, ingratitude,

unthankful friends, much disquiet and molest some. Unkind
speeches trouble as many, uncivil carriage or dogged answers,
weak women above the rest; if they proceed from their surly
husbands, are as bitter as gall, and not to be digested.[1] A glass-
man's wife in Basil became melancholy because her husband
said he would marry again if she died. "No cut to unkind-
ness," as the saying is; a frown and hard speech, ill respect, a
brow-beating, or bad look, especially to courtiers, or such as
attend upon great persons, is present death: *Ingenium vultu
statque caditque suo*, they ebb and flow with their masters'
favours. Some persons are at their wits' ends, if by chance
they overshoot themselves in their ordinary speeches or actions,
which may after turn to their disadvantage or disgrace, or have
any secret disclosed. Ronseus, *Epist. miscel.* 3, reports of a
gentlewoman twenty-five years old, that, falling foul with one
of her gossips, was upbraided with a secret infirmity (no matter
what) in public, and so much grieved with it, that she did
thereupon *solitudines quærere, omnes ab se ablegare, ac tandem,
in gravissimam incidens melancholiam, contabescere*, forsake all
company, quite moped, and in a melancholy humour pine
away. Others are as much tortured to see themselves
rejected, contemned, scorned, disabled, diffamed, detracted,
undervalued, or "left behind their fellows." [2] Lucian brings
in Hetœmocles, a philosopher, in his *Lapith. convivio*, much
discontented that he was not invited amongst the rest, expostu-
lating the matter, in a long epistle, with Aristænetus their host.
Prætextatus, a robed gentleman in Plutarch, would not sit
down at a feast, because he might not sit highest, but went his
ways all in a chafe. We see the common quarrellings that are
ordinary with us, for taking of the wall, precedency, and the
like, which though toys in themselves, and things of no moment,
yet they cause many distempers, much heart-burning amongst
us. Nothing pierceth deeper than a contempt or disgrace,
especially if they be generous spirits,[3] scarce anything affects
them more than to be despised or vilified. Crato, *consil.* 16,
lib. 2, exemplifies it, and common experience confirms it. Of
the same nature is oppression: "Surely oppression makes a man
mad" (Eccles. vii, 7); loss of liberty, which made Brutus venture
his life, Cato kill himself, and Tully complain,[4] *Omnem hilari-
tatem in perpetuum amisi*,[5] Mine heart's broken, I shall never
look up, or be merry again; *hæc jactura intolerabilis*, to some
parties 'tis a most intolerable loss. Banishment, a great misery,
as Tyrtæus describes it in an epigram of his:

Nam miserum est patria amissa, laribusque, vagari
Mendicum, et timida voce rogare cibos:
Omnibus invisus, quocunque accesserit, exul
Semper erit, semper spretus egensque jacet, etc.

A miserable thing 'tis so to wander,
And like a beggar for to whine at door,
Contemn'd of all the world an exile is,
Hated, rejected, needy still and poor.

Polynices, in his conference with Jocasta in Euripides,[1] reckons
up five miseries of a banished man, the least of which alone
were enough to deject some pusillanimous creatures. Oftentimes a too great feeling of our own infirmities or imperfections
of body or mind will rivel us up; as if we be long sick:

O beata sanitas! te præsente, amœnum
Ver floret gratiis, absque te nemo beatus.

[O blessed health! when thou art with us the spring is
full of charms, without thee no one is happy.]

O blessed health! "thou art above all gold and treasure"
(Ecclus. xxx, 15), the poor man's riches, the rich man's bliss,
without thee there can be no happiness: or visited with some
loathsome disease, offensive to others, or troublesome to ourselves; as a stinking breath, deformity of our limbs, crookedness,
loss of an eye, leg, hand, paleness, leanness, redness, baldness,
loss or want of hair, etc., *hic ubi fluere cœpit, diros ictus cordi*
infert, saith Synesius[2] (he himself troubled not a little *ob comæ*
defectum), the loss of hair alone strikes a cruel stroke to the heart.
Acco, an old woman, seeing by chance her face in a true glass
(for she used false flattering glasses belike at other times, as most
gentlewomen do), *animi dolore in insaniam delapsa est* (Cælius
Rhodiginus, *lib.* 17, *cap.* 2), ran mad. Broteas, the son of
Vulcan, because he was ridiculous for his imperfections, flung
himself into the fire.[3] Lais of Corinth, now grown old, gave
up her glass to Venus, for she could not abide to look upon it.
Qualis sum nolo, qualis eram nequeo [what I am I fain would not
be, what I was I cannot be].[4] Generally to fair nice pieces, old
age and foul linen are two most odious things, a torment of
torments, they may not abide the thought of it.

O deorum
Quisquis hæc audis, utinam inter errem
Nuda leones,
Antequam turpis macies decentes
Occupet malas, teneræque succus
Defluat prædæ, speciosa quæro
Pascere tigres.[5]

[Hear me, some gracious heavenly power,
Let lions this naked corse devour.
My cheeks ere hollow wrinkles seize,
Ere yet their rosy bloom decays;
While youth yet rolls its vital flood,
Let tigers fiercely riot in my blood.]

To be foul, ugly, and deformed! much better be buried alive.
Some are fair but barren, and that galls them: "Hannah wept
sore, did not eat, and was troubled in spirit, and all for her
barrenness" (1 Sam. 1); and (Gen. 30), Rachel said "in the
anguish of her soul, Give me a child, or I shall die"; another
hath too many: one was never married, and that's his hell,
another is, and that's his plague. Some are troubled in that they
are obscure; others by being traduced, slandered, abused, disgraced, vilified, or anyway injured: *minime miror eos* (as he said)
qui insanire occipiunt ex injuria, I marvel not at all if offences
make men mad. Seventeen particular causes of anger and
offence Aristotle reckons them up, which for brevity's sake I
must omit. No tidings troubles one; ill reports, rumours, bad
tidings or news, hard hap, ill success, cast in a suit, vain hopes,
or hope deferred, another: expectation, *adeo omnibus in rebus
molesta semper est expectatio* [expectation in all circumstances
brings annoyance] as Polybius observes; [1] one is too eminent,
another too base-born, and that alone tortures him as much as
the rest: one is out of action, company, employment; another
overcome and tormented with worldly cares and onerous business. But what tongue can suffice to speak of all? [2]

Many men catch this malady by eating certain meats, herbs,
roots, at unawares; as henbane, nightshade, cicuta, mandrakes,
etc. A company of young men at Agrigentum, in Sicily, came
into a tavern; [3] where after they had freely taken their liquor,
whether it were the wine itself, or something mixed with it 'tis
not yet known, but upon a sudden they began to be so troubled
in their brains, and their phantasy so crazed, that they thought
they were in a ship at sea, and now ready to be cast away by
reason of a tempest. [4] Wherefore, to avoid shipwreck and
present drowning, they flung all the goods in the house out at
the windows into the street, or into the sea, as they supposed;
thus they continued mad a pretty season, and being brought
before the magistrate to give an account of this their fact, they
told him (not yet recovered of their madness) that what was
done they did for fear of death, and to avoid imminent danger.
The spectators were all amazed at this their stupidity, and gazed

on them still, whilst one of the ancientest of the company, in a grave tone, excused himself to the magistrate upon his knees, *O viri Tritones, ego in imo jacui,* I beseech your deities, etc., for I was in the bottom of the ship all the while: another besought them, as so many sea-gods, to be good unto them, and if ever he and his fellows came to land again, he would build an altar to their service.[1] The magistrate could not sufficiently laugh at this their madness, bid them sleep it out, and so went his ways. Many such accidents frequently happen upon these unknown occasions. Some are so caused by philters, wandering in the sun, biting of a mad dog, a blow on the head, stinging with that kind of spider called tarantula, an ordinary thing, if we may believe Sckenkius, *lib.* 6 *de venenis*, in Calabria and Apulia in Italy, Cardan, *Subtil. lib.* 9, Scaliger, *exercitat.* 185. Their symptoms are merrily described by Jovianus Pontanus, *Ant. dial.*, how they dance altogether, and are cured by music. Cardan [2] speaks of certain stones, if they be carried about one, which will cause melancholy and madness; he calls them unhappy, as an adamant, selenites, etc. "which dry up the body, increase cares, diminish sleep": [3] Ctesias, *in Persicis*, makes mention of a well in those parts, of which if any man drink, "he is mad for twenty-four hours." [4] Some lose their wits by terrible objects (as elsewhere I have more copiously dilated,[5] and life itself many times, as Hippolytus affrighted by Neptune's sea-horses, Athamas by Juno's Furies: but these relations are common in all writers.

> *Hic alias poteram, et plures subnectere causas,*
> *Sed jumenta vocant, et sol inclinat, eundum est.*[6]

> Many such causes, much more could I say,
> But that for provender my cattle stay:
> The sun declines, and I must needs away.

These causes, if they be considered and come alone, I do easily yield, can do little of themselves, seldom, or apart (an old oak is not felled at a blow), though many times they are all-sufficient every one: yet if they concur, as often they do, *vis unita fortior; et quæ non absunt singula, multa nocent* [union gives strength; things which singly hurt not can do injury when in a mass], they may batter a strong constitution; as Austin said, "many grains and small sands sink a ship, many small drops make a flood," etc.,[7] often reiterated; many dispositions produce an habit.

MEMB. V.

Subsect. I.—*Continent, inward, antecedent, next Causes, and how the Body works on the Mind*

As a purly hunter, I have hitherto beaten about the circuit of the forest of this microcosm, and followed only those outward adventitious causes. I will now break into the inner rooms, and rip up the antecedent immediate causes which are there to be found. For as the distraction of the mind, amongst other outward causes and perturbations, alters the temperature of the body, so the distraction and distemper of the body will cause a distemperature of the soul, and 'tis hard to decide which of these two do more harm to the other. Plato, Cyprian, and some others, as I have formerly said, lay the greatest fault upon the soul, excusing the body; others again, accusing the body, excuse the soul, as a principal agent. Their reasons are, because "the manners do follow the temperature of the body,"[1] as Galen proves in his book of that subject, Prosper Calenius, *de atra bile*, Jason Pratensis, *cap. de mania*, Lemnius, *lib.* 4, *cap.* 16, and many others. And that which Gualter hath commented, *Hom.* 10 *in epist. Johannis*, is most true, concupiscence and original sin, inclinations, and bad humours are radical[2] in every one of us, causing these perturbations, affections, and several distempers, offering many times violence unto the soul. "Every man is tempted by his own concupiscence" (James i, 14), "the spirit is willing but the flesh is weak, and rebelleth against the spirit," as our apostle teacheth us:[3] that methinks the soul hath the better plea against the body, which so forcibly inclines us, that we cannot resist, *Nec nos obniti contra, nec tendere tantum Sufficimus* [To make a stand, and manfully resist, Our strength avails not]. How the body, being material, worketh upon the immaterial soul, by mediation of humours and spirits, which participate of both, and ill-disposed organs, Cornelius Agrippa hath discoursed, *lib.* 1 *de occult. Philos.*, *cap.* 63, 64, 65; Levinus Lemnius, *lib.* 1 *de occult. nat. mir. cap.* 12 *et* 16 *et* 21, *Institut. ad opt. vit.*; Perkins, *lib.* 1, Cases of Conscience, *cap.* 12; T. Bright, *capp.* 10, 11, 12, in his Treatise of Melancholy. For as anger,[4] fear, sorrow, obtrectation, emulation, etc., *si mentis intimos recessus occuparint*, saith Lemnius,[5] *corpori quoque infesta sunt, et illi teterrimos morbos inferunt*, cause grievous diseases in the body, so bodily diseases affect the soul by consent. Now the

chiefest causes proceed from the heart, humours, spirits: [1] as they
are purer, or impurer, so is the mind, and equally suffers, as a lute
out of tune; if one string or one organ be distempered, all the
rest miscarry, *Corpus onustum Hesternis vitiis, animum quoque
prægravat una* [2] [By yesterday's excesses still oppressed, The body
suffers not the mind to rest].   The body is *domicilium animæ* [the
dwelling of the soul], her house, abode, and stay; and as a torch
gives a better light, a sweeter smell, according to the matter it
is made of, so doth our soul perform all her actions, better or
worse, as her organs are disposed; or as wine savours of the cask
wherein it is kept, the soul receives a tincture from the body,
through which it works.   We see this in old men, children,
Europeans, Asians, hot and cold climes; sanguine are merry,
melancholy sad, phlegmatic dull, by reason of abundance of
those humours, and they cannot resist such passions which are
inflicted by them.   For in this infirmity of human nature, as
Melancthon declares, the understanding is so tied to and captivated by his inferior senses, that without their help he cannot
exercise his functions, and the will, being weakened, hath but a
small power to restrain those outward parts, but suffers herself
to be overruled by them; that I must needs conclude with
Lemnius, *spiritus et humores maximum nocumentum obtinent*,
spirits and humours do most harm in troubling the soul. [3]   How
should a man choose but be choleric and angry, that hath his
body so clogged with abundance of gross humours? or melancholy, that is so inwardly disposed?   That thence comes then
this malady, madness, apoplexies, lethargies, etc. it may not
be denied.

Now this body of ours is most part distempered by some
precedent diseases, which molest his inward organs and instruments, and so *per consequens* [consequently] cause melancholy,
according to the consent of the most approved physicians.
"This humour" [4] (as Avicenna, *lib. 3, fen. 1, tract. 4, cap.* 18,
Arnoldus, *Breviar. lib. 1, cap.* 18, Jacchinus, *Comment. in* 9
Rhasis, cap. 15, Montaltus, *cap.* 10, Nicholas Piso, *cap. de melan.*,
etc., suppose) "is begotten by the distemperature of some inward
part, innate, or left after some inflammation, or else included in
the blood after an ague, [5] or some other malignant disease."
This opinion of theirs concurs with that of Galen, *lib. 3, cap.* 6,
de locis affect.   Guianerius gives an instance in one so caused by
a quartan ague, and Montanus, *consil.* 32, in a young man of
twenty-eight years of age, so distempered after a quartan, which
had molested him five years together; Hildesheim, *Spicil.* 2 *de*

mania, relates of a Dutch baron, grievously tormented with melancholy after a long ague:[1] Galen, *lib. de atra bile, cap.* 4, puts the plague a cause; Botaldus, in his book *de lue vener. cap.* 2, the French pox for a cause; others frenzy, epilepsy, apoplexy, because those diseases do often degenerate into this. Of suppression of hemrods, hæmorrhagia, or bleeding at the nose, menstruous retentions (although they deserve a larger explication, as being the sole cause of a proper kind of melancholy, in more ancient maids, nuns and widows, handled apart by Rodericus à Castro and Mercatus, as I have elsewhere signified), or any other evacuation stopped, I have already spoken. Only this I will add, that this melancholy, which shall be caused by such infirmities, deserves to be pitied of all men, and to be respected with a more tender compassion, according to Laurentius, as coming from a more inevitable cause.

SUBSECT. II.—*Distemperature of particular Parts, Causes*

There is almost no part of the body which, being distempered, doth not cause this malady, as the brain and his parts, heart, liver, spleen, stomach, matrix or womb, pylorus, myrach, mesentery, hypochondries, meseraic veins; and in a word, saith Arculanus,[2] "there is no part which causeth not melancholy, either because it is adust, or doth not expel the superfluity of the nutriment." Savonarola, *Pract. major, rubric.* 11, *tract.* 6, *cap.* 1, is of the same opinion, that melancholy is engendered in each particular part, and Crato[3] *in consil.* 17, *lib.* 2. Gordonius, who is *instar omnium* [the pick of the bunch], *lib. med. partic.* 2, *cap.* 19, confirms as much, putting the "matter of melancholy sometimes in the stomach, liver, heart, brain, spleen, myrach, hypochondries, whenas the melancholy humour resides there, or the liver is not well cleansed from melancholy blood."[4]

The brain is a familiar and frequent cause, too hot, or too cold, "through adust blood so caused," as Mercurialis will have it, "within or without the head,"[5] the brain itself being distempered. Those are most apt to this disease, "that have a hot heart and moist brain,"[6] which Montaltus, *cap.* 11 *de melanch.*, approves out of Halyabbas, Rhasis, and Avicenna. Mercurialis, *consil.* 11, assigns the coldness of the brain a cause, and Sallustius Salvianus, *Med. lect. lib.* 2, *cap.* 1, will have it arise from a "cold and dry distemperature of the brain."[7] Piso, Benedictus Victorius Faventinus, will have it proceed from a "hot distemperature of the brain";[8] and Montaltus, *cap*. 10, from the brain's heat, scorching the blood.[1]   The brain is still distempered by himself, or by consent: by himself or his proper affection, as Faventinus calls it, "or by vapours which arise from the other parts, and fume up into the head, altering the animal faculties." [2]

Hildesheim, *Spicil*. 2, *de mania*, thinks it may be caused from a "distemperature of the heart; sometimes hot; sometimes cold." [3]   A hot liver, and a cold stomach, are put for usual causes of melancholy: Mercurialis, *consil*. 11, *et consil*. 6, *consil*. 86, assigns a hot liver and cold stomach for ordinary causes.   Monavius, in an epistle of his to Crato, in Scoltzius,[4] is of opinion that hypochondriacal melancholy may proceed from a cold liver; the question is there discussed.   Most agree that a hot liver is in fault.   "The liver is the shop of humours, and especially causeth melancholy by his hot and dry distemperature.[5]   The stomach and meseraic veins do often concur, by reason of their obstructions, and thence their heat cannot be avoided, and many times the matter is so adust and inflamed in those parts, that it degenerates into hypochondriacal melancholy." [6]   Guianerius, *cap*. 2, *tract*. 15, holds the meseraic veins to be a sufficient cause alone.[7]   The spleen concurs to this malady, by all their consents, and suppression of hemrods, *dum non expurget altera causa lien*, saith Montaltus, if it be "too cold and dry,[8] and do not purge the other parts as it ought," *consil*. 23.   Montanus puts the "spleen stopped" [9] for a great cause.   Christopherus à Vega reports,[10] of his knowledge, that he hath known melancholy caused from putrefied blood in those seed-veins and womb; Arculanus, "from that menstruous blood turned into melancholy, and seed too long detained" (as I have already declared) "by putrefaction or adustion." [11]

The mesenterium, or midriff, diaphragma, is a cause, which the Greeks called φρένες, because by his inflammation the mind is much troubled with convulsions and dotage.[12]   All these, most part, offend by inflammation, corrupting humours and spirits, in this non-natural melancholy: for from these are engendered fuliginous and black spirits.   And for that reason Montaltus, *cap*. 10 *de causis melan*., will have "the efficient cause of melancholy to be hot and dry, not a cold and dry distemperature, as some hold, from the heat of the brain roasting the blood, immoderate heat of the liver and bowels, and inflammation of the pylorus.   And so much the rather, because that," as Galen holds, "all spices inflame the blood, solitariness, waking, agues, study, meditation, all which heat: and therefore he concludes that this distemperature causing adventitious melancholy is not cold and dry, but hot and dry." [1]   But of this I have sufficiently treated in the matter of melancholy, and hold that this may be true in non-natural melancholy, which produceth madness, but not in that natural, which is more cold, and being immoderate, produceth a gentle dotage.   Which opinion Geraldus de Solo maintains in his comment upon Rhasis.[2]

SUBSECT. III.—*Causes of Head-Melancholy*

After a tedious discourse of the general causes of melancholy, I am now returned at last to treat in brief of the three particular species, and such causes as properly appertain unto them. Although these causes promiscuously concur to each and every particular kind, and commonly produce their effects in that part which is most weak, ill-disposed, and least able to resist, and so cause all three species, yet many of them are proper to some one kind, and seldom found in the rest. As for example, head-melancholy is commonly caused by a cold or hot distemperature of the brain, according to Laurentius, *cap.* 5 *de melan.*, but, as Hercules de Saxonia contends,[3] from that agitation or distemperature of the animal spirits alone. Sallust. Salvianus, before mentioned, *lib.* 2, *cap.* 3, *de re med.*, will have it proceed from cold: but that I take of natural melancholy, such as are fools and dote: for as Galen writes, *lib.* 4 *de puls.* 8, and Avicenna, "a cold and moist brain is an inseparable companion of folly." [4] But this adventitious melancholy which is here meant, is caused of a hot and dry distemperature, as Damascen the Arabian, *lib.* 3, *cap.* 22,[5] thinks, and most writers; Altomarus and Piso call it "an innate burning untemperateness, turning blood and choler into melancholy." [6]   Both these opinions may stand good, as Bruel maintains, and Capivaccius, *si cerebrum sit calidius*: "if the brain be hot, the animal spirits will be hot, and thence comes madness; if cold, folly." [7]   David Crusius, *Theat. morb. Hermet. lib.* 2, *cap.* 6, *de atra bile*, grants melancholy to be a disease of an inflamed brain, but cold notwithstanding of itself: *calida per accidens, frigida per se*, hot by accident only; I am of Capivaccius' mind for my part. Now this humour, according to Salvianus, is sometimes in the substance of the brain, sometimes contained in the membranes and tunicles that cover the brain, sometimes in the passages of the ventricles of the brain, or veins of those ventricles. It follows many times "frenzy, long diseases, agues, long abode in hot places, or under the sun, a blow on the head," as Rhasis informeth us: [1] Piso adds solitariness, waking, inflammations of the head, proceeding most part from much use of spices, hot wines, hot meats: [2] all which Montanus reckons up, *consil.* 22, for a melancholy Jew; and Heurnius repeats, *cap.* 12 *de mania*: hot baths, garlic, onions, saith Guianerius, bad air, corrupt, much waking, etc.,[3] retention of seed or abundance, stopping of hæmorrhagia, the midriff misaffected; and according to Trallianus, *lib.* 1, 16, immoderate cares, troubles, griefs, discontent, study, meditation, and, in a word, the abuse of all those six non-natural things. Hercules de Saxonia, *cap.* 16, *lib.* 1, will have it caused from a cautery, or boil dried up, or any issue.[4] Amatus Lusitanus, *cent.* 2, *cura* 67, gives instance in a fellow that had a hole in his arm, "after that was healed, ran mad, and when the wound was open, he was cured again." [5] Trincavellius, *consil.* 13, *lib.* 1, hath an example of a melancholy man so caused by overmuch continuance in the sun, frequent use of venery, and immoderate exercise: and, in his *cons.* 49, *lib.* 3, from an headpiece overheated,[6] which caused head-melancholy. Prosper Calenus brings in Cardinal Cæsius for a pattern of such as are so melancholy by long study; but examples are infinite.

SUBSECT. IV.—*Causes of Hypochondriacal or Windy Melancholy*

In repeating of these causes, I must *cramben bis coctam apponere*, say that again which I have formerly said, in applying them to their proper species. Hypochondriacal or flatuous melancholy is that which the Arabians call myrachial, and is in my judgment the most grievous and frequent, though Bruel and Laurentius make it least dangerous, and not so hard to be known or cured. His causes are inward or outward. Inward from divers parts or organs, as midriff, spleen, stomach, liver, pylorus, womb, diaphragma, meseraic veins, stopping of issues, etc. Montaltus, *cap.* 15, out of Galen, recites, "heat and obstruction of those meseraic veins, as an immediate cause, by which means the passage of the chylus to the liver is detained, stopped, or corrupted, and turned into rumbling and wind." [7] Montanus, *consil.* 233, hath an evident demonstration, Trincavellius another, *lib.* 1, *cap.* 12, and Plater a third, *Observat. lib.* 1, for a doctor of the law visited with this infirmity, from the said obstruction and heat of these meseraic veins, and bowels: *quoniam inter ventriculum et jecur venæ effervescunt*, the veins are inflamed about the liver and stomach. Sometimes those

other parts are together misaffected, and concur to the produc-
tion of this malady: a hot liver and cold stomach, or cold belly;
look for instances in Hollerius, Victor Trincavellius, *consil.* 35,
lib. 3, Hildesheim, *Spicil.* 2, *fol.* 132, Solenander, *consil.* 9, *pro
cive Lugdunensi*, Montanus, *consil.* 229, for the Earl of Monttort
in Germany, 1549, and Frisimelica in the 233rd consultation of
the said Montanus. J. Cæsar Claudinus gives instance of a
cold stomach and over-hot liver, almost in every consultation,
cons. 89, for a certain count, and *cons.* 106, for a Polonian baron;
by reason of heat the blood is inflamed, and gross vapours sent
to the heart and brain. Mercurialis subscribes to them, *cons.* 89,
"the stomach being misaffected," [1] which he calls the king of the
belly, because if he be distempered, all the rest suffer with him,
as being deprived of their nutriment, or fed with bad nourishment, by means of which come crudities, obstructions, wind,
rumbling, griping, etc. Hercules de Saxonia, besides heat,
will have the weakness of the liver and his obstruction a cause,
facultatem debilem jecinoris, which he calls the mineral of melancholy. Laurentius assigns this reason, because the liver over-
hot draws the meat undigested out of the stomach, and burneth
the humours. Montanus, *cons.* 244, proves that sometimes a
cold liver may be a cause. Laurentius, *cap.* 12, Trincavellius,
lib. 12 *consil.*, and Gualter Bruel, seem to lay the greatest fault
upon the spleen, that doth not his duty in purging the liver as
he ought, being too great, or too little, in drawing too much blood
sometimes to it, and not expelling it, as P. Cnemander in a
consultation of his noted; [2] *tumorem lienis* [swelling of the
spleen], he names it, and the fountain of melancholy. Diocles
supposed the ground of this kind of melancholy to proceed from
the inflammation of the pylorus, which is the nether mouth of
the ventricle. Others assign the mesenterium or midriff distempered by heat, the womb misaffected, stopping of hemrods,
with many such. All which Laurentius, *cap.* 12, reduceth to
three, mesentery, liver, and spleen, from whence he denominates
hepatic, splenetic, and meseraic melancholy. Outward causes
are bad diet, care, griefs, discontents, and in a word all those
six non-natural things, as Montanus found by his experience,
consil. 244. Solenander, *consil.* 9, for a citizen of Lyons in
France, gives his reader to understand that he knew this mischief
procured by a medicine of cantharides, which an unskilful
physician ministered his patient to drink *ad venerem excitandam*
[to excite desire]. But most commonly fear, grief, and some
sudden commotion or perturbation of the mind begin it, in

such bodies especially as are ill disposed. Melancthon, *tract.* 14, *cap.* 2, *de anima*, will have it as common to men, as the mother to women, upon some grievous trouble, dislike, passion, or discontent. For as Camerarius records in his life, Melancthon himself was much troubled with it, and therefore could speak out of experience. Montanus, *consil.* 22, *pro delirante Judæo*, confirms it, grievous symptoms of the mind brought him to it.[1] Rondeletius relates of himself, that being one day very intent to write out a physician's notes, molested by an occasion, he fell into a hypochondriacal fit, to avoid which he drank the decoction of wormwood, and was freed. Melancthon ("being the disease is so troublesome and frequent") holds it "a most necessary and profitable study for every man to know the accidents of it, and a dangerous thing to be ignorant,"[2] and would therefore have all men in some sort to understand the causes, symptoms, and cures of it.

SUBSECT. V.—*Causes of Melancholy from the whole Body*

As before, the cause of this kind of melancholy is inward or outward. Inward, "when the liver is apt to engender such a humour, or the spleen weak by nature, and not able to discharge his office."[3] A melancholy temperature, retention of hemrods, monthly issues, bleeding at nose, long diseases, agues, and all those six non-natural things increase it; but especially bad diet, as Piso thinks,[4] pulse, salt meat, shell-fish, cheese, black wine, etc. Mercurialis, out of Averroes and Avicenna, condemns all herbs; Galen, *lib.* 3 *de loc. affect. cap.* 7, especially cabbage. So likewise fear, sorrow, discontents, etc., but of these before. And thus in brief you have had the general and particular causes of melancholy.

Now go and brag of thy present happiness, whosoever thou art, brag of thy temperature, of thy good parts, insult, triumph, and boast; thou seest in what a brittle state thou art, how soon thou mayest be dejected, how many several ways, by bad diet, bad air, a small loss, a little sorrow or discontent, an ague, etc.; how many sudden accidents may procure thy ruin, what a small tenure of happiness thou hast in this life, how weak and silly a creature thou art. "Humble thyself therefore under the mighty hand of God" (1 Peter, v, 6), know thyself, acknowledge thy present misery, and make right use of it. *Qui stat videat ne cadat* [let him that is upright see that he fall not]. Thou dost

now flourish, and hast *bona animi, corporis, et fortunæ*, goods of
body, mind, and fortune, *nescis quid serus secum vesper ferat*,
thou knowest not what storms and tempests the late evening
may bring with it. Be not secure then, "be sober and watch,"
fortunam reverenter habe[1] [be not puffed up by good fortune], if
fortunate and rich; if sick and poor, moderate thyself. I
have said.

SECT. III. MEMB. I.

SUBSECT. I.—*Symptoms, or Signs of Melancholy in the Body*

PARRHASIUS, a painter of Athens, amongst those Olynthian
captives Philip of Macedon brought home to sell, bought one
very old man; and when he had him at Athens, put him to
extreme torture and torment, the better by his example to
express the pains and passions of his Prometheus, whom he
was then about to paint.[2] I need not be so barbarous, inhuman,
curious, or cruel, for this purpose to torture any poor melancholy man; their symptoms are plain, obvious and familiar, there
needs no such accurate observation or far-fetched object, they
delineate themselves, they voluntarily bewray themselves, they
are too frequent in all places, I meet them still as I go, they cannot conceal it, their grievances are too well known, I need not
seek far to describe them.

Symptoms therefore are either universal or particular, saith
Gordonius, *lib. med. cap.* 19, *part.* 2, to persons, to species;[3]
"some signs are secret, some manifest, some in the body, some
in the mind, and diversely vary, according to the inward or
outward causes" (Capivaccius); or from stars, according to
Jovianus Pontanus, *de reb. cœlest. lib.* 10, *cap.* 13, and celestial
influences, or from the humours diversely mixed (Ficinus, *lib.* 1,
cap. 4, *de sanit. tuenda*). As they are hot, cold, natural, unnatural, intended or remitted, so will Aetius have *melancholica
deliria multiformia*, diversity of melancholy signs. Laurentius
ascribes them to their several temperatures, delights, natures,
inclinations, continuance of time, as they are simple or mixed
with other diseases, as the causes are divers, so must the signs
be almost infinite (Altomarus, *cap.* 7 *art. med.*). And as wine
produceth divers effects, or that herb Tortocolla in Laurentius,[4]
"which makes some laugh, some weep, some sleep, some dance

some sing, some howl, some drink, etc.," so doth this our
melancholy humour work several signs in several parties.

But to confine them, these general symptoms may be reduced
to those of the body or the mind. Those usual signs appearing
in the bodies of such as are melancholy be these, cold and dry,
or they are hot and dry, as the humour is more or less adust.
From these first qualities arise many other second,[1] as that of
colour,[2] black, swarthy, pale, ruddy, etc., some are *impense rubri*,
as Montaltus, *cap.* 16, observes out of Galen, *lib. 3 de locis affectis*,
very red and high coloured. Hippocrates in his book *de insania
et melan.*[3] reckons up these signs, that they are "lean, withered,
hollow-eyed, look old, wrinkled, harsh, much troubled with wind
and a griping in their bellies, or belly-ache, belch often, dry
bellies and hard, dejected looks, flaggy beards, singing of the
ears, vertigo, light-headed, little or no sleep, and that interrupt,
terrible and fearful dreams." [4]

> *Anna soror, quae me suspensum insomnia terrent!* [5]
>
> [O sister Anna, terrifying dreams
> My sleep have troubled.]

The same symptoms are repeated by Melanelius (in his book
of Melancholy, collected out of Galen), Ruffus, Aetius, by
Rhasis, Gordonius, and all the juniors, "continual, sharp, and
stinking belchings, as if their meat in their stomachs were
putrefied, or that they had eaten fish, dry bellies, absurd and
interrupt dreams, and many phantastical visions about their
eyes, vertiginous, apt to tremble, and prone to venery." [6]
Some [7] add palpitation of the heart, cold sweat, as usual
symptoms, and a leaping in many parts of the body, *saltum
in multis corporis partibus*, a kind of itching, saith Laurentius,
on the superficies of the skin, like a flea-biting sometimes.
Montaltus, *cap.* 21, puts fixed eyes and much twinkling of their
eyes for a sign,[8] and so doth Avicenna, *oculos habentes palpitantes,
trauli, vehementer rubicundi, etc., lib. 3, fen. 1, tract. 4, cap.* 18.
They stut most part, which he took out of Hippocrates'
Aphorisms. Rhasis [9] makes "headache and a binding heaviness" for a principal token, "much leaping of wind about the
skin, as well as stutting, or tripping in speech, etc., hollow eyes,
gross veins, and broad lips." To some too, if they be far gone,
mimical gestures are too familiar, laughing, grinning, fleering,
murmuring, talking to themselves, with strange mouths and
faces, inarticulate voices, exclamations, etc. And although
they be commonly lean, hirsute, uncheerful in countenance,

withered, and not so pleasant to behold, by reason of those
continual fears, griefs, and vexations, dull, heavy, lazy, restless,
unapt to go about any business; yet their memories are most
part good, they have happy wits, and excellent apprehensions.
Their hot and dry brains make them they cannot sleep, *Ingentes
habent et crebras vigilias* (Aretæus), mighty and often watchings,
sometimes waking for a month, a year together. Hercules de
Saxonia [1] faithfully averreth, that he hath heard his mother
swear, she slept not for seven months together: Trincavellius,
tom. 2, cons. 16, speaks of one that waked fifty days, and
Sckenkius hath examples of two years, and all without offence.
In natural actions their appetite is greater than their concoction,
multa appetunt, pauca digerunt, as Rhasis hath it, they covet to
eat, but cannot digest. And although they "do eat much, yet
they are lean, ill-liking," saith Aretæus, "withered and hard,
much troubled with costiveness," [2] crudities, oppilations, spitting,
belching, etc. Their pulse is rare and slow, except it be of the
carotides, which is very strong; [3] but that varies according to
their intended passions or perturbations, as Struthius hath
proved at large, *Sphygmaticæ artis lib.* 4, *cap.* 13. To say truth,
in such chronic diseases the pulse is not much to be respected,
there being so much superstition in it, as Crato [4] notes, and so
many differences in Galen, that he dares say thay may not be
observed or understood of any man.

Their urine is most part pale, and low coloured, *urina pauca,
acris, biliosa* (Aretæus), not much in quantity; but this, in my
judgment, is all out as uncertain as the other, varying so often
according to several persons, habits, and other occasions not
to be respected in chronic diseases. "Their melancholy excrements in some very much, in others little, as the spleen plays
his part," [5] and thence proceeds wind, palpitation of the heart,
short breath, plenty of humidity in the stomach, heaviness of
heart and heartache, and intolerable stupidity and dullness of
spirits. Their excrements or stool hard, black to some, and
little. If the heart, brain, liver, spleen, be misaffected, as
usually they are, many inconveniences proceed from them,
many diseases accompany, as incubus, apoplexy,[6] epilepsy,
vertigo, those frequent wakings and terrible dreams, intempestive
laughing, weeping, sighing, sobbing, bashfulness, blushing,
trembling, sweating, swooning, etc.[7] All their senses are
troubled,[8] they think they see, hear, smell, and touch that which
they do not, as shall be proved in the following discourse.

SUBSECT. II.—*Symptoms or Signs in the Mind*

Arculanus, *in* 9 *Rhasis ad Almansor. cap.* 16, will have these symptoms to be infinite, as indeed they are, varying according to the parties, "for scarce is there one of a thousand that dotes alike" (Laurentius, *cap.* 16).[1] Some few of greater note I will point at; and amongst the rest, fear and sorrow, which, as they are frequent causes, so if they persevere long, according to Hippocrates' and Galen's [2] aphorisms, they are most assured signs, inseparable companions, and characters of melancholy; of present melancholy and habituated, said Montaltus, *cap.* 11, and common to them all, as the said Hippocrates, Galen, Avicenna, and all neoterics hold. But as hounds many times run away with a false cry, never perceiving themselves to be at a fault, so do they. For Diocles of old (whom Galen confutes), and, amongst the juniors, Hercules de Saxonia,[3] with Lod. Mercatus, *cap.* 17, *lib.* 1 *de melan.*, take just exceptions at this aphorism of Hippocrates; 'tis not always true, or so generally to be understood. Fear and sorrow are no common symptoms to all melancholy; "Upon more serious consideration, I find some" (saith he) "that are not so at all. Some indeed are sad, and not fearful; some fearful, and not sad; some neither fearful nor sad; some both." Four kinds he excepts: fanatical persons, such as were Cassandra, Manto, Nicostrata, Mopsus, Proteus, the Sibyls, whom Aristotle [4] confesseth to have been deeply melancholy. Baptista Porta seconds him, *Physiog. lib.* 1, *cap.* 8, they were *atra bile perciti.* Demoniacal persons, and such as speak strange languages, are of this rank: some poets; such as laugh always, and think themselves kings, cardinals, etc.; sanguine they are, pleasantly disposed most part, and so continue. Baptista Porta [5] confines fear and sorrow to them that are cold; but lovers, sibyls, enthusiasts, he wholly excludes. So that I think I may truly conclude, they are not always sad and fearful, but usually so: and that without a cause,[6] *timent de non timendis* (Gordonius), *quæque momenti non sunt* [they fear where there is no ground for fear, they are alarmed about trifles]; "although not all alike" (saith Altomarus), "yet all likely fear,[7] some with an extraordinary and a mighty fear" [8] (Aretæus). "Many fear death, and yet, in a contrary humour, make away themselves" [9] (Galen, *lib.* 3 *de loc. affec. cap.* 7) Some are afraid that heaven will fall on their heads: some they are damned, or shall be. "They are troubled with scruples of conscience, distrusting God's mercies, think they shall go certainly to hell, the devil will have them, and make great lamentation"[1] (Jason Pratensis). Fear of devils, death, that they shall be so sick, of some such or such disease, ready to tremble at every object, they shall die themselves forthwith, or that some of their dear friends or near allies are certainly dead; imminent danger, loss, disgrace still torment others, etc.; that they are all glass, and therefore will suffer no man to come near them: that they are all cork, as light as feathers; others as heavy as lead; some are afraid their heads will fall off their shoulders, that they have frogs in their bellies, etc. Montanus, *consil.* 23, speaks of one "that durst not walk alone from home, for fear he should swoon or die."[2] A second "fears every man he meets will rob him, quarrel with him, or kill him."[3] A third dares not venture to walk alone, for fear he should meet the devil, a thief, be sick; fears all old women as witches, and every black dog or cat he sees he suspecteth to be a devil, every person comes near him is maleficiated, every creature, all intend to hurt him, seek his ruin; another dares not go over a bridge, come near a pool, rock, steep hill, lie in a chamber where cross-beams are, for fear he be tempted to hang, drown, or precipitate himself. If he be in a silent auditory, as at a sermon, he is afraid he shall speak aloud at unawares, something undecent, unfit to be said. If he be locked in a close room, he is afraid of being stifled for want of air, and still carries biscuit, aquavitæ, or some strong waters about him, for fear of deliquiums, or being sick; or if he be in a throng, middle of a church, multitude, where he may not well get out, though he sit at ease, he is so misaffected. He will freely promise, undertake any business beforehand, but when it comes to be performed, he dare not adventure, but fears an infinite number of dangers, disasters, etc. Some are "afraid to be burned,[4] or that the ground will sink under them,[5] or swallow them quick,[6] or that the king will call them in question for some fact they never did" (Rhasis, *Cont.*), "and that they shall surely be executed." The terror of such a death troubles them, and they fear as much, and are equally tormented in mind, "as they that have committed a murder, and are pensive without a cause, as if they were now presently to be put to death"[7] (Plater, *cap.* 3 *de mentis alienat.*). They are afraid of some loss, danger, that they shall surely lose their lives, goods, and all they have, but why they know not. Trincavellius, *consil.* 13, *lib.* 1, had a patient that would needs make away himself, for fear of being hanged, and could not be persuaded for three years together, but that he had killed a

man.   Plater, *Observat. lib.* 1, have two other examples of such
as feared to be executed without a cause.   If they come in a
place where a robbery, theft, or any such offence hath been
done, they presently fear they are suspected, and many times
betray themselves without a cause.   Louis the Eleventh, the
French king, suspected every man a traitor that came about
him, durst trust no officer.   *Alii formidolosi omnium, alii
quorundam* (Fracastorius, *lib.* 2 *de intellect.*), "some fear all
alike, some certain men," [1] and cannot endure their companies,
are sick in them, or if they be from home.   Some suspect
treason [2] still, others "are afraid of their dearest and nearest
friends" [3] (Melanelius, *e Galeno, Ruffo, Aetio*), and dare not be
alone in the dark for fear of hobgoblins and devils: he suspects
everything he hears or sees to be a devil, or enchanted, and
imagineth a thousand chimeras and visions, which to his thinking he certainly sees, bugbears, talks with black men, ghosts,
goblins, etc.,

> *Omnes se terrent auræ, sonus excitat omnis.* [4]

> [At every rustle of the breeze he quakes,
> He starts at every sound.]

Another through bashfulness, suspicion, and timorousness will
not be seen abroad, "loves darkness as life, and cannot endure
the light," [5] or to sit in lightsome places, his hat still in his eyes,
he will neither see nor be seen by his good will (Hippocrates,
lib. de insania et melancholia).   He dare not come in company for
fear he should be misused, disgraced, overshoot himself in
gesture or speeches, or be sick; he thinks every man observes
him, aims at him, derides him, owes him malice.   Most part
"they are afraid they are bewitched, possessed, or poisoned by
their enemies," and sometimes they suspect their nearest friends:
"he thinks something speaks or talks within him, or to him, and
he belcheth of the poison." [6]   Christopherus à Vega, *lib.* 2,
cap. 1, had a patient so troubled, that by no persuasion or physic
he could be reclaimed.   Some are afraid that they shall have
every fearful disease they see others have, hear of, or read, and
dare not therefore hear or read of any such subject, no, not of
melancholy itself, lest by applying to themselves that which
they hear or read, they should aggravate and increase it.   If they
see one possessed, bewitched, an epileptic paroxysm, a man
shaking with the palsy, or giddy-headed, reeling or standing in
a dangerous place, etc., for many days after it runs in their minds,
they are afraid they shall be so too, they are in like danger, as

Perkins, *cap.* 12, *sect.* 2, well observes in his Cases of Conscience, and many times by violence of imagination they produce it. They cannot endure to see any terrible object, as a monster, a man executed, a carcass, hear the devil named, or any tragical relation seen, but they quake for fear, *Hecatas somniare sibi videntur* (Lucian), they dream of hobgoblins, and may not get it out of their minds a long time after: they apply (as I have said) all they hear, see, read, to themselves; as Felix Plater notes [1] of some young physicians, that studying to cure diseases, catch them themselves, will be sick, and appropriate all symptoms they find related of others to their own persons.   And therefore (*quod iterum moneo, licet nauseam paret lectori, malo decem potius verba, decies repetita licet, abundare, quam unum desiderari*) [I repeat my warning, though it be *ad nauseam*; I had rather say a hundred words too much than one too little] I would advise him that is actually melancholy not to read this tract of Symptoms, lest he disquiet or make himself for a time worse, and more melancholy than he was before.   Generally of them all take this, *de inanibus semper conqueruntur et timent*, saith Aretæus; they complain of toys, and fear without a cause,[2] and still think their melancholy to be most grievous, none so bad as they are, though it be nothing in respect, yet never any man sure was so troubled, or in this sort: as really tormented and perplexed, in as great an agony for toys and trifles (such things as they will after laugh at themselves) as if they were most material and essential matters indeed, worthy to be feared, and will not be satisfied.   Pacify them for one, they are instantly troubled with some other fear; always afraid of something which they foolishly imagine or conceive to themselves, which never peradventure was, never can be, never likely will be; troubled in mind upon every small occasion, unquiet, still complaining, grieving, vexing, suspecting, grudging, discontent, and cannot be freed so long as melancholy continues.   Or if their minds be more quiet for the present, and they free from foreign fears, outward accidents, yet their bodies are out of tune, they suspect some part or other to be amiss; now their head aches, heart, stomach, spleen, etc., is misaffected, they shall surely have this or that disease; still troubled in body, mind, or both, and through wind, corrupt phantasy, some accidental distemper, continually molested.   Yet for all this, as Jacchinus notes,[3] "in all other things they are wise, staid, discreet, and do nothing unbeseeming their dignity, person, or place, this foolish, ridiculous, and childish fear excepted"; which so much, so continually tortures and crucifies their souls, like a barking dog that always bawls, but seldom bites, this fear ever molesteth, and, so long as melancholy lasteth, cannot be avoided.

Sorrow is that other character, and inseparable companion, as individual as Saint Cosmus and Damian, *fidus Achates*, as all writers witness, a common symptom, a continual, and still without any evident cause, *mœrent omnes, et si roges eos reddere causam, non possunt*:[1] grieving still, but why they cannot tell: *agelasti, mœsti, cogitabundi* [never smiling, gloomy, wrapt in thought], they look as if they had newly come forth of Trophonius' den. And though they laugh many times, and seem to be extraordinary merry (as they will by fits), yet extreme lumpish again in an instant, dull and heavy, *semel et simul* [both at once], merry and sad, but most part sad: *Si qua placent, abeunt; inimica tenacius hærent*[2] [that which pleases soon departs, that which hurts clings fast]: sorrow sticks by them still continually, gnawing as the vulture did Tityus' bowels,[3] and they cannot avoid it. No sooner are their eyes open, but after terrible and troublesome dreams their heavy hearts begin to sigh: they are still fretting, chafing, sighing, grieving, complaining, finding faults, repining, grudging, weeping, *Heautontimorumenoi*, vexing themselves, disquieted in mind,[4] with restless, unquiet thoughts, discontent, either for their own, other men's or public affairs, such as concern them not; things past, present, or to come, the remembrance of some disgrace, loss, injury, abuse, etc. troubles them now being idle afresh, as if it were new done; they are afflicted otherwise for some danger, loss, want, shame, misery, that will certainly come, as they suspect and mistrust. *Lugubris Ate* [mournful Ate] frowns upon them, insomuch that Aretæus well calls it *angorem animi*, a vexation of the mind, a perpetual agony. They can hardly be pleased or eased, though in other men's opinion most happy; go, tarry, run, ride, *post equitem sedet atra cura*[5] [close behind the rider sits black care]: they cannot avoid this feral plague; let them come in what company they will, *hæret lateri lethalis arundo*[6] [the deadly arrow in his side is fixed], as to a deer that is struck, whether he run, go, rest with the herd, or alone, this grief remains: irresolution, inconstancy, vanity of mind, their fear, torture, care, jealousy, suspicion, etc., continues, and they cannot be relieved. So he complained[7] in the poet:

> *Domum revortor mœstus, atque animo fere*
> *Perturbato, atque incerto præ ægritudine,*
> *Assido: accurrunt servi, soccos detrahunt:*

Video alios festinare, lectos sternere,
Cœnam apparare, pro se quisque sedulo
Faciebant, quo illam mihi lenirent miseriam.

He came home sorrowful and troubled in his mind; his
servants did all they possibly could to please him; one pulled
off his socks, another made ready his bed, a third his supper,
all did their utmost endeavours to ease his grief and exhilarate
his person; he was profoundly melancholy, he had lost his son,
illud angebat [that was torturing him], that was his *cordolium*
[heart-sorrow], his pain, his agony which could not be removed.
Hence it proceeds many times that they are weary of their
lives, and feral thoughts to offer violence to their own persons
come into their minds; *tædium vitæ* [weariness of life] is a common
symptom, *tarda fluunt, ingrataque tempora* [time passes slowly
and without enjoyment], they are soon tired with all things;
they will now tarry, now be gone; now in bed they will rise,
now up, then go to bed, now pleased, then again displeased;
now they like, by and by dislike all, weary of all, *sequitur nunc*
vivendi, nunc moriendi cupido [at one time they want to live,
at another to die], saith Aurelianus, *lib.* 1, *cap.* 6, but most part
vitam damnant [1] [they declare life not worth living], discontent,
disquieted, perplexed upon every light or no occasion, object:
often tempted, I say, to make away themselves: *Vivere nolunt,*
mori nesciunt: [2] they cannot die, they will not live: they complain, weep, lament, and think they lead a most miserable life,
never was any man so bad, or so before, every poor man they see
is most fortunate in respect of them, every beggar that comes to
the door is happier than they are, they could be contented to
change lives with them, especially if they be alone, idle, and
parted from their ordinary company, molested, displeased, or
provoked: grief, fear, agony, discontent, wearisomeness, laziness, suspicion, or some such passion, forcibly seizeth on them.
Yet by and by, when they come in company again which they
like, or be pleased, *suam sententiam rursus damnant, et vitæ*
solatio delectantur, as Octavius Horatianus observes, *lib.* 2, *cap.* 5,
they condemn their former mislike, and are well pleased to live.
And so they continue, till with some fresh discontent they be
molested again, and then they are weary of their lives, weary of
all, they will die, and show rather a necessity to live than a
desire. Claudius the emperor, as Suetonius describes him,[3] had
a spice of this disease, for when he was tormented with the pain
of his stomach, he had a conceit to make away himself. Julius
Cæsar Claudinus, *consil.* 84, had a Polonian to his patient so

affected, that through fear and sorrow, with which he was still disquieted, hated his own life, wished for death every moment, and to be freed of his misery; [1] Mercurialis another, and another that was often minded to dispatch himself, and so continued for many years.

Suspicion and jealousy are general symptoms: they are commonly distrustful, apt to mistake, and amplify, *facile irascibiles*, testy, [2] pettish, peevish, and ready to snarl upon every small occasion, [3] *cum amicissimis* [with their dearest friends], and without a cause, *datum vel non datum*, it will be *scandalum acceptum* [they will take offence, whether it is given or not]. If they speak in jest, he takes it in good earnest. If they be not saluted, invited, consulted with, called to counsel, etc., or that any respect, small compliment, or ceremony be omitted, they think themselves neglected and contemned; for a time that tortures them. If two talk together, discourse, whisper, jest, or tell a tale in general, he thinks presently they mean him, applies all to himself, *de se putat omnia dici*. Or if they talk with him, he is ready to misconster every word they speak, and interpret it to the worst; he cannot endure any man to look steadily on him, speak to him almost, laugh, jest, or be familiar, or hem, or point, cough, or spit, or make a noise sometimes, etc. He thinks they laugh or point at him, or do it in disgrace of him, circumvent him, contemn him; [4] every man looks at him, he is pale, red, sweats for fear and anger, lest somebody should observe him. He works upon it, and long after this false conceit of an abuse troubles him. Montanus, *consil.* 22, gives instance in a melancholy Jew, that was *iracundior Adria* [more tempestuous than the Adriatic Sea], so waspish and suspicious, *tam facile iratus* [so quick to anger], that no man could tell how to carry himself in his company.

Inconstant they are in all their actions, vertiginous, restless, unapt to resolve of any business, they will and will not, persuaded to and fro upon every small occasion, or word spoken: and yet if once they be resolved, obstinate, hard to be reconciled. If they abhor, dislike, or distaste, once settled, though to the better by odds, by no counsel or persuasion to be removed; yet in most things wavering, irresolute, unable to deliberate, through fear, *faciunt, et mox facti pænitent* (Aretæus), *avari, et paulo post prodigi*: now prodigal, and then covetous, they do, and by and by repent them of that which they have done, so that both ways they are troubled, whether they do or do not, want or have, hit or miss, disquieted of all hands, soon weary, and still seeking

change, restless, I say, fickle, fugitive, they may not abide to
tarry in one place long:

> *Romæ rus optans, absentem rusticus urbem*
> *Tollit ad astra;* [1]

> [At Rome, he fain would to the country fly;
> When there, he lauds the city to the sky;]

no company long, or to persevere in any action or business:

> *Et similis regum pueris, pappare minutum*
> *Poscit, et iratus mammæ lallare recusat;* [2]

> [Like the children of the rich, he wants his food cut up
>   small, and being cross with his nurse will not let
>   her sing him to sleep;]

eftsoons pleased, and anon displeased; as a man that's bitten
with fleas, or that cannot sleep, turns to and fro in his bed,
their restless minds are tossed and vary, they have no patience
to read out a book, to play out a game or two, walk a mile, sit
an hour, etc.; erected and dejected in an instant; animated to
undertake, and upon a word spoken again discouraged.

Extreme passionate, *Quicquid volunt valde volunt*; and what
they desire, they do most furiously seek: anxious ever and very
solicitous, distrustful and timorous, envious, malicious, profuse
one while, sparing another, but most part covetous, muttering,
repining, discontent, and still complaining, grudging, peevish,
injuriarum tenaces, prone to revenge, soon troubled, and most
violent in all their imaginations, not affable in speech, or apt to
vulgar compliment, but surly, dull, sad, austere; *cogitabundi* still,
very intent, and as Albertus Durer paints Melancholy,[3] like a
sad woman leaning on her arm with fixed looks, neglected habit,
etc.; held therefore by some proud, soft, sottish, or half-mad,
as the Abderites esteemed of Democritus, and yet of a deep
reach, excellent apprehension, judicious, wise and witty: for
I am of that nobleman's mind,[4] "Melancholy advanceth men's
conceits more than any humour whatsoever," improves their
meditations more than any strong drink or sack. They are of
profound judgment in some things, although in others *non recte
judicant inquieti* [people in a passion do not judge correctly],
saith Fracastorius, *lib. 2 de intell.* And as Arculanus, *cap.* 16
in 9 *Rhasis*, terms it, *Judicium plerumque perversum, corruptum,
cum judicant honesta inhonesta, et amicitiam habent pro inimicitia,*
[their judgment is generally perverse and corrupt, since] they
count honesty dishonesty, friends as enemies, they will abuse
their best friends, and dare not offend their enemies.   Cowards

most part, *et ad inferendam injuriam timidissimi*, saith Cardan,
lib. 8, *cap.* 4, *de rerum varietate* : loath to offend; and if they
chance to overshoot themselves in word or deed, or any small
business or circumstance be omitted, forgotten, they are miserably tormented, and frame a thousand dangers and inconveniences to themselves, *ex musca elephantem* [make a fly into
an elephant], if once they conceit it: overjoyed with every
good rumour, tale, or prosperous event, transported beyond
themselves: with every small cross again, bad news, misconceived injury, loss, danger, afflicted beyond measure, in great
agony, perplexed, dejected, astonished, impatient, utterly
undone: fearful, suspicious of all. Yet again, many of them
desperate hairbrains, rash, careless, fit to be assassinates, as being
void of all fear and sorrow, according to Hercules de Saxonia,[1]
"most audacious, and such as dare walk alone in the night,
through deserts and dangerous places, fearing none."

They are prone to love, and easy to be taken:[2] *propensi
ad amorem et excandescentiam* (Montaltus, *cap.* 21), quickly
enamoured, and dote upon all, love one dearly, till they see
another, and then dote on her, *et hanc, et hanc, et illam, et omnes*
[this one, and that one, and all of them]; the present moves most,
and the last commonly they love best. Yet some again *anterotes*
[enemies of love], cannot endure the sight of a woman, abhor the
sex, as that same melancholy duke of Muscovy, that was instantly
sick if he came but in sight of them;[3] and that anchorite, that
fell into a cold palsy when a woman was brought before him.[4]

Humorous they are beyond all measure, sometimes profusely
laughing, extraordinarily merry, and then again weeping without a cause (which is familiar with many gentlewomen) groaning,
sighing, pensive, sad, almost distracted, *multa absurda fingunt,
et a ratione aliena* (saith Frambesarius [5]), they feign many
absurdities, vain, void of reason. One supposeth himself to be
a dog, cock, bear, horse, glass, butter, etc. He is a giant, a
dwarf, as strong as an hundred men, a lord, duke, prince, etc.
And if he be told he hath a stinking breath, a great nose, that
he is sick, or inclined to such or such a disease, he believes it
eftsoons, and peradventure by force of imagination will work it
out. Many of them are immovable, and fixed in their conceits,
others vary upon every object, heard or seen. If they see a
stage-play, they run upon that a week after; if they hear music,
or see dancing, they have naught but bagpipes in their brain;
if they see a combat, they are all for arms. If abused, an abuse
troubles them long after; if crossed, that cross, etc.[6] Restless in

their thoughts and actions, continually meditating, *velut ægri somnia, vanæ finguntur species*, more like dreams than men awake, they feign a company of antic, phantastical conceits, they have most frivolous thoughts, impossible to be effected; and sometimes think verily they hear and see present before their eyes such phantasms or goblins, they fear, suspect, or conceive, they still talk with, and follow them. In fine, *cogitationes somniantibus similes, id vigilant, quod alii somniant cogitabundi*: still, saith Avicenna, they wake, as others dream, and such for the most part are their imaginations and conceits, absurd, vain, foolish toys,[1] yet they are most curious [2] and solicitous, continual, *et supra modum* (Rhasis, *Cont. lib.* 1, *cap.* 9) *præmeditantur de aliqua re* [and are excessively engrossed in one thing or other]; as serious in a toy, as if it were a most necessary business, of great moment, importance, and still, still, still thinking of it: *sæviunt in se*, macerating themselves. Though they do talk with you, and seem to be otherwise employed, and to your thinking very intent and busy, still that toy runs in their mind, that fear, that suspicion, that abuse, that jealousy, that agony, that vexation, that cross, that castle in the air, that crotchet, that whimsy, that fiction, that pleasant waking dream, whatsoever it is. *Nec interrogant* (saith Fracastorius [3]) *nec interrogatis recte respondent* [they do not ask questions themselves nor answer properly the questions put to them]; they do not much heed what you say, their mind is on another matter; ask what you will, they do not attend, or much intend that business they are about, but forget themselves what they are saying, doing, or should otherwise say or do, whither they are going, distracted with their own melancholy thoughts. One laughs upon a sudden, another smiles to himself, a third frowns, calls, his lips go still, he acts with his hand as he walks, etc. "'Tis proper to all melancholy men," saith Mercurialis, *consil.* 11, "what conceit they have once entertained, to be most intent, violent, and continually about it."[4] *Invitis occurrit*, do what they may, they cannot be rid of it, against their wills they must think of it a thousand times over, *perpetuo molestantur, nec oblivisci possunt*, they are continually troubled with it, in company, out of company; at meat, at exercise, at all times and places, *non desinunt ea, quæ minime volunt, cogitare* [5] [they cannot put out of their minds the matters they least wish to think of]; if it be offensive especially, they cannot forget it, they may not rest or sleep for it, but still tormenting themselves, *Sisyphi saxum volvunt sibi ipsis* [they endure the torments of Sisyphus], as Brunner observes,[1] *perpetua calamitas et miserabile flagellum* [perpetually in suffering and under the lash].

Crato,[2] Laurentius,[3] and Fernelius put bashfulness for an ordinary symptom; *subrusticus pudor*, or *vitiosus pudor* [*mauvaise honte*], is a thing which much haunts and torments them. If they have been misused, derided, disgraced, chidden, etc., or by any perturbation of mind misaffected, it so far troubles them, that they become quite moped many times, and so disheartened, dejected, they dare not come abroad, into strange companies especially, or manage their ordinary affairs, so childish, timorous, and bashful, they can look no man in the face; some are more disquieted in this kind, some less, longer some, others shorter, by fits, etc., though some on the other side (according to Fracastorius[4]) be *inverecundi et pertinaces*, impudent and peevish. But most part they are very shamefaced, and that makes them with Pet. Blesensis, Christopher Urswick, and many such, to refuse honours, offices, and preferments, which sometimes fall into their mouths; they cannot speak, or put forth themselves as others can, *timor hos, pudor impedit illos*, timorousness and bashfulness hinder their proceedings, they are contented with their present estate, unwilling to undertake any office, and therefore never likely to rise. For that cause they seldom visit their friends, except some familiars: *pauciloqui*, of few words, and oftentimes wholly silent. Frambesarius, a Frenchman,[5] had two such patients, *omnino taciturnos* [completely taciturn], their friends could not get them to speak: Rodericus à Fonseca, *Consult. tom. 2, 85 consil.* gives instance in a young man, of twenty-seven years of age, that was frequently silent, bashful, moped, solitary, that would not eat his meat, or sleep, and yet again by fits apt to be angry, etc.

Most part they are, as Plater notes, *desides, taciturni, ægre impulsi* [indolent, taciturn, sluggish], *nec nisi coacti procedunt*, etc., they will scarce be compelled to do that which concerns them, though it be for their good, so diffident, so dull, of small or no compliment, unsociable, hard to be acquainted with, especially of strangers; they had rather write their minds than speak, and above all things love solitariness. *Ob voluptatem, an ob timorem soli sunt?* Are they so solitary for pleasure (one asks) or pain? for both; yet I rather think for fear and sorrow, etc.

> *Hinc metuunt cupiuntque, dolent fugiuntque, nec auras*
> *Respiciunt, clausi tenebris, et carcere cæco.*[6]

> Hence 'tis they grieve and fear, avoiding light,
> And shut themselves in prison dark from sight.

As Bellerophon in Homer,[1]

> *Qui miser in silvis mœrens errabat opacis,*
> *Ipse suum cor edens, hominum vestigia vitans:*
>
> That wandered in the woods sad all alone,
> Forsaking men's society, making great moan;

they delight in floods and waters, desert places, to walk alone
in orchards, gardens, private walks, back lanes; averse from
company, as Diogenes in his tub, or Timon Misanthropus, they
abhor all companions at last,[2] even their nearest acquaintances
and most familiar friends, for they have a conceit (I say) every
man observes them, will deride, laugh to scorn, or misuse them,
confining themselves therefore wholly to their private houses
or chambers, *fugiunt homines sine causa* (saith Rhasis) *et odio
habent* [they shun people for no reason, and hate them], *Cont.
lib.* ɪ, *cap.* 9, they will diet themselves, feed and live alone.
It was one of the chiefest reasons why the citizens of Abdera
suspected Democritus to be melancholy and mad, because that,
as Hippocrates related in his epistle to Philopœmen, "he forsook the city, lived in groves and hollow trees, upon a green
bank by a brook side, or confluence of waters all day long, and
all night." [3]   *Quæ quidem* (saith he) *plurimum atra bile vexatis
et melancholicis eveniunt, deserta frequentant, hominumque congressum aversantur;* which is an ordinary thing with melancholy
men.[4]   The Egyptians therefore in their hieroglyphics expressed
a melancholy man by a hare sitting in her form, as being a
most timorous and solitary creature (Pierius, *Hieroglyph. lib.* ɪ2).
But this and all precedent symptoms are more or less apparent,
as the humour is intended or remitted, hardly perceived in
some, or not at all, most manifest in others.   Childish in some,
terrible in others; to be derided in one, pitied or admired in
another; to him by fits, to a second continuate: and howsoever
these symptoms be common and incident to all persons, yet
they are the more remarkable, frequent, furious, and violent in
melancholy men.   To speak in a word, there is nothing so vain,
absurd, ridiculous, extravagant, impossible, incredible, so
monstrous a chimera, so prodigious and strange, such as painters
and poets durst not attempt,[5] which they will not really fear,
feign, suspect and imagine unto themselves: and that which
Lod. Vives [6] said in a jest of a silly country fellow, that killed
his ass for drinking up the moon, *ut lunam mundo redderet* [that

he might restore the moon to the world], you may truly say of them in earnest; they will act, conceive all extremes, contrarieties, and contradictions, and that in infinite varieties. *Melancholici plane incredibilia sibi persuadent, ut vix omnibus sæculis duo reperti sint, qui idem imaginati sint* (Erastus, *de lamiis*), scarce two of two thousand that concur in the same symptoms. The tower of Babel never yielded such confusion of tongues, as the chaos of melancholy doth variety of symptoms. There is in all melancholy *similitudo dissimilis*, like men's faces, a disagreeing likeness still; and as in a river we swim in the same place, though not in the same numerical water; as the same instrument affords several lessons, so the same disease yields diversity of symptoms. Which howsoever they be diverse, intricate, and hard to be confined, I will adventure yet in such a vast confusion and generality to bring them into some order; and so descend to particulars.

SUBSECT. III.—*Particular Symptoms from the influence of Stars, parts of the Body, and Humours*

Some men have peculiar symptoms, according to their temperament and *crasis* [constitution], which they had from the stars and those celestial influences, variety of wits and dispositions, as Anthony Zara contends, *Anat. ingen. sect.* I, *memb.* II, 12, 13, 14, *Plurimum irritant influentiæ cœlestes, unde cientur animi ægritudines et morbi corporum.* One saith,[1] diverse diseases of the body and mind proceed from their influences, as I have already proved [2] out of Ptolemy, Pontanus, Lemnius, Cardan, and others, as they are principal significators of manners, diseases, mutually irradiated, or lords of the geniture, etc. Ptolemæus in his Centiloquy, Hermes, or whosoever else the author of that tract, attributes all these symptoms which are in melancholy men to celestial influences: which opinion Mercurialis, *de affect. lib.* I, *cap.* 10, rejects; but, as I say, Jovianus Pontanus [3] and others stiffly defend. That some are solitary, dull, heavy, churlish, some again blithe, buxom, light, and merry, they ascribe wholly to the stars. As if Saturn be predominant in his nativity, and cause melancholy in his temperature, then he shall be very austere, sullen, churlish, black of colour, profound in his cogitations, full of cares, miseries, and discontents, sad and fearful, always silent, solitary, still delighting in husbandry, in woods, orchards, gardens, rivers,

ponds, pools, dark walks and close:[1] *cogitationes sunt velle
ædificare, velle arbores plantare, agros colere* [their thoughts
turn on plans of building, planting trees, tilling fields], etc.,
to catch birds, fishes, etc., still contriving and musing of such
matters. If Jupiter domineers, they are more ambitious, still
meditating of kingdoms, magistracies, offices, honours, or that
they are princes, potentates, and how they would carry themselves, etc. If Mars, they are all for wars, brave combats,
monomachies, testy, choleric, harebrain, rash, furious, and
violent in their actions. They will feign themselves victors,
commanders, are passionate and satirical in their speeches,
great braggers, ruddy of colour. And though they be poor in
show, vile and base, yet like Telephus and Peleus in the poet,[2]
ampullas jactant et sesquipedalia verba [they fling about their
swelling and gigantic words], their mouths are full of myriads,
and tetrarchs at their tongues' end. If the Sun, they will be
lords, emperors, in conceit at least, and monarchs, give offices,
honours, etc. If Venus, they are still courting of their mistresses,
and most apt to love, amorously given, they seem to hear
music, plays, see fine pictures, dancers, merriments, and the
like; ever in love, and dote on all they see. Mercurialists are
solitary, much in contemplation, subtle, poets, philosophers,
and musing most part about such matters. If the Moon have
a hand, they are all for peregrinations, sea voyages, much
affected with travels, to discourse, read, meditate of such things;
wandering in their thoughts, diverse, much delighting in waters,
to fish, fowl, etc.

But the most immediate symptoms proceed from the temperature itself and the organical parts, as head, liver, spleen,
meseraic veins, heart, womb, stomach, etc., and most especially
from distemperature of spirits (which, as Hercules de Saxonia
contends,[3] are wholly immaterial), or from the four humours in
those seats, whether they be hot or cold, natural, unnatural,
innate or adventitious, intended or remitted, simple or mixed,
their diverse mixtures and several adustions, combinations,
which may be as diversely varied as those four first qualities [4]
in Clavius,[5] and produce as many several symptoms and monstrous fictions as wine doth effects, which, as Andreas Bachius
observes, *lib. 3 de vino, cap.* 20, are infinite. Of greater note
be these.

If it be natural melancholy, as Lod. Mercatus, *lib. 1, cap.* 17,
de melan., T. Bright, *cap.* 16, hath largely described, either of
the spleen or of the veins, faulty by excess of quantity or

thickness of substance, it is a cold and dry humour, as Montanus affirms, *consil.* 26, the parties are sad, timorous and fearful. Prosper Calenus, in his book *de atra bile*, will have them to be more stupid than ordinary, cold, heavy, dull, solitary, sluggish, *si multam atram bilem et frigidam habent* [if they have a quantity of black and cold bile]. Hercules de Saxonia, *cap.* 19, *lib.* 7, holds these that are naturally melancholy to be of a leaden colour or black,[1] and so doth Guianerius, *cap.* 3, *tract.* 15, and such as think themselves dead many times, or that they see, talk with black men, dead men, spirits and goblins frequently, if it be in excess. These symptoms vary according to the mixture of those four humours adust, which is unnatural melancholy. For, as Trallianus hath written, *cap.* 16, *lib.* 7, "There is not one cause of this melancholy, nor one humour which begets, but divers diversely intermixed, from whence proceeds this variety of symptoms": [2] and those varying again as they are hot or cold. "Cold melancholy" (saith Benedictus Victorius Faventinus, *Pract. Mag.*) "is a cause of dotage, and more mild symptoms; if hot or more adust, of more violent passions and furies." [3] Fracastorius, *lib.* 2 *de intellect.*, will have us to consider well of it, "with what kind of melancholy every one is troubled, for it much avails to know it; one is enraged by fervent heat, another is possessed by sad and cold; one is fearful, shamefaced; the other impudent and bold"; [4] as Ajax, *Arma rapit superosque furens in prælia poscit* [snatches his arms and challenges the gods], quite mad or tending to madness: *nunc hos, nunc impetit illos* [now these he rushes at, now those]. Bellerophon, on the other side, *solis errat male sanus in agris*, wanders alone in the woods; one despairs, weeps, and is weary of his life, another laughs, etc. All which variety is produced from the several degrees of heat and cold, which Hercules de Saxonia [5] will have wholly proceed from the distemperature of spirits alone, animal especially, and those immaterial, the next and immediate causes of melancholy, as they are hot, cold, dry, moist, and from their agitation proceeds that diversity of symptoms which he reckons up in the thirteenth chapter of his Tract of Melancholy, and that largely through every part.[6] Others will have them come from the diverse adustion of the four humours, which in this unnatural melancholy, by corruption of blood, adust choler, or melancholy natural, "by excessive distemper of heat turned, in comparison of the natural, into a sharp lye by force of adustion, cause, according to the diversity of their matter, diverse and strange symptoms," [7] which T. Bright reckons up in his following chapter. So doth Arculanus,[1] according to the four principal humours adust, and many others.

For example, if it proceed from phlegm (which is seldom and not so frequently as the rest), it stirs up dull symptoms, and a kind of stupidity, or impassionate hurt:[2] they are sleepy, saith Savonarola,[3] dull, slow, cold, blockish, ass-like, *asininam melancholiam*, Melancthon[4] calls it; "they are much given to weeping, and delight in waters, ponds, pools, rivers, fishing, fowling, etc." (Arnoldus, *Breviar.* 1, *cap.* 18). They are pale of colour,[5] slothful, apt to sleep, heavy; "much troubled with headache,"[6] continual meditation, and muttering to themselves; they dream of waters, that they are in danger of drowning, and fear such things (Rhasis).[7] They are fatter than others that are melancholy, of a muddy complexion, apter to spit, sleep,[8] more troubled with rheum than the rest, and have their eyes still fixed on the ground. Such a patient had Hercules de Saxonia, a widow in Venice, that was fat and very sleepy still; Christophorus à Vega another affected in the same sort. If it be inveterate or violent, the symptoms are more evident, they plainly dote and are ridiculous to others, in all their gestures, actions, speeches; imagining impossibilities, as he in Christophorus à Vega, that thought he was a tun of wine, and that Siennois, that resolved within himself not to piss, for fear he should drown all the town.[9]

If it proceed from blood adust, or that there be a mixture of blood in it, "such are commonly ruddy of complexion, and high-coloured,"[10] according to Sallust. Salvianus and Hercules de Saxonia; and as Savonarola, Victorius Faventius Empir. farther add, "the veins of their eyes be red, as well as their faces."[11] They are much inclined to laughter, witty and merry conceited in discourse, pleasant, if they be not far gone, much given to music, dancing, and to be in women's company. They meditate wholly on such things, and think "they see or hear plays, dancing, and such-like sports"[12] (free from all fear and sorrow, as Hercules de Saxonia supposeth[13]), if they be more strongly possessed with this kind of melancholy, Arnoldus adds *Breviar. lib.* 1, *cap.* 18, like him of Argos in the poet, that sat laughing all day long, as if he had been at a theatre.[14] Such another is mentioned by Aristotle,[15] living at Abydos, a town of Asia Minor, that would sit after the same fashion, as if he had been upon a stage, and sometimes act himself; now clap his hands, and laugh, as if he had been well pleased with the sight. Wolfius relates of a country fellow called Brunsellius, subject to this humour, "that being by chance at a sermon, saw a woman fall off from a form half asleep, at which object most of the company laughed, but he for his part was so much moved, that for three whole days after he did nothing but laugh, by which means he was much weakened, and worse a long time following." [1] Such a one was old Sophocles, and Democritus himself had *hilare delirium* [a merry madness], much in this vein. Laurentius, *cap. 3 de melan.*, thinks this kind of melancholy, which is a little adust with some mixture of blood, to be that which Aristotle meant, when he said melancholy men of all others are most witty, which causeth many times a divine ravishment, and a kind of *enthusiasmus*, which stirreth them up to be excellent philosophers, poets, prophets, etc. Mercurialis, *consil.* 110, gives instance in a young man his patient, sanguine melancholy, "of a great wit, and excellently learned." [2]

If it arise from choler adust, they are bold and impudent, and of a more hairbrain disposition, apt to quarrel and think of such things, battles, combats, and their manhood; furious, impatient in discourse, stiff, irrefragable and prodigious in their tenents; and if they be moved, most violent, outrageous, ready to disgrace, provoke any, to kill themselves and others; [3] Arnoldus adds, stark mad by fits, "they sleep little, their urine is subtile and fiery." [4] Guianerius: "In their fits you shall hear them speak all manner of languages, Hebrew, Greek, and Latin, that never were taught or knew them before." Apponensis, *in com. in Pro. sec.* 30, speaks of a mad woman that spake excellent good Latin: and Rhasis knew another, that could prophesy in her fit, and foretell things truly to come. Guianerius [5] had a patient could make Latin verses when the moon was combust, otherwise illiterate. Avicenna and some of his adherents will have these symptoms, when they happen, to proceed from the devil, and that they are rather *demoniaci*, possessed, than mad or melancholy, or both together, as Jason Pratensis thinks, *immiscent se mali genii* [evil spirits insinuate themselves], etc., but most ascribe it to the humour, which opinion Montaltus, *cap.* 21, stiffly maintains, confuting Avicenna and the rest, referring it wholly to the quality and disposition of the humour and subject. Cardan, *de rerum var. lib.* 8, *cap.* 10, holds these men of all others fit to be assassinates, bold, hardy, fierce, and adventurous, to undertake anything by reason of their choler adust. "This humour," saith he, "prepares them to endure death itself, and all manner of torments, with invincible courage, and 'tis a wonder to see with what alacrity they will

undergo such tortures," [1] *ut supra naturam res videatur* [so that
it seems to be unnatural]: he ascribes this generosity, fury, or
rather stupidity, to this adustion of choler and melancholy: but
I take these rather to be mad or desperate than properly
melancholy; for commonly this humour, so adust and hot,
degenerates into madness.

If it come from melancholy itself adust, "those men," saith
Avicenna, "are usually sad and solitary, and that continually,
and in excess, more than ordinarily suspicious, more fearful,
and have long, sore, and most corrupt imaginations"; [2] cold
and black, bashful, and so solitary, that as Arnoldus writes,
"they will endure no company, they dream of graves still, and
dead men, and think themselves bewitched or dead": [3] if it be
extreme, they think they hear hideous noises, see and talk
"with black men, and converse familiarly with devils, and such
strange chimeras and visions" [4] (Gordonius), or that they are
possessed by them, that somebody talks to them, or within
them. *Tales melancholici plerumque dæmoniaci* [melancholy
persons of this kind are usually possessed with a spirit] (Montaltus, *consil. 26, ex Avicenna*). Valescus de Taranta had such
a woman in cure, "that thought she had to do with the devil": [5]
and Gentilis Fulgosus, *quæst. 55*, writes that he had a melancholy
friend, that "had a black man in the likeness of a soldier" still
following him wheresoever he was.[6] Laurentius, *cap. 7*, hath
many stories of such as have thought themselves bewitched by
their enemies; and some that would eat no meat as being dead.
Anno 1550, an advocate of Paris fell into such a melancholy
fit, that he believed verily he was dead; he could not be persuaded otherwise, or to eat or drink, till a kinsman of his, a
scholar of Bourges, did eat before him dressed like a corse.[7]
The story, saith Serres, was acted in a comedy before Charles
the Ninth. Some think they are beasts, wolves, hogs, and cry
like dogs, foxes, bray like asses, and low like kine, as King
Prœtus' daughters.[8] Hildesheim, *Spicil. 2 de mania*, hath an
example of a Dutch baron so affected, and Trincavellius, *lib. 1
consil. 11*, another of a nobleman in his country, "that thought
he was certainly a beast, and would imitate most of their voices,"[9]
with many such symptoms, which may properly be reduced to
this kind.

If it proceed from the several combinations of these four
humours, or spirits (Hercules de Saxonia adds hot, cold, dry,
moist, dark, confused, settled, constringed, as it participates of
matter, or is without matter), the symptoms are likewise mixed

One thinks himself a giant, another a dwarf; one is heavy as lead, another is as light as a feather. Marcellus Donatus, *lib.* 2, *cap.* 41, makes mention out of Seneca, of one Senecio, a rich man, that "thought himself and everything else he had great—great wife, great horses; could not abide little things, but would have great pots to drink in, great hose, and great shoes bigger than his feet." [1] Like her in Trallianus, that "supposed she could shake all the world with her finger," [2] and was afraid to clinch her hand together, lest she should crush the world like an apple in pieces: or him in Galen, that thought he was Atlas, and sustained heaven with his shoulders. [3] Another thinks himself so little, that he can creep into a mouse-hole: one fears heaven will fall on his head; a second is a cock; and such a one Guianerius [4] saith he saw at Padua, that would clap his hands together and crow. Another thinks he is a nightingale, and therefore sings all the night long; [5] another he is all glass, a pitcher, and will therefore let nobody come near him, and such a one Laurentius gives out upon his credit, that he knew in France. [6] Christophorus à Vega, *cap.* 3, *lib.* 14, Sckenkius, and Marcellus Donatus, *lib.* 2, *cap.* 1, have many such examples, and one amongst the rest of a baker in Ferrara, that thought he was composed of butter, and durst not sit in the sun or come near the fire for fear of being melted: of another that thought he was a case of leather, stuffed with wind. Some laugh, weep; some are mad, some dejected, moped, in much agony, some by fits, others continuate, etc. Some have a corrupt ear—they think they hear music, or some hideous noise as their phantasy conceives—corrupt eyes; some smelling, some one sense, some another. Louis the Eleventh had a conceit everything did stink about him; all the odoriferous perfumes they could get would not ease him, but still he smelled a filthy stink. [7] A melancholy French poet in Laurentius, [8] being sick of a fever, and troubled with waking, by his physicians was appointed to use *unguentum populeum* [an ointment made of poplar] to anoint his temples; but he so distasted the smell of it, that for many years after, all that came near him he imagined to scent of it, and would let no man talk with him but aloof off, or wear any new clothes, because he thought still they smelled of it; in all other things wise and discreet, he would talk sensibly, save only in this. A gentleman in Limousin, saith Anthony de Verdeur, was persuaded he had but one leg, affrighted by a wild boar that by chance struck him on the leg; he could not be satisfied his leg was sound (in all other things well) until two

Franciscans, by chance coming that way, fully removed him
from the conceit. *Sed abunde fabularum audivimus* [but we
have heard enough tales].

SUBSECT. IV.—*Symptoms from Education, Custom, Continuance
of Time, our Condition, mixed with other Diseases, by Fits,
Inclination, etc.*

Another great occasion of the variety of these symptoms
proceeds from custom, discipline, education, and several inclinations "This humour will imprint in melancholy men the objects
most answerable to their condition of life, and ordinary actions,
and dispose men according to their several studies and callings." [1]
If an ambitious man become melancholy, he forthwith thinks
he is a king, an emperor, a monarch, and walks alone, pleasing
himself with a vain hope of some future preferment, or present
as he supposeth, and withal acts a lord's part, takes upon him
to be some statesman or magnifico, makes congees, gives entertainment, looks big, etc. Francisco Sansovino records of a
melancholy man in Cremona, that would not be induced to
believe but that he was pope, gave pardons, made cardinals,
etc. Christophorus à Vega makes mention of another of his
acquaintance, that thought he was a king, driven from his
kingdom,[2] and was very anxious to recover his estate. A
covetous person is still conversant about purchasing of lands
and tenements, plotting in his mind how to compass such and
such manors, as if he were already lord of, and able to go through
with it; all he sees is his, *re* or *spe*, he hath devoured it in hope,
or else in conceit esteems it his own; like him in Athenæus,[3]
that thought all the ships in the haven to be his own. A lascivious *inamorato* plots all the day long to please his mistress,
acts and struts, and carries himself as if she were in presence,
still dreaming of her, as Pamphilus of his Glycerium, or as some
do in their morning sleep. Marcellus Donatus [4] knew such a
gentlewoman in Mantua, called Elionora Meliorina, that constantly believed she was married to a king, and "would kneel
down and talk with him, as if he had been there present with
his associates; and if she had found by chance a piece of glass
in a muck-hill or in the street, she would say that it was a jewel
sent from her lord and husband." [5] If devout and religious,
he is all for fasting, prayer, ceremonies, alms, interpretations,
visions, prophecies, revelations, he is inspired by the Holy
Ghost, full of the spirit: [6] one while he is saved, another while

damned, or still troubled in mind for his sins, the devil will surely have him, etc. More of these in the third Partition, of Love-melancholy. A scholar's mind is busied about his studies, he applauds himself for that he hath done, or hopes to do, one while fearing to be out in his next exercise, another while contemning all censures; envies one, emulates another; or else with indefatigable pains and meditation consumes himself.[1] So of the rest, all which vary according to the more remiss and violent impression of the object, or as the humour itself is intended or remitted. For some are so gently melancholy, that in all their carriage, and to the outward apprehension of others, it can hardly be discerned, yet to them an intolerable burden, and not to be endured. *Quædam occulta, quædam manifesta*,[2] some signs are manifest and obvious to all at all times, some to few, or seldom, or hardly perceived; let them keep their own counsel, none will take notice or suspect them. "They do not express in outward show their depraved imaginations," as Hercules de Saxonia observes, "but conceal them wholly to themselves, and are very wise men, as I have often seen; some fear, some do not fear at all, as such as think themselves kings or dead, some have more signs, some fewer, some great, some less," [3] some vex, fret, still fear, grieve, lament, suspect, laugh, sing, weep, chafe, etc., by fits (as I have said) or more during and permanent. Some dote in one thing, are most childish and ridiculous and to be wondered at in that, and yet for all other matters most discreet and wise. To some it is in disposition, to another in habit; and as they write of heat and cold, we may say of this humour, one is *melancholicus ad octo* [eight degrees melancholy], a second two degrees less, a third half-way. 'Tis superparticular, *sesquialtera, sesquitertia,* and *superbipartiens tertias, quintas melancholiæ*,[4] etc.; all those geometrical proportions are too little to express it. "It comes to many by fits, and goes; to others it is continuate": [5] many (saith Faventinus [6]) "in spring and fall only are molested," some once a year, as that Roman Galen speaks of; [7] one, at the conjunction of the moon alone, or some unfortunate aspects, at such and such set hours and times, like the sea-tides; [8] to some women when they be with child, as Plater notes,[9] never otherwise: to others 'tis settled and fixed. To one, led about and variable still by that *ignis fatuus* of phantasy, like an *arthritis* or running gout, 'tis here and there, and in every joint, always molesting some part or other; or if the body be free, in a myriad of forms exercising the mind. A second once peradventure in his life hath a most

grievous fit, once in seven years, once in five years, even to the
extremity of madness, death, or dotage, and that upon some feral
accident or perturbation, terrible object, and that for a time,
never perhaps so before, never after. A third is moved upon all
such troublesome objects, cross fortune, disaster, and violent
passions, otherwise free, once troubled in three or four years.
A fourth, if things be to his mind, or he in action, well pleased,
in good company, is most jocund, and of a good complexion: if
idle, or alone, all amort, or carried away wholly with pleasant
dreams and phantasies, but if once crossed and displeased,

Pectore concipiet nil nisi triste suo ;

[He will imagine naught save sadness in his heart;]

his countenance is altered on a sudden, his heart heavy, irksome
thoughts crucify his soul, and in an instant he is moped or
weary of his life, he will kill himself. A fifth complains in his
youth, a sixth in his middle age, the last in his old age.

Generally thus much we may conclude of melancholy: that it
is most pleasant at first,[1] I say, *mentis gratissimus error* [a most
pleasing delusion], a most delightsome humour, to be alone,
dwell alone, walk alone, meditate, lie in bed whole days, dreaming awake as it were, and frame a thousand phantastical imaginations unto themselves. They are never better pleased than
when they are so doing, they are in paradise for the time, and
cannot well endure to be interrupt; with him in the poet, *Pol,
me occidistis, amici, non servastis, ait*[2] [" In sooth, good friends,
you have killed, not cured me," says he]; you have undone him,
he complains, if you trouble him: tell him what inconvenience
will follow, what will be the event, all is one, *canis ad vomitum*
[like a dog to his vomit], 'tis so pleasant he cannot refrain.[3]
He may thus continue peradventure many years by reason of a
strong temperature, or some mixture of business, which may
divert his cogitations: but at the last *læsa imaginatio*, his
phantasy is crazed, and, now habituated to such toys, cannot
but work still like a fate; the scene alters upon a sudden, fear
and sorrow supplant those pleasing thoughts, suspicion, discontent, and perpetual anxiety succeed in their places; so by
little and little, by that shoeing-horn of idleness, and voluntary
solitariness, melancholy, this feral fiend, is drawn on, *et quantum
vertice ad auras Æthereas, tantum radice in Tartara tendit*[4] [High
as his topmost boughs to heaven ascend, So low his roots to
hell's dominions tend]; it was not so delicious at first, as now it
is bitter and harsh; a cankered soul macerated with cares and

discontents, *tædium vitæ*, impatience, agony, inconstancy, irresolution, precipitate them unto unspeakable miseries. They cannot endure company, light, or life itself; some unfit for action, and the like. Their bodies are lean and dried up,[1] withered, ugly, their looks harsh, very dull, and their souls tormented, as they are more or less entangled, as the humour hath been intended, or according to the continuance of time they have been troubled.

To discern all which symptoms the better, Rhasis the Arabian [2] makes three degrees of them. The first is *falsa cogitatio*, false conceits and idle thoughts: to misconster and amplify, aggravating everything they conceive or fear; the second is *falso cogitata loqui*, to talk to themselves, or to use inarticulate, incondite voices, speeches, obsolete gestures, and plainly to utter their minds and conceits of their hearts by their words and actions, as to laugh, weep, to be silent, not to sleep, eat their meat, etc.; the third is to put in practice that which they think or speak.[3] Savonarola, *rub.* 11, *tract.* 8, *cap.* 1, *de ægritudine*, confirms as much: "when he begins to express that in words, which he conceives in his heart, or talks idly, or goes from one thing to another," [4] which Gordonius [5] calls *nec caput habentia, nec caudam* [having neither head nor tail], he is in the middle way: "but when he begins to act it likewise, and to put his fopperies in execution, he is then in the extent of melancholy, or madness itself." [6] This progress of melancholy you shall easily observe in them that have been so affected; they go smiling to themselves at first, at length they laugh out; at first solitary, at last they can endure no company: or if they do, they are now dizzards, past sense and shame, quite moped, they care not what they say or do, all their actions, words, gestures, are furious or ridiculous. At first his mind is troubled, he doth not attend what is said, if you tell him a tale, he cries at last, "What said you?" but in the end he mutters to himself, as old women do many times, or old men when they sit alone, upon a sudden they laugh, whoop, halloo, or run away, and swear they see or hear players, devils,[7] hobgoblins, ghosts, strike or strut, etc., grow humorous in the end: like him in the poet, *sæpe ducentos, sæpe decem servos* [often he keeps two hundred servants, often only ten], he will dress himself, and undress, careless at last, grows insensible, stupid, or mad. He howls like a wolf, barks like a dog, and raves like Ajax and Orestes, hears music and outcries which no man else hears.[8] As he [9] did whom Amatus Lusitanus mentioneth, *cent.* 3, *cura* 55, or that woman in Sprenger,[1] that spake many languages, and said she was possessed: that farmer in Prosper Calenius,[2] that disputed and discoursed learnedly in philosophy and astronomy with Alexander Achilles, his master, at Bologna in Italy. But of these I have already spoken.

Who can sufficiently speak of these symptoms, or prescribe rules to comprehend them? as Echo to the painter in Ausonius, *Vane, quid affectas*, etc., Foolish fellow, what wilt? if you must needs paint me, paint a voice, *et similem si vis pingere, pinge sonum;* if you will describe melancholy, describe a phantastical conceit, a corrupt imagination, vain thoughts and different, which who can do? The four-and-twenty letters make no more variety of words in divers languages than melancholy conceits produce diversity of symptoms in several persons. They are irregular, obscure, various, so infinite, Proteus himself is not so diverse; you may as well make the moon a new coat as a true character of a melancholy man; as soon find the motion of a bird in the air as the heart of man, a melancholy man. They are so confused, I say, diverse, intermixed with other diseases. As the species be confounded (which I have showed [3]), so are the symptoms; sometimes with headache, cachexia, dropsy, stone, as you may perceive by those several examples and illustrations collected by Hildesheim, *Spicil.* 2: [4] Mercurialis, *consil.* 118, *cap.* 6 *et* 11, with headache, epilepsy, priapismus; Trincavellius, *consil.* 12, *lib.* 1, *consil.* 49, with gout, *caninus appetitus*; Montanus, *consil.* 26, etc., 23, 234, 249, with falling sickness, headache, vertigo, lycanthropia, etc.; J. Cæsar Claudinus, *consult.* 4 *consult.* 89 *et* 116, with gout, agues, hemrods, stone, etc. Who can distinguish these melancholy symptoms so intermixed with others, or apply them to their several kinds, confine them into method? 'Tis hard, I confess; yet I have disposed of them as I could, and will descend to particularize them according to their species. For hitherto I have expatiated in more general lists or terms, speaking promiscuously of such ordinary signs, which occur amongst writers. Not that they are all to be found in one man, for that were to paint a monster or chimera, not a man; but some in one, some in another, and that successively or at several times.

Which I have been the more curious to express and report, not to upbraid any miserable man, or by way of derision (I rather pity them), but the better to discern, to apply remedies unto them; and to show that the best and soundest of us all is in great danger, how much we ought to fear our own fickle

estates, remember our miseries and vanities, examine and
humiliate ourselves, seek to God, and call to Him for mercy;
that needs not look for any rods to scourge ourselves, since we
carry them in our bowels, and that our souls are in a miserable
captivity, if the light of grace and heavenly truth doth not shine
continually upon us: and by our discretion to moderate ourselves,
to be more circumspect and wary in the midst of these dangers.

MEMB. II.

SUBSECT. I.—*Symptoms of Head-Melancholy*

"IF no symptoms appear about the stomach, nor the blood be
misaffected, and fear and sorrow continue, it is to be thought
the brain itself is troubled, by reason of a melancholy juice
bred in it, or otherwise conveyed into it, and that evil juice is
from the distemperature of the part, or left after some inflammation." [1] Thus far Piso. But this is not always true, for
blood and hypochondries both are often affected even in head-
melancholy. Hercules de Saxonia differs here from the common
current of writers, putting peculiar signs of head-melancholy
from the sole distemperature of spirits in the brain, as they are
hot, cold, dry, moist, "all without matter, from the motion
alone, and tenebrosity of spirits"; [2] of melancholy which proceeds from humours by adustion he treats apart, with their
several symptoms and cures. The common signs, if it be by
essence in the head, are ruddiness of face, high sanguine complexion, most part *rubore saturato* [with a flushed red colour] (one
calls it a bluish, and sometimes full of pimples), with red eyes [3]
(Avicenna, *lib.* 3, *fen.* 2, *tract.* 4, *cap.* 18, Duretus and others
out of Galen, *de affect. lib.* 3, *cap.* 6). Hercules de Saxonia to
this of redness of face adds "heaviness of the head, fixed and
hollow eyes." [4] "If it proceed from dryness of the brain,
then their heads will be light, vertiginous, and they most apt
to wake, and to continue whole months together without sleep.
Few excrements in their eyes and nostrils," [5] "and often bald
by reason of excess of dryness," Montaltus adds, *cap.* 17. If
it proceed from moisture, dullness, drowsiness, headache
follows; and as Sallust. Salvianus, *cap.* 2, *lib.* 2, out of his own
experience found, epileptical, with a multitude of humours in
the head. They are very bashful; if ruddy, apt to blush, and

to be red upon all occasions, *præsertim si metus accesserit*
[especially if any fear troubles them].   But the chiefest symptom
to discern this species, as I have said, is this, that there be no
notable signs in the stomach, hypochondries, or elsewhere, *digna*,
as Montaltus terms them,[1] or of greater note, because oftentimes
the passions of the stomach concur with them.   Wind is common
to all three species, and is not excluded, only that of the hypochondries is more windy than the rest,[2] saith Hollerius. Aetius,
Tetrab. lib. 2, sec. 2, cap. 9 et 10, maintains the same; if there
be more signs, and more evident in the head than elsewhere,
the brain is primarily affected; and prescribes head-melancholy
to be cured by meats amongst the rest, void of wind, and good
juice, not excluding wind, or corrupt blood, even in head-
melancholy itself: [3] but these species are often confounded, and
so are their symptoms, as I have already proved.   The symptoms
of the mind are superfluous and continual cogitations: "for
when the head is heated, it scorcheth the blood, and from thence
proceed melancholy fumes, which trouble the mind" [4] (Avicenna).
They are very choleric, and soon hot, solitary, sad, often silent,
watchful, discontent (Montaltus, *cap*. 24).   If anything trouble
them, they cannot sleep, but fret themselves still, till another
object mitigate, or time wear it out.   They have grievous
passions, and immoderate perturbations of the mind, fear,
sorrow, etc., yet not so continuate but that they are sometimes
merry, apt to profuse laughter, which is more to be wondered
at, and that by the authority of Galen himself,[5] by reason of
mixture of blood, *prærubri jocosis delectantur et irrisores plerumque
sunt*, if they be ruddy, they are delighted in jests, and oftentimes scoffers themselves, conceited, and, as Rodericus à Vega
comments on that place of Galen, merry, witty, of a pleasant
disposition, and yet grievously melancholy anon after.   *Omnia
discunt sine doctore*, saith Aretæus, they learn without a teacher:
and, as Laurentius [6] supposeth, those feral passions and symptoms of such as think themselves glass, pitchers, feathers, etc.,
speak strange languages, proceed *a calore cerebri* (if it be in
excess), from the brain's distempered heat.

SUBSECT. II.—*Symptoms of Windy Hypochondriacal
Melancholy*

"In this hypochondrical or flatuous melancholy, the symptoms
are so ambiguous," saith Crato in a counsel of his for a noble-
woman,[7] "that the most exquisite physicians cannot determine

of the part affected." Matthew Flaccius, consulted about a
noble matron, confessed as much, that in this malady he with
Hollerius, Fracastorius, Fallopius, and others, being to give
their sentence of a party labouring of hypochondriacal melancholy, could not find out by the symptoms which part was most
especially affected; some said the womb, some heart, some
stomach, etc., and therefore Crato, *consil.* 24, *lib.* 1, boldly avers
that, in this diversity of symptoms which commonly accompany
this disease, "no physician can truly say what part is affected." [1]
Galen, *lib. 3 de loc. affect.*, reckons up these ordinary symptoms,
which all the neoterics repeat, of Diocles; only this fault he
finds with him, that he puts not fear and sorrow amongst the
other signs. Trincavellius excuseth Diocles, *lib. 3, consil.* 35,
because that oftentimes in a strong head and constitution, a
generous spirit, and a valiant, these symptoms appear not, by
reason of his valour and courage. Hercules de Saxonia [2] (to
whom I subscribe) is of the same mind (which I have before
touched) that fear and sorrow are not general symptoms; some
fear and are not sad; some be sad and fear not; some neither
fear nor grieve. The rest are these, beside fear and sorrow,
"sharp belchings, fulsome crudities, heat in the bowels, wind and
rumbling in the guts, vehement gripings, pain in the belly and
stomach sometimes after meat that is hard of concoction, much
watering of the stomach, and moist spittle, cold sweat," [3]
importunus sudor, unseasonable sweat all over the body, as
Octavius Horatianus, *lib. 2, cap.* 5, calls it; "cold joints, indigestion, they cannot endure their own fulsome belchings, continual
wind about their hypochondries, heat and griping in their
bowels, *præcordia sursum convelluntur*, midriff and bowels are
pulled up, the veins about their eyes look red, and swell from
vapours and wind." [4] Their ears sing now and then, vertigo
and giddiness come by fits, turbulent dreams, dryness, leanness;
apt they are to sweat upon all occasions, of all colours and
complexions. Many of them are high-coloured, especially after
meals, which symptom Cardinal Cæsius was much troubled with,
and of which he complained to Prosper Calenus his physician;
he could not eat, or drink a cup of wine, but he was as red in
the face as if he had been at a mayor's feast. That symptom
alone vexeth many. Some again are black, pale, ruddy, sometimes their shoulders, and shoulder-blades ache, there is a
leaping all over their bodies, sudden trembling, a palpitation of
the heart, and that *cardiaca passio*, grief in the mouth of the
stomach, which maketh the patient think his heart itself acheth,

and sometimes suffocation, *difficultas anhelitus*, short breath, hard wind, strong pulse, swooning.[1] Montanus, *consil.* 55; Trincavellius, *lib.* 3, *consil.* 36 *et* 37; Fernelius, *cons.* 43; Frambesarius, *Consult. lib.* 1, *consil.* 17; Hildesheim, Claudinus, etc., give instance of every particular. The peculiar symptoms which properly belong to each part be these. If it proceed from the stomach, saith Savonarola,[2] 'tis full of pain, wind. Guianerius adds vertigo, nausea, much spitting, etc. If from the myrach, a swelling and wind in the hypochondries, a loathing, and appetite to vomit, pulling upward. If from the heart, aching and trembling of it, much heaviness. If from the liver, there is usually a pain in the right hypochondry. If from the spleen, hardness and grief in the left hypochondry, a rumbling, much appetite and small digestion (Avicenna). If from the meseraic veins and liver on the other side, little or no appetite (Hercules de Saxonia). If from the hypochondries, a rumbling inflation, concoction is hindered, often belching, etc. And from these crudities, windy vapours ascend up to the brain, which trouble the imagination, and cause fear, sorrow, dullness, heaviness, many terrible conceits and chimeras, as Lemnius well observes, *lib.* 1, *cap.* 16: "As a black and thick cloud covers the sun, and intercepts his beams and light, so doth this melancholy vapour obnubilate the mind, enforce it to many absurd thoughts and imaginations,"[3] and compel good, wise, honest, discreet men (arising to the brain from the lower parts, "as smoke out of a chimney"[4]) to dote, speak and do that which becomes them not, their persons, callings, wisdoms. One, by reason of those ascending vapours and gripings rumbling beneath, will not be persuaded but that he hath a serpent in his guts, a viper; another frogs. Trallianus relates a story of a woman that imagined she had swallowed an eel or a serpent; and Felix Platerus, *Observat. lib.* 1, hath a most memorable example of a countryman of his, that by chance falling into a pit where frogs and frogs' spawn was, and a little of that water swallowed began to suspect that he had likewise swallowed frogs' spawn and with that conceit and fear, his phantasy wrought so far that he verily thought he had young live frogs in his belly *qui vivebant ex alimento suo*, that lived by his nourishment and was so certainly persuaded of it, that for many years following he could not be rectified in his conceit. He studied physic seven years together to cure himself, travelled into Italy France and Germany to confer with the best physicians about it, and, *anno* 1609, asked his counsel amongst the rest; he tol him it was wind, his conceit, etc., but *mordicus contradicere, et ore et scriptis probare nitebatur* [he obstinately contradicted him, and maintained his view both in speech and writing]: no saying would serve, it was no wind, but real frogs: "and do you not hear them croak?" Platerus would have deceived him by putting live frogs into his excrements; but he, being a physician himself, would not be deceived, *vir prudens alias, et doctus,* a wise and learned man otherwise, a doctor of physic, and after seven years' dotage in this kind, *a phantasia liberatus est,* he was cured. Laurentius and Goulart have many such examples, if you be desirous to read them. One commodity, above the rest which are melancholy, these windy flatuous have, *lucida intervalla* [lucid intervals], their symptoms and pains are not usually so continuate as the rest, but come by fits, fear and sorrow and the rest: yet in another they exceed all others; and that is, they are luxurious, incontinent, and prone to venery, by reason of wind,[1] *et facile amant, et quamlibet fere amant* [and easily fall in love, and with any woman almost] (Jason Pratensis). Rhasis[2] is of opinion that Venus doth many of them much good. The other symptoms of the mind be common with the rest.

SUBSECT. III.—*Symptoms of Melancholy abounding in the whole Body*

Their bodies that are affected with this universal melancholy are most part black, "the melancholy juice is redundant all over,"[3] hirsute they are, and lean, they have broad veins, their blood is gross and thick. "Their spleen is weak,"[4] and liver apt to engender the humour; they have kept bad diet, or have had some evacuation stopped, as hemrods, or months in women, which Trallianus,[5] in the cure, would have carefully to be inquired, and withal to observe of what complexion the party is of, black or red. For, as Forestus and Hollerius contend, if they be black,[6] it proceeds from abundance of natural melancholy; if it proceed from cares, agony, discontents, diet, exercise, etc., they may be as well of any other colour, red, yellow, pale, as black, and yet their whole blood corrupt: *prærubri colore sæpe sunt tales, sæpe flavi* [such people are often ruddy, often yellowish] (saith Montaltus, *cap.* 22). The best way to discern this species is to let them bleed;[7] if the blood be corrupt, thick and black, and they withal free from these hypochondriacal symptoms, and not so grievously troubled with them or those of the head, it argues they are melancholy *a toto corpore* [throughout the whole body]. The fumes which arise from this corrupt blood disturb the mind, and make them fearful and sorrowful, heavy-hearted, as the rest, dejected, discontented, solitary, silent, weary of their lives, dull and heavy, or merry, etc., and if far gone, that which Apuleius wished to his enemy, by way of imprecation, is true in them: "Dead men's bones, hobgoblins, ghosts are ever in their minds, and meet them still in every turn; all the bugbears of the night, and terrors, fairybabes of tombs and graves are before their eyes and in their thoughts, as to women and children, if they be in the dark alone." [1] If they hear, or read, or see any tragical object, it sticks by them; they are afraid of death, and yet weary of their lives; in their discontented humours they quarrel with all the world, bitterly inveigh, tax satirically, and because they cannot otherwise vent their passions, or redress what is amiss as they mean, they will by violent death at last be revenged on themselves.

SUBSECT. IV.—*Symptoms of Maids', Nuns', and Widows' Melancholy*

Because Lodovicus Mercatus, in his second book *de mulier. affect. cap.* 4, and Rodericus à Castro, *de morb. mulier. cap.* 3, *lib.* 2, two famous physicians in Spain, Daniel Sennertus of Wittenberg, *lib.* 1, *part.* 2, *cap.* 13, with others, have vouchsafed, in their works not long since published, to write two just treatises *de melancholia virginum, monialium et viduarum* [of the melancholy of maids, nuns, and widows], as a particular species of melancholy (which I have already specified) distinct from the rest, for it much differs from that which commonly befalls men and other women, as having one only cause proper to women alone,[2] I may not omit, in this general survey of melancholy symptoms, to set down the particular signs of such parties so misaffected.

The causes are assigned out of Hippocrates, Cleopatra, Moschion, and those old *gynæciorum scriptores* [writers on women's diseases], of this feral malady, in more ancient maids, widows, and barren women, *ob septum transversum violatum,* saith Mercatus, by reason of the midriff or *diaphragma,* heart and brain offended with those vicious vapours which come from menstruous blood; *inflammationem arteriæ circa dorsum,* Roderi-cus adds, an inflammation of the back, which with the rest is offended by that fuliginous exhalation of corrupt seed, troubling the brain, heart and mind; [3] the brain, I say, not in essence, but by consent; *universa enim hujus affectus causa ab utero pendet, et a sanguinis menstrui malitia*, for, in a word, the whole malady proceeds from that inflammation, putridity, black smoky vapours, etc.; from thence comes care, sorrow, and anxiety, obfuscation of spirits, agony, desperation, and the like, which are intended or remitted, *si amatorius accesserit ardor* [should the amatory passion be aroused], or any other violent object or perturbation of mind. This melancholy may happen to widows, with much care and sorrow, as frequently it doth, by reason of a sudden alteration of their accustomed course of life, etc.; to such as lie in child-bed, *ob suppressam purgationem*; but to nuns and more ancient maids, and some barren women, for the causes abovesaid, 'tis more familiar, *crebrius his quam reliquis accidit, inquit Rodericus* [it happens to these more frequently than to the rest, saith Rodericus]; the rest are not altogether excluded.

Out of these causes Rodericus defines it, with Aretæus, to be *angorem animi*, a vexation of the mind, a sudden sorrow from a small, light, or no occasion, with a kind of still dotage and grief of some part or other, head, heart, breasts, sides, back, belly, etc., with much solitariness, weeping, distraction, etc., from which they are sometimes suddenly delivered, because it comes and goes by fits, and is not so permanent as other melancholy.[1]

But, to leave this brief description, the most ordinary symptoms be these: *pulsatio juxta dorsum*, a beating about the back, which is almost perpetual; the skin is many times rough, squalid, especially, as Aretæus observes, about the arms, knees, and knuckles. The midriff and heart-strings do burn and beat very fearfully, and when this vapour or fume is stirred, flieth upward, the heart itself beats, is sore grieved, and faints,[2] *fauces siccitate præcluduntur, ut difficulter possit ab uteri strangulatione decerni*, like fits of the mother; *alvus plerisque nil reddit, aliis exiguum, acre, biliosum, lotium flavum*. They complain many times, saith Mercatus, of a great pain in their heads, about their hearts and hypochondries, and so likewise in their breasts, which are often sore; sometimes ready to swoon, their faces are inflamed and red, they are dry, thirsty, suddenly hot, much troubled with wind, cannot sleep, etc. And from hence proceed *ferina deliramenta*, a brutish kind of dotage, troublesome sleep, terrible dreams in the night, *subrusticus pudor, et verecundia ignava*, a foolish kind of bashfulness to some, perverse conceits and opinions, dejection of mind, much discontent, preposterous judgment.[3] They are apt to loathe, dislike, disdain, to be weary

of every object, etc., each thing almost is tedious to them, they
pine away, void of counsel, apt to weep and tremble, timorous,
fearful, sad, and out of all hope of better fortunes. They take
delight in nothing for the time, but love to be alone and solitary,
though that do them more harm: and thus they are affected
so long as this vapour lasteth; but by and by as pleasant and
merry as ever they were in their lives, they sing, discourse, and
laugh in any good company, upon all occasions; and so by fits it
takes them now and then, except the malady be inveterate,
and then 'tis more frequent, vehement, and continuate. Many
of them cannot tell how to express themselves in words, or how
it holds them, what ails them; you cannot understand them, or
well tell what to make of their sayings; so far gone sometimes,
so stupefied and distracted, they think themselves bewitched,
they are in despair, *aptæ ad fletum, desperationem* [prone to
weeping, despondency]; *dolores mammis et hypochondriis*, Mercatus therefore adds, now their breasts, now their hypochondries,
belly and sides, then their heart and head aches; now heat, then
wind, now this, now that offends, they are weary of all; and
yet will not, cannot again tell how, where, or what offends
them,[1] though they be in great pain, agony, and frequently
complain, grieving, sighing, weeping, and discontented still,
sine causa manifesta [without apparent cause], most part; yet,
I say, they will complain, grudge, lament, and not be persuaded
but that they are troubled with an evil spirit, which is frequent
in Germany, saith Rodericus, amongst the common sort; and
to such as are most grievously affected (for he makes three
degrees of this disease in women), they are in despair, surely
forspoken or bewitched, and in extremity of their dotage (weary
of their lives), some of them will attempt to make away themselves. Some think they see visions, confer with spirits and
devils, they shall surely be damned, are afraid of some treachery,
imminent danger, and the like, they will not speak, make answer
to any question, but are almost distracted, mad, or stupid for
the time, and by fits: and thus it holds them, as they are more or
less affected, and as the inner humour is intended or remitted,
or by outward objects and perturbations aggravated, solitariness,
idleness, etc.

Many other maladies there are incident to young women,
out of that one and only cause above specified, many feral
diseases. I will not so much as mention their names; melancholy alone is the subject of my present discourse, from which
I will not swerve. The several cures of this infirmity, concerning

diet, which must be very sparing, phlebotomy, physic, internal, external remedies, are at large in great variety in Rodericus à Castro,[1] Sennertus, and Mercatus, which whoso will, as occasion serves, may make use of. But the best and surest remedy of all, is to see them well placed, and married to good husbands in due time; *hinc illæ lachrymæ* [hence those tears], that's the primary cause, and this the ready cure, to give them content to their desires. I write not this to patronize any wanton, idle flirt, lascivious or light huswives, which are too forward many times, unruly, and apt to cast away themselves on him that comes next, without all care, counsel, circumspection, and judgment. If religion, good discipline, honest education, wholesome exhortation, fair promises, fame, and loss of good name cannot inhibit and deter such (which to chaste and sober maids cannot choose but avail much), labour and exercise, strict diet, rigour, and threats may more opportunely be used, and are able of themselves to qualify and divert an ill-disposed temperament. For seldom should you see an hired servant, a poor handmaid, though ancient, that is kept hard to her work and bodily labour, a coarse country wench, troubled in this kind, but noble virgins, nice gentlewomen, such as are solitary and idle, live at ease, lead a life out of action and employment, that fare well, in great houses and jovial companies, ill-disposed peradventure of themselves, and not willing to make any resistance, discontented otherwise, of weak judgment, able bodies, and subject to passions (*grandiores virgines*, saith Mercatus, *steriles, et viduæ plerumque melancholicæ* [grown-up girls, barren women, and widows are usually melancholy]); such for the most part are misaffected, and prone to this disease. I do not so much pity them that may otherwise be eased, but those alone that out of a strong temperament, innate constitution, are violently carried away with this torrent of inward humours, and though very modest of themselves, sober, religious, virtuous, and well given (as many so distressed maids are), yet cannot make resistance; these grievances will appear, this malady will take place, and now manifestly shows itself, and may not otherwise be helped. But where am I? Into what subject have I rushed? What have I to do with nuns, maids, virgins, widows? I am a bachelor myself, and lead a monastic life in a college, *næ ego sane ineptus qui hæc dixerim* [it is certainly very foolish of me to speak thus], I confess 'tis an indecorum, and as Pallas, a virgin, blushed when Jupiter by chance spake of love matters in her presence, and turned away her face, *me reprimam* [I will check myself]; though my subject necessarily require it, I will say no more.

And yet I must and will say something more, add a word or two *in gratiam virginum et viduarum* [in favour of maids and widows], in favour of all such distressed parties, in commiseration of their present estate. And as I cannot choose but condole their mishap that labour of this infirmity and are destitute of help in this case, so must I needs inveigh against them that are in fault, more than manifest causes, and as bitterly tax those tyrannizing pseudo-politicians, superstitious orders, rash vows, hard-hearted parents, guardians, unnatural friends, allies (call them how you will), those careless and stupid overseers, that, out of worldly respects, covetousness, supine negligence, their own private ends (*cum sibi sit interim bene* [being themselves comfortably situated in the meanwhile]), can so severely reject, stubbornly neglect, and impiously contemn, without all remorse and pity, the tears, sighs, groans, and grievous miseries of such poor souls committed to their charge. How odious and abominable are those superstitious and rash vows of popish monasteries, so to bind and enforce men and women to vow virginity, to lead a single life, against the laws of nature, opposite to religion, policy, and humanity, so to starve, to offer violence, to suppress the vigour of youth! by rigorous statutes, severe laws, vain persuasions, to debar them of that to which by their innate temperature they are so furiously inclined, urgently carried, and sometimes precipitated, even irresistibly led, to the prejudice of their souls' health, and good estate of body and mind! and all for base and private respects, to maintain their gross superstition, to enrich themselves and their territories, as they falsely suppose, by hindering some marriages, that the world be not full of beggars, and their parishes pestered with orphans! Stupid politicians! *hæccine fieri flagitia?* ought these things so to be carried? Better marry than burn, saith the Apostle, but they are otherwise persuaded. They will by all means quench their neighbour's house if it be on fire, but that fire of lust, which breaks out into such lamentable flames, they will not take notice of; their own bowels oftentimes, flesh and blood, shall so rage and burn, and they will not see it: *Miserum est*, saith Austin, *seipsum non miserescere*, and they are miserable in the meantime that cannot pity themselves, the common good of all, and *per consequens* their own estates. For let them but consider what fearful maladies, feral diseases, gross inconveniences, come to both sexes by this enforced temperance;

it troubles me to think of, much more to relate, those frequent
aborts and murdering of infants in their nunneries (read
Kemnisius [1] and others), their notorious fornications, those
spintrias, tribadas, ambubaias, etc., those rapes, incests, adulteries,
mastuprations, sodomies, buggeries of monks and friars. See
Bale's Visitation of Abbeys, Mercurialis,[2] Rodericus à Castro,
Peter Forestus, and divers physicians; I know their ordinary
apologies and excuses for these things, *sed viderint politici, medici,
theologi* [but let the politicians, the physicians and the theologians
look out]; I shall more opportunely meet with them elsewhere.[3]

> *Illius viduæ, aut patronum virginis hujus,*
> *Ne me forte putes, verbum non amplius addam.*

> [Lest you should think I am pleading the cause of
> this widow or that virgin, I will say no more.]

MEMB. III.

Immediate Cause of these precedent Symptoms

To give some satisfaction to melancholy men that are troubled
with these symptoms, a better means in my judgment cannot
be taken than to show them the causes whence they proceed;
not from devils as they suppose, or that they are bewitched or
forsaken of God, hear or see, etc., as many of them think, but
from natural and inward causes; that so knowing them, they
may better avoid the effects, or at least endure them with
more patience. The most grievous and common symptoms
are fear and sorrow, and that without a cause, to the wisest
and discreetest men, in this malady not to be avoided. The
reason why they are so Aetius discusseth at large, *Tetrabib*, 2, 2,
in his first problem out of Galen, *lib. 2 de causis, sympt.* 1.
For Galen imputeth all to the cold that is black, and thinks
that the spirits being darkened, and the substance of the brain
cloudy and dark, all the objects thereof appear terrible, and the
mind itself, by those dark, obscure, gross fumes, ascending
from black humours,[4] is in continual darkness, fear, and sorrow;
divers terrible monstrous fictions in a thousand shapes and
apparitions occur, with violent passions, by which the brain
and phantasy are troubled and eclipsed. Fracastorius, *lib. 2
de intellect.*, will have cold to be the cause of fear and sorrow;

"for such as are cold are ill-disposed to mirth, dull, and heavy,
by nature solitary, silent; and not for any inward darkness (as
physicians think), for many melancholy men dare boldly be,
continue, and walk in the dark, and delight in it":[1] *solum
frigidi timidi* [only the cold are timid]: if they be hot, they are
merry; and the more hot, the more furious, and void of fear,
as we see in madmen: but this reason holds not, for then no
melancholy, proceeding from choler adust, should fear. Averroes
scoffs at Galen for his reasons, and brings five arguments to
refel them: so doth Hercules de Saxonia, *tract. de melanch.
cap.* 3, assigning other causes, which are copiously censured and
confuted by Ælianus Montaltus, *cap.* 5 *et* 6; Lod. Mercatus,
de inter. morb. cur. lib. 1, *cap.* 17; Altomarus, *cap.* 7 *de mel.*;
Guianerius, *tract.* 15, *cap.* 1; Bright, *cap.* 37; Laurentius,
cap. 5; Valesius, *Med. cont. lib.* 5, *cont.* 1. "Distemperature,"
they conclude, "makes black juice, blackness obscures the
spirits, the spirits obscured cause fear and sorrow."[2] Laurentius, *cap.* 13, supposeth these black fumes offend specially the
diaphragma or midriff, and so *per consequens* the mind, which is
obscured as the sun by a cloud.[3] To this opinion of Galen almost
all the Greeks and Arabians subscribe, the Latins new and old;
internæ tenebræ offuscant animum, ut externæ nocent pueris, as
children are affrighted in the dark, so are melancholy men at
all times, as having the inward cause with them, and still
carrying it about.[4] Which black vapours, whether they proceed
from the black blood about the heart, as T[homas] W[right],
Jes[uit], thinks in his Treatise of the Passions of the Mind, or
stomach, spleen, midriff, or all the misaffected parts together,
it boots not; they keep the mind in a perpetual dungeon, and
oppress it with continual fears, anxieties, sorrows, etc. It is
an ordinary thing for such as are sound to laugh at this dejected
pusillanimity and those other symptoms of melancholy, to make
themselves merry with them, and to wonder at such, as toys
and trifles, which may be resisted and withstood, if they will
themselves: but let him that so wonders consider with himself,
that if a man should tell him on a sudden some of his especial
friends were dead, could he choose but grieve? Or set him upon
a steep rock, where he should be in danger to be precipitated,
could he be secure? His heart would tremble for fear, and his
head be giddy. P. Byarus, *tract. de pest.*, gives instance (as
I have said): "And put case" (saith he) "in one that walks
upon a plank; if it lie on the ground, he can safely do it, but if
the same plank be laid over some deep water, instead of a

bridge, he is vehemently moved, and 'tis nothing but his imagination, *forma cadendi impressa* [the idea of falling], to which his other members and faculties obey." [1]   Yea, but you infer that such men have a just cause to fear, a true object of fear; so have melancholy men an inward cause, a perpetual fume and darkness, causing fear, grief, suspicion, which they carry with them, an object which cannot be removed, but sticks as close, and is as inseparable, as a shadow to a body, and who can expel or overrun his shadow? Remove heat of the liver, a cold stomach, weak spleen; remove those adust humours and vapours arising from them, black blood from the heart, all outward perturbations; take away the cause, and then bid them not grieve nor fear, or be heavy, dull, lumpish; otherwise counsel can do little good; you may as well bid him that is sick of an ague not to be adry, or him that is wounded not to feel pain.

Suspicion follows fear and sorrow at heels, arising out of the same fountain, so thinks Fracastorius,[2] "that fear is the cause of suspicion, and still they suspect some treachery, or some secret machination to be framed against them," still they distrust. Restlessness proceeds from the same spring, variety of fumes make them like and dislike. Solitariness, avoiding of light, that they are weary of their lives, hate the world, arise from the same causes, for their spirits and humours are opposite to light, fear makes them avoid company, and absent themselves, lest they should be misused, hissed at, or overshoot themselves, which still they suspect. They are prone to venery by reason of wind. Angry, waspish, and fretting still, out of abundance of choler, which causeth fearful dreams, and violent perturbations to them both sleeping and waking. That they suppose they have no heads, fly, sink, they are pots, glasses, etc., is wind in their heads. Hercules de Saxonia [3] doth ascribe this to the several motions in the animal spirits, "their dilation, contraction, confusion, alteration, tenebrosity, hot or cold distemperature," excluding all material humours. Fracastorius accounts it "a thing worthy of inquisition, why they should entertain such false conceits, as that they have horns, great noses, that they are birds, beasts," etc.,[4] why they should think themselves kings, lords, cardinals. For the first, Fracastorius gives two reasons: "One is the disposition of the body; the other the occasion of the phantasy,"[5] as if their eyes be purblind, their ears sing, by reason of some cold and rheum, etc. To the second Laurentius answers, the imagination, inwardly or outwardly moved, represents to the understanding, not enticements only, to favour the passion or dislike, but a very intensive pleasure follows the passion or displeasure, and the will and reason are captivated by delighting in it.

Why students and lovers are so often melancholy and mad, the philosophers of Coimbra [1] assign this reason, "because by a vehement and continual meditation of that wherewith they are affected, they fetch up the spirits into the brain, and with the heat brought with them they incend it beyond measure: and the cells of the inner senses dissolve their temperature, which being dissolved, they cannot perform their offices as they ought."

Why melancholy men are witty, which Aristotle hath long since maintained in his Problems, and that all learned men, famous philosophers, and lawgivers, *ad unum fere omnes melancholici*, have still been melancholy,[2] is a problem much controverted. Jason Pratensis will have it understood of natural melancholy, which opinion Melancthon inclines to, in his book *de anima*, and Marsilius Ficinus, *de san. tuend. lib.* 1, *cap.* 5, but not simple, for that makes men stupid, heavy, dull, being cold and dry, fearful, fools, and solitary, but mixed with the other humours, phlegm only excepted; and they not adust, but so mixed as that blood be half,[3] with little or no adustion, that they be neither too hot nor too cold. Apponensis, cited by Melancthon, thinks it proceeds from melancholy adust, excluding all natural melancholy as too cold. Laurentius condemns his tenent, because adustion of humours makes men mad, as lime burns when water is cast on it. It must be mixed with blood, and somewhat adust, and so that old aphorism of Aristotle may be verified, *Nullum magnum ingenium sine mixtura dementiæ*, no excellent wit without a mixture of madness. Fracastorius shall decide the controversy: [4] "Phlegmatic are dull; sanguine lively, pleasant, acceptable, and merry, but not witty; choleric are too swift in motion, and furious, impatient of contemplation, deceitful wits; melancholy men have the most excellent wits, but not all; this humour may be hot or cold, thick, or thin; if too hot, they are furious and mad: if too cold, dull, stupid, timorous, and sad: if temperate, excellent, rather inclining to that extreme of heat than cold." This sentence of his will agree with that of Heraclitus, a dry light makes a wise mind; temperate heat and dryness are the chief causes of a good wit; therefore, saith Ælian, an elephant is the wisest of all brute beasts, because his brain is driest, *et ob atræ bilis copiam* [and on account of his abundance of black bile]: this reason Cardan approves, *Subtil. lib.* 12. Jo. Baptista Silvaticus, a physician of Milan, in his first Controversy, hath copiously handled this question; Rulandus in his Problems; Cœlius Rhodiginus, *lib.* 17; Valleriola, 6*to narrat. med.*; Hercules de Saxonia, *tract. posth. de mel. cap.* 3; Lodovicus Mercatus, *de inter. morb. cur. lib. cap.* 17; Baptista Porta, *Physiog. lib.* 1, *cap.* 13; and many others.

Weeping, sighing, laughing, itching, trembling, sweating, blushing, hearing and seeing strange noises, visions, wind, crudity, are motions of the body, depending upon these precedent motions of the mind: neither are tears affections, but actions (as Scaliger holds): "The voice of such as are afraid trembles, because the heart is shaken" [1] (*Conimb. prob.* 6, *sec.* 3, *de som.*). Why they stut or falter in their speech, Mercurialis and Montaltus, *cap.* 17, give like reasons out of Hippocrates, "dryness, which makes the nerves of the tongue torpid." [2] Fast speaking (which is a symptom of some few) Aetius will have caused from abundance of wind, and swiftness of imagination: [3] baldness comes from excess of dryness,[4] hirsuteness from a dry temperature. The cause of much waking is a dry brain, continual meditation, discontent, fears, and cares, that suffer not the mind to be at rest; incontinency is from wind, and a hot liver (Montanus, *cons.* 26). Rumbling in the guts is caused from wind, and wind from ill concoction, weakness of natural heat, or a distempered heat and cold; palpitation of the heart from vapours, heaviness and aching from the same cause.[5] That the belly is hard, wind is a cause, and of that leaping in many parts. Redness of the face, and itching, as if they were flea-bitten, or stung with pismires, from a sharp subtile wind; cold sweat from vapours arising from the hypochondries, which pitch upon the skin;[6] leanness for want of good nourishment. Why their appetite is so great, Aetius answers: [7] *Os ventris frigescit*, cold in those inner parts, cold belly, and hot liver, causeth crudity, and intention proceeds from perturbations; our soul for want of spirits cannot attend exactly to so many intentive operations; being exhaust, and overswayed by passion, she cannot consider the reasons which may dissuade her from such affections.[8]

Bashfulness and blushing [9] is a passion proper to men alone, and is not only caused for some shame and ignominy, or that they are guilty unto themselves of some foul fact committed,[10] but, as Fracastorius well determines,[11] *ob defectum proprium, et timorem*, "from fear, and a conceit of our defects; the face

labours and is troubled at his presence that sees our defects,
and nature, willing to help, sends thither heat, heat draws the
subtilest blood, and so we blush. They that are bold, arrogant,
and careless, seldom or never blush, but such as are fearful."
Anthonius Lodovicus, in his book *de pudore*, will have this subtile
blood to arise in the face, not so much for the reverence of our
betters in presence, "but for joy and pleasure, or if anything
at unawares shall pass from us, a sudden accident, occurse, or
meeting"[1] (which Disarius in Macrobius confirms), any object
heard or seen, for blind men never blush, as Dandinus observes,[2]
the night and darkness make men impudent. Or that we be
stayed before our betters, or in company we like not, or if
anything molest and offend us, *erubescentia* turns to *rubor*,
blushing to a continuate redness.[3] Sometimes the extremity of
the ears tingle, and are red, sometimes the whole face, *etsi
nihil vitiosum commiseris* [although you have done nothing
wrong] as Lodovicus holds: though Aristotle is of opinion,
omnis pudor ex vitio commisso, all shame [is] for some offence.
But we find otherwise; it may as well proceed from fear, from
force and inexperience (so Dandinus holds[4]), as vice; a hot
liver, saith Duretus (*notis in Hollerium*); "from a hot brain,
from wind, the lungs heated, or after drinking of wine, strong
drink, perturbations," etc.[5]

"Laughter, what it is," saith Tully,[6] "how caused, where,
and so suddenly breaks out that, desirous to stay it, we cannot,
how it comes to possess and stir our face, veins, eyes, countenance, mouth, sides, let Democritus determine." The cause
that it often affects melancholy men so much, is given by
Gomesius, *lib. 3 de sale genial. cap.* 18, abundance of pleasant
vapours, which, in sanguine melancholy especially, break from
the heart, "and tickle the midriff, because it is transverse and
full of nerves: by which titillation the sense being moved, and
arteries distended, or pulled, the spirits from thence move and
possess the sides, veins, countenance, eyes."[7] See more in
Jossius, *de risu et fletu*, Vives, 3 *de anima*. Tears, as Scaliger
defines, proceed from grief and pity, "or from the heating of a
moist brain, for a dry cannot weep."[8]

That they see and hear so many phantasms, chimeras, noises,
visions, etc., as Fienus hath discoursed at large in his book of
Imagination, and Lavater, *de spectris*, *part.* 1, *cap.* 2, 3, 4, their
corrupt phantasy makes them see and hear that which indeed
is neither heard nor seen.[9] *Qui multum jejunant, aut noctes
ducunt insomnes*, they that much fast, or want sleep, as melan-

choly or sick men commonly do, see visions, or such as are weak-sighted, very timorous by nature, mad, distracted, or earnestly seek. *Sabini quod volunt somniant*, as the saying is, they dream of that they desire.   Like Sarmiento the Spaniard, who, when he was sent to discover the Straits of Magellan and confine places by the Prorex [Viceroy] of Peru, standing on the top of a hill, *amœnissimam planitiem despicere sibi visus fuit, ædificia magnifica, quamplurimos pagos, altas turres, splendida templa* [imagined he was looking down on a most pleasant valley, with splendid buildings, numerous villages, lofty towers, glittering temples], and brave cities, built like ours in Europe, not, saith mine author,[1] that there was any such thing, but that he was *vanissimus et nimis credulus* [very untrustworthy and credulous], and would fain have had it so.   Or as Lod. Mercatus proves,[2] by reason of inward vapours, and humours from blood, choler, etc., diversely mixed, they apprehend and see outwardly, as they suppose, divers images, which indeed are not.   As they that drink wine think all runs round, when it is in their own brain; so is it with these men, the fault and cause is inward, as Galen affirms, madmen and such as are near death, *quas extra se videre putant imagines, intra oculos habent*[3] [the figures which they think they see before them are really in their own eyes], 'tis in their brain, which seems to be before them; the brain, as a concave glass, reflects solid bodies.   *Senes etiam decrepiti cerebrum habent concavum et aridum, ut imaginentur se videre* (saith Boissardus[4]) *quæ non sunt* [old men have a concave and dry brain which makes them think they see non-existent objects], old men are too frequently mistaken and dote in like case; or, as he that looketh through a piece of red glass judgeth everything he sees to be red, corrupt vapours mounting from the body to the head, and distilling again from thence to the eyes, when they have mingled themselves with the watery crystal which receiveth the shadows of things to be seen, make all things appear of the same colour, which remains in the humour that overspreads our sight, as to melancholy men all is black, to phlegmatic all white, etc.   Or else, as before, the organs, corrupt by a corrupt phantasy, as Lemnius, *lib.* 1, *cap.* 16, well quotes, "cause a great agitation of spirits and humours, which wander to and fro in all the creeks of the brain, and cause such apparitions before their eyes."[5]   One thinks he reads something written in the moon, as Pythagoras is said to have done of old; another smells brimstone, hears Cerberus bark; Orestes, now mad, supposed he saw the

Furies tormenting him, and his mother still ready to run
upon him:

> *O mater, obsecro noli me persequi*
> *His furiis, aspectu anguineis, horribilibus,*
> *Ecce ! ecce ! me invadunt, in me jam ruunt ;*

> [Mother, I beseech thee, persecute me not with furies
> of horrid, snaky aspect. Look, look how they
> rush upon me and assail me;]

but Electra told him thus raving in his mad fit, he saw no such
sights at all, it was but his crazed imagination.

> *Quiesce, quiesce, miser, in linteis tuis,*
> *Non cernis etenim quæ videre te putas.*

> [Lie quiet, poor soul, upon thy couch, for thou seest
> these things but in fancy.]

So Pentheus (*in Bacchis Euripidis*) saw two suns, two Thebes,
his brain alone was troubled. Sickness is an ordinary cause of
such sights. Cardan, *Subtil.* 8, *Mens ægra laboribus et jejuniis
fracta, facit eos videre, audire*, etc. [over-exertion and want of
food affect their minds so that they see and hear, etc.]. And.
Osiander beheld strange visions, and Alexander ab Alexandro,
both in their sickness, which he relates, *de rerum varietat. lib.* 8,
cap. 44. Albategnius, that noble Arabian, on his death-bed
saw a ship ascending and descending, which Fracastorius records
of his friend Baptista Turrianus. Weak sight, and a vain
persuasion withal, may effect as much, and second causes concurring, as an oar in water makes a refraction, and seems bigger,
bended double, etc. The thickness of the air may cause such
effects; or any object not well discerned in the dark, fear and
phantasy will suspect to be a ghost, a devil, etc. *Quod nimis
miseri timent, hoc facile credunt* [1] [persons in great misery readily
believe what they fear], we are apt to believe, and mistake in
such cases. Marcellus Donatus, *lib.* 2, *cap.* 1, brings in a story
out of Aristotle, of one Antipheron, which likely saw, wheresoever he was, his own image in the air, as in a glass. Vitellio,
lib. 10 *Perspect.*, hath such another instance of a familiar
acquaintance of his, that after the want of three or four nights'
sleep, as he was riding by a river side, saw another riding with
him, and using all such gestures as he did, but when more
light appeared, it vanished. Eremites and anachorites have
frequently such absurd visions, revelations by reason of much
fasting and bad diet; many are deceived by legerdemain, as Scot
hath well showed in his book of the Discovery of Witchcraft,

and Cardan, *Subtil.* 18. Suffites, perfumes, suffumigations, mixed candles, perspective glasses, and such natural causes, make men look as if they were dead, or with horse-heads, bull's horns, and such-like brutish shapes, the room full of snakes, adders, dark, light, green, red, of all colours, as you may perceive in Baptista Porta, Alexis, Albertus, and others; glowworms, fire-drakes, meteors, *ignis fatuus*, which Plinius, *lib.* 2, *cap.* 37, calls Castor and Pollux, with many such that appear in moorish grounds, about churchyards, moist valleys, or where battles have been fought, the causes of which read in Goclenius, Velcurius, Finkius, etc. Such feats are often done, to frighten children with squibs, rotten wood, etc., to make folks look as if they were dead, *solito majores*,[1] bigger [than usual], lesser, fairer, fouler; *ut astantes sine capitibus videantur, aut toti igniti, aut forma dæmonum, accipe pilos canis nigri, etc.* [to make them appear headless, or on fire, or in the form of devils, take the hairs of a black dog, etc.], saith Albertus; and so 'tis ordinary to see strange uncouth sights by catoptrics; who knows not that if in a dark room the light be admitted at one only little hole, and a paper or glass put upon it, the sun shining will represent on the opposite wall all such objects as are illuminated by his rays? With concave and cylinder glasses, we may reflect any shape of men, devils, antics (as magicians most part do, to gull a silly spectator in a dark room), we will ourselves, and that hanging in the air, when 'tis nothing but such an horrible image as Agrippa demonstrates,[2] placed in another room. Roger Bacon of old is said to have represented his own image walking in the air by this art, though no such thing appear in his Perspectives. But most part it is in the brain that deceives them, although I may not deny but that oftentimes the devil deludes them, takes his opportunity to suggest, and represent vain objects to melancholy men, and such as are ill affected. To these you may add the knavish impostures of jugglers, exorcists, mass-priests, and mountebanks, of whom Roger Bacon speaks, etc., *de miraculis naturæ et artis*, [of the wonders of nature and art] *cap.* 1. They can counterfeit the voices of all birds and brute beasts almost, all tones and tunes of men, and speak within their throats, as if they spoke afar off, that they make their auditors believe they hear spirits, and are thence much astonished and affrighted with it.[3] Besides, those artificial devices to overhear their confessions, like that whispering place of Gloucester[4] with us, or like the duke's place at Mantua in Italy, where the sound is reverberated by a concave wall;

a reason of which Blancanus in his *Echometria* gives, and mathematically demonstrates.

So that the hearing is as frequently deluded as the sight, from the same causes almost, as he that hears bells will make them sound what he list. "As the fool thinketh, so the bell clinketh." Theophilus in Galen thought he heard music, from vapours which made his ears sound, etc. Some are deceived by echoes, some by roaring of waters, or concaves and reverberation of air in the ground, hollow places and walls. At Cadurcum, in Aquitaine, words and sentences are repeated by a strange echo to the full, or whatsoever you shall play upon a musical instrument, more distinctly and louder than they are spoken at first.[1] Some echoes repeat a thing spoken seven times, as at Olympus, in Macedonia, as Pliny relates, *lib.* 36, *cap.* 15; some twelve times, as at Charenton, a village near Paris, in France. At Delphi, in Greece, heretofore was a miraculous echo, and so in many other places. Cardan, *Subtil. lib.* 18, hath wonderful stories of such as have been deluded by these echoes. Blancanus the Jesuit, in his *Echometria*, hath variety of examples, and gives his reader full satisfaction of all such sounds by way of demonstration. At Barry, an isle in the Severn mouth, they seem to hear a smith's forge: [2] so at Lipari, and those sulphureous isles, and many such-like which Olaus speaks of in the continent of Scandia, and those northern countries. Cardan, *de rerum var. lib.* 15, *cap.* 84, mentioneth a woman that still supposed she heard the devil call her, and speaking to her; she was a painter's wife in Milan: and many such illusions and voices, which proceed most part from a corrupt imagination.

Whence it comes to pass that they prophesy, speak several languages, talk of astronomy, and other unknown sciences to them (of which they have been ever ignorant), I have in brief touched;[3] only this I will here add, that Arculanus,[4] Bodine, *lib.* 3, *cap.* 6, *Dæmon.*, and some others, hold as a manifest token that such persons are possessed with the devil; [5] so doth Hercules de Saxonia,[6] and Apponensis, and fit only to be cured by a priest. But Guianerius,[7] Montaltus,[8] Pomponatius of Padua, and Lemnius, *lib.* 2, *cap.* 2, refer it wholly to the ill disposition of the humour,[9] and that out of the authority of Aristotle, *Prob.* 30, 1, because such symptoms are cured by purging; and as by the striking of a flint fire is enforced, so, by the vehement motion of spirits, they do *elicere voces inauditas*, compel strange speeches to be spoken: another argument he hath from Plato's *reminiscentia* [recollection], which is all out as likely as that which Marsilius Ficinus speaks of his friend Pierleonus;[1] by a divine kind of infusion he understood the secrets of nature, and tenents of Grecian and barbarian philosophers, before ever he heard of, saw, or read their works: but in this I should rather hold with Avicenna and his associates, that such symptoms proceed from evil spirits, which take all opportunities of humours decayed, or otherwise, to pervert the soul of man: and besides, the humour itself is *balneum diaboli*, the devil's bath, and, as Agrippa proves, doth entice him to seize upon them.

SECT. IV. MEMB. I.

Prognostics of Melancholy

PROGNOSTICS, or signs of things to come, are either good or bad. If this malady be not hereditary, and taken at the beginning, there is good hope of cure, *recens curationem non habet difficilem*, saith Avicenna, *lib.* 3, *fen.* 1, *tract.* 4, *cap.* 18. That which is with laughter, of all others is most secure, gentle, and remiss (Hercules de Saxonia). "If that evacuation of hemrods, or *varices*, which they call the water between the skin, shall happen to a melancholy man, his misery is ended"[2] (Hippocrates, *Aphor.* 6, 11). Galen, *lib.* 6, *de morbis vulgar. com.* 8, confirms the same; and to this aphorism of Hippocrates all the Arabians, new and old Latins subscribe: Montaltus, *cap.* 25, Hercules de Saxonia, Mercurialis, Victorius Faventinus, etc. Sckenkius, *lib.* 1 *Observat. med. cap. de mania*, illustrates this aphorism with an example of one Daniel Federer, a coppersmith, that was long melancholy, and in the end mad about the twenty-seventh year of his age; these *varices* or water began to arise in his thighs, and he was freed from his madness. Marius the Roman was so cured, some say, though with great pain. Sckenkius hath some other instances of women that have been helped by flowing of their months, which before were stopped. That the opening of the hemrods will do as much for men, all physicians jointly signify. so they be voluntary, some say, and not by compulsion. All melancholy are better after a quartan; Jobertus saith,[3] scarce any man hath that ague twice; but whether it free him from this malady, 'tis a question;

for many physicians ascribe all long agues for especial causes,
and a quartan ague amongst the rest. Rhasis, *Cont. lib.* 1,
tract. 9: "When melancholy gets out at the superficies of the
skin, or settles, breaking out in scabs, leprosy, morphew, or is
purged by stools, or by the urine, or that the spleen is enlarged,
and those *varices* appear, the disease is dissolved." [1] Guianerius,
cap. 5, *tract.* 15, adds dropsy, jaundice, dysentery, leprosy, as
good signs, to these scabs, morphews, and breaking out, and
proves it out of the sixth of Hippocrates' Aphorisms.

Evil prognostics on the other part. *Inveterata melancholia
incurabilis,* if it be inveterate, it is incurable,[2] a common axiom,
aut difficulter curabilis, [or], as they say that make the best,
hardly cured. This Galen witnesseth, *lib. 3 de loc. affect. cap.* 6:
"Be it in whom it will, or from what cause soever, it is ever
long, wayward, tedious, and hard to be cured, if once it be
habituated." [3] As Lucian said of the gout, she was "the queen
of diseases, and inexorable," [4] may we say of melancholy. Yet
Paracelsus will have all diseases whatsoever curable, and laughs
at them which think otherwise, as T. Erastus, *part.* 3, objects
to him; although in another place, hereditary diseases he
accounts incurable, and by no art to be removed.[5] Hildesheim,
Spicil. 2 de mel., holds it less dangerous if only "imagination
be hurt, and not reason; [6] the gentlest is from blood, worse
from choler adust, but the worst of all from melancholy
putrefied." [7] Bruel esteems hypochondriacal least dangerous,
and the other two species (opposite to Galen) hardest to be
cured.[8] The cure is hard in man, but much more difficult in
women.[9] And both men and women must take notice of that
saying of Montanus, *consil.* 230, *pro Abbate Italo*: "This malady
doth commonly accompany them to their grave; physicians
may ease, and it may lie hid for a time, but they cannot quite
cure it, but it will return again more violent and sharp than at
first, and that upon every small occasion or error": [10] as in
Mercury's weather-beaten statue, that was once all over gilt,
the open parts were clean, yet there was *in fimbriis aurum,*
in the chinks a remnant of gold: there will be some relics of
melancholy left in the purest bodies (if once tainted), not so
easily to be rooted out. Oftentimes it degenerates into epilepsy,
apoplexy, convulsions, and blindness; [11] by the authority of
Hippocrates and Galen, all aver,[12] if once it possess the ventricles
of the brain, Frambesarius, and Sallust. Salvianus adds, if it
get into the optic nerves, blindness. Mercurialis, *consil.* 20,
had a woman to his patient, that from melancholy became

epileptic and blind. If it come from a cold cause, or so continue cold, or increase, epilepsy, convulsions follow, and blindness, or else in the end they are moped, sottish, and in all their actions, speeches, gestures ridiculous.[1] If it come from a hot cause, they are more furious and boisterous, and in conclusion mad.[2] *Calescentem melancholiam sæpius sequitur mania.* If it heat and increase, that is the common event,[3] *per circuitus, aut semper, insanit*,[4] he is mad by fits, or altogether. For, as Sennertus contends out of Crato,[5] there is *seminarius ignis* in this humour, the very seeds of fire. If it come from melancholy natural adust, and in excess, they are often demoniacal (Montanus).

Seldom this malady procures death, except (which is the greatest, most grievous calamity, and the misery of all miseries) they make away themselves,[6] which is a frequent thing, and familiar amongst them. 'Tis Hippocrates' observation,[7] Galen's sentence, *Etsi mortem timent, tamen plerumque sibi ipsis mortem consciscunt* [although they fear death, yet many of them commit suicide], *lib. 3 de locis affect. cap.* 7, the doom of all physicians. 'Tis Rabbi Moses' aphorism,[8] the prognosticon of Avicenna, Rhasis, Aetius, Gordonius, Valescus, Altomarus, Sallustius Salvianus, Capivaccius, Mercatus, Hercules de Saxonia, Piso, Bruel, Fuchsius, all, etc.

> *Et sæpe usque adeo mortis formidine vitæ*
> *Percipit infelix odium lucisque videndæ,*
> *Ut sibi consciscat mærenti pectore letum.*[9]

And so far forth death's terror doth affright,
He makes away himself, and hates the light:
To make an end of fear and grief of heart,
He voluntary dies to ease his smart.

In such sort doth the torture and extremity of his misery torment him, that he can take no pleasure in his life, but is in a manner enforced to offer violence unto himself, to be freed from his present insufferable pains. So some (saith Fracastorius[10]) "in fury, but most in despair, sorrow, fear, and out of the anguish and vexation of their souls, offer violence to themselves: for their life is unhappy and miserable. They can take no rest in the night, nor sleep, or if they do slumber, fearful dreams astonish them." In the day-time they are affrighted still by some terrible object, and torn in pieces with suspicion, fear, sorrow, discontents, cares, shame, anguish, etc., as so many wild horses, that they cannot be quiet an hour, a minute of time, but even against their wills they are intent, and still thinking of it, they cannot forget it, it grinds their souls day and night, they are perpetually tormented, a burden to themselves, as Job was, they can neither eat, drink, nor sleep. Ps. cvii, 18: "Their soul abhorreth all meat, and they are brought to death's door," "being bound in misery and iron";[1] they curse their stars with Job, "and day of their birth,[2] and wish for death"[3] for, as Pineda and most interpreters hold, Job was even melancholy to despair, and almost madness itself;[4] they murmur many times against the world, friends, allies, all mankind, even against God Himself in the bitterness of their passion, *vivere nolunt, mori nesciunt*,[5] live they will not, die they cannot. And in the midst of these squalid, ugly, and such irksome days, they seek at last, finding no comfort, no remedy in this wretched life, to be eased of all by death.[6] *Omnia appetunt bonum*, all creatures seek the best, and for their good as they hope, *sub specie*, in show at least, *vel quia mori pulchrum putant* (saith Hippocrates[7]) *vel quia putant inde se majoribus malis liberari* [either because they count it best to die or because they think in this way to be freed from greater evils], to be freed as they wish. Though many times, as Æsop's fishes, they leap from the frying-pan into the fire itself, yet they hope to be eased by his means: and therefore (saith Felix Platerus[8]) "after many tedious days, at last, either by drowning, hanging, or some such fearful end, they precipitate or make away themselves; many lamentable examples are daily seen amongst us:" *alius ante fores se laqueo suspendit* (as Seneca notes), *alius se præcipitavit a tecto, ne dominum stomachantem audiret, alius ne reduceretur a fuga ferrum redegit in viscera* [one hanged himself before his own door; another threw himself from the house-top, to avoid his master's anger; a third, to escape return from exile, plunged a dagger into his heart], so many causes there are—*His amor exitio est, furor his*—love, grief, anger, madness, and shame, etc. 'Tis a common calamity, a fatal end to this disease,[9] they are condemned to a violent death by a jury of physicians, furiously disposed, carried headlong by their tyrannizing wills, enforced by miseries, and there remains no more to such persons, if that heavenly Physician, by His assisting grace and mercy alone, do not prevent (for no human persuasion or art can help), but to be their own butchers, and execute themselves. Socrates his *cicuta* [hemlock], Lucretia's dagger, Timon's halter, are yet to be had; Cato's knife and Nero's sword are left behind them, as so many fatal engines, bequeathed to posterity, and will be used to the world's end by such distressed souls: so intolerable, insufferable, grievous, and violent is their pain, so unspeakable and continuate.[1] One day of grief is an hundred years, as Cardan observes: 'tis *carnificina hominum* [a man-killer], *angor animi*, as well saith Aretæus, a plague of the soul, the cramp and convulsion of the soul, an epitome of hell; and if there be a hell upon earth, it is to be found in a melancholy man's heart.

> For that deep torture may be call'd an hell,
> When more is felt than one hath power to tell.

Yea, that which scoffing Lucian said of the gout in jest, I may truly affirm of melancholy in earnest.

> *O triste nomen! o diis odibile!*
> *Melancholia lacrimosa,[2] Cocyti filia,*
> *Tu Tartari specubus opacis edita*
> *Erinnys, utero quam Megæra suo tulit,*
> *Et ab uberibus aluit, cuique parvulæ*
> *Amarulentum in os lac Alecto dedit,*
> *Omnes abominabilem te dæmones*
> *Produxere in lucem, exitio mortalium.*

Et paulo   *Non Jupiter ferit tale telum fulminis,*
post.   *Non ulla sic procella sævit æquoris,*
> *Non impetuosi tanta vis est turbinis.*
> *An asperos sustineo morsus Cerberi?*
> *Num virus echidnæ membra mea depascitur?*
> *Aut tunica sanie tincta Nessi sanguinis?*
> *Illacrimabile et immedicabile malum hoc.*

> O sad and odious name! a name so fell,
> Is this of melancholy, brat of hell.
> There born in hellish darkness doth it dwell.
> The Furies brought it up, Megæra's teat,
> Alecto gave it bitter milk to eat.
> And all conspired a bane to mortal men,
> To bring this devil out of that black den. . . . .
> Jupiter's thunderbolt, not storm at sea,
> Nor whirlwind doth our hearts so much dismay
> What? am I bit by that fierce Cerberus?
> Or stung by serpent[3] so pestiferous?
> Or put on shirt that 's dipt in Nessus' blood?
> My pain 's past cure; physic can do no good.

To torture of body like unto it, *Siculi non invenere tyranni majus tormentum* [the Sicilian tyrants invented no worse torture], no strappadoes, hot irons, Phalaris' bulls,

> *Nec ira deum tantum, nec tela, nec hostis,*
> *Quantum sola noces animis illapsa.*[4]

> Jove's wrath, nor devils can
> Do so much harm to th' soul of man.

All fears, griefs, suspicions, discontents, imbonities, insuavities
are swallowed up and drowned in this Euripus, this Irish Sea,
this ocean of misery, as so many small brooks; 'tis *coagulum
omnium ærumnarum* [a banding together of all griefs], which
Ammianus [1] applied to his distressed Palladius. I say of our
melancholy man, he is the cream of human adversity, the
quintessence,[2] and upshot; all other diseases whatsoever are
but flea-bitings to melancholy in extent: 'tis the pith of them all.

> *Hospitium est calamitatis; quid verbis opus est?*
> *Quamcunque malam rem quæris, illic reperies:*[3]
>
> What need more words? 'tis calamity's inn,
> Where seek for any mischief, 'tis within;

and a melancholy man is that true Prometheus, which is bound
to Caucasus; the true Tityus, whose bowels are still by a vulture
devoured (as poets feign), for so doth Lilius Giraldus interpret
it,[4] of anxieties and those griping cares, and so ought it to be
understood. In all other maladies we seek for help; if a leg or
an arm ache, through any distemperature or wound, or that
we have an ordinary disease, above all things whatsoever we
desire help and health, a present recovery, if by any means
possible it may be procured; we will freely part with all our
other fortunes, substance, endure any misery, drink bitter
potions, swallow those distasteful pills, suffer our joints to be
seared, to be cut off, anything for future health: so sweet, so
dear, so precious above all other things in this world is life;
'tis that we chiefly desire, long life and happy days, *Multos da,
Jupiter, annos*,[5] increase of years all men wish; but to a melancholy man, nothing so tedious, nothing so odious; that which
they so carefully seek to preserve he abhors, he alone;[6] so
intolerable are his pains. Some make a question, *graviores
morbi corporis an animi*, whether the diseases of the body or
mind be more grievous, but there is no comparison, no doubt
to be made of it, *multo enim sævior longeque est atrocior animi,
quam corporis cruciatus* (Lemnius, *lib. 1, cap.* 12), the diseases
of the mind are far more grievous. *Totum hic pro vulnere
corpus*, body and soul is misaffected here, but the soul especially.
So Cardan testifies, *de rerum var. lib.* 8, 40. Maximus Tyrius,
a Platonist, and Plutarch[7] have made just volumes to prove it.
Dies adimit ægritudinem hominibus[8] [time cures men's sorrows];
in other diseases there is some hope likely, but these unhappy
men are born to misery, past all hope of recovery, incurably

sick, the longer they live the worse they are, and death alone
must ease them.

Another doubt is made by some philosophers, whether it be
lawful for a man, in such extremity of pain and grief, to make
away himself: and how these men that so do are to be censured.
The Platonists approve of it, that it is lawful in such cases, and
upon a necessity (Plotinus, *lib. de beatitud. cap.* 7), and Socrates
himself defends it in Plato's *Phædo*: "If any man labour of an
incurable disease, he may dispatch himself, it it be to his good."
Epicurus and his followers, the Cynics and Stoics in general
affirm it, Epictetus and Seneca [1] amongst the rest, *quamcunque
veram esse viam ad libertatem*, any way is allowable that leads
to liberty; "Let us give God thanks, that no man is compelled
to live against his will"; [2] *Quid ad hominem claustra, carcer,
custodia? liberum ostium habet* [3] [What need a man care about
bars or prison? The way of escape is at hand], death is always
ready and at hand. *Vides illum præcipitem locum, illud flumen?*
dost thou see that steep place, that river, that pit, that tree?
there's liberty at hand, *effugia servitutis et doloris sunt* [there
are ways of escape from servitude and pain], as that Laconian
lad cast himself headlong (*non serviam, aiebat puer* [I will not
be a slave, said the boy]) to be freed of his misery: every vein
in thy body, if these be *nimis operosi exitus* [too troublesome
means of egress], will set thee free; *quid tua refert finem facias
an accipias?* [what matters whether you make or await your
end?] there's no necessity for a man to live in misery. *Malum
est in necessitate vivere; sed in necessitate vivere, necessitas nulla
est* ['tis evil to live in need; but there is no need to live in need].
Ignavus qui sine causa moritur, et stultus qui cum dolore vivit
[he is a coward who kills himself for nothing, and a fool who
lives on in pain] (*idem, Epist.* 58). Wherefore hath our mother
the earth brought out poisons, saith Pliny,[4] in so great a
quantity, but that men in distress might make away themselves? which kings of old had ever in a readiness, *ad incerta
fortunæ venenum sub custode promptum* [had poison ready to
hand in case of emergency], Livy writes, and executioners
always at hand. Speusippus being sick was met by Diogenes,
and, carried on his slaves' shoulders, he made his moan to the
philosopher; "But I pity thee not," quoth Diogenes, "*qui cum
talis vivere sustines* [since being in such plight thou endurest to
live]; thou mayst be freed when thou wilt," meaning by death.
Seneca therefore [5] commends Cato, Dido, and Lucretia, for their
generous courage in so doing, and others that voluntarily die.

to avoid a greater mischief, to free themselves from misery, to save their honour, or vindicate their good name, as Cleopatra did, as Sophonisba, Syphax' wife, did, Hannibal did, as Junius Brutus, as Vibius Virius, and those Campanian senators in Livy (*Dec.* 3, *lib.* 6), to escape the Roman tyranny that poisoned themselves. Themistocles drank bull's blood, rather than he would fight against his country, and Demosthenes chose rather to drink poison, Publius *Crassi filius* [the son of Crassus], Censorius, and Plancus, those heroical Romans, to make away themselves, than to fall into their enemies' hands. How many myriads besides in all ages might I remember, *qui sibi letum Insontes peperere manu* [who though innocent committed suicide], etc. Razis in the Maccabees is magnified for it,[1] Samson's death approved. So did Saul and Jonas sin, and many worthy men and women, *quorum memoria celebratur in Ecclesia* [whose memory is celebrated in the Church], saith Leminchus,[2] for killing themselves to save their chastity and honour, when Rome was taken, as Austin instances, *lib.* 1 *de Civit. Dei, cap.* 16. Jerome vindicateth the same, *in Jonam*, and Ambrose, *lib.* 3 *de virginitate*, commendeth Pelagia for so doing. Eusebius, *lib.* 8, *cap.* 15, admires a Roman matron for the same fact to save herself from the lust of Maxentius the tyrant. Adelhelmus, Abbot of Malmesbury, calls them *beatas virgines quæ sic* [blessed virgins who], etc. Titus Pomponius Atticus, that wise, discreet, renowned Roman senator, Tully's dear friend, when he had been long sick, as he supposed of an incurable disease, *vitamque produceret ad augendos dolores, sine spe salutis* [by prolonging his life only increased his pain, without hope of cure], was resolved voluntarily by famine to dispatch himself to be rid of his pain; and whenas Agrippa and the rest of his weeping friends earnestly besought him, *osculantes obsecrarent, ne id quod natura cogeret ipse acceleraret*, not to offer violence to himself, "with a settled resolution he desired again they would approve of his good intent, and not seek to dehort him from it"; and so constantly died, *precesque eorum taciturna sua obstinatione depressit* [and silenced their prayers by his determined attitude]. Even so did Corellius Rufus, another grave senator, by the relation of Plinius Secundus, *Epist. lib.* 1, *epist.* 12, famish himself to death; *pedibus correptus cum incredibiles cruciatus et indignissima tormenta pateretur, a cibis omnino abstinuit* [being terribly tortured by the gout, he entirely abstained from food]; neither he nor Hispulla his wife could divert him, but *destinatus mori obstinate magis*, etc., die he would and die he did. So did Lycurgus. Aristotle, Zeno, Chrysippus, Empedocles, with myriads, etc. In wars, for a man to run rashly upon imminent danger and present death is accounted valour and magnanimity, to be the cause of his own, and many a thousand's ruin besides, to commit wilful murder in a manner, of himself and others, is a glorious thing, and he shall be crowned for it.[1] The Massagetæ[2] in former times, Derbiccians,[3] and I know not what nations besides, did stifle their old men after seventy years, to free them from those grievances incident to that age. So did the inhabitants of the island of Choa; because their air was pure and good, and the people generally long-lived, *antevertebant fatum suum, priusquam manci forent, aut imbecillitas accederet, papavere vel cicuta*, with poppy or hemlock, [before they became infirm or imbecile], they prevented death. Sir Thomas More in his *Utopia* commends voluntary death, if he be *sibi aut aliis molestus*, troublesome to himself or others "(especially if to live be a torment to him), let him free himself with his own hands from this tedious life, as from a prison, or suffer himself to be freed by others."[4] And 'tis the same tenent which Laertius related of Zeno of old, *Juste sapiens sibi mortem consciscit, si in acerbis doloribus versetur, membrorun mutilatione aut morbis ægre curandis* [the wise man rightly commits suicide if through accident or disease he suffers acute pain], and which Plato, 9 *de legibus*, approves, if old age, poverty, ignominy, etc. oppress, and which Fabius expresseth in effect (*Præfat.* 7 *Institut.*), *nemo nisi sua culpa diu dolet*[5] [if any one suffers pain long, it is his own fault]. It is an ordinary thing in China (saith Mat. Riccius the Jesuit), "if they be in despair of better fortunes, or tired and tortured with misery, to bereave themselves of life, and many times, to spite their enemies the more, to hang at their door."[6] Tacitus the historian, Plutarch the philosopher, much approve a voluntary departure, and Austin, *de Civ. Dei, lib.* 1, *cap.* 29, defends a violent death, so that it be undertaken in a good cause: *Nemo sic mortuus, qui non fuerat aliquando moriturus; quid autem interest, quo mortis genere vita ista finiatur, quando ille cui finitur iterum mori non cogitur?* [No one dies in this way who would not have had to die at some time or other. What difference then does it make by what kind of death life is finished, seeing that he whose life is finished has not to die again?], etc. No man so voluntarily dies, but *volens nolens*, he must die at last, and our life is subject to innumerable casualties, who knows when they may happen? *utrum satius est unam perpeti moriendo, an omnes timere vivendo?*

rather suffer one [death] than fear all.[1] "Death is better than
a bitter life" (Eccl. xxx, 17), and a harder choice to live in fear
than by once dying to be freed from all.[2] Cleombrotus Ambraciotes persuaded I know not how many hundreds of his
auditors, by a luculent oration he made of the miseries of this,
and happiness of that other life, to precipitate themselves; and,
having read Plato's divine tract *de anima*, for example's sake
led the way first. That neat epigram of Callimachus will tell
you as much:

> *Jamque vale soli cum diceret Ambraciotes,*
> *In Stygios fertur desiluisse lacus,*
> *Morte nihil dignum passus: sed forte Platonis*
> *Divini eximium de nece legit opus.*

> [To daylight having bid his last farewell,
> The Ambraciot plunged into the Stygian hole,
> Although no crime or sorrow did compel—
> He simply had read Plato on the Soul.]

Calenus and his Indians hated of old to die a natural death:[3]
the Circumcellions and Donatists, loathing life, compelled others
to make them away, with many such:[4] but these are false and
pagan positions, profane Stoical paradoxes, wicked examples;
it boots not what heathen philosophers determine in this kind,
they are impious, abominable, and upon a wrong ground.
"No evil is to be done that good may come of it"; *reclamat
Christus, reclamat Scriptura* [Christ and Scripture cry out against
it], God and all good men are against it.[5] He that stabs another
can kill his body; but he that stabs himself kills his own soul.
*Male meretur, qui dat mendico quod edat; nam et illud quod dat
perit; et illi producit vitam ad miseriam:*[6] he that gives a beggar
an alms (as that comical poet said) doth ill, because he doth but
prolong his miseries. But Lactantius, *lib.* 6, *cap.* 7, *de vero
cultu*, calls it a detestable opinion, and fully confutes it, *lib.* 3
de sap. cap. 18, and St. Austin, *Ep.* 52 *ad Macedonium, cap.* 61
ad Dulcitium Tribunum; so doth Hierome to Marcella of Blæsilla's
death, *Non recipio tales animas*, etc., he calls such men *martyres
stultæ philosophiæ* [the victims of a stupid philosophy]; so doth
Cyprian, *de duplici martyrio : Si qui sic moriantur, aut infirmitas
aut ambitio, aut dementia cogit eos* [those who so die are driven
to it by illness or ambition or madness]; 'tis mere madness so
to do, *furor est ne moriare mori*[7] ['tis mad for fear of death to
kill oneself]. To this effect writes Arist., 3 *Ethic.*, Lipsius
Manuduc. ad Stoicam philosophiam, lib. 3, *dissertat.* 23, but i

needs no confutation. This only let me add, that in some cases those hard censures of such as offer violence to their own persons,[1] or in some desperate fit to others, which sometimes they do, by stabbing, slashing, etc., are to be mitigated, as in such as are mad, beside themselves for the time, or found to have been long melancholy, and that in extremity; they know not what they do, deprived of reason, judgment, all, as a ship that is void of a pilot must needs impinge upon the next rock or sands, and suffer shipwreck.[2] P. Forestus [3] hath a story of two melancholy brethren that made away themselves, and for so foul a fact were accordingly censured to be infamously buried, as in such cases they use, to terrify others, as it did the Milesian virgins of old; but upon farther examination of their misery and madness, the censure was revoked,[4] and they were solemnly interred, as Saul was by David (2 Sam. ii, 4); and Seneca well adviseth, *Irascere interfectori, sed miserere interfecti:* be justly offended with him as he was a murderer, but pity him now as a dead man. Thus of their goods and bodies we can dispose; but what shall become of their souls, God alone can tell; His mercy may come *inter pontem et fontem, inter gladium et jugulum,* betwixt the bridge and the brook, the knife and the throat. *Quod cuiquam contigit, cuivis potest* [what happens to someone may happen to any one]. Who knows how he may be tempted? It is his case, it may be thine: *Quæ sua sors hodie est, cras fore vestra potest.*[5] We ought not to be so rash and rigorous in our censures as some are; charity will judge and hope the best; God be merciful unto us all!

NOTES

Page 3

[1] Hæc comice dicta cave ne male capias.

Page 7

[1] These verses refer to the frontispiece, which is divided into ten compartments that are here severally explained.

Page 15

[1] Seneca, in ludo in mortem Claudii Cæsaris.
[2] Lib. de Curiositate.
[3] Modo hæc tibi usui sint, quemvis auctorem fingito.—Wecker.
[4] Lib. 10, cap. 12.   Multa a male feriatis in Democriti nomine commenta data, nobilitatis auctoritatisque ejus perfugio utentibus.
[5] Martialis, lib. 10, epigr. 4.

Page 16

[1] Juv. Sat. 1.
[2] Auth. Pet. Besseo, edit. Coloniæ, 1616.   [4] Laert. lib. 9.
[3] Hip. Epist. Damaget.
[5] Hortulo sibi cellulam seligens, ibique, seipsum includens, vixit solitarius.
[6] Floruit Olympiade 80; 700 annis post Troiam.
[7] Diacos. quod cunctis operibus facile excellit.—Laert.
[8] Col. lib. 1, cap. 1.   [9] Const. lib. de agric. passim.
[10] Volucrum voces et linguas intelligere se dicit Abderitani.—Ep. Hip.
[11] Sabellicus, Exempl. lib. 10.   Oculis se privavit, ut melius contemplationi operam daret, sublimi vir ingenio, profundæ cogitationis, etc.
[12] Naturalia, moralia, mathematica, liberales disciplinas, artiumque omnium peritiam callebat.
[13] Veni Athenas, et nemo me novit.
[14] Idem contemptui et admirationi habitus.
[15] Solebat ad portam ambulare, et inde, etc.—Hip. Ep. Damag.
[16] Perpetuo risu pulmonem agitare solebat Democritus.—Juv., Sat. 10.

Page 17

[1] Non sum dignus præstare matellam.—Mart.
[2] Christ Church in Oxford.   [3] Præfat. Hist.
[4] Keeper of our college library, lately revived by Otho Nicolson, Esq.
[5] Scaliger.   [6] In Theæt.
[7] Phil. Stoic. li. diff. 8.   Dogma cupidis et curiosis ingeniis imprimendum, ut sit talis qui nulli rei serviat, aut exacte unum aliquid elaboret, alia negligens, ut artifices, etc.
[8] Delibare gratum de quocunque cibo, et pittisare de quocunque dolio jucundum.
[9] Essays, lib. 3.   [10] Præfat. Bibliothec.

Page 18

[1] Ambo fortes et fortunati, Mars idem magisterii dominus juxta primam Leovitii regulam.

[2] Heinsius Primerio.

[3] Calide ambientes, sollicite litigantes, aut misere excidentes, voces, strepitum, contentiones, etc.

[4] Cyp. ad Donat. Unice securus, ne excidam in foro, aut in mari Indico bonis eluam, de dote filiæ, patrimonio filii non sum sollicitus.

Page 19

[1] Hor.   [2] Per.   [3] Hor.

[4] Secundum mœnia locus erat frondosis populis opacus, vitibusque sponte natis, tenuis prope aqua defluebat, placide murmurans, ubi sedile et domus Democriti conspiciebatur.

[5] Ipse composite considebat, super genua volumen habens, et utrinque alia patentia parata, dissectaque animalia cumulatim strata, quorum viscera rimabatur.

Page 20

[1] Cum mundus extra se sit, et mente captus sit, e nesciat se languere, ut medelam adhibeat.

[2] Scaliger, Ep. ad Patissonem. Nihil magis lectorem invitat quam inopinatum argumentum, neque vendibilior merx est quam petulans liber.

[3] Lib. 20, cap. 11. Miras sequuntur inscriptionum festivitates.

[4] Præfat. Nat. Hist. Patri obstetricem parturienti filiæ accersenti moram injicere possunt.

[5] Anatomy of Popery, Anatomy of Immortality, Angelus Salas' Anatomy of Antimony, etc.

[6] Cont. lib. 4, cap. 9. Non est cura melior quam labor.

Page 21

[1] Hor. de Arte Poet.

[2] Non quod de novo quid addere, aut a veteribus prætermissum, sed propriæ exercitationis causa.

[3] Qui novit, neque id quod sentit exprimit, perinde est ac si nesciret.

[4] Jovius, Præf. Hist.   [5] Erasmus.

[6] Otium otio dolorem dolore sum solatus.   [7] Observat. lib. 1.

[8] Mr. Joh. Rouse, our Protobib. Oxon., Mr. Hopper, Mr. Guthridge, etc.

Page 22

[1] Quæ illi audire et legere solent, eorum partim vidi egomet, alia gessi, quæ illi literis, ego militando didici, nunc vos existimate facta an dicta pluris sint.

[2] Dido Virg. [Taught by that Power that pities me, I learn to pity them.]

[3] Camden. Ipsa elephantiasi correpta elephantiasis hospitium construxit.

[4] Iliada post Homerum.   [5] [To bring twice-boiled cabbage to table.]

[6] Nihil prætermissum quod a quovis dici possit.   [7] Martialis.

[8] Magis impium mortuorum lucubrationes, quam vestes furari.

[9] [Many are possessed with an incurable itch for writing.]

[10] Eccles. ult.

[11] Libros eunuchi gignunt, steriles pariunt.

[12] D. King, præfat. lect. Jonas, the late Right Reverend Lord B. of London.

[13] Homines famelici gloriæ ad ostentationem eruditionis undique congerunt.—Buchananus.

[14] Effascinati etiam laudis amore, etc.—Justus Baronius.

[15] Ex ruinis alienæ existimationis sibi gradum ad famam struunt.

PAGE 23

[1] Exercit. 288.
[2] Omnes sibi famam quærunt et quovis modo in orbem spargi contendunt, ut novæ alicujus rei habeantur auctores.—Præf. Biblioth.
[3] Præfat. Hist.   [4] Plautus.   [Three-letter men (*f u r* = thief).]
[5] E Democriti puteo.   [6] Non tam refertæ bibliothecæ quam cloacæ.
[7] Et quicquid chartis amicitur ineptis.
[8] Epist. ad Patiss. In regno Franciæ omnibus scribendi datur libertas, paucis facultas.
[9] Olim literæ ob homines in pretio, nunc sordent ob homines.
[10] Aus. Pacat.
[11] Inter tot mille volumina vix unus a cujus lectione quis melior evadat, immo potius non pejor.

PAGE 24

[1] Palingenius.
[2] Lib. 5 de sap.
[3] Sterile oportet esse ingenium quod in hoc scripturientum pruritu, etc.
[4] Cardan, præf. ad Consol.   [5] Hor. lib. 1, Sat. 4.
[6] Epist. lib. 1. Magnum poetarum proventum annus hic attulit, mense Aprili nullus fere dies quo non aliquis recitavit.
[7] Idem.
[8] Principibus et doctoribus deliberandum relinquo, ut arguantur auctorum furta et millies repetita tollantur, et temere scribendi libido coerceatur, aliter in infinitum progressura.
[9] Onerabuntur ingenia, nemo legendis sufficit.
[10] Libris obruimur, oculi legendo, manus volutando dolent.—Fam. Strada, Momo.

PAGE 25

[1] Quicquid ubique bene dictum facio meum, et illud nunc meis ad compendium, nunc ad fidem et auctoritatem alienis exprimo verbis, omnes auctores meos clientes esse arbitror, etc.—Sarisburiensis ad Polycrat. prol.
[2] In Epitaph. Nep. Illud Cyp. hoc Lact. illud Hilar. est, ita Victorinus, in hunc modum locutus est Arnobius, etc.
[3] Præf. ad Syntax. med.
[4] In Luc. 10, tom. 2. Pigmæi gigantum humeris impositi plusquam ipsi gigantes vident.

PAGE 26

[1] Nec aranearum textus ideo melior quia ex se fila gignuntur, nec noster ideo vilior, quia ex alienis libamus ut apes.—Lipsius adversus dialogist.
[2] Uno absurdo dato mille sequuntur.
[3] Non dubito multos lectores hic fore stultos.   [4] Martial, 13, 2.

PAGE 27

[1] Ut venatores feram e vestigio impresso, virum scriptiuncula.—Lips.
[2] Hor.   [3] Hor.   [4] Antwerp, fol. 1607.
[5] Muretus.   [6] Lipsius.

PAGE 28

[1] Hor.
[2] Fieri non potest, ut quod quisque cogitat, dicat unus.—Muretus.
[3] Lib. 1 de ord. cap. 11.   [4] Erasmus.
[5] Annal. tom. 3, ad annum 360. Est porcus ille qui sacerdotem ex amplitudine redituum sordide demetitur.
[6] Erasm. Dial.
[7] Epist. lib. 6. Cujusque ingenium non statim emergit, nisi materiæ autor, occasio, commendatorque contingat.   [8] Præf. Hist.

PAGE 29

[1] Laudari a laudato laus est. [2] Vit. Persii. ["Which Probus" = what Probus said.]

[3] Minuit præsentia famam. [4] Lipsius, Judic. de Seneca.

[5] Lib. 10. Plurimum studii, multam rerum cognitionem, omnem studiorum materiam, etc.; multa in eo probanda, multa admiranda.

[6] Suet. Arena sine calce. [7] Introduct. ad Sen.

[8] Judic. de Sen. Vix aliquis tam absolutus, ut alteri per omnia satis-faciat, nisi longa temporis præscriptio, semota judicandi libertate, religione quadam animos occuparit.

PAGE 30

[1] Hor. Ep. lib. 1, 19.

[2] Æque turpe frigide laudari ac insectanter vituperari. Favorinus, A. Gel. lib. 19, cap. 2.

[3] Ovid. Trist. 1, eleg. 7. [4] Juven. Sat. 9.

[5] Aut artis inscii aut quæstui magis quam literis student. Hab. Cantab. et Lond. excus. 1576.

[6] Ovid. de Pont. Eleg. 1, 5.

PAGE 31

[1] Hor.

[2] Tom. 3, Philopseud. Accepto pessulo, quum carmen quoddam dixisset, effecit ut ambularet, aquam hauriret, urnam pararet, etc.

[3] Eusebius, Eccles. Hist. lib. 6.

[4] Stans pede in uno [standing on one foot] as he [Lucilius] made verses.

[5] Virg. [6] Non eadem a summo expectes, minimoque poeta.

[7] Stilus hic nullus, præter parrhesiam.

PAGE 32

[1] Qui rebus se exercet, verba negligit, et qui callet artem dicendi, nullam disciplinam habet recognitam.

[2] Palingenius.

[3] Cujuscunque orationem vides politam et sollicitam, scito animum in pusillis occupatum, in scriptis nil solidum.—Epist. lib. 1, 21.

[4] Philostratus, lib. 8, vit. Apol. Negligebat oratoriam facultatem, et penitus aspernabatur ejus professores, quod linguam duntaxat, non autem mentem redderent eruditiorem.

[5] Hic enim, quod Seneca de Ponto, bos herbam, ciconia lacertum, canis leporem, virgo florem legat.

[6] Pet. Nannius, not. in Hor.

PAGE 33

[1] Non hic colonus domicilium habeo, sed topiarii in morem, hinc inde florem vellico, ut canis Nilum lambens.

[2] Supra bis mille notabiles errores Laurentii demonstravi, etc.

[3] Philo de Con. [4] Virg.

PAGE 34

[1] Frambesarius, Sennertus, Ferrandus, etc. [2] Ter. Adelph.

[3] Heaut. Act. 1, sc. 1. [4] Gellius, lib. 18, cap. 3.

PAGE 35

[1] Et inde catena quædam fit, quæ hæredes etiam ligat.—Cardan. Heinsius.

[2] Malle se bellum cum magno principe gerere, quam cum uno ex fratrum mendicantium ordine.

[3] Hor. Epod. lib. od. 7. [4] Epist. 86, ad Casulam presb.

[5] Lib. 12, cap. 1. Mutos nasci, et omni scientia egere satius fuisset, quam sic in propriam perniciem insanire.

NOTES

445

Page 36

[1] Infelix mortalitas! inutilibus quæstionibus ac disceptationibus vitam traducimus, naturæ principes thesauros, in quibus gravissimæ morborum medicinæ collocatæ sunt, interim intactos relinquimus. Nec ipsi solum relinquimus, sed et alios prohibemus, impedimus, condemnamus, ludibriisque afficimus.

[2] [Let the shoemaker stick to his last.]

[3] Quod in praxi minime fortunatus esset, medicinam reliquit, et ordinibus initiatus in theologia postmodum scripsit.—Gesner, Bibliotheca.

[4] P. Jovius.

[5] Mr. W. Burton, Preface to his Description of Leicestershire, printed at London by W. Jaggard for J. White, 1622.

Page 37

[1] In Hygiasticon. Neque enim hæc tractatio aliena videri debet a theologo, etc., agitur de morbo animæ.

[2] Dr. Clayton in comitiis, anno 1621.   [3] Hor.

[4] In Newark in Nottinghamshire. Cum duo edificasset castella, ad tollendam structionis invidiam, et expiandam maculam, duo instituit cœnobia, et collegis religiosis implevit.

Page 38

[1] Ferdinando de Quiros, anno 1612 Amstelodami impress.

[2] Præfat. ad Characteres. Spero enim (O Polycles) libros nostros meliores inde futuros, quod istiusmodi memoriæ mandata reliquerimus, ex preceptis et exemplis nostris ad vitam accommodatis, ut se inde corrigant.

[3] Part. 1, sect. 3.   [4] Præf. lectori.

Page 39

[1] Ep. 2, lib. 2, ad Donatum. Paulisper te crede subduci in ardui montis verticem celsiorem, speculare inde rerum jacentium facies, et oculis in diversa porrectis, fluctuantis mundi turbines intuere, jam simul aut ridebis aut misereberis, etc.

[2] Controv. lib. 2, cont. 7, and lib. 6, cont.   [3] Horatius.

[4] Idem Hor. lib. 2, Satira 3. Damasippus Stoicus probat omnes stultos insanire.

Page 40

[1] Tom. 2, Sympos. lib. 5, cap. 6. Animi affectiones, si diutius inhæreant, pravos generant habitus.

[2] Lib. 28, cap. 1, Synt. art. mir. Morbus nihil est aliud quam dissolutio quædam ac perturbatio fœderis in corpore existentis, sicut et sanitas est consentientis bene corporis consummatio quædam.

[3] Lib. 9 Geogr. Plures olim gentes navigabant illuc sanitatis causa.

[4] Eccles. ii, 26.

Page 41

[1] [Isaiah.]

[2] Jure hæreditario sapere jubentur.—Euphormio Satyr.

[3] Apud quos virtus, insania et furor esse dicitur.

[4] Calcagninus, Apol. Omnes mirabantur, putantes illisam iri stultitiam. Sed præter expectationem res evenit. Audax stultitia in eam irruit, etc., illa cedit irrisa, et plures hinc habet sectatores stultitia.

[5] Non est respondendum stulto secundum stultitiam.

[6] 2 Reg. vii.   [7] Lib. 10, ep. 97.   [8] Aug. Ep. 178.

Page 42

[1] Quis nisi mentis inops, etc.

[2] Quid insanius quam pro momentanea felicitate æternis te mancipare suppliciis?

³ In fine Phædonis. Hic finis fuit amici nostri, o Echecrates, nostro quidem judicio omnium quos experti sumus optimi et apprime sapientissimi, et justissimi.

⁴ Xenoph. lib. 4 de dictis Socratis, ad finem. Talis fuit Socrates, quem omnium optimum et felicissimum statuam.

⁵ Lib. 25 Platonis Convivio.

Page 43

¹ Lucretius.   ² Anaxagoras olim mens dictus ab antiquis.

³ Regula naturæ, naturæ miraculum, ipsa eruditio dæmonium hominis, sol scientiarum, mare, sophia, antistes literarum et sapientiæ, ut Scioppius olim de Scal.; et Heinsius: Aquila in nubibus, Imperator literatorum, columen literarum, abyssus eruditionis, ocellus Europæ, Scaliger.

⁴ Lib. 3 de sap. cap. 17 et 20. Omnes philosophi aut stulti aut insani; nulla anus, nullus æger ineptius deliravit.

⁵ Democritus, a Leucippo doctus, hæreditatem stultitiæ reliquit Epicuro.

⁶ Hor. Car. lib. 1, od. 34, in Epicur.

⁷ Nihil interest inter hos et bestias nisi quod loquantur.—De sap. lib. 26, cap. 8.

⁸ Cap. de virt.

Page 44

¹ Neb. et Ranis.

² Omnium disciplinarum ignarus.

³ Pulchorum adolescentum causa frequenter gymnasium obibat, etc.

⁴ Seneca. Scis rotunda metiri, sed non tuum animum.

⁵ Ab uberibus sapientia lactati cæcutire non possunt.

⁶ Cor Zenodoti et jecur Cratetis.

Page 45

¹ Lib. de nat. boni.

² Hic profundissimæ Sophiæ fodinæ.

³ Panegyr. Trajano. Omnes actiones exprobrare stultitiam videntur.

⁴ Ser. 4, in domi Pal. Mundus qui ob antiquitatem deberet esse sapiens, semper stultizat, et nullis flagellis alteratur, sed ut puer vult rosis et floribus coronari.

⁵ [Apuleius was regarded as the hero as well as the author of the Golden Ass.]

⁶ Insanum te omnes pueri, clamantque puellæ.—Hor.

⁷ Plautus, Aulular.

Page 46

¹ Adelph. Act. 5, sc. 8.   ² Tully, Tusc. 5.

³ Plato, Apologia Socratis.   ⁴ Ant. Dial.

⁵ Lib. 3 de sap. Pauci vid video sanæ mentis sunt.

⁶ Stulte et incaute omnia agi video.

⁷ Insania non omnibus eadem (Erasm. chil. 3, cent. 10). Nemo mortalium qui non aliqua in re desipit, licet alius alio morbo laboret, hic libidinis, ille avaritiæ, ambitionis, invidiæ.

⁸ Hor. lib. 2, sat. 3.

⁹ Lib. 1 de Aulico. Est in unoquoque nostrum seminarium aliquod stultitiæ, quod si quando excitetur, in infinitum facile excrescit.

Page 47

¹ Primaque lux vitæ prima erroris erat.

² Tibullus. Stulti prætereunt dies, their wits are a-woolgathering. So fools commonly dote.

³ Dial. Contemplantes, tom. 2.   ⁴ Catullus.

Page 48

[1] Sub ramosa platano sedentem, solum, discalceatum, super lapidem, valde pallidum ac macilentum, promissa barba, librum super genibus habentem.

[2] De furore, mania, melancholia scribo, ut sciam quo pacto in hominibus gignatur, fiat, crescat, cumuletur, minuatur; hæc, inquit, animalia quæ vides propterea seco, non Dei opera perosus, sed fellis bilisque naturam disquirens.

[3] Aust. lib. 1 in Gen. Jumenti et servi tui obsequium rigide postulas, et tu nullum præstas aliis, nec ipsi Deo.

[4] Uxores ducunt, mox foras ejiciunt.   [5] Pueros amant, mox fastidiunt.

[6] Quid hoc ab insania deest?   [7] Reges eligunt, deponunt.

Page 49

[1] Contra parentes, frates, cives perpetuo rixantur, et inimicitias agunt.

[2] Credo equidem vivos ducent e marmore vultus.

[3] Idola inanimata amant, animata odio habent; sic pontificii.

[4] Suam stultitiam perspicit nemo, sed alter alterum deridet.

Page 50

[1] Denique sit finis quærendi, cumque habeas plus, Pauperiem metuas minus, et finire laborem Incipias, partis quod avebas, utere.—Hor.

[2] Astutam vapido servat sub pectore vulpem. Et cum vulpe positus pariter vulpinarier. Cretizandum cum Crete.

[3] Qui fit, Mæcenas, ut nemo quam sibi sortem, Seu ratio dederit, seu sors objecerit, illa Contentus vivat, etc.—Hor.

[4] Diruit, ædificat, mutat quadrata rotundis. Trajanus pontem struxit super Danubium, quem successor ejus Adrianus statim demolitus.

[5] Qua quid in re ab infantibus differunt, quibus mens et sensus sine ratione inest, quicquid sese his offert volupe est? [Plut.]

Page 51

[1] Idem Plut.

[2] Ut insaniæ causam disquiram bruta macto et seco, cum hoc potius in hominibus investigandum esset.

[3] Totus a nativitate morbus est.

[4] In vigore furibundus, quum decrescit insanabilis.

[5] Cyprian. ad Donatum. Qui sedet crimina judicaturus, etc.

[6] Tu pessimus omnium latro es, as a thief told Alexander in Curtius. Damnat foras judex, quod intus operatur.—Cyprian.

[7] Vultus magna cura, magna animi incuria.—Am. Marcel.

[8] Horrenda res est, vix duo verba sine mendacio proferuntur: et quamvis solenniter homines ad veritatem dicendam invitentur, pejerare tamen non dubitant, ut ex decem testibus vix unus verum dicat.—Calv. in viii John, serm. 1.

[9] Sapientiam insaniam esse dicunt.

Page 52

[1] Siquidem sapientiæ suæ admiratione me complevit, offendi sapientissimum virum, qui salvos potest omnes homines reddere.

[2] E Græc. epig.

[3] Plures Democriti nunc non sufficiunt, opus Democrito qui Democritum rideat.—Eras. Moria.

[4] Polycrat. lib. 3, cap. 8, e Petron.

[5] Ubi omnes delirabant, omnes insani, etc.; hodie nauta, cras philosophus; hodie faber, cras pharmacopola; hic modo regem agebat multo satellitio, tiara, et sceptro ornatus, nunc vili amictus centiculo, asinum clitellarium impellit.

⁶ Calcagninus, Apol. Chrysalus e cæteris auro dives, manicato peplo et tiara conspicuus, levis alioquin et nullius consilii, etc. Magno fastu ingredienti assurgunt dii, etc.

Page 53

¹ Sed hominis levitatem Jupiter perspiciens, At tu (inquit) esto bombilio, etc., protinusque vestis illa manicata in alas versa est, et mortales inde Chrysalides vocant hujusmodi homines.

² [Provinces of Moronia, or Foolsland, in Joseph Hall's Mundus Alter et Idem.]

³ Hor.   ⁴ Juven.

⁵ De bello Jud. l. 8, cap. 11. Iniquitates vestræ neminem latent, inque dies singulos certamen habetis quis pejor sit.

⁶ Hor.   ⁷ Lib. 5, epist. 8.   ⁸ Hor.

Page 54

¹ Superstitio est insanus error.   ² Lib. 8 Hist. Belg.

³ Lucan.

⁴ Father Angelo, the Duke of Joyeux, going barefoot over the Alps to Rome, etc.

⁵ Si cui intueri vacet quæ patiuntur superstitiosi, invenies tam indecora honestis, tam indigna liberis, tam dissimilia sanis, ut nemo fuerit dubitaturus furere eos, si cum paucioribus furerent.—Senec.

⁶ Quid dicam de eorum indulgentiis, oblationibus, votis, solutionibus, jejuniis, cœnobiis, somniis, horis, organis, cantilenis, campanis, simulacris, missis, purgatoriis, mitris, breviariis, bullis, lustralibus, aquis, rasuris, unctionibus, candelis, calicibus, crucibus, mappis, cereis, thuribulis, incantationibus, exorcismis, sputis, legendis, etc.—Baleus, de actis Rom. Pont.

⁷ Th. Naogeor.

Page 55

¹ Dum simulant spernere, acquisiverunt sibi 30 annorum spatio bis centena millia librarum annua.—Arnold.

² Et quum interdiu de virtute locuti sunt, sero in latibulis clunes agitant labore nocturno.—Agrippa.

³ 1 Tim. iii, 13. But they shall prevail no longer, their madness shall be known to all men.

⁴ Benignitatis sinus solebat esse, nunc litium officina curia Romana.—Budæus.

⁵ Quid tibi videtur facturus Democritus, si horum spectator contigisset?

Page 56

¹ Ob inanes ditionum titulos, ob præreptum locum, ob interceptam mulierculam, vel quod e stultitia natum, vel e malitia, quod cupido dominandi, libido nocendi, etc.

² Bellum rem plane belluinam vocat Morus, Utop. lib. 2.

³ Munster, Cosmog. lib. 5, cap. 3, e Dict. Cretens.

⁴ Jovius, vit. ejus.   ⁵ Comineus.   ⁶ Lib. 3.

Page 57

¹ Hist. of the Siege of Ostend, fol. 23.

² Erasmus de bello. Ut placidum illud animal benevolentiæ natum tam ferina vecordia in mutuam rueret perniciem.

³ Rich. Dinoth. præfat. Belli civilis Gal.   ⁴ Jovius.

⁵ Dolus, asperitas, injustitia propria bellorum negotia.—Tertul.

⁶ Tully.   ⁷ Lucan.

⁸ Pater in filium, affinis in affinem, amicus in amicum, etc. Regio cum regione, regnum regno colliditur. Populus populo in mutuam perniciem, belluarum instar sanguinolente ruentium.

Page 58

[1] Libanii Declam.

[2] Ira enim et furor Bellonæ consultores, etc., dementes sacerdotes sunt.

[3] Bellum quasi bellua et ad omnia scelera furor immissus.

[4] Gallorum decies centum millia ceciderunt. Ecclesiarum 20 millia fundamentis excisa.

[5] Belli civilis Gal. lib. 1. Hoc ferali bello et cædibus omnia repleverunt, et regnum amplissimum a fundamentis pene everterunt, plebis tot myriades gladio, bello, fame miserabiliter perierunt. [6] Pont. Heuterus.

[7] Comineus. Ut nullus non execretur et admiretur crudelitatem, et barbaram insaniam, quæ inter homines eodem sub cœlo natos, ejusdem linguæ, sanguinis, religionis, exercebatur.

[8] Lucan. [9] Virg. [10] Bishop of Cusco, an eye-witness.

Page 59

[1] Read Meteran of his stupend cruelties.

[2] Heinsius Austriaco. [3] Virg. Georg.

[4] Jansenius Gallobelgicus, 1596. Mundus furiosus, inscriptio libri.

[5] Exercitat. 250, serm. 4. [6] Fleat Heraclitus an rideat Democritus?

[7] Curæ leves loquuntur, ingentes stupent.

[8] Arma amens capio, nec sat rationis in armis. [9] Erasmus.

[10] Pro Murena. Omnes urbanæ res, omnia studia, omnis forensis laus et industria latet in tutela et præsidio bellicæ virtutis, et simul atque increpuit suspicio tumultus, artes illico nostræ conticescunt.

[11] Ser. 13.

[12] Eobanus Hessus. Quibus omnis in armis Vita placet, non ulla juvat nisi morte, nec ullam Esse putant vitam, quæ non assueverit armis.

Page 60

[1] Crudelissimos sævissimosque latrones, fortissimos haberi propugnatores, fidissimos duces habent, bruta persuasione donati.

[2] Lib. 10 vit. Scanderbeg.

[3] De benef. lib. 2, cap. 16. [4] Nat. quæst. lib. 3.

[5] Nulli beatiores habiti, quam qui in prœliis cecidissent.—Brisonius, de rep. Persarum, lib. 3, fol. 3, 44. Idem Lactantius de Romanis et Græcis. Idem Ammianus, lib. 23, de Parthis. Judicatur is solus beatus apud eos, qui in prœlio fuderit animam.

Page 61

[1] Boterus, Amphitridion. Busbequius, Turc. Hist. Per cædes et sanguinem parare hominibus ascensum in cœlum putant.—Lactan. de falsa relig. lib. 1, cap. 8.

[2] Quoniam bella acerbissima Dei flagella sunt quibus hominum pertinaciam punit, ea perpetua oblivione sepelienda potius quam memoriæ mandanda plerique judicant.—Rich. Dinoth, præf. Hist. Gall.

[3] Cruentam humani generis pestem, et perniciem divinitatis nota insigniunt.

[4] Et quod dolendum, applausum habent et occursum viri tales.

[5] Herculi eadem porta ad cœlum patuit, qui magnam generis humani partem perdidit.

[6] Virg. Æneid 7.

[7] Homicidium quum committunt singuli, crimen est, quum publice geritur, virtus vocatur.—Cyprianus.

[8] Seneca. [9] Juven.

[10] De vanit. scient., de princip. nobilitatis.

Page 62

[1] Juven. Sat. 4.

[2] Pansa rapit, quod Natta reliquit. Tu pessimus omnium latro es, as Demetrius the pirate told Alexander in Curtius.

[3] Non ausi mutire, etc.—Æsop.

[4] Improbum et stultum, si divitem, multos bonos viros in servitutem habentem, ob id duntaxat quod ei contingat aureorum numismatum cumulus, ut appendices et additamenta numismatum.—Morus, Utopia.

[5] Eorumque detestantur Utopienses insaniam, qui divinos honores iis impendunt, quos sordidos et avaros agnoscunt; non alio respectu honorantes, quam quod dites sint.—Idem, lib. 2.

Page 63

[1] Cyp. 2 ad Donat. ep. Ut reus innocens pereat, fit nocens. Judex damnat foras, quod intus operatur.

[2] Sidonius, Apo. [3] Salvianus, lib. 3, de providen.

[4] Ergo judicium nihil est nisi publica merces.—Petronius. Quid faciant leges ubi sola pecunia regnat?—Idem.

[5] Hic arcentur hæreditatibus liberi, hic donatur bonis alienis, falsum consulit, alter testamentum corrumpit, etc.—Idem.

[6] Vexat censura columbas. [7] Plaut. Mostel.

[8] Idem. [9] Juven. Sat. 4.

[10] Quod tot sint fures et mendici, magistratuum culpa fit, qui malos imitantur præceptores, qui discipulos libentius verberant quam docent.—Morus, Utop. lib. 1.

Page 64

[1] Decernuntur furi gravia et horrenda supplicia, quum potius providendum multo foret ne fures sint, ne cuiquam tam dira furandi aut pereundi sit necessitas.—Idem.

[2] Boterus de augment. urb. lib. 3, cap. 3.

[3] E fraterno corde sanguinem eliciunt.

[4] [Go it, Socrates! go it, Xanthippe!]

[5] Milvus rapit ac deglubit. [6] Petronius de Crotone civit.

[7] Quid forum? locus quo alius alium circumvenit.

[8] Vastum chaos, larvarum emporium, theatrum hypocrisios, etc.

[9] Nemo cœlum, nemo jusjurandum, nemo Jovem pluris facit, sed omnes apertis oculis bona sua computant.—Petron.

Page 65

[1] Plutarch. vit. ejus. Indecorum animatis ut calceis uti aut vitris, quæ ubi fracta abjicimus, nam, ut de meipso dicam, nec bovem senem vendiderim, nedum hominem natu grandem laboris socium.

[2] Jovius. Cum innumera illius beneficia rependere non posset aliter, interfici jussit.

[3] Beneficia eo usque læta sunt, dum videntur solvi posse, ubi multum antevenere pro gratia odium redditur.—Tac.

[4] Paucis carior est fides quam pecunia.—Sallust.

[5] Prima fere vota et cunctis, etc.

[6] Et genus et formam regina pecunia donat. Quantum quisque sua nummorum servat in arca, Tantum habet et fidei.

[7] Non a peritia sed ab ornatu et vulgi vocibus habemur excellentes.—Cardan, lib. 2 de cons.

[8] Perjurata suo postponit numina lucro Mercator. Ut necessarium sit vel Deo displicere, vel ab hominibus contemni, vexari, negligi.

[9] Qui Curios simulant et Bacchanalia vivunt.

[10] Tragelapho similes vel centauris, sursum homines, deorsum equi.

PAGE 66

[1] Præceptis suis cœlum promittunt, ipsi interim pulveris terreni vilia mancipia.

[2] Æneas Sylv.

[3] Arridere homines ut sæviant, blandiri ut fallant.—Cyp. ad Donatum.

[4] Love and hate are like the two ends of a perspective glass, the one multiplies, the other makes less.

[5] Ministri locupletiores iis quibus ministratur, servus majores opes habens quam patronus.

[6] Qui terram colunt equi paleis pascuntur, qui otiantur caballi avena saginantur, discalceatus discurrit qui calces aliis facit.

[7] Juven. [8] Bodine, lib. 4 de repub. cap. 6.

[9] Plinius, lib. 37, cap. 3. Capillos habuit succineos, exinde factum ut omnes puellæ Romanæ colorem illum affectarent.

[10] Odit damnatos.—Juv.

PAGE 67

[1] Agrippa, Ep. 28, lib. 7. Quorum cerebrum est in ventre, ingenium in patinis.

[2] Psal. [liii, 4]. They eat up my people as bread.

[3] Absumit hæres Cæcuba dignior Servata centum clavibus, et mero Tinguet pavimentis superbo, Pontificum potiore cœnis.—Hor.

[4] Qui Thaidem pingere, inflare tibiam, crispare crines.

[5] Doctus spectare lacunar.

[6] Tullius. Est enim proprium stultitiæ aliorum cernere vitia, oblivisci suorum. Idem Aristippus Charidemo apud Lucianum. Omnino stultitiæ cujusdam esse puto, etc.

[7] Execrari publice quod occulte agat. Salvianus, lib. de prov. Acres ulciscendis vitiis quibus ipsi vehementer indulgent.

PAGE 68

[1] Adamus, Eccl. Hist. cap. 212. Siquis damnatus fuerit, lætus esse gloria est; nam lacrimas et planctum cæteraque compunctionum genera quæ nos salubria censemus, ita abominantur Dani, ut nec pro peccatis nec pro defunctis amicis ulli flere liceat.

[2] Orbi dat leges foras, vix famulum regit sine strepitu domi.

[3] Quicquid ego volo hoc vult mater mea, et quod mater vult, facit pater.

[4] Oves, olim mite pecus, nunc tam indomitum et edax ut homines devorent, etc.—Morus, Utop. lib. 1.

[5] Diversos variis tribuit natura furores.

[6] Democrit. Ep. præd. Hos dejerantes et potantes deprehendet, hos vomentes, illos litigantes, insidias molientes, suffragantes, venena miscentes, in amicorum accusationem subscribentes, hos gloria, illos ambitione, cupiditate, mente captos, etc.

[7] Ad Donat. ep. 2, cap. 9. O si posses in specula sublimi constitutus, etc.

PAGE 69

[1] Lib. 1 de nup. Philol. In qua quid singuli nationum populi quotidianis motibus agitarent, relucebat.

[2] O Jupiter! contingat mihi aurum, hæreditas, etc. Multos da Jupiter annos! Dementia quanta est hominum, turpissima vota diis insusurrant, si quis admoverit aurem, conticescunt; et quod scire homines nolunt Dec narrant.—Senec. Ep. 10.

[3] Plautus, Menæch. Non potest hæc res hellebori jugere obtinerier.

[4] Eoque gravior morbus quo ignotior periclitanti.

[5] Quæ lædunt oculos, festinas demere; si quid Est animum, differs curandi tempus in annum.—Hor.

⁶ Si caput, crus dolet, brachium, etc., medicum accersimus, recte et honeste, si par etiam industria in animi morbis poneretur.—Joh. Pelezius, Jesuita, lib. 2 de hum. affec. morborumque cura.

⁷ Et quotusquisque tamen est qui contra tot pestes medicum requirat vel ægrotare se agnoscat? Ebullit ira, etc. Et nos tamen ægros esse negamus. Incolumes medicum recusant. Præsens ætas stultitiam priscis exprobrat.—Bud. de affec. lib. 5.

⁸ Senes pro stultis habent juvenes.—Balth. Cast.

PAGE 70

¹ Clodius accusat mœchos.
² Omnium stultissimi qui auriculas studiose tegunt.—Sat. Menip.
³ Hor. Epist. 2.   ⁴ Prosper.
⁵ Statim sapiunt, statim sciunt, neminem reverentur, neminem imitantur, ipsi sibi exemplo.—Plin. Epist. lib. 8.
⁶ Nulli alteri sapere concedit, ne desipere videatur.—Agrip.
⁷ Omnis orbis percæcus a Persis ad Lusitaniam.   ⁸ Florid.

PAGE 71

¹ August. Qualis in oculis hominum qui inversis pedibus ambulat, talis in oculis sapientum et angelorum qui sibi placet, aut cui passiones dominantur.
² Plautus, Menæchmi.
³ Governor of Africa by Cæsar's appointment.
⁴ Nunc sanitatis patrocinium est insanientium turba.—Sen.
⁵ Pro Roscio Amerino. Et quod inter omnes constat insanissimus, nisi inter eos, qui ipsi quoque insaniunt.
⁶ Necesse est cum insanientibus furere, nisi solus relinqueris.—Petronius.
⁷ Quoniam non est genus unum stultitiæ qua me insanire putas.
⁸ Stultum me fateor, liceat concedere verum, Atque etiam insanum.—Hor.
⁹ Odi, nec possum cupiens non esse quod odi.—Ovid. Errore grato libenter omnes insanimus.

PAGE 72

¹ Amator scortum vitæ præponit, iracundus vindictam, fur prædam, parasitus gulam, ambitiosus honores, avarus opes, etc., odimus hæc et accersimus.—Cardan. lib. 2 de consol.
² Prov. xxvi, 11.
³ Plutarch. Gryllo. Suilli homines, sic Clem. Alex.
⁴ Non persuadebis, etiamsi persuaseris.   ⁵ Tully.
⁶ Malo cum illis insanire, quam cum aliis bene sentire.
⁷ Qui inter hos enutriuntur, non magis sapere possunt, quam qui in culina bene olere.—Petron.
⁸ Persius.   ⁹ Hor. Sat. 2.
¹⁰ Vesanum exagitant pueri, innuptæque puellæ.   ¹¹ Plautus.

PAGE 73

¹ Hor. Sat. 2, 3. Superbam stultitiam Plinius vocat, Epist. 7, 21, quod semel dixi, fixum ratumque sit.
² Multi sapientes proculdubio fuissent, si se non putassent ad sapientiæ summum pervenisse.
³ Idem.   ⁴ Plutarchus, Solone. Detur sapientiori.
⁵ Tam præsentibus plena est numinibus, ut facilius possis deum quam hominem invenire.

PAGE 74

¹ Pulchrum bis dicere non nocet.   ² Malefactors.
³ Who can find a faithful man?—Prov. xx, 6.

⁴ In Ps. xlix. Qui momentanea sempiternis, qui dilapidat heri absentis bona, mox in jus vocandus et damnandus.

⁵ Perquam ridiculum est homines ex animi sententia vivere, et quæ diis ingrata sunt exequi, et tamen a solis diis velle salvos heri, quum propriæ salutis curam abjecerint.—Theod. cap. 6, de provid. lib. de curat. Græc. affect.

⁶ Sapiens sibi qui imperiosus, etc.—Hor. Sat. 2, 7.

⁷ Conclus. lib. de vic. offer. Certum est animi morbis laborantes pro mortuis censendos.

⁸ Lib. de sap. Ubi timor adest, sapientia adesse nequit.

PAGE 75

¹ Quid insanius Xerxe Hellespontum verberante, etc.

² Eccles. xxi, 12. "Where is bitterness, there is no understanding." Prov. xii, 16. "An angry man is a fool."

³ 3 Tusc. Injuria in sapientem non cadit.

⁴ Hom. 6, in 2 Epist. ad Cor. Hominem te agnoscere nequeo, cum tanquam asinus recalcitres, lascivias ut taurus, hinnias ut equus post mulieres, ut ursus ventri indulgeas, quum rapias ut lupus, etc. At, inquis, formam hominis habeo. Id magis terret, quum feram humana specie videre me putem.

⁵ Epist. lib. 2, ep. 13. Stultus semper incipit vivere. Fœda hominum levitas, nova quotidie fundamenta vitæ ponere, novas spes, etc.

⁶ De curial. miser. Stultus, qui quærit quod nequit invenire, stultus qui quærit quod nocet inventum, stultus qui cum plures habet calles, deteriorem deligit. Mihi videntur omnes deliri, amentes, etc.

PAGE 76

¹ Ep. Damageto.

² Amicis nostris Rhodi dicito, ne nimium rideant, aut nimium tristes sint.

³ Per multum risum poteris cognoscere stultum.—Offic. 3, cap. 9.

⁴ Sapientes liberi, stulti servi, libertas est potestas, etc.

⁵ Hor. 2, ser. 7. ⁶ Juven.

⁷ [Charles the Wise (of France), Philip the Good (of Burgundy), Louis the Pious (St. Louis of France).]

PAGE 77

¹ Hypocrit. ² Ut mulier aulica nullius pudens.

³ Epist. 33. Quando fatuo delectari volo, non est longe quærendus, me video.

⁴ Primo Contradicentium. ⁵ Lib. de causis corrupt. artium.

⁶ Actione ad subtil. in Scal. fol. 1226. ⁷ Lib. 1 de sap.

⁸ Vide, miser homo, quia totum est vanitas, totum stultitia, totum dementia, quicquid facis in hoc mundo, præter hoc solum quod propter Deum facis.—Ser. de miser. hom.

⁹ In 2 Platonis dial. lib. de justo.

PAGE 78

¹ Dum iram et odium in Deo revera ponit. ² Virg. Ecl. 3.

³ Ps. Inebriabuntur ab ubertate domus. ⁴ In Ps. civ, Anstin.

⁵ In Platonis Tim. sacerdos Ægyptius. ⁶ Hor. Vulgus insanum.

⁷ Patet ea divisio probabilis, etc., ex Arist. Top. lib. 1, cap. 8. Rog. Bac. Epist. de secret. art. et nat., cap. 8. Non est judicium in vulgo.

⁸ [i.e. not a pin to choose between them. See Apperson's English Proverbs, p. 27.]

PAGE 79

[1] De occult. philosoph. lib. 1, cap. 25 et 19 ejusd. lib.; lib. 10, cap. 4.
[2] See Lipsius, Epist.
[3] De politia illustrium, lib. 1, cap. 4. Ut in humanis corporibus variæ accidunt mutationes corporis, animique, sic in republica, etc.
[4] Ubi reges philosophantur.—Plato.   [5] Lib. de re rust.
[6] Vel publicam utilitatem: Salus publica suprema lex esto. Beata civitas non ubi pauci beati, sed tota civitas beata.—Plato, quinto de republica.

PAGE 80

[1] Mantua væ miseræ nimium vicina Cremonæ.
[2] Interdum a feris, ut olim Mauritania, etc.
[3] Deliciis Hispaniæ, anno 1604. Nemo malus, nemo pauper, optimus quisque atque ditissimus. Pie sancteque vivebant, summaque cum veneratione et timore, divino cultui, sacrisque rebus incumbebant.
[4] [Barcelona.]   [5] Polit. lib. 5, cap. 3.

PAGE 81

[1] Boterus, Polit. lib. 1, cap. 1. Cum nempe princeps rerum gerendarum imperitus, segnis, oscitans, suique muneris immemor, aut fatuus est.
[2] Non viget respublica cujus caput infirmatur.—Sarisburiensis, cap. 22.
[3] See Dr. Fletcher's Relation, and Alexander Gaguinus' History.
[4] Abundans omni divitiarum affluentia, incolarum multitudine, splendore ac potentia.
[5] Not above two hundred miles in length, sixty in breadth, according to Adricomius.
[6] Romulus Amaseus.
[7] Sabellicus. Si quis incola vetus, non agnosceret, si quis peregrinus, ingemisceret.
[8] Polit. lib. 5, cap. 6. Crudelitas principum, impunitas scelerum, violatio legum, peculatus pecuniæ publicæ, etc.
[9] Epist.
[10] De increm. urb. cap. 20. Subditi miseri, rebelles, desperati, etc.
[11] R. Dallington, 1596, conclusio libri.

PAGE 82

[1] Boterus, lib. 9, cap. 4 Polit. Quo fit ut aut rebus desperatis exulent, aut conjuratione subditorum crudelissime tandem trucidentur.
[2] [Galeazzo Sforza, Duke of Milan.]
[3] Mutuis odiis et cædibus exhausti, etc.
[4] Lucra ex malis, sceleratisque causis.   [5] Sallust.
[6] For most part we mistake the name of politicians, accounting such as read Machiavel and Tacitus great statesmen, that can dispute of political precepts, supplant and overthrow their adversaries, enrich themselves get honours, dissemble; but what is this to the *bene esse*, or preservation of a commonwealth?
[7] Imperium suapte sponte corruit.
[8] Apul. Prim. Flor. Ex innumerabilibus, pauci senatores genere nobiles, e consularibus pauci boni, e bonis adhuc pauci eruditi.
[9] Non solum vitia concipiunt ipsi principes, sed etiam infundunt in civitatem, plusque exemplo quam peccato nocent.—Cic. de legibus.
[10] Epist. ad Zen. Juven. Sat. 4. Paupertas seditionem gignit et maleficium.—Arist. Pol. 2, 3, 7.

PAGE 83

[1] Sallust. Semper in civitate quibus opes nullæ sunt bonis invident, vetera odere, nova exoptant, odio suarum rerum mutari omnia petunt.

² De legibus. Profligatæ in repub. disciplinæ est indicium juris-
peritorum numerus, et medicorum copia.
³ In præf. Stud. juris. Multiplicantur nunc in terris ut locustæ, non
patriæ parentes, sed pestes, pessimi homines, majore ex parte superciliosi,
contentiosi, etc., licitum latrocinium exercent.
⁴ Dousa, Epod. Loquutuleia turba, vultures togati.
⁵ Barc. Argen.
⁶ Jurisconsulti domus oraculum civitatis.—Tully.   ⁷ Lib. 3.
⁸ Lib. 1 de rep. Gallorum. Incredibilem reipub. perniciem afferunt.

PAGE 84

¹ Polycrat. lib.
² Is stipe contentus, at hi asses integros sibi multiplicari jubent.
³ Plus accipiunt tacere, quam nos loqui.
⁴ Totius injustitiæ nulla capitalior, quam eorum qui cum maxime
decipiunt, id agunt, ut boni viri esse videantur.
⁵ Nam quocunque modo causa procedat, hoc semper agitur, ut loculi
impleantur, etsi avaritia nequit satiari.
⁶ Camden, in Norfolk. Qui si nihil sit litium e juris apicibus lites tamen
serere callent.
⁷ Plutarch, Vit. Cat. Causas apud inferos quas in suam fidem re-
ceperunt, patrocinio suo tuebuntur.
⁸ Lib. 2 de Helvet. repub. Non explicandis, sed moliendis controversiis operam dant, ita ut lites in multos annos extrahantur summa cum
molestia utriusque partis et dum interea patrimonia exhauriantur.

PAGE 85

¹ Lupum auribus tenent.   ² Hor.
³ Lib. de Helvet. repub. Judices quocunque pago constituunt qui amica
aliqua transactione si fieri possit, lites tollant. Ego majorum nostrorum
simplicitatem admiror, qui sic causas gravissimas composuerint, etc.
⁴ Clenard. Ep. lib. 1. Si quæ controversiæ utraque pars judicem adit, is
semel et simul rem transigit, audit: nec quid sit appellatio, lacrimosæque
moræ noscunt.
⁵ Camden.
⁶ [Lacedæmonian cylinder: a secret letter written on a slip of papyrus
and rolled round a cylinder.]
⁷ Lib. 10 Epist. ad Atticum, epist. 10.
⁸ Biblioth. lib. 3.   ⁹ Lib. de Anim.
¹⁰ Lib. major morb. corp. an animi. Hi non conveniunt ut diis more
majorum sacra faciant, non ut Jovi primitias offerant, aut Baccho com-
missationes, sed anniversarius morbus exasperans Asiam huc eos coegit,
ut contentiones hic peragant.

PAGE 86

¹ 1 Cor. vi, 5, 6.
² Stulti, quando demum sapietis?—Ps. xciv, 8.
³ Of which text read two learned sermons, so intituled [i.e. "Christ's
Counsel," etc.] and preached by our Regius Professor, Dr. Prideaux;
printed at London by Felix Kingston, 1621.
⁴ Sæpius bona materia cessat sine artifice. Sabellicus de Germania:
Si quis videret Germaniam urbibus hodie excultam, non diceret ut olim
tristem cultu, asperam cœlo, terram informem.
⁵ By his Majesty's Attorney-General there.

PAGE 87

¹ As Zeipland, Bemster in Holland, etc.
² From Gaunt [Ghent] to Sluce [Sluys], from Bruges to the sea, etc.

³ Ortelius, Boterus, Mercator, Meteranus, etc.

⁴ Jam inde non minus belli gloria, quam humanitatis cultu inter floren-tissimas orbis Christiani gentes imprimis floruit.—Camden, Brit., de Normannis.

⁵ Geog. Kecker.

⁶ Tam hieme quam æstate intrepide sulcant Oceanum, et duo illorum duces non minore audacia quam fortuna totius orbem terræ circum-navigarunt.—Amphitheatro Boterus.

⁷ A fertile soil, good air, etc. Tin, lead, wool, saffron, etc.

⁸ Tota Britannia unica velut arx.—Boter.

Page 88

¹ Lib. 1 Hist.   ² Increment. urb. lib. 1, cap. 9.

³ Angliæ, excepto Londinio, nulla est civitas memorabilis, licet ea natio rerum omnium copia abundet.

⁴ Cosmog. lib. 3, cap. 119. Villarum non est numerus, nullus locus otiosus aut incultus.

⁵ Chytræus, Orat. edit. Francof. 1583.

⁶ [Thuringia.]   ⁷ Maginus, Geog.

⁸ Ortelius, e Vaseo et Pet. de Medina.

⁹ ["Portugal between two rivers," i.e. the province of Entre-Douro-e-Minho, or Minho.]

¹⁰ An hundred families in each.

Page 89

¹ Populi multitudo diligente cultura fecundat solum.—Boter. lib. 8, cap. 3.

² Orat. 35.   Terra ubi oves stabulantur optima agricolis ob stercus.

³ De re rust. lib. 2, cap. 1.

⁴ Hodie urbibus desolatur, et magna ex parte incolis destituitur.—Gerbelius, Desc. Græciæ, lib. 6.

Page 90

¹ Videbit eas fere omnes aut eversas, aut solo æquatas, aut in rudera fœdissime dejectas.—Gerbelius.

² Lib. 7. Septuaginta olim legiones scriptæ dicuntur; quas vires hodie, etc.

³ [Lucca and Siena.]   ⁴ Polit. lib. 3, cap. 8.

⁵ For dyeing of cloths, and dressing, etc.

⁶ Valer. lib. 2, cap. 1.   ⁷ [i.e. the first of that name.]

Page 91

¹ Hist. Scot. lib. 10.   Magnis propositis præmiis, ut Scoti ab iis edocerentur.

² Munst. Cosm. lib. 5, cap. 74. Agro omnium rerum infecundissimo, aqua indigente, inter saxeta, urbs tamen elegantissima, ob Orientis negotiationes et Occidentis.

³ Lib. 8 Geogr.: ob asperum situm.

⁴ Lib. edit. a Nic. Tregant. Belg. anno 1616, Expedit. in Sinas.

Page 92

¹ Ubi nobiles probri loco habent artem aliquam profiteri.—Cleonard. Ep. lib. 1.

² Lib. 13 Belg. Hist.   Non tam laboriosi ut Belgæ, sed ut Hispani otiatores vitam ut plurimum otiosam agentes: artes manuariæ quæ plurimum habent in se laboris et difficultatis, majoremque requirunt industriam, a peregrinis et exteris exercentur; habitant in piscosissimo mari, interea tantum non piscantur quantum insulæ suffecerit, sed a vicinis emere coguntur.

² Grotii liber.
⁴ Urbs animis numeroque potens, et robore gentis.—Scaliger.
⁵ Camden.   ⁶ York, Bristow, Norwich, Worcester, etc.
⁷ Mr. Gainsford's argument, "Because gentlemen dwell with us in the
country villages, our cities are less," is nothing to the purpose: put three
hundred or four hundred villages in a shire, and every village yield a gentleman, what is four hundred families to increase one of our cities, or to
contend with theirs, which stand thicker? And whereas ours usually
consist of seven thousand, theirs consist of forty thousand inhabitants.
⁸ Maxima pars victus in carne consistit.—Polyd. lib. 1 Hist.

PAGE 93

¹ Refrænate monopolii licentiam, pauciores alantur otio, redintegretur
agricolatio, lanificium instauretur, ut sit honestum negotium quo se
exerceat otiosa illa turba. Nisi his malis medentur, frustra exercent
justitiam.—Mor. Utop. lib. 1.
² Mancipiis locuples eget æris Cappadocum rex.—Hor.
³ Regis dignitatis non est exercere imperium in mendicos sed in opulentos.
Non est regni decus, sed carceris esse custos.—Mor. Utop. lib. 1.
⁴ Colluvies hominum mirabiles excocti sole, immundi veste, fœdi visu,
furti imprimis acres, etc.
⁵ Cosmog. lib. 3, cap. 5.
⁶ Seneca. Haud minus turpia principi multa supplicia, quam medico
multa funera.
⁷ Ac pituitam et bilem a corpore (8 de Rep.) omnes vult exterminari.
⁸ See Lipsius, Admiranda.
⁹ De quo Suet. in Claudio, et Plinius, cap. 36.
¹⁰ [The Baths of Diocletian at Salona.]
¹¹ [Lago Fucino, or di Celano, drained in 1862.]
¹² Ut egestati simul et ignaviæ occurratur, opificia condiscantur, tenues
subleventur.—Bodin. lib. 6, cap. 2, num. 6, 7.
¹³ Amasis Ægypti rex legem promulgavit, ut omnes subditi quotannis
rationem redderent unde viverent.
¹⁴ Buscoldus, Discursu polit. cap. 2.
¹⁵ Lib. 1 de increm. urb. cap. 6.
¹⁶ Cap. 5 de increm. urb. Quas flumen, lacus, aut mare alluit.

PAGE 94

¹ Incredibilem commoditatem, vectura mercium tres fluvii navigabiles,
etc.—Boterus de Gallia.
² Ind. Orient. cap. 2. Rotam in medio flumine constituunt, cui ex
pellibus animalium consutos uteres appendunt, hi dum rota movetur,
aquam per canales, etc.
³ Herodotus.   ⁴ Centum pedes lata fossa, 30 alta.
⁵ Contrary to that of Archimedes, who holds the superficies of all waters
even.   ⁶ Lib. 1, cap. 3.
⁷ Dion, Pausanias, et Nic. Gerbelius. Munster, Cosm. lib. 4, cap. 36.
Ut brevior foret navigatio et minus periculosa.
⁸ Charles the Great went about to make a channel from the Rhine to
the Danube (Bil. Pirckheimerus, Descript. Ger. The ruins are yet seen about
Weissenburg from Rednich to Altimul [from the Rednitz to the Altmühl]),
ut navigabilia inter se Occidentis et Septentrionis littora fierent.

PAGE 95

¹ Maginus, Geogr. Simlerus, de rep. Helvet. lib. 1, describit.
² [The Douro.]   ³ Camden, in Lincolnshire. Fossdyke.
⁴ Near St. Albans.

Page 96

[1] [Rosicrucians.]
[2] Lilius Giraldus, Nat. Comes.
[3] Apuleius, lib. 4 Flor. Lar familiaris inter homines ætatis suæ cultus est, litium omnium et jurgiorum inter propinquos arbiter et disceptator. Adversus iracundiam, invidiam, avaritiam, libidinem, ceteraque animi humani vitia et monstra philosophus iste Hercules fuit. Pestes eas mentibus exegit omnes, etc. [4] Votis Navig.

Page 97

[1] [The Unknown Southern Land, i.e. Australia.]
[2] Ragguaglios, part. 2, cap. 2, et part. 3, cap. 17.
[3] Valent. Andreæ Apolog. manip. 604.
[4] Qui sordidus est, sordescat adhuc.   [5] Hor.

Page 98

[1] Ferdinando de Quiros, 1612.
[2] [The South Sea, Pacific Ocean.]
[3] Vide Acosta et Laiet.
[4] Vide Patricium, lib. 8, tit. 10, de Instit. Reipub.
[5] Sic olim Hippodamus Milesius, Arist. Polit. cap. 11, et Vitruvius, lib. 1, cap. ult.

Page 99

[1] With walls of earth, etc.
[2] De his Plin. epist. 42, lib. 2, et Tacit. Annal. lib. 15.
[3] Vide Brisonium de regno Pers. lib. 3, de his, et Vegetium, lib. 2, cap. 3, de Annona.
[4] Not to make gold, but for matters of physic.
[5] Brisonius; Josephus, lib. 21 Antiquit. Jud. cap. 6; Herod. lib. 3.
[6] So Lod. Vives thinks best, Comineus, and others.

Page 100

[1] Plato de leg. lib. 6. Ædiles creari vult, qui fora, fontes, vias, portus, plateas, et id genus alia procurent. Vide Isaacum Pontanum de civ. Amstel. (hæc omnia, etc.), Gotardum et alios.
[2] De increm. urb. cap. 13. Ingenue fateor me non intelligere cur ignobilius sit urbes bene munitas colere nunc quam olim, aut casæ rusticæ præesse quam urbi. Idem Ubertus Foliot, de Neapoli.
[3] Ne tantillum quidem soli incultum relinquitur, ut verum sit ne pollicem quidem agri in his regionibus sterilem aut infecundum reperiri. —Marcus Hemingius Augustanus de regno Chinæ, lib. 1, cap. 3.
[4] Mr. Carew, in his Survey of Cornwall, saith that before that country was enclosed, the husbandmen drank water, did eat little or no bread (fol. 66, lib. 1), their apparel was coarse, they went bare-legged, their dwelling was correspondent; but since enclosure they live decently, and have money to spend (fol. 23); when their fields were common, their wool was coarse, Cornish hair; but since enclosure, it is almost as good as Cotswold, and their soil much mended. Tusser, cap. 52 of his Husbandry, is of his opinion, one acre enclosed is worth three common: "The country enclosed I praise; The other delighteth not me, For nothing of wealth it doth raise," etc.
[5] Incredibilis navigiorum copia, nihilo pauciores in aquis, quam in continenti commorantur.—M. Riccius, Expedit. in Sinas, lib. 1, cap. 3.
[6] To this purpose Aristotle (Polit. 2, cap. 6) allows a third part of their revenues, Hippodamus half.
[7] Ita lex Agraria olim Romæ.

Page 101

¹ Lucanus, lib. 6.   ² Virg. Georg. 1.
³ Joh. Valent. Andreas.   ⁴ Lord Verulam.
⁵ So is it in the kingdom of Naples and France.
⁶ See Contarenus, and Osorius de rebus gestis Emanuelis.
⁷ Claudian.

Page 102

¹ Herodotus, Erato, lib. 6. Cum Ægyptiis Lacedæmonii in hoc congruunt, quod eorum præcones, tibicines, coqui, et reliqui artifices, in paterno artificio succedunt, et coquus a coquo gignitur et paterno opere perseverat. Idem Marcus Polus de Quinzay. Idem Osorius de Emanuele rege Lusitano, Riccius de Sinis.

² Hippol. à Collibus de increm. urb. cap. 20. Plato, 8 de legibus. Quæ ad vitam necessaria, et quibus carere non possumus, nullum dependi vectigal, etc.

³ Plato, 12 de legibus, 40 annos natos vult, ut si quid memorabile viderent apud exteros, hoc ipsum in rempub. recipiatur.

⁴ Simlerus, in Helvetia.

Page 103

¹ Utopienses causidicos excludunt, qui causas callide et vafre tractent et disputent. Iniquissimum censent hominem ullis obligari legibus, quæ aut numerosiores sunt, quam ut perlegi queant, aut obscuriores quam ut a quovis possint intelligi. Volunt ut suam quisque causam agat, eamque referat judici quam narraturus fuerat patrono, sic minus erit ambagum, et veritas facilius elicietur.—Mor. Utop. lib. 2.

² Medici ex publico victum sumunt.—Boter. lib. 1, cap. 5, de Ægyptiis.
³ De his lege Patricium, lib. 3, tit. 8, de reip. instit.
⁴ Nihil a clientibus patroni accipiant, priusquam lis finita est.—Barcl. Argen. lib. 3.
⁵ It is so in most free cities in Germany.
⁶ Mat. Riccius, Exped. in Sinas, lib. 1, cap. 5, de examinatione electionum copiose agit, etc.
⁷ Contar. de repub. Venet. lib. 1. [The reference is to the elaborate system of lot and ballot by which the doges were chosen.]
⁸ Osor. lib. 11 de reb. gest. Eman. Qui in literis maximos progressus fecerint maximis honoribus afficiuntur, secundus honoris gradus militibus assignatur, postremi ordinis mechanicis. Doctorum hominum judiciis in altiorem locum quisque præfertur, et qui a plurimis approbatur, ampliores in rep. dignitates consequitur. Qui in hoc examine primas habet, insigni per totam vitam dignitate insignitur, marchioni similis, aut duci apud nos.
⁹ Cedant arma togæ.
¹⁰ As in Berne, Lucerne, Freiburg in Switzerland, a vicious liver is incapable of any office; if a senator, instantly deposed.—Simlerus.
¹¹ Not above three years.—Arist. Polit. 5, cap. 8.
¹² Nam quis custodiet ipsos custodes?
¹³ Chytræus, in Greisgeia. Qui non ex sublimi despiciant inferiores, nec ut bestias conculcent sibi subditos, auctoritatis nomini confisi, etc.

Page 104

¹ Sesellius de rep. Gallorum, lib. 1 et 2.
² Si quis egregium aut bello aut pace perfecerit.—Sesel. lib. 1.
³ Ad regendam rempub. soli literati admittuntur, nec ad eam rem gratia magistratuum aut regis indigent, omnia explorata cujusque scientia et virtute pendent.—Riccius, lib. 1, cap. 5.
⁴ In defuncti locum eum jussit subrogari, qui inter majores virtute reliquis præiret; non fuit apud mortales ullum excellentius certamen, aut

cujus victoria magis esset expetenda, non enim inter celeres celerrimo, non inter robustos robustissimo, etc.

[5] Nullum videres vel in hac vel in vicinis regionibus pauperem, nullum obæratum, etc.

[6] Nullus mendicus apud Sinas, nemini sano quamvis oculis turbatus sit, mendicare permittitur, omnes pro viribus laborare coguntur, cæci molis trusatilibus versandis addicuntur, soli hospitiis gaudent, qui ad labores sunt inepti. Osor. lib. 11 de reb. gest. Eman. Heming. de reg. Chin. lib. 1, cap. 3. Gotard. Arth. Orient. Ind. descr.

[7] Alex. ab Alex. 3, cap. 12.

[8] Sic olim Romæ. Isaac. Pontan. de his optime, Amstel. lib. 2, cap. 9.

[9] Idem Aristot. Pol. 5, cap. 8. Vitiosum quum soli pauperum liberi educantur ad labores, nobilium et divitum in voluptatibus et deliciis.

PAGE 105

[1] Quæ hæc injustitia ut nobilis quispiam, aut fænerator qui nihil agat, lautam et splendidam vitam agat, otio et deliciis, quum interim auriga, faber, agricola, quo respub. carere non potest, vitam adeo miseram ducat, ut pejor quam jumentorum sit ejus conditio? Iniqua resp. quæ dat parasitis, adulatoribus, inanium voluptatum artificibus generosis et otiosis tanta munera prodigit, at contra agricolis, carbonariis, aurigis, fabris, etc., nihil prospicit, sed eorum abusa labore florentis ætatis fame penset et ærumnis.—Mor. Utop. lib. 2.

[2] In Segovia nemo otiosus, nemo mendicus nisi per ætatem aut morbum opus facere non potest: nulli deest unde victum quærat, aut quo se exerceat. —Cypr. Echovius, Delic. Hispan. Nullus Genevæ otiosus, ne septennis puer.—Paulus Heutzner, Itiner.

[3] Athenæus, lib. 14.   [4] Simlerus de repub. Helvet.

[5] [Horsed and flogged in the Amphitheatre.] Spartian. Olim Romæ sic.

[6] He that provides not for his family is worse than a thief.—Paul.

[7] Alfredi lex. Utraque manus et lingua præcidatur, nisi eam capite redemerit.

[8] Si quis nuptam stuprarit, virga virilis ei præcidatur; si mulier, nasus et auricula præcidantur.—Alfredi lex. En leges ipsi Veneri Martique timendas.

[9] Pauperes non peccant, quum extrema necessitate coacti rem alienam capiunt.—Maldonat. Summula, quæst. 8, art. 3. Ego cum illis sentio qui licere putant a divite clam accipere, qui tenetur pauperi subvenire.—Emmanuel Sa, Aphor. confess.

[10] Lib. 2 de reg. Persarum.   [11] Lib. 23.

[12] Aliter Aristoteles, a man at twenty-five, a woman at twenty.—Polit.

[13] Lex olim Lycurgi, hodie Chinensium ; vide Plutarchum, Riccium, Hemingium, Arnisæum, Nevisanum, et alios de hac quæstione.

[14] Alfredus.

[15] Apud Lacones olim virgines sine dote nubebant.—Boter. lib. 3, cap. 3.

[16] Lege cautum non ita pridem apud Venetos, ne quis patricius dotem excederet 1500 coron.

[17] Bux. Synag. Jud. Sic Judæi. Leo Afer, Africæ descript. Ne sint aliter incontinentes ob reipub. bonum. Ut August. Cæsar orat. ad cælibes Romanos olim edocuit.

[18] Speciosissimi juvenes liberis dabunt operam.—Plato de Rep. lib. 5.

[19] Morbo laborans, qui in prolem facile diffunditur, ne genus humanum fœda contagione lædatur, juventute castratur, mulieres tales procul a consortio virorum ablegantur, etc.—Hector Boethius, Hist. lib. 1, de vet. Scotorum moribus.

[20] The Saxons exclude dumb, blind, leprous, and such-like persons from all inheritance, as we do fools.

[21] Ut olim Romani, Hispani hodie, etc.

[22] Riccius, lib. 11, cap. 5, de Sinarum expedit. Sic Hispani cogunt Mauros arma deponere. So it is in most Italian cities.

PAGE 106

[1] Idem Plato, 12 de legibus. It hath ever been immoderate, vide Guil. Stuckium, Antiq. convival. lib. 1, cap. 26.

[2] Plato, 6 de legibus.

[3] As those Lombards beyond seas, though with some reformation, mons pietatis, or bank of charity, as Malines terms it (cap. 33, Lex mercat. part. 2), that lend money upon easy pawns, or take money upon adventure for men's lives.

[4] That proportion will make merchandise increase, land dearer, and better improved, as he [Malines] hath judicially proved in his tract of usury, exhibited to the Parliament *anno* 1621.

[5] Hoc fere Zanchius, Com. in 4 cap. ad Ephes. Æquissimam vocat usuram et caritati Christianæ consentaneam, modo non exigant, etc., nec omnes dent ad fœnus, sed ii qui in pecuniis bona habent, et ob ætatem, sexum, artis alicujus ignorantiam, non possunt uti. Nec omnibus, sed mercatoribus et iis qui honeste impendent, etc.

[6] Idem apud Persas olim; lege Brisonium.

[7] Idem Plato de Rep.

PAGE 107

[1] Lib. 30. Optimum quidem fuerat eam patribus nostris mentem a diis datam esse, ut vos Italiæ, nos Africæ imperio contenti essemus. Neque enim Sicilia aut Sardinia satis digna pretia sunt pro tot classibus, etc.

[2] Claudian.   [3] Thucydides.

[4] A depopulatione, agrorum incendiis, et ejusmodi factis immanibus.—Plato.

[5] Hungar. dec. 1, lib. 9.

[6] Sesellius, lib. 2 de repub. Gal. Valde enim est indecorum, ubi quod præter opinionem accidit dicere, Non putaram, presertim si res præcaveri potuerit. Livius, lib. 1. Dion, lib. 2. Diodorus Siculus, lib. 2.

[7] Peragit tranquilla potestas, Quod violenta nequit.—Claudian.

[8] Bellum nec timendum nec provocandum.—Plin. Panegyr. Trajano.

[9] Lib. 3 Poet. cap. 19.   [10] Lib. 4 de repub. cap. 2.

[11] Peucer, lib. 1 de divinat.   [12] Camden, in Cheshire.

PAGE 108

[1] Iliad 6.

[2] Vide Puteani Comum, Goclenium de portentosis cœnis nostrorum temporum.

[3] Mirabile dictu est, quantum opsoniorum una domus singulis diebus absumat; sternuntur mensæ in omnes pene horas calentibus semper eduliis.—Descrip. Britan.

[4] Lib. 1 de rep. Gallorum. Quod tot lites et causæ forenses, aliæ ferantur ex aliis, in immensum producantur, et magnos sumptus requirant, unde fit ut juris administri plerumque nobilium possessiones adquirant, tum quod sumptuose vivant, et a mercatoribus absorbentur et splendissime vestiantur, etc.

PAGE 109

[1] Ter.   [2] Plaut. Captivi.   [3] Paling. Filius aut fur.

[4] Catus cum mure, duo galli simul in æde, Et glotes binæ nunquam vivunt sine lite.

[5] Res angusta domi.

[6] When pride and beggary meet in a family, they roar and howl, and cause as many flashes of discontents as fire and water, when they concur, make thunderclaps in the skies.

[7] Plautus, Aulular.

I—Q 886

Page 110

[1] Lib. 7, cap. 6.
[2] Pellitur in bellis sapientia, vi geritur res. Vetus proverbium, aut regem aut fatuum nasci oportere.
[3] Lib. 5 Hist. Rom. Similes tot bacculorum calculis, secundum computantis arbitrium, modo ærei sunt, modo aurei; ad nutum regis nunc beati sunt, nunc miseri.
[4] Ærumnosique Solones in Sa, 3 de miser. curialium.

Page 111

[1] Hoc cognomento cohonestati Romæ, qui cæteros mortales sapientia præstarent. Testis Plin. lib. 7, cap. 34.
[2] J. Dousæ Epod. lib. 1, cap. 13.
[3] Insanire parant certa ratione modoque; mad by the book they, etc.
[4] Juvenal.   [5] Solomon.
[6] Communis irrisor stultitiæ.   [7] [Objections and solutions.]
[8] Wit, whither wilt?   [9] Scaliger, exercitat. 324.   [10] Vit. ejus.

Page 112

[1] Ennius.
[2] Lucian. Ter mille drachmis olim empta; studens inde sapientiam adipiscetur.
[3] Epist. 21, lib. 1. Non oportet orationem sapientis esse politam aut sollicitam.
[4] Lib. 3, cap. 13. Multo anhelitu jactatione furentes pectus, frontem cædentes, etc.
[5] Lipsius. Voces sunt, præterea nihil.
[6] Lib. 30. Plus mali facere videtur qui oratione quam qui pretio quemvis corrumpit: nam, etc.
[7] In Gorg. Platonis.   [8] In Naugerio.
[9] Si furor sit Lyæus, etc., quoties furit, furit, furit, amans, bibens, et poeta, etc.

Page 113

[1] Morus, Utop. lib. 11.   [2] Macrob. Satur. 7, 16.
[3] Epist. 88.   [4] Lib. de causis corrup. artium.
[5] Lib. 2 in Ausonium, cap. 19 et 32.   [6] Edit. 7 volum. Jano Gutero.
[7] Aristophanis Ranis.   [8] Lib. de beneficiis.

Page 114

[1] Delirus et amens dicatur merito. Hor. Seneca.
[2] Ovid. Met.
[3] Plutarch. Amatorio est amor insanus.   [4] Epist. 39.
[5] Sylvæ nuptialis lib. 1, num. 11. Omnes mulieres ut plurimum stultæ
[6] Aristotle.
[7] Dolere se dixit quod tum vita egrederetur.
[8] Lib. 1, num. 11. Sapientia et divitiæ vix simul possideri possunt.
[9] They get their wisdom by eating pie-crust, some. [An allusion to the proverb, "Pie-lid makes people wise"—i.e. its removal reveals what the pie is made of.]
[10] χρήματα τοῖς θνητοῖς γίγνεται ἀφεοσύνη. Opes quidem mortabilus sun amentia.—Theognis.
[11] Fortuna nimium quem fovet, stultum facit.   [12] Job xxviii.

Page 115

[1] Mag. moral. lib. 2.   [2] Hor. lib. 1, sat. 4.
[3] Insana gula, insanæ substructiones, insanum venandi studium; discordia demens (Virg. Æn.).

⁴ Heliodorus Carthaginiensis ad extremum orbis sarcophago testamento me hic jussi condier, ut viderem an quis insanior ad me visendum usque ad hæc loca penetraret.—Ortelius, in Gad.
⁵ If it be his work, which Gaspar Veretus suspects.
⁶ Livy.   Ingentes virtutes, ingentia vitia.   ⁷ [Cosmo de' Medici.]

Page 116

¹ Hor.   Quisquis Ambitione mala aut argenti pallet amore, Quisquis luxuria, tristique superstitione.   Persius.
² Chronica Slavonica, ad annum 1257: de cujus pecunia jam incredibilia dixerunt.
³ A fool and his money are soon parted.
⁴ Orat. de imag.   Ambitiosus et audax naviget Anticyras.
⁵ Navis stulta, quæ continuo movetur, nautæ stulti qui se periculis exponunt, aqua insana quæ sic fremit, etc., aer jactatur, etc.; qui mari se committit stolidum unum terra fugiens, 40 mari invenit.—Gaspar Ens, Moros.
⁶ Cap. de alien. mentis.   ⁷ Deipnosophist. lib. 8.
⁸ Tibicines mente capti.—Erasm. Chi. 14, cer. 7.
⁹ Prov. xxxi.   Insana libido.   Hic rogo non furor est, non est hæc mentula demens?—Mart. ep. 76, lib. 3.
¹⁰ Mille puellarum et puerorum mille furores.
¹¹ Uter est insanior horum?—Hor.   Ovid, Virg., Plin.
¹² Plin. lib. 36.

Page 117

¹ Tacitus, 3 Annal.
² [The "good, doting citizen" in Jonson's Every Man out of His Humour.]
³ Ovid. 7 Met. E fungis nati homines ut olim Corinthi primævi illius loci accolæ, quia stolidi et fatui fungis nati dicebantur, idem et alibi dicas.
⁴ Famian. Strada: de bajulis, de marmore semisculptis.
⁵ Arrianus periplo maris Euxini portus ejus meminit, et Gillius, l. 3 de Bosphor. Thracio. Et laurus insana quæ allata in convivium convivas omnes insania affecit. Guliel. Stuckius, Comment., etc. [The "insane laurel" is probably *Azalea pontica*, the honey from which drove Xenophon's soldiers out of their wits (*Anab.* 4, 8, 20).]
⁶ Lepidum poema sic inscriptum [a witty poem so entitled].

Page 118

¹ Stultitiam simulare non potes nisi taciturnitate.
² Extortus non cruciatur, ambustus non læditur, prostratus in lucta, non vincitur; non fit captivus ab hoste venundatus.   Etsi rugosus, senex dentulus, luscus, deformis, formosus tamen, et deo similis, felix, dives, rex nullius egens, etsi denario non sit dignus.
³ Illum contendunt non injuria affici, non insania, non inebriari, quia virtus non eripitur ob constantes comprehensiones.—Lips. Phys. Stoic. lib. 3, diffi. 18.
⁴ Taraeus Hebius, epig. 102, lib. 8.   ⁵ Hor.
⁶ Fratres sancti Roseæ Crucis.
⁷ An sint, quales sint, unde nomen illud asciverint.
⁸ Turri Babel.
⁹ Omnium artium et scientiarum instaurator.
¹⁰ Divinus ille vir. Auctor notarum in Epist. Rog. Bacon. ed. Hambur. 608.
¹¹ Sapientiæ desponsati.

Page 119

[1] Justus is the first name of Lipsius and the quotation refers to him.
[2] Solus hic est sapiens, alii volitant velut umbræ.
[3] In ep. ad Balthas. Moretum.
[4] Rejectiunculæ ad Patavium; Felinus cum reliquis.
[5] Magnum virum sequi est sapere, some think; others desipere. Catul.
[6] Plaut. Menæchmi.   [7] Juv. Sat. 14.
[8] Or to send for a cook to the Anticyræ, to make hellebore pottage, settle-brain pottage.
[9] Aliquantulum tamen inde me solabor, quod una cum multis et sapientibus et celeberrimis viris ipse insipiens sim, quod se Menippus Luciani in Necyomantia.

Page 120

[1] Petronius, in Catalect.
[2] That I mean of Andr. Vale. Apolog. manip. lib. 1 et 26 apol.
[3] Hæc affectio nostris temporibus frequentissima.
[4] Cap. 15 de Mel.
[5] De anima. Nostro hoc sæculo morbus frequentissimus.
[6] Consult. 98.   Adeo nostris temporibus frequenter ingruit ut nullus fere ab ejus labe immunis reperiatur et omnium fere morborum occasio existat.

Page 121

[1] Mor. Encom. Si quis calumnietur levius esse quam decet theologum, aut mordacius quam deceat Christianum.
[2] Hor. Sat. 4, lib. 1.
[3] Epi. ad Dorpium de Moria. Si quispiam offendatur et sibi vindicet, non habet quod expostulet cum eo qui scripsit; ipse si volet, secum agat injuriam, utpote sui proditor, qui declaravit hoc ad se proprie pertinere.
[4] Si quis se læsum clamabit, aut conscientiam prodit suam, aut certe metum.—Phædr. lib. 3 Æsop. Fab.

Page 122

[1] Hor.   [2] Mart. lib. 7, 25.
[3] Ut lubet feriat, abstergant hos ictus Democriti pharmaco.
[4] Rusticorum dea præesse vacantibus et otiosis putabatur, cui post labores agricola sacrificabat.—Plin. lib. 3, cap. 12. Ovid. lib. 6. Fast. Jam quoque cum fiunt antiquæ sacra Vacunæ, Ante Vacunales stantque sedentque focos. Rosinus. [Vacuna was the goddess of rural leisure.]
[5] Ter. Prol. Eunuch.   [6] [A gesture of anger.]
[7] Ariost. lib. 39, staff 58.
[8] Ut enim ex studiis gaudium sic studia ex hilaritate proveniunt.—Plinius Maximo suo, Ep. lib. 8.

Page 123

[1] Annal. 15.
[2] Sir Francis Bacon in his Essays, now Viscount St. Albans.
[3] Quod Probus, Persii βιογράφος, virginali verecundia Persium fuisse dicit, ego, etc.
[4] Quas aut incuria fudit, Aut humana parum cavit natura.—Hor.
[5] Prol. quer. Plaut.

Page 124

[1] Si me commorit, melius non tangere clamo.—Hor.
[2] Hippoc. epist. Damageto. Accersitus sum ut Democritum tanquam insanum curarem, sed postquam conveni, non per Jovem desipientia negotium, sed rerum omnium receptaculum deprehendi, ejusque ingenium

demiratus sum. Abderitanos vero tanquam non sanos accusavi, veratri
potione ipsos potius eguisse dicens.
  [3] Mart.

Page 130

[1] Magnum miraculum.
[2] Mundi epitome, naturæ deliciæ.
[3] Finis rerum omnium, cui sublunaria serviunt.—Scalig. exercit. 365,
sec. 3. Vales. de sacr. Phil. cap. 5.
[4] Ut in numismate Cæsaris imago, sic in homine Dei. [5] Gen. i.
[6] Imago mundi in corpore, Dei in anima. Exemplumque dei quisque
est in imagine parva.
  [7] Eph. iv, 24. [8] Palanterius. [9] Ps. xlix, 20.
[10] Lascivia superat equum, impudentia canem, astu vulpem, furore
leonem.—Chrys. 23 Gen.
[11] Gen. iii, 13.

Page 131

[1] Ecclus. xl, 1, 2, 3, 4, 5, 8. [2] Gen. iii, 17.
[3] Illa cadens tegmen manibus decussit, et unà Perniciem immisit miseris
mortalibus atram.—Hesiod. Oper.
  [4] Hom. 5 ad pop. Antioch.
[5] Ps. cvii, 17. [6] Prov. i, 27.
[7] Quod autem crebrius bella concutiant, quod sterilitas et fames
sollicitudinem cumulent, quod sævientibus morbis valitudo frangitur,
quod humanum genus luis populatione vastatur; ob peccatum omnia.
—Cypr.
[8] Si raro desuper pluvia descendat, si terra situ pulveris squaleat, si
vix jejunas et pallidas herbas sterilis gleba producat, si turbo vineam
debilitet, etc.—Cypr.

Page 132

[1] Mat. xiv, 3.
[2] Philostratus, lib. 8 vit. Apollonii. Injustitiam ejus, et sceleratus
nuptias, et cætera quæ præter rationem fecerat, morborum causas dixit.
  [3] 16. [4] 18. [5] 20. [6] Verse 27.
[7] 28. Deus quos diligit, castigat. [8] Isa. v, 13, 25.
[9] Nostræ salutis avidus continenter aures vellicat, ac calamitate subinde
nos exercet.—Levinus Lemn. lib. 2, cap. 29, de occult. nat. mir.
[10] Vexatio dat intellectum. Isa. xxviii, 19.

Page 133

[1] Lib. 7. Cum judicio mores et facta recognoscit et se intuetur. Dum
fero languorem, fero religionis amorem. Expers languoris non sum
memor hujus amoris.
[2] Summum esse totius philosophiæ, ut tales esse sani perseveremus, quales
nos futuros esse infirmi profitemur.
[3] Petrarch. [4] Prov. iii, 12.
[5] Hor. Epist. lib. 1, 4.
[6] Deut. viii, 11. Qui stat videat ne cadat.
[7] Quanto majoribus beneficiis a Deo cumulatur, tanto obligatiorem se
debitorem fateri.

Page 134

[1] Boterus de inst. urbium.
[2] Lege hist. relationem Lod. Frois de rebus Japonicis ad annum 1596.
[3] Guicciard. descript. Belg. anno 1421.
[4] Giraldus Cambrensis. [5] Janus Dousa, Ep. lib. 1, car. 10.
[6] Munster, lib. 3, Cos. cap. 462. [7] Buchanan. Baptist.

Page 135

[1] Homo homini lupus, homo homini dæmon.
[2] Ovid. Trist. lib. 5, eleg. 8.   [3] Miscent aconita novercæ.
[4] Lib. 2, epist. 2, ad Donatum.   [5] Ezech. xviii, 2.
[6] Hor. lib. 3, Od. 6.   [7] 2 Tim. iii, 2.

Page 136

[1] Ezech. xviii, 31.   [2] 1 Macc. iii, 12.
[3] Part. 1, sec. 2, memb. 2.
[4] Nequitia est quæ te non sinet esse senem.   [5] Homer. Iliad.

Page 137

[1] Intemperantia, luxus, ingluvies, et infinita hujusmodi flagitia, quæ divinas pœnas merentur.—Crato.
[2] Fern. Path. lib. 1, cap. 1.   Morbus est affectus contra naturam corporis insidens.
[3] Fuchs. Instit. lib. 3, sect. 1, cap. 3: a quo primum vitiatur actio.
[4] Dissolutio fœderis in corpore, ut sanitas est consummatio.
[5] Lib. 4, cap. 2. Morbus est habitus contra naturam, qui usum ejus, etc.
[6] Cap. 11, lib. 7.   [7] Horat. lib. 1, ode 3.
[8] Cap. 50, lib. 7.   Centum et quinque vixit annos sine ullo incommodo.
[9] Intus mulso, foras oleo.
[10] Exemplis genitur. præfixis Ephemer. cap. de infirmitat.

Page 138

[1] Qui, quoad pueritiæ ultimam memoriam recordari potest, non meminit se ægrotum decubuisse.
[2] Lib. de vita longa.   [3] Opera et Dies.
[4] See Fernelius, Path. lib. 1, cap. 9, 10, 11, 12; Fuchsius, Instit. lib. 3, sect. 1, cap. 7; Wecker, Synt.
[5] Præfat. de morbis capitis.   In capite ut variæ habitant partes, ita variæ querelæ ibi eveniunt.
[6] Of which read Heurnius, Montaltus, Hildesheim, Quercetan, Jason Pratensis, etc.

Page 139

[1] [?caros, torpor.]
[2] ["A distemper accompanied with a strong inclination to sleep, without being able to do so."—Bailey's Dictionary.]
[3] Cap. 2 de melanchol.
[4] Cap. 2 de physiologia sagarum. Quod alii minus recte fortasse dixerint nos examinare, melius dijudicare, corrigere studeamus.
[5] Cap. 4 de mel.   [6] Art. Med. cap. 7.

Page 140

[1] Plerique medici uno complexu perstringunt hos duos morbos, quod ex eadem causa oriantur, quodque magnitudine et modo solum distent, et alter gradus ad alterum existat.—Jason Pratens.
[2] Lib. Med.   [3] Pars maniæ mihi videtur.
[4] Insanus est, qui ætate debita et tempore debito per se, non momentaneam et fugacem, ut vini, solani, hyoscyami, sed confirmatam habet impotentiam bene operandi circa intellectum.—Lib 2, de intellectione.
[5] Of which read Felix Plater, cap. 3 de mentis alienatione.

Page 141

[1] Lib. 6, cap. 11.   [2] Lib. 3, cap. 16.
[3] Cap. 9, Art. med.   [4] De præstig. dæmonum, lib. 3, cap. 21.
[5] Observat. lib. 10, de morbis cerebri, cap. 15.

⁶ Hippocrates, lib. de insania.
⁷ Lib. 8, cap. 22.   Homines interdum lupos fieri; et contra.
⁸ Met. lib. 1.   ⁹ Cap. de mania.
¹⁰ Ulcerata crura, sitis ipsis adest immodica, pallidi, lingua sicca.
¹¹ Cap, 9, art. Hydrophobia.

PAGE 142

¹ Lib. 3, cap. 9.   ² Lib. 7, de venenis.
³ Lib. 3, cap. 13, de morbis acutis.   ⁴ Spicil. 2.
⁵ Sckenkius, 7 lib. de venenis.   ⁶ Lib. de hydrophobia.
⁷ Observat. lib. 10, 25.
⁸ Lascivam choream.—Tom. 4, de morbis amentium, tract. 1.
⁹ Eventu, ut plurimum rem, ipsam comprobante.

PAGE 143

¹ Lib. 1, cap. de mania.   ² Cap. 3 de mentis alienat.
³ Cap. 4 de mel.   ⁴ Part. 3.

PAGE 144

¹ De quo homine securitas, de quo certum gaudium? Quocunque se convertit, in terrenis rebus amaritudinem animi inveniet.—Aug. in Psal. viii, 5.
² Job. xiv, 1.
³ Omni tempore Socratem eodem vultu videri, sive domum rediret, sive domo egrederetur.
⁴ Lib. 7, cap. 1.   Natus in florentissima totius orbis civitate, nobilissimis parentibus, corporis vires habuit et rarissimas animi dotes, uxorem conspicuam, pudicam, felices liberos, consulare decus, sequentes triumphos, etc.
⁵ Ælian.   ⁶ Homer. Iliad.
⁷ Lipsius, cent. 3, ep. 45.   Ut cœlum, sic nos homines sumus: illud ex intervallo nubibus obducitur et obscuratur.   In rosario flores spinis intermixti.   Vita similis aeri, udum modo, sudum, tempestas, serenitas: ita vices rerum sunt, præmia gaudiis, et sequaces curæ.
⁸ Lucretius, lib. 4, 1134.
⁹ Prov. xiv, 13.   Extremum gaudii luctus occupat.
¹⁰ Natalitia, inquit, celebrantur, nuptiæ hic sunt; at ibi quid celebratur quod non dolet, quod non transit?

PAGE 145

¹ Apuleius, 4 Florid.   Nihil quicquam homini tam prosperum divinitus datum, quin ei admixtum sit aliquid difficultatis ut etiam amplissima quaque lætitia, subsit quæpiam vel parva querimonia conjugatione quadam mellis et fellis.
² Caduca nimirum et fragilia, et puerilibus consentanea crepundiis, sunt ista quæ vires et opes humanæ vocantur; affluunt subito, repente dilabuntur, nullo in loco, nulla in persona, stabilibus nixa radicibus consistunt, sed incertissimo flatu fortunæ quos in sublime extulerunt improviso recursu destitutos in profundo miseriarum valle miserabiliter immergunt.—Valerius, lib. 6, cap. 11.
³ Huic seculo parum aptus es, aut potius omnium nostrorum conditionem gnoras, quibus reciproco quodam nexu, etc.—Lorchanus Gallobelgicus, ib. 3, ad annum 1598.
⁴ Horum omnia studia dirigi debent, ut humana fortiter feramus.
⁵ 2 Tim. ii, 3.
⁶ Epist. 96, lib. 10.   Affectus frequentes contemptique morbum faciunt. Distillatio una nec adhuc in morem adaucta, tussim facit, assidua et violenta phthisim.

PAGE 146

[1] Calidum ad octo: frigidum ad octo.
[2] Una hirundo non facit æstatem.   [One swallow doesn't make a summer.]
[3] Lib. 1, cap. 6.
[4] Fuchsius, lib. 3, sec. 1, cap. 7.   Hildesheim, fol. 130.
[5] Psal. cxxxix, 14, 15.

PAGE 147

[1] De anima.   Turpe enim est homini ignorare sui corporis (ut ita dicam) ædificium, præsertim cum ad valetudinem et mores hæc cognitio plurimum conducat.
[2] De usu part.   [3] History of Man.
[4] Dr. Crooke.   [5] In Syntaxi.
[6] De anima.   [7] Instit. lib. 1.
[8] Physiol. lib. 1, 2.   [9] Anat. lib. 1, cap. 18.
[10] In Micro.   Succos, sine quibus animal sustentari non potest.
[11] Morbosos humores.

PAGE 148

[1] Spiritalis anima.

PAGE 149

[1] Laurentius, cap. 20, lib. 1, Anat.
[2] In these they observe the beating of the pulse.

PAGE 150

[1] Cujus est pars similaris a vi cutifica, ut interiora muniat.—Capivac. Anat. pag. 252.
[2] Anat. lib. 1, cap. 19.   Celebris est et pervulgata partium divisio in principes et ignobiles partes.

PAGE 151

[1] Dr. Crooke, out of Galen, and others.
[2] Vos vero veluti in templum ac sacrarium quoddam vos duci putetis, etc. Suavis et utilis cognitio.
[3] Lib. 1, cap. 12, sect. 5.

PAGE 153

[1] Hæc res est præcipue digna admiratione, quod tanta affectuum varietate cietur cor, quod omnes res tristes et lætæ statim corda feriunt et movent.
[2] Physio. lib. 1, cap. 8.
[3] Ut orator regi: sic pulmo vocis instrumentum annectitur cordi, etc.—Melancth.

PAGE 154

[1] De anima, cap. 1.
[2] Scalig. Exerc. 307; Tolet. in lib. de anima, cap. 1, etc.
[3] Lib. de anima, cap. 1.   [4] Tuscul. quæst.
[5] Lib. 6, Doct. Val. Gentil. cap. 13, pag. 1216.   [6] Aristot.
[7] Anima quæque intelligimus, et tamen quæ sit ipsa intelligere non valemus.
[8] Spiritualem animam a reliquis distinctam tuetur, etiam in cadavere inhærentem post mortem per aliquot menses.

PAGE 155

[1] Lib. 3, cap. 31.
[2] Cœlius, lib. 2, cap. 31; Plutarch in Gryllo; Lips. Cen. 1, ep. 50; Jossius de risu et fletu; Averroes, Campanella, etc.

³ Philip. de anima, cap. 1. Cœlius, 20 Antiq. cap. 3. Plutarch. de placit. philos.

⁴ De vit. et mort. part. 2, cap. 3, prop. 1; De vit. et mort. 2, cap. 22.

⁵ Nutritio est alimenti transmutatio, viro naturalis.—Scal. Exerc. 101, sec. 17.

⁶ See more of attraction in Scal. Exer. 343.

PAGE 156

¹ Vita consistit in calido et humido.

PAGE 158

¹ Lumen est actus perspicui. Lumen a luce provenit, lux est in corpore lucido.

² In Phædone.　　³ De pract. philos. 4.

⁴ Saturn. 7, cap. 14.　　⁵ Lac. cap. 8 de opif. Dei, 1.　　⁶ Lib. 19, cap. 2.

PAGE 159

¹ Phys. lib. 5, cap. 8.

PAGE 160

¹ Exercit. 280.

PAGE 161

¹ T[homas] W[right], Jesuit, in his Passions of the Mind.

² Velcurio.

PAGE 162

¹ Nervi a spiritu moventur, spiritus ab anima.—Melanct.

² Velcurio.　Jucundum et anceps subjectum.

³ Goclenius in Ψυχολ. pag. 302; Bright in Phys. Scrib. lib. 1; David Crusius, Melancthon, Hippius Heurnius, Levinus Lemnius, etc.

⁴ Lib. an mores sequantur, etc.

⁵ Cæsar, 6 Com.

⁶ Read Æneas Gazæus' dial. of the immortality of the soul.

PAGE 163

¹ Ovid. Met. 15.　　　　² In Gallo.

³ Ovid. Met. 15.　　　　⁴ Nicephorus, Hist. lib. 10, cap. 35.

⁵ Phædo.　　　　⁶ Claudian, lib. 1. de rap. Proserp.

⁷ [Pliny the Elder; "Uncle Pliny," as Burton calls him elsewhere.]

⁸ Hæc quæstio multos per annos varie ac mirabiliter impugnata, etc.

⁹ Colerus, ibid.

PAGE 164

¹ De eccles. dog. cap. 16.　　² Ovid. 4 Met.

³ Bonorum lares, malorum vero larvas et lemures.

⁴ Some say at three days, some six weeks, others otherwise.

PAGE 165

¹ Melancthon.

² Nihil in intellectu, quod non prius fuerat in sensu.—Velcurio.

PAGE 166

¹ [=*tabula rasa*, a smooth tablet, "clean slate."]

² The pure part of the conscience.

³ Quod tibi fieri non vis, alteri ne feceris.

I—*Q 886

PAGE 167

[1] Res ab intellectu monstratas recipit, vel rejicit; approbat, vel improbat.—Philip. Ignoti nulla cupido.

[2] Melancthon. Operationes plerumque feræ, etsi libera sit illa in essentia sua.

[3] In civilibus libera, sed non in spiritualibus.—Osiander.

[4] Tota voluntas aversa a Deo. Omnis homo mendax.

[5] Virg.

[6] Vel propter ignorantiam, quod bonis studiis non sit instructa mens ut debuit, aut divinis præceptis exculta.

PAGE 168

[1] Medea, Ovid.   [2] Ovid.   Seneca, Hipp.

PAGE 169

[1] Melancholicos vocamus, quos exuperantia vel pravitas melancholiæ ita male habet, ut inde insaniant vel in omnibus, vel in pluribus, iisque manifestis sive ad rectam rationem, voluntatem pertinent, vel electionem, vel intellectus operationes.

[2] Pessimum et pertinacissimum morbum qui homines in bruta degenerare cogit.

[3] Panth. Med.

[4] Angor animi in una contentione defixus, absque febre.

PAGE 170

[1] Cap. 16, lib. 1.

[2] Eorum definitio morbus quid non sit, potius quam quid sit, explicat.

[3] Animæ functiones imminuuntur in fatuitate, tolluntur in mania, depravantur solum in melancholia.—Herc. de Sax. cap. 1, tract. de Melanch.

[4] Cap. 4 de mel.

[5] Per consensum sive per essentiam.   [6] Cap. 4 de mel.

PAGE 171

[1] Sec. 7, de mor. vulgar. lib. 6.   [2] Spicil. de melancholia.

[3] Cap. 3 de mel. Pars affecta cerebrum sive per consensum, sive per cerebrum contingat, et procerum auctoritate et ratione stabilitur.

[4] Lib. de mel. Cor vero vicinitatis ratione una afficitur, ac septum transversum ac stomachus cum dorsali spina, etc.

[5] Lib. 1, cap. 10. Subjectum est cerebrum interius.

[6] Raro quisquam tumorem effugit lienis, qui hoc morbo afficitur.—Piso.

[7] See Donat. ab Altomar.

[8] Facultas imaginandi, non cogitandi, nec memorandi læsa hic.

[9] Lib. 3, fen. 1, tract. 4, cap. 8.   [10] Lib. 3, cap. 5.

[11] Lil. Med. cap. 19, part. 2. Tract. 15, cap. 2.

[12] Hildesheim, Spicil. 2 de melanc. fol. 207, et fol. 127. Quandoque etiam rationalis si affectus inveteratus sit.

PAGE 172

[1] Lib. posthumo de melanc. edit. 1620. Deprivatur fides, discursus, opinio, etc., per vitium imaginationis, ex accidenti.

[2] Qui parvum caput habent, insensati plerique sunt.—Arist. in Physiognomia.

[3] Aretæus, lib. 3, cap. 5.

[4] Qui prope statum sunt.—Aret. Mediis convenit ætatibus.—Piso.

[5] De quartano.   [6] Lib. 1, part. 2, cap. 11.

[7] Primus ad melancholiam non tam mœstus sed et hilares, jocosi, cachinnantes, irrisores, et qui plerumque præubri sunt.

[8] Qui sunt subtilis ingenii, et multæ perspicacitatis, de facili incidunt in melancholiam.—Lib. 1 Cont. tract. 9.

[9] Nunquam sanitate mentis excidit aut dolore capitur.—Erasmus.

[10] In laud. calvit.

[11] Vacant conscientiæ carnificina, nec pudefiunt, nec verentur, nec dilacerantur millibus curarum, quibus tota vita obnoxia est.

Page 173

[1] Lib. 1, tract. 3, contradic. 18.   [2] Lib. 1, cont. 21.

[3] Bright, cap. 16.   [4] Lib. 1, cap. 6, de sanit. tuenda.

[5] Quisve aut qualis sit humor aut quæ istius differentiæ, et quomodo gignantur in corpore, scrutandum, hac enim re multi veterum laboraverunt, nec facile accipere ex Galeno sententiam ob loquendi varietatem.—Leon. Jacch. Com. in 9 Rhasis, cap. 15, cap. 16 in 9 Rhasis.

[6] Lib. postum. de melan. edit. Venetiis 1620, cap. 7 et 8. Ab intemperie calida, humida, etc.

[7] Secundum magis aut minus si in corpore fuerit, ad intemperiem plusquam corpus salubriter ferre poterit: inde corpus morbosum efficitur.

[8] Lib. 1 Controvers. cap. 21.   [9] Lib. 1, sect. 4, cap. 4.

[10] Consil. 26.   [11] Lib. 2 Contradic. cap. 11.

[12] De feb. tract. diff. 2, cap. 1. Non est negandum ex hac fieri melancholicos.

Page 174

[1] In Syntax.

[2] Varie aduritur, et miscetur, unde variæ amentium species.—Melanct

[3] Humor frigidus delirii causa, furoris calidus, etc.

[4] Lib. i, cap. 10, de affect. cap.

[5] Nigrescit hic humor, aliquando supercalefactus, aliquando superfrigefactus, cap. 7.

[6] Humor hic niger aliquando præter modum calefactus, et alias refrigeratus evadit: nam recentibus carbonibus ei quid simile accidit, qui durante flamma pellucidissime candent, ea extincta prorsus nigrescunt.—Hippocrates.

[7] Guianerius, diff. 2, cap. 7.

[8] Non est mania, nisi extensa melancholia.   [9] Cap. 6, lib. 1.

Page 175

[1] 2 Ser. 2, cap. 9. Morbus hic est omnifarius.

[2] Species indefinitæ sunt.

[3] Si aduratur naturalis melancholia, alia fit species, si sanguis alia, si flava bilis, alia, diversa a primis: maxima est inter has differentia, et tot doctorum sententiæ, quot ipsi numero sunt.

[4] Tract. de mel. cap. 7.

[5] Quædam incipiens, quædam consummata.

[6] Cap. de humor. lib. de anima. Varie aduritur et miscetur ipsa melancholia, unde variæ amentium species.

[7] Cap. 16, in 9 Rhasis.

[8] Laurentius, cap. 4 de mel.   [9] Cap. 13.

Page 176

[1] 480 et 116 consult. consil. 12.   [2] Hildesheim, Spicil. 2, fol. 166.

[3] Trincavellius, tom. 2, consil. 15 et 16.

[4] Cap. 13, tract. posth. de melan.   [5] Guarion. Cons. med. 2.

Page 177

[1] Laboravit per essentiam et a toto corpore.

[2] Machiavel, etc. Smithus, de rep. Angl. cap. 8, lib. 1; Buscoldus, Discurs. Polit. discurs. 5, cap. 7; Arist. lib. 3 Polit. cap. ult; Keckerm., alii, etc.

³ Lib. 6.

⁴ Primo Artis curativæ.

⁵ Nostri primum sit propositi affectionum causas indagare; res ipsa hortari videtur, nam alioqui earum curatio manca et inutilis esset.

⁶ Path. lib. 1, cap. 11. Rerum cognoscere causas, medicis imprimis necessarium, sine qua nec morbum curare, nec præcavere licet.

⁷ Tanta enim morbi varietas ac differentia ut non facile dignoscatur, unde initium morbus sumpserit.—Melanelius, e Galeno.

⁸ Felix qui potuit rerum cognoscere causas.

PAGE 178

¹ 1 Sam. xvi, 14.   ² Dan. v, 21.

³ Lactant. Instit. lib. 2, cap. 8.

⁴ Mente captus, et summo animi mœrore consumptus.

⁵ Munster. Cosmog. lib. 4, cap. 43. De cœlo substernebantur, tanquam insani de saxis præcipitati, etc.

⁶ Livius, lib. 38.

⁷ Gaguin. lib. 3, cap. 4. Quod Dionysii corpus discooperuerat, in insaniam incidit.

⁸ Idem, lib. 9, sub Carol. 6. Sacrorum contemptor, templi foribus effractis, dum s. Johannis argenteum simulacrum rapere contendit, simulacrum aversâ facie dorsum ei versat, nec mora sacrilegus mentis inops, atque in semet insaniens in proprios artus desævit.

⁹ Giraldus Cambrensis, lib. 1, cap. 1, Itinerar. Cambriæ.

PAGE 179

¹ Delrio, tom. 3 lib. 6, sect. 3, quæst. 3.   ² Psal. xliv, 1.

³ Lib. 8, cap. de Hierar.   ⁴ Claudian.

⁵ [Thou hast conquered, O Galilean.]

⁶ De Babila Martyre.   ⁷ Lib. 1, cap. 5, Prog.

⁸ Lib. 1, de abditis rerum causis.

⁹ Respons. med. resp. 12.   ¹⁰ 1 Pet. v, 6.

PAGE 180.

¹ Lib. 1, cap. 7, de orbis concordia. In nulla re major fuit altercatio, major obscuritas, minor opinionum concordia, quam de dæmonibus et substantiis separatis.

² Lib. 3 de Trinit. cap. 1.

³ Pererius in Genesin, lib. 4, in cap. iii, v. 23.

⁴ See Strozzius Cicogna, Omnifariæ mag. lib. 2, cap. 15, Jo. Aubanus, Bredenbachius.

PAGE 181

¹ Angelus per superbiam separatus a Deo, qui in veritate non stetit.—Austin.

² Nihil aliud sunt dæmones quam nudæ animæ quæ corpore deposito priorem miserati vitam, cognatis succurrunt commoti misericordia, etc.

³ De Deo Socratis.

⁴ He lived five hundred years since.

PAGE 182

¹ Apuleius. Spiritus animalia sunt animo passibilia, mente rationalia, corpore aeria, tempore sempiterna.

² Nutriuntur, et excrementa habent; quod pulsata doleant solido percussa corpore.

³ Lib. 4 Theol. nat. fol. 535.

⁴ Cyprianus, in Epist. Montes etiam et animalia transferri possunt: as the devil did Christ to the top of the pinnacle; and witches are often translated. See more in Strozzius Cicogna, lib. 3, cap. 4, Omnif. mag. Per aera subducere et in sublime corpora ferre possunt.—Biarmannus. Percussi dolent et uruntur in conspicuos cineres.—Agrippa, lib. 3, cap. 18, de occult. philos.

⁵ [Bel and the Dragon, 36.]

Page 183

¹ Agrippa de occult. philos. lib. 3, cap. 18.
² Part. 3, sect. 2, mem. 1, subs. 1, Love Melancholy.
³ Genial. dierum. Ita sibi visum et compertum quum prius an essent ambigeret. Fidem suam liberet.
⁴ Lib. 1 de verit. fidei. Benzo, etc.

Page 184

¹ Lib. de divinatione et magia.
² Cap. 8. Transportavit in Livoniam cupiditate videndi, etc.
³ Sic Hesiodus, de nymphis, vivere dicit 10 ætates phœnicum, vel 9720. [See Pantagruel's discourse on the subject of Rabelais, iv. 27.]
⁴ Custodes hominum et provinciarum, etc., tanto meliores hominibus, quanto hi brutis animantibus.
⁵ Præsides, pastores, gubernatores hominum, ut illi animalium.

Page 185

¹ Natura familiares ut canes hominibus; multi aversantur et abhorrent.
² Ab homine plus distant quam homo ab ignobilissimo verme, et tamen quidam ex his ab hominibus superantur ut homines a feris, etc.
³ Cibo et potu uti et venere cum hominibus ac tandem mori.—Cicogna, part. 1, lib. 2, cap. 3.
⁴ Plutarch. de defect. oraculorum.
⁵ Lib. de Zilphis et Pigmæis.
⁶ Dii gentium a Constantio profligati sunt, etc.
⁷ Octavian. dial. Judæorum deum fuisse Romanorum numinibus una cum gente captivum.
⁸ Omnia spiritibus plena, et ex eorum concordia et discordia omnes boni et mali effectus promanant, omnia humana reguntur: paradoxa veterum de quo Cicogna, Omnif. mag. lib. 2, cap. 3.

Page 186

¹ Oves quas abacturus erat in quascunque formas vertebat. Pausanias, Hyginus.
² Austin in lib. 2 de Gen. ad literam, cap. 17. Partim quia subtilioris sensus acumine, partim scientia callidiore vigent et experientia propter magnam longitudinem vitæ, partim ab angelis discunt, etc.
³ Lib. 3 Omnif. mag. cap. 3. ⁴ Lib. 18 Quest.
⁵ Quum tanta sit et tam profunda spirituum scientia, mirum non est tot tantasque res visu admirabiles ab ipsis patrari, et quidem rerum naturalium ope quas multo melius intelligunt, multoque peritius suis locis et temporibus applicare norunt, quam homo.—Cicogna.
⁶ Aventinus. Quicquid interdiu exhauriebatur, noctu explebatur. Inde pavefacti curatores, etc.
⁷ In lib. 2 de anima, text. 29. Homerus discriminatim omnes spiritus dæmones vocat.

PAGE 187

[1] A Jove ad inferos pulsi, etc.

[2] De Deo Socratis. Adest mihi divina sorte dæmonium quoddam a prima pueritia me secutum; sæpe dissuadet, impellit nonnunquam instar vocis. —Plato.

[3] Agrippa, lib. 3 de occul. ph. cap. 18, Zanch., Pictorius, Pererius, Cicogna, lib. 3, cap. 1.

[4] Vasa iræ, cap. 13.

[5] Quibus datum est nocere terræ et mari, etc.

PAGE 188

[1] [Meririm, according to Cornelius Agrippa.]

[2] Physiol. Stoicorum e Senec. lib. 1, cap. 28.

[3] Usque ad lunam animas esse ætherias vocarique heroas, lares, genios.

[4] Mart. Capella.

[5] Nihil vacuum ab his ubi vel capillum in aerem vel aquam jacias.

[6] Lib. de Zilph.   [7] Palingenius.

[8] Lib. 7, cap. 34 et 35, Syntax. art. mirab.

PAGE 189

[1] Comment in dial. Plat. de amore, cap. 5. Ut sphæra quælibet super nos, ita præstantiores habent habitatores suæ sphæræ consortes, ut habet nostra.

[2] Lib. de anima. et dæmone. Med. inter deos et homines, diva ad nos et nostra æqualiter ad deos ferunt.

[3] Saturninas et Joviales accolas. [The reference is to Kepler's *Dissertatio cum Nuncio Sidereo*, in which he discourses with a messenger from the stars concerning Galileo's discoveries.]

[4] In loca detrusi sunt infra cœlestes orbes in aerem scilicet et infra ubi Judicio generali reservantur.

[5] Q. 36, art. 9.

PAGE 190

[1] Virg. Ecl. 8.   [2] Æn. 4.

[3] Austin. Hoc dixi, ne quis existimet habitare ibi mala dæmonia ubi Solem et Lunam et Stellas Deus ordinavit, et alibi nemo arbitraretur Dæmonem cœlis habitare cum Angelis suis unde lapsum credimus. Idem Zanch. lib. 4, cap. 3, de Angel. malis; Pererius in Gen. cap. 6, lib. 8, in ver. 2.

[4] Peregrin. Hierosol.

PAGE 191

[1] Domus diruunt, muros dejiciunt, immiscent se turbinibus et procellis, et pulverem instar columnæ evehunt.—Cicogna, lib. 5, cap. 5.

[2] Quæst. in Liv.

[3] De præstigiis dæmonum, cap. 16. Convelli culmina videmus, prosterni sata, etc.

[4] De bello Neapolitano, lib. 5.

[5] Suffitibus gaudent. Idem Just. Mart. Apol. pro Christianis.

[6] In Dei imitationem, saith Eusebius.

[7] Dii gentium dæmonia, etc.; ego in eorum statuas pellexi.

[8] Et nunc sub divorum nomine coluntur a pontificiis.

PAGE 192

[1] Lib. 11 de rerum var.

[2] Lib. 3, cap. 3, de magis et veneficis, etc.   [3] Nereides.

[4] Lib. de Zilphis.   [5] Lib. 3.

[6] Pro salute hominum excubare se simulant, sed in eorum perniciem omnia moliuntur.—Aust.

[7] Dryades, Oreades, Hamadryades.

[8] Elvas Olaus vocat [Olaus calls them elves], lib. 3.

Page 193

[1] Part 1, cap. 19.
[2] Lib. 3, cap. 11. Elvarum choreas Olaus, lib. 3, vocat. Saltum adeo profunde in terras imprimunt, ut locus insigni deinceps virore orbicularis sit, et gramen non pereat.
[3] Lib. de Zilph. et Pigmæis. Olaus, lib. 3.
[4] Lib. 7, cap. 14. Qui et in famulitio viris et feminis inserviunt, conclavia scopis purgant, patinas mundant, ligna portant, equos curant, etc.
[5] Ad ministeria utuntur.
[6] Where treasure is hid (as some think) or some murder, or such-like villainy committed.
[7] Lib. 16, de rerum varietat.
[8] Quidam lemures domesticis instrumentis noctu ludunt: patinas, ollas, cantharas, et alia vasa dejiciunt, et quidam voces emittunt, ejulant, risum emittunt, etc.; ut canes nigri, feles, variis formis, etc.

Page 194

[1] Vel spiritus sunt hujusmodi damnatorum, vel e purgatorio, vel ipsi dæmones.—Cap. 4.
[2] Epist. lib. 7.
[3] Meridionales dæmones Cicogna calls them, or Alastores, lib. 3, cap. 9.
[4] Sueton. cap. 59 in Caligula.
[5] Strozzius Cicogna, lib. 3 Mag. cap. 5.   [3] Idem, cap. 18.

Page 195

[1] [Logs of wood that appeared floating in a pool at Brereton in Cheshire.]
[2] Mr. Carew, Survey of Cornwall, lib. 2, folio 140. [The Lanhadron or Arundell oak, which usually bore white or variegated leaves; it foretold the death of the lord of the manor by leafing normally.]
[3] Horto Geniali, folio 137
[4] Part. 1, cap. 19. Abducunt eos a recta via, et viam iter facientibus intercludunt.
[5] Lib. 1, cap. 44. Dæmonum cernuntur et audiuntur ibi frequentes illusiones, unde viatoribus cavendum ne se dissocient, aut a tergo maneant, voces enim fingunt sociorum, ut a recto itinere abducant, etc.
[6] Mons sterilis et nivosus, ubi intempesta nocte umbræ apparent.
[7] Lib. 2, cap. 21. Offendicula faciunt transeuntibus in via et petulanter rident cum vel hominem vel jumentum ejus pedes atterere faciant, et maxime si homo maledictis et calcaribus sæviat.

Page 196

[1] In Cosmogr.
[2] Vestiti more metallicorum, gestus et opera eorum imitantur.
[3] Immisso in terræ carceres vento horribiles terræ motus efficiunt, quibus sæpe non domus modo et turres, sed civitates integræ et insulæ haustæ sunt.
[4] Hierom. in 3 Ephes. Idem Michaelis, cap. 4 de spiritibus. Idem Thyræus de locis infestis.
[5] Lactantius, 2 de origine erroris, cap. 15. Hi maligni spiritus per omnem terram vagantur, et solatium perditionis suæ perdendis hominibus operantur.
[6] Mortalium calamitates epulæ sunt malorum dæmonum.—Synesius.
[7] Dominus mendacii a seipso deceptus, alios decipere cupit, adversarius humani generis, inventor mortis, superbiæ institutor, radix malitiæ, scelerum caput, princeps omnium vitiorum, furit inde in Dei contumeliam, hominum perniciem. De horum conatibus et operationibus lege Epiphanium, 2 tom. lib. 2; Dionysium, cap. 4; Ambros. Epistol. lib. 10, ep. 84; August. de Civ. Dei, lib. 5, cap. 9, lib. 8, cap. 22, lib. 9, 18, lib. 10, 21;

Theophil. in 12 Mat.; Basil. ep. 141; Leonem, Ser.; Theodoret. in 11 Cor. ep. 22; Chrys. hom. 53 in 12 Gen.; Greg. in 1 cap. John; Barthol. de prop. lib. 2, cap. 20; Zanch. lib. 4 de malis angelis; Perer. in Gen. lib. 8, in cap. 6, 2; Origen. Sæpe præliis intersunt, itinera et negotia nostra quæcunque dirigunt, clandestinis subsidiis optatos sæpe præbent successus. Pet. Mar. in Sam. etc.; Ruscam de Inferno.

PAGE 197

[1] Et velut mancipia circumfert.—Psellus.   [2] Lib. de transmut. Malac. ep.
[3] Custodes sunt hominum, et eorum, ut nos animalium: tum et provinciis præpositi regunt auguriis, somniis, oraculis, præmiis, etc.
[4] Lipsius, Physiol. Stoic. lib. 1, cap. 19.
[5] Leo Suavius. Idem et Trithemius.

PAGE 198

[1] Omnif. mag. lib. 2, cap. 23.
[2] Ludus deorum sumus.   [3] Lib. de anima et dæmone.
[4] Quoties fit, ut principes novitium aulicum divitiis et dignitatibus pene obruant, et multorum annorum ministrum, qui non semel pro hero periculum subiit, ne teruncio donent, etc. Idem. Quod philosophi non remunerentur, cum scurra et ineptus ob insulsum jocum sæpe præmium reportet, inde fit, etc.

PAGE 199

[1] Lib. de cruent. cadaver.   [2] Boissardus, cap. 6, Magia.
[3] Godelmannus, cap. 3, lib. 1, de magis. Idem Zanchius, lib. 4, cap. 10 et 11, de malis angelis.
[4] Nociva melancholia furiosos efficit, et quandoque penitus interficit.— G. Piccolomineus. Idemque Zanch. cap. 10, lib. 4. Si Deus permittat, corpora nostra movere possunt, alterare, quovis morborum et malorum genere afficere, imo et in ipsa penetrare et sævire.
[5] Inducere potest morbos et sanitates.
[6] Viscerum actiones potest inhibere latenter, et venenis nobis ignotis corpus inficere.
[7] Irrepentes corporibus occulto morbos fingunt, mentes terrent, membra distorquent.—Lips. Phys. Stoic. lib. 1, cap. 19.
[8] De rerum var. lib. 16, cap. 93.
[9] Quum mens immediate decipi nequit, primum movet phantasiam, et ita obfirmat vanis conceptibus ut ne quem facultati æstimativæ rationive locum relinquat. Spiritus malusi nvadit animam, turbat sensus, in furorem conjicit.—Austin, de vit. Beat.

PAGE 200

[1] Lib. 3, fen. 1, tract. 4, cap. 18.
[2] A Dæmone maxime proficisci, et sæpe solo.   [3] Lib. de incant.
[4] Cap. de mania, lib. de morbis cerebri. Dæmones, quum sint tenues et incomprehensibiles spiritus, se insinuare corporibus humanis possunt, et occulte in visceribus operti, valetudinem vitiare, somniis animas terrere et mentes furoribus quatere.
[5] Insinuant se melancholicorum penetralibus intus, ibique considunt et deliciantur tanquam in regione clarissimorum siderum, coguntque animum furere.
[6] Lib. 1, cap. 6, Occult. Philos.   [7] Part. 1, cap. 1, de spectris.

PAGE 201

[1] [*Malleus Maleficarum* or *Hexenhammer*, the standard textbook on witchcraft, by Jakob Sprenger and Heinrich Krämer.]
[2] Sine cruce et sanctificatione sic a dæmone obsessa.—Dial. Greg. Pag. cap. 9.

PAGE 202

[1] Penult. de opific. Dei.   [2] Lib. 28, cap. 26, tom. 2.   [3] De lamiis.
[4] [Reginald Scot, or Scott, author of the Discovery of Witchcraft.]

PAGE 203

[1] Et quomodo venefici fiant enarrat.
[2] De quo plura legas in Boissardo, lib. 1 de præstig.
[3] Rex Jacobus, Dæmonol. lib. 1, cap. 3.
[4] An university in Spain in Old Castile.   [5] The chief town in Poland.
[6] Oxford and Paris, see finem P. Lombardi.
[7] Præfat. de magis et veneficis.
[8] Rotatum pileum habebat, quo ventos violentos cieret, aerem turbaret, et in quam partem, etc.   [9] Erastus.

PAGE 204

[1] Ministerio hirci nocturni.
[2] Steriles nuptos et inhabiles. Vide Petrum de Palude, lib. 4, distinct. 34; Paulum Guiclandum.
[3] Infantes matribus suffurantur, aliis suppositivis in locum verorum conjectis.
[4] Milles.
[5] D. Luther, in primum præceptum, et Leon. Varius, lib. 1 de fascinat.
[6] Lavat., Cicog.   [7] Boissardus, de Magia.   [8] Dæmon. lib. 3, cap. 3.

PAGE 205

[1] Vide Philostratum, vita ejus; Boissardum de Magia.
[2] Vide Suidam de Pasete.   [3] Nubrigensem lege, lib. 1, cap. 19.
[4] Erastus. Adolphus Scribanius.
[5] Virg. Æneid. 4, incantatricem describens: Hæc se carminibus promittit solvere mentes, Quas velit, ast aliis duras immittere curas.
[6] Godelmannus, cap. 7, lib. 1. Nutricum mammas præsiccant, solo tactu podagram, apoplexiam, paralysin, et alios morbos, quos medicina curare non poterat.
[7] Factus inde maniacus.   [8] Spic. 2, fol. 147.
[9] Omnia philtra etsi inter se differant, hoc habent commune, quod hominem efficiant melancholicum.—Epist. 231 Scholtzii.
[10] De cruent. cadaver.

PAGE 206

[1] Astra regunt homines, et regit astra Deus.
[2] Chirom. lib. Quæris a me quantum operantur astra? dico, in nos nihil astra urgere, sed animos proclives trahere: qui sic tamen liberi sunt, ut si ducem sequantur rationem, nihil efficiant, sin vero naturam, id agere quod in brutis fere.
[3] Cœlum vehiculum divinæ virtutis, cujus mediante motu, lumine et influentia, Deus elementaria corpora ordinat et disponit.—Th. de Vio, Cajetanus, in Psa. civ.
[4] Mundus iste quasi lyra ab excellentissimo quodam artifice concinnata, quem qui norit mirabiles eliciet harmonias.—J. Dee, Aphorismo 11.

PAGE 207

[1] Medicus sine cœli peritia nihil est, etc., nisi genesim sciverit, ne tantillum poterit.—Lib. de podag.
[2] Constellatio in causa est; et influentia cœli morbum hunc movet, interdum omnibus aliis amotis. Et alibi: Origo ejus a cœlo petenda est.—Tr. de morbis amentium.
[3] Lib. de anima, cap. de humorib. Ea varietas in Melancholia habet cœlestes causas ♂ ♄ et ♃ in ♎ ♂ ♂ et ☾ in ♏.

⁴ Ex atra bile varii generantur morbi perinde ut ipse multum calid aut frigidi in se habuerit, quum utrique suscipiendo quam aptissima sit tametsi suapte natura frigida sit. Annon aqua sic afficitur a calore u adreat; et a frigore, ut in glaciem concrescat? et hæc varietas distinctionum, alii flent, rident, etc.

⁵ Hanc ad intemperantiam gignendam plurimum confert ♂ et ♄ positus, etc.

⁶ ☿ quoties alicujus genitura in ♍ et ♓ adverso signo positus, horoscopum partiliter tenuerit atque etiam a ♂ vel ♄ □ radio percussus fuerit, natus ab insania vexabitur.

⁷ Qui ♄ et ♂ habet, alterum in culmine, alterum imo cœlo, cum in lucem venerit, melancholicus erit, à qua sanabitur, si ☿ illos irradiarit.

⁸ Hac configuratione natus, aut lunaticus, aut mente captus.

PAGE 208

¹ Ptolemæus centiloquio, et quadripartito tribuit omnium melancholicorum symptomata siderum influentiis.

² Arte Medica. Accedunt ad has causas affectiones siderum. Plurimum incitant et provocant influentiæ cælestes.—Velcurio, lib. 4, cap. 15.

³ Hildesheim, Spicil. 2, de mel.

⁴ Joh. de Indag. cap. 9; Montaltus, cap. 22.

⁵ Caput parvum qui habent cerebrum et spiritus plerumque angustos; facile incident in melancholiam rubicundi.—Aetius. Idem Montaltus, cap. 21, e Galeno.

PAGE 209

¹ Saturnina a rascetta per mediam manum decurrens, usque ad radicem montis Saturni, a parvis lineis intersecta, arguit melancholicos.—Aphoris.78.

² Agitantur miseriis, continuis inquietudinibus, neque unquam a sollicitudine liberi sunt, anxie affliguntur amarissimis intra cogitationibus, semper tristes, suspiciosi, meticulosi: cogitationes sunt, velle agrum colere, stagna amant et paludes, etc.—Jo. de Indagine, lib. 1.

³ Cælestis Physiognom. lib. 10.

⁴ Cap. 14, lib. 5, idem. Maculæ in ungulis nigræ, lites, rixas, melancholiam significant, ab humore in corde tali.

PAGE 210

¹ Lib. 1 Path. cap. 11.

² Venit enim properata malis inopina senectus: Et dolor ætatem jussit inesse meam.—Boethius, met. 1, de consol. Philos.

³ Cap. de humoribus, lib. de anima.

⁴ Necessarium accidens decrepitis, et inseparabile.

⁵ Ps. xc, 10. ⁶ Meteran. Belg. hist. lib. 1.

⁷ Sunt morosi, et anxii, et iracundi, et difficiles senes, si quærimus, etiam avari.—Tull. de senectute.

⁸ Lib. 2 de Aulico. Senes avari, morosi, jactabundi, philauti, deliri, superstitiosi, suspiciosi, etc.

⁹ Lib. 3 de lamiis, cap. 17 et 18.

PAGE 211

¹ Solanum, opium, lupi adeps, lacr. asini, etc., sanguis infantum, etc.

² Corrupta est iis ab humore melancholico phantasia.—Nymannus.

³ Putant se lædere quando non lædunt.

⁴ Qui hæc in imaginationis vim referre conati sunt, aut atræ bilis, inanem prorsus laborem susceperunt.

⁵ Lib. 3, cap. 4, Omnif. mag. ⁶ Lib. 1, cap. 11, Path.

⁷ Ut arthritici, epileptici, etc.

⁸ Ut filii non tam possessionum quam morborum hæredes sint.

[9] Epist. de secretis artis et naturæ, cap. 7. Nam in hoc quod patres corrupti sunt, generant filios corruptæ complexionis, et compositionis, et filii eorum eadem de causa se corrumpunt, et sic derivatur corruptio a patribus ad filios.
[10] Non tam (inquit Hippocrates) gibbos et cicatrices oris et corporis habitum agnoscis ex iis, sed verum incessum gestus, mores, morbos, etc.
[11] Synagog. Jud.

PAGE 212

[1] Affectus parentum in fœtus transeunt, et puerorum malitia parentibus imputanda.—Lib. 4, cap. 3, de occult. nat. mirac.
[2] Ex pituitosis pituitosi, ex biliosis biliosi, ex lienosis et melancholicis melancholici.
[3] Epist. 174, in Scoltz. Nascitur nobiscum illa aliturque et una cum parentibus habemus malum hunc assem. Jo. Pelezius, lib. 2 de cura humanorum affectuum.
[4] Lib. 10, observat. 15.
[5] Maginus, Geog. [For Galbots, Southey and Shilleto suggest Cagots.]
[6] Sæpe non eundem, sed similem producit effectum, et illæso parente transit in nepotem.
[7] Dial. præfix. genituris Leovitii.

PAGE 213

[1] Bodin. de rep. cap. de periodis reip.
[2] Claudius Albaville, Capuchin, in his voyage to Maragnan, 1614, cap. 45. Nemo fere ægrotus, sano omnes et robusto corpore, vivunt annos 120, 140, sine medicina. Idem Hector Boethius de insulis Orcad. et Damianus à Goes de Scandia.
[3] Lib. 4, cap. 3, de occult. nat. mir. Tetricos plerumque filios senes progenerant et tristes, rarius exhilaratos.
[4] Coitus super repletionem pessimus, et filii qui tum gignuntur, aut morbosi sunt, aut stolidi.
[5] Dial. præfix. Leovitio.   [6] Lib. de ed. liberis.
[7] De occult. nat. mir. Temulentæ et stolidæ mulieres liberos plerumque producunt sibi similes.
[8] Lib. 2, cap, 8. de occult. nat. mir. Good Master Schoolmaster, do not English this.

PAGE 214

[1] De nat. mul. lib. 3, cap. 4.   [2] Buxtorfius, cap. 31 Synag. Jud. Ezek. xviii.
[3] Drusius, Obs. lib. 3, cap. 20.
[4] Beda, Eccl. hist. lib. 1, cap. 27, respons. 10.
[5] Nam spiritus cerebri si tum male afficiantur, tales procreant, et quales fuerint affectus, tales filiorum: ex tristibus tristes, ex jucundis jucundi nascuntur, etc.
[6] Fol. 129. Socrates' children were fools.—Sabel.

PAGE 215

[1] De occul. nat. mir.
[2] Baptista Porta, loco præd. Ex leporum intuitu plerique infantes edunt bifido superiore labello.
[3] Quasi mox in terram collapsurus, per omnem vitam incedebat, cum mater gravida ebrium hominem sic incedentem viderat.
[4] Civem facie cadaverosa, qui dixit, etc.
[5] Optimum bene nasci, maxima pars felicitatis nostræ bene nasci ; quamobrem præclare humano generi consultum videretur, si soli parentes bene habiti et sani, liberis operam darent.
[6] Infantes infirmi præcipitio necati. Bohemus, lib. 3, cap. 3. Apud Laconas olim. Lipsius, epist. 85, cent. ad Belgas, Dionysio Villerio. Si quos aliqua membrorum parte inutiles notaverint, necari jubent.

PAGE 216

[1] Lib. 1, de veterum Scotorum moribus. Morbo comitiali, dementia, mania, lepra, etc., aut simili labe, quæ facile in prolem transmittitur, laborantes inter eos, ingenti facta indagine, inventos, ne gens fæda contagione læderetur ex iis nata, castraverunt, mulieres hujusmodi procul a virorum consortio ablegarunt, quod si harum aliqua concepisse inveniebatur, simul cum fœtu nondum edito defodiebatur viva.

[2] Euphormio Satyr.

PAGE 217

[1] Fecit omnia delicta quæ fieri possunt circa res sex non naturales, et eæ fuerunt causæ extrinsecæ, ex quibus postea ortæ sunt obstructiones.

[2] Path. lib. 1, cap. 2. Maximam in gignendis morbis vim obtinet, pabulum, materiamque morbi suggerens: nam nec ab aere, nec a perturbationibus, vel aliis evidentibus causis morbi sunt, nisi consentiat corporis præparatio, et humorum constitutio. Ut semel dicam, una gula est omnium morborum mater, etiamsi alius est genitor. Ab hac morbi sponte sæpe emanant nulla alia cogente causa.

[3] Shilleto omits "also four." Perhaps some name should replace "also."

[4] Cogan, Elyot, Vaughan, Venner.

PAGE 218

[1] Freitagius.   [2] Isaac.

[3] Non laudatur quia melancholicum præbet alimentum.

[4] Male alit cervina (inquit Freitagius) crassissimum eb atribilarium suppeditat alimentum.

[5] Lib. de subtiliss. diæta. Equina caro et asinina equinis danda est hominibus et asininis.

[6] Parum absunt a natura leporum. Bruerinus, lib. 13, cap. 25. Pullorum tenera et optima.

PAGE 219

[1] Illaudabilis succi nauseam provocant.   [2] Piso, Altomarus.

[3] Curio. Freitagius, Magninus, part. 3, cap. 17. Mercurialis, de affect. lib. 1, cap. 10, excepts all milk meats in hypochondriacal melancholy.

[4] Wecker, Syntax. theor., p. 2; Isaac; Bruer. lib. 15, cap. 30 et 31.

[5] Cap. 18, part. 3.

PAGE 220

[1] Omni loco et omni tempore medici detestantur anguillas, præsertim circa solstitium. Damnantur tum sanis tum ægris.

[2] Cap. 6 in his Tract of Melancholy.

[3] Optime nutrit omnium judicio inter primæ notæ pisces gustu præstanti.

[4] Non est dubium, quin pro vivariorum situ, ac natura, magnas alimentorum sortiantur differentias, alibi suaviores, alibi lutulentiores.

[5] Observat. 16, lib. 10.

PAGE 221

[1] Pseudolus, Act. 3, sc. 2.   [2] Plautus, ibid.

[3] Quare rectius valetudini suæ quisque consulet, qui lapsus priorum parentum memor, eas plane vel omiserit vel parce degustarit.—Kersleius, cap. 4 de vero usu med.

[4] In Mizaldo de Horto, P. Crescent., Herbastein, etc.

[5] Cap. 13, part. 3, Bright in his Tract of Melancholy.

[6] Intellectum turbant, producunt insaniam.

[7] Audivi (inquit Magnin.) quod si quis ex iis per annum continue comedat, in insaniam caderet (cap. 13). Improbi succi sunt (cap. 12).

PAGE 222

¹ De rerum varietat. In Fessa plerumque morbosi, quod fructus comedant ter in die.
² Cap. de Mel. ³ Lib. 11, cap. 3.
⁴ Bright, cap. 6, excepts honey. ⁵ Hor. apud Scoltzium, consil. 186.
⁶ Ne comedas crustam, choleram quia gignit adustam.—Schol. Sal.

PAGE 223

¹ Vinum turbidum.
² Ex vini potentis bibitione, duo Alemanni in uno mense melancholici facti sunt.
³ Hildesheim, Spicil. fol. 273. ⁴ Crassum generat sanguinem.
⁵ About Dantzic in Spruce [Prussia], Hamburg, Leipsic.

PAGE 224

¹ Henricus Abrincensis.
² Potus tum salubris tum jucundus, l. 1.
³ Galen, lib. 1 de san. tuend. Cavendæ sunt aquæ quæ ex stagnis hauriuntur, et quæ turbidæ et male olentes, etc.
⁴ Innoxium reddit et bene olentem.
⁵ Contendit hæc vitia coctione non emendari.
⁶ Lib. de bonitate aquæ. Hydropem auget, febres putridas, splenem, tusses, nocet oculis, malum habitum corporis et colorem.
⁷ [Vardar.] ⁸ Mag. Nigritatem inducit si pecora biberint.

PAGE 225

¹ Aquæ ex nivibus coactæ strumosos faciunt.
² Cosmog. lib. 3, cap. 36.
³ Method. hist. cap. 5. Balbutiunt Labdoni in Aquitania ob aquas, atque hi morbi ab aquis in corpora derivantur.
⁴ Edulia ex sanguine et suffocato parta.—Hildesheim.
⁵ Cupedia vero, placentæ, bellaria, commentaque alia curiosa pistorum et coquorum gustui servientium, conciliant morbos tum corpori tum animo insanabiles.—Philo Judæus, lib. de victimis.
⁶ P. Jov. vita ejus.
⁷ As lettuce steeped in wine, birds fed with fennel and sugar, as a Pope's concubine used in Avignon.—Stephan.
⁸ Animæ negotium illa facessit, et de templo Dei immundum stabulum facit.—Pelezius, cap. 10.
⁹ Lib. 11, cap. 52. Homini cibus utilissimus simplex, acervatio ciborum pestifera, et condimenta perniciosa, multos morbos multa fercula ferunt.

PAGE 226

¹ Dec. 31, cap. 2. Nihil deterius quam si tempus justo longius comedendo protrahatur, et varia ciborum genera conjungantur: inde morborum scaturigo, quæ ex repugnantia humorum oritur.
² Path. lib. 1, cap. 14. ³ Juv. Sat. 1.
⁴ Nimia repletio ciborum facit melancholicum.
⁵ Comestio superflua cibi, et potus quantitas nimia.
⁶ Impura corpora, quanto magis nutris, tanto magis lædis: putrefacit enim alimentum vitiosus humor.
⁷ Vid. Goclen. de portentosis cœnis, etc., Puteani Com.
⁸ Amb. lib. de jeju. cap. 14. ⁹ Juvenal. ¹⁰ Guicciardine.
¹¹ Nat. quæst. 4, cap. ult. Fastidio est lumen gratuitum, dolet quod sole, quod spiritum emere non possimus, quod hic aer non emptus ex facili, etc., adeo nihil placet, nisi quod carum est.
¹² Ingeniosi ad gulam.

Page 227

[1] Olim vile mancipium, nunc in omni æstimatione, nunc ars haber coepta, etc.

[2] Epist. 28, lib. 7. Quorum in ventre ingenium, in patinis, etc.

[3] In lucem coenat Sertorius.   [4] Seneca.

[5] Mancipia gulæ, dapes non sapore sed sumptu æstimantes.—Seneca Consol. ad Helviam.

[6] Sævientia guttura satiare non possunt fluvii et maria.—Æneas Sylvius de miser. curial.   [7] Plautus.

Page 228

[1] Hor. lib. 1, sat. 3.

[2] Diei brevitas conviviis, noctis longitudo stupris conterebatur.

[3] Et quo plus capiant, irritamenta excogitantur.

[4] Foras portantur ut ad convivium reportentur, repleri ut exhauriant, e exhauriri ut bibant.—Ambros.

[5] Ingentia vasa velut ad ostentationem, etc.   [6] Plautus.

Page 229

[1] Lib. 3 Anthol. cap. 20.   [2] Gratiam conciliant potando.

[3] Notis ad Cæsares.   [4] Lib. de educandis principum liberis.

[5] Virg. Æn. 1.

[6] Idem strenui potatoris episcopi sacellanus, cum ingentem pateram exhaurit princeps.

[7] Bohemus in Saxonia. Adeo immoderate et immodeste ab ipsis bibitur ut in compotationibus suis non cyathis solum et cantharis sat infunder possint, sed impletum mulctrale apponant, et scutella injecta hortantu quemlibet ad libitum potare.

[8] Dictu incredibile, quantum hujusce liquoris immodesta gens capiat plus potantem amicissimum habent, et serto coronant, inimicissimum contra qui non vult, et cæde et fustibus expiant.

[9] Qui potare recusat, hostis habetur, et cæde nonnunquam res expiatur.

[10] Qui melius bibit pro salute domini, melior habetur minister.

[11] Græc. poeta apud Stobæum, ser. 18.

Page 230

[1] Qui de die jejunant, et nocte vigilant, facile cadunt in melancholiam; e qui naturæ modum excedunt, cap. 5, tract. 15; cap. 2: Longa famis tolerantia ut iis sæpe accidit qui tanto cum fervore Deo servire cupiunt per jejunium quod maniaci efficiantur, ipse vidi sæpe.

[2] In tenui victu ægri delinquunt, ex quo fit ut majori afficiantur detri mento, majorque fit error tenui quam pleniore victu.

[3] Quæ longo tempore consueta sunt, etiamsi deteriora, minus in assueti molestare solent.

[4] Qui medice vivit, misere vivit.   [5] Consuetudo altera natura.

[6] Herefordshire, Gloucestershire, Worcestershire.

[7] Leo Afer, lib. 1. Solo camelorum lacte contenti, nil præterea deliciarun ambiunt.

Page 231

[1] Flandri vinum butyro dilutum bibunt (nauseo referens), ubique butyrun inter omnia fercula et bellaria locum obtinet.—Steph. præfat. Herod.

[2] Delectantur Græci piscibus magis quam carnibus.

[3] Lib. 1 Hist. Ang.

[4] P. Jovius, Descript. Britonum. They sit, eat and drink all day a dinner in Iceland, Muscovy, and those northern parts.

[5] Suidas, vit. Herod. Nihilo cum eo melius quam si quis cicutam aconitum, etc.

⁶ Expedit. in Sinas, lib. 1, cap. 3. Hortensium herbarum et olerum apud Sinas quam apud nos longe frequentior usus, complures quippe de vulgo reperias nulla alia re vel tenuitatis, vel religionis causa vescentes. Equos, mulos, asellos, etc., æque fere vescuntur ac pabula omnia.—Mat. Riccius, lib. 5, cap. 12.

⁷ Tartari mulis, equis vescuntur et crudis carnibus, et fruges contemnunt, dicentes hoc jumentorum pabulum et boum, non hominum.

⁸ [Peking.]

⁹ Islandiæ descriptione. Victus eorum butyro, lacte, caseo consistit: pisces loco panis habent, potus aqua, aut serum, sic vivunt sine medicina multi ad annos 200.

¹⁰ Laet. occident. Ind. descrip. lib. 11, cap. 10. Aquam marinam bibere sueti absque noxa.

¹¹ Davies' second voyage.   ¹² Patagones.

¹³ Benzo et Fer. Cortesius, lib. Novus Orbis inscrip.

¹⁴ Linschoten, cap. 56. Palmæ instar totius orbis arboribus longe præstantior.

PAGE 232

¹ Lips. epist.   ² Teneris assuescere multum.

³ Repentinæ mutationes noxam pariunt.—Hippocrat. Aphorism. 21, Epist. 6, sect. 3.

⁴ Bruerinus, lib. 1, cap. 23.   ⁵ Simpl. med. cap. 4, lib. 1.

⁶ Heurnius, lib. 3, cap. 19, Prax. med.   ⁷ Aphoris. 17.

⁸ In dubiis consuetudinem sequatur adolescens, et inceptis perseveret.

PAGE 233

¹ Qui cum voluptate assumuntur cibi, ventriculus avidius complectitur, expeditiusque concoquit, et quæ displicent aversatur.

² Nothing against a good stomach, as the saying is.

³ Lib. 7 Hist. Scot.   ⁴ 30 Artis.

⁵ Quæ excernuntur aut subsistunt.

⁶ Ex ventre suppresso, inflammationes, capitis dolores, caligines crescunt.

⁷ Excrementa retenta mentis agitationem parere solent.

⁸ Cap. de mel.   ⁹ Tam delirus, ut vix se hominem agnosceret.

PAGE 234

¹ Alvus astrictus causa.

² Per octo dies alvum siccum habet, et nihil reddit.

³ Sive per nares, sive hæmorrhoides.

⁴ Multi intempestive ab hæmorrhoidibus curati, melancholia corrupti sunt. Incidit in Scyllam, etc.

⁵ Lib. 1 de mania.   ⁶ Breviar. lib. 7, cap. 18.

⁷ Non sine magno incommodo ejus, cui sanguis a naribus promanat, noxii sanguinis vacuatio impediri potest.

⁸ Novi quosdam præ pudore a coitu abstinentes, torpidos pigrosque actos; nonnullos etiam melancholicos, præter modum mœstos timidosque.

⁹ Nonnulli nisi coeant, assidue capitis gravitate infestantur. Dicit se novisse quosdam tristes et ita factos ex intermissione Veneris.

¹⁰ Vapores venenatos mittit sperma ad cor et cerebrum.

¹¹ Sperma plus diu retentum transit in venenum.

¹² Graves producit corporis et animi ægritudines.

PAGE 235

¹ Ex spermate supra modum retento monachos et viduas melancholicos sæpe fieri vidi.

² Melancholia orta a vasis seminariis in utero.

² Nobilis senex Alsatus juvenem uxorem duxit, at ille, colico dolore et

multis morbis correptus, non potuit præstare officium mariti, vix inito matrimonio ægrotus. Illa in horrendum furorum incidit, ob Venerem cohibitam ut omnium eam invisentium congressum, voce, vultu, gestu expeteret, et quum non consentirent, molossos Anglicanos magno expetiit clamore.

⁴ Vidi sacerdotem optimum et pium, qui, quod nollet uti Venere, in melancholica symptomata incidit.

⁵ Ob abstinentiam a concubitu incidit in melancholiam.

⁶ Quæ a coitu exacerbantur.

⁷ Superfluum coitum causam ponunt.

⁸ Exsiccat corpus, spiritus consumit, etc. Caveant ab hoc sicci, velut inimico mortali.

Page 236

¹ Ita exsiccatus ut e melancholico statim fuerit insanus; ab humectantibus curatus.

² Ex cauterio et ulcere exsiccato.

³ Gord., cap. 10, lib. 1, discommends cold baths as noxious.

⁴ Siccum reddunt corpus.

⁵ Si quis longius moretur in iis, aut nimis frequenter, aut importune utatur, humores putrefacit.

⁶ Ego anno superiore quendam guttosum vidi adustum, qui ut liberaretur de gutta, ad balnea accessit, et de gutta liberatus, maniacus factus est.

⁷ On Schola Salernitana.

⁸ Calefactio et ebullitio per venæ incisionem magis sæpe incitatur et augetur, majore impetu humores per corpus discurrunt.

⁹ Lib. de flatulenta melancholia. Frequens sanguinis missio corpus extenuat.

¹⁰ In 9 Rhasis. Atram bilem parit, et visum debilitat.

Page 237

¹ Multo nigrior spectatur sanguis post dies quosdam, quam fuit ab initio.

² Non laudo eos qui in desipientia docent secandam esse venam frontis, quia spiritus debilitatur inde, et ego longa experientia observavi in proprio xenodochio, quod desipientes ex phlebotomia magis læduntur, et magis desipiunt, et melancholici sæpe fiunt inde pejores.

³ De mentis alienat. cap. 3. Etsi multos hoc improbasse sciam, innumeros hac ratione sanatos longa observatione cognovi, qui vigesies, sexagies venas tundendo, etc.

⁴ Vires debilitat.

⁵ Impurus aer spiritus dejicit, infecto corde gignit morbos.

⁶ Sanguinem densat, et humores.—Path. lib. 1, cap. 13.

⁷ Lib. 3, cap. 3.

⁸ Lib. de quartana. Ex aere ambiente contrahitur humor melancholicus.

⁹ Qualis aer, talis spiritus: et cujusmodi spiritus, humores.

¹⁰ Ælianus Montaltus, cap. 11, Calidus et siccus, frigidus et siccus, paludinosus, crassus.

Page 238

¹ Multa hic in xenodochiis fanaticorum millia quæ strictissime catenata servantur.

² Lib. med. part. 2, cap. 19. Intellige quod in calidis regionibus frequenter accidit mania, in frigidis autem tarde.

³ Lib. 2.   ⁴ Hodœporicon, cap. 7.

⁵ Apulia æstivo calore maxime fervet, ita ut ante finem Maii pene exusta sit.   ⁶ Maginus, Pers.

⁷ Pantheo seu Pract. med. lib. 1, cap. 16. Venetæ mulieres, quæ diu sub sole vivunt, aliquando melancholicæ evadunt.

⁸ Navig. lib. 2, cap. 4.   Commercia nocte, hora secunda, ob nimios qui sæviunt interdiu æstus, exercent.
⁹ Morbo Gallico laborantes exponunt ad solem ut morbos exsiccent.

PAGE 239

¹ Sir Richard Hawkins in his Observations, sect. 13.
² Hippocrates, 3 Aphorismorum, idem ait.
³ [Diarbekr.]   ⁴ Idem Maginus in Persia.   ⁵ Descrip. Ter. Sanctæ.
⁶ Quum ad solis radios in Leone longam moram traheret, ut capillos salvos redderet, in maniam incidit.
⁷ Mundus Alter et Idem, seu Terra Australis Incognita.   [Joseph Hall's satirical Utopia, published in 1607, under the name of Mercurius Britannicus.]
⁸ Crassus et turbidus aer tristem efficit animam.
⁹ Commonly called Scandaroon in Asia Minor.
¹⁰ [The Pontine Marshes.]

PAGE 240

¹ Atlas Geographicus.   Memoria valent Pisani, quod crassiore fruantur aere.
² Lib. 1 Hist.
³ Lib. 2, cap. 41: Aura densa ac caliginosa tetrici homines existunt, et subtristes. Et cap. 3: Flante subsolano et Zephyro, maxima in mentibus hominum alacritas existit, mentisque erecto ubi telum solis splendore nitescit.   Maxima dejectio mærorque si quando aura caliginosa est.
⁴ Geor.

PAGE 241

¹ Hor.
² Mens quibus vacillat, ab aere cito offenduntur, et multi insani apud Belgas ante tempestates sæviunt, aliter quieti. Spiritus quoque aeris et mali genii aliquando se tempestatibus ingerunt, et menti humanæ se latenter insinuant, eamque vexant, exagitant, et ut fluctus marin humanum corpus ventis agitatur.
³ Aer noctu densatur, et cogit mœstitiam.
⁴ Lib. de Iside et Osiride.
⁵ Multa defatigatio spiritus viriumque substantiam exhaurit, et corpus refrigerat. Humores corruptos qui aliter a natura concoqui et domari possint, et demum blande excludi, irritat, et quasi in furorem agit, qui postea, mota Camarina, tetro vapore corpus varie lacessunt, animumque.

PAGE 242

¹ In Veni mecum, libro sic inscripto.
² Instit. ad vit. Christ. cap. 44. Cibos crudos in venas rapit, qui putrescentes illic spiritus animales inficiunt.
³ Crudi hæc humoris copia per venas aggreditur, unde morbi multiplices.
⁴ Immodicum exercitium.
⁵ Hom. 31, in 1 Cor. vi.   Nam qua mens hominis quiescere non possit, sed continuo circa varias cogitationes discurrat, nisi honesto aliquo negotio occupetur, ad melancholiam sponte delabitur.
⁶ Crato, consil. 21. Ut immodica corporis exercitatio nocet corporibus, ita vita deses et otiosa: otium animal pituitosum reddit, viscerum obstructiones, et crebras fluxiones, et morbos concitat.
⁷ Et vidi quod una de rebus quæ magis generat melancholiam, est otiositas.
⁸ Reponitur otium ab aliis causa, et hoc a nobis observatum eos huic malo magis obnoxios qui plane otiosi sunt, quam eos qui aliquo munere versantur exsequendo.

[9] De tranquil. animæ. Sunt quos ipsum otium in animi conjicit ægritudinem.

[10] Nihil est quod æque melancholiam alat ac augeat, ac otium et absti nentia a corporis et animi exercitationibus.

[11] Nihil magis excæcat intellectum quam otium.—Gordonius, de observat. vit. hum. lib. 1.

PAGE 243

[1] Path. lib. 1, cap. 17. Exercitationis intermissio, inertem calorem, languidos spiritus, et ignavos, et ad omnes actiones segniores reddit; cruditates, obstructiones, et excrementorum proventus facit.

[2] Hor. Ser. 1, sat. 3.

[3] Seneca.   [4] Mœrorem animi, et maciem, Plutarch calls it.

[5] [The greatest harm to the soul.]

[6] Sicut in stagno generantur vermes, sic et otioso malæ cogitationes.—Sen.

PAGE 244

[1] Now this leg, now that arm, now their head, heart, etc.

[2] Exod. v.

[3] (For they cannot well tell what aileth them, or what they would have themselves) my heart, my head, my husband, my son, etc.

[4] Prov. xviii. Pigrum dejiciet timor. Heautontimorumenos.

[5] Lib. 19, cap. 10.

PAGE 245

[1] Plautus, Prol. Mostel.

[2] Piso, Montaltus, Mercurialis, etc.

PAGE 246

[1] A quibus malum, velut a primaria causa, occasionem nactum est.

[2] Jucunda rerum præsentium, præteritarum, et futurarum meditatio.

PAGE 247

[1] Facilis descensus Averni: Sed revocare gradum, superasque evadere ad auras, Hic labor, hoc opus est.—Virg.

[2] Hieronymus, ep. 72, dixit oppida et urbes videri sibi tetros carceres. solitudinem Paradisum: solum scorpionibus infectum, sacco amictus, humi cubans, aqua et herbis victitans, Romanis prætulit deliciis.

PAGE 248

[1] Offic. 3.   [2] Eccles. iv.

PAGE 249

[1] Natura de te videtur conqueri posse, quod cum ab ea temperatissimum corpus adeptus sis, tam præclarum a Deo ac utile donum, non contempsisti modo, verum corrupisti, fœdasti, prodidisti, optimam temperaturam otio, crapula, et aliis vitæ erroribus, etc.

[2] Path. lib. cap. 17 Fernel. Corpus infrigidat, omnes sensus, mentisque vires, torpore debilitat.

[3] Lib. 2, sect. 2, cap. 4. Magnam excrementorum vim cerebro et aliis partibus conservat.

[4] Jo. Ratzius, lib. de rebus 6 non naturalibus. Præparat corpus talis somnus ad multus periculosas ægritudines.

PAGE 250

[1] Instit. ad vitam optimam, cap. 26. Cerebro siccitatem adfert, phrenesin et delirium, corpus aridum facit, squalidum, strigosum, humores adurit, temperamentum cerebri corrumpit, maciem inducit: exsiccat corpus, bilem accendit, profundos reddit oculos, calorem auget.

² Naturalem calorem dissipat, læsa concoctione cruditates facit. Attenuant juvenum vigilatæ corpora noctes.
³ Vita Alexan. ⁴ Grad. 1, cap. 14. ⁵ Hor.
⁶ Perturbationes clavi sunt, quibus corpori animus seu patibulo affigitur. —Iambl. de myst.
⁷ Lib. de sanitat. tuend.

PAGE 251

¹ Prolog. de virtute Christi. Quæ utitur corpore, ut faber malleo.
² Vita Apollonii, lib. 1.
³ Lib. de anim. Ab inconsiderantia et ignorantia omnes animi motus.
⁴ De Physiol. Stoic. ⁵ Grad. 1, cap. 32.
⁶ Epist. 104. ⁷ Ælianus.
⁸ Lib. 1, cap. 6. Si quis ense percusserit eos, tantum respiciunt.
⁹ Terror in sapiente esse non debet.
¹⁰ De occult nat. mir. lib. 1, cap. 16. Nemo mortalium qui affectibus non ducatur: qui non movetur, aut saxum, aut deus est.
¹¹ Instit. lib. 2, de humanorum affect. morborumque curat.
¹² Epist. 105. ¹³ Granatensis. ¹⁴ Virg.
¹⁵ De Civit. Dei, lib. 14, cap. 9. Qualis in oculis hominum qui inversis pedibus ambulat, talis in oculis sapientum, cui passiones dominantur.

PAGE 252

¹ Lib. de Decal. Passiones maxime corpus offendunt et animam, et frequentissimæ causæ melancholiæ, dimoventes ab ingenio et sanitate pristina (lib. 3, de anima).
² Fræna et stimuli animi, velut in mari quædam auræ leves, quædam placidæ, quædam turbulentæ: sic in corpore quædam affectiones excitant tantum, quædam ita movent, ut de statu judicii depellant.
³ Ut gutta lapidem, sic paulatim hæ penetrant animum.
⁴ Usu valentes recte morbi animi vocantur.
⁵ Imaginatio movet corpus, ad cujus motum excitantur humores, et spiritus vitales, quibus alteratur.
⁶ Eccles. xiii, 26. "The heart alters the countenance to good or evil, and distraction of the mind causeth distemperature of the body."
⁷ Spiritus et sanguis a læsa imaginatione contaminantur, humores enim mutati actiones animi immutant.—Piso.
⁸ Montani consil. 22. Hæ vero quomodo causent melancholiam, clarum; et quod concoctionem impediant, et membra principalia debilitent.

PAGE 253

¹ Breviar. lib. 1, cap. 18.
² Solent hujusmodi egressiones favorabiliter oblectare, et lectorem lassum jucunde refovere, stomachumque neauseantem quodam quasi condimento reficere, et ego libenter excurro.
³ Ab imaginatione oriuntur affectiones, quibus anima componitur, aut turbata deturbatur.—Jo. Sarisbur. Metolog. lib. 4, cap. 10.
⁴ Scalig. exercit.

PAGE 254

¹ Qui, quoties volebat, mortuo similis jacebat, auferens se a sensibus, et quum pungeretur dolorem non sensit.
² Idem Nymannus, Orat. de imaginat.
³ Verbis et unctionibus se consecrant dæmoni pessimæ mulieres qui iis ad opus suum utitur, et earum phantasiam regit, ducitque ad loca ab ipsis desiderata, corpora vero earum sine sensu permanent, quæ umbra cooperit diabolus, ut nulli sint conspicua, et post, umbra sublata, propriis corporibus eas restituit.—Wier. lib. 3, cap. 11.

⁴ Denario medico.
⁵ Solet timor, præ omnibus affectibus, fortes imaginationes gignere; post amor, etc.—Lib. 2, cap. 8.
⁶ Ex viso urso, talem peperit.

PAGE 255

¹ Lib. 1, cap. 4, de occult. nat. mir. Si inter amplexus et suavia cogitet de uno, aut alio absente, ejus effigies solet in fœtu elucere.
² Quid non fœtui adhuc matri unito, subita spirituum vibratione per nervos, quibus matrix cerebro conjuncta est, imprimit impregnatæ imaginatio? ut si imaginetur malum granatum, illius notas secum proferet fœtus : si leporem, infans editur supremo labello bifido et dissecto. Vehemens cogitatio movet rerum species.—Wier. lib. 3, cap. 8.
³ Ne, dum uterum gestent, admittant absurdas cogitationes, sed et visu audituque fœda et horrenda devitent.
⁴ Occult. Philos. lib. 1, cap. 64.
⁵ Lib. 3 de lamiis, cap. 10.   ⁶ Agrippa, lib. 1, cap. 64.
⁷ Sect. 3, memb. 1, subsect. 3.
⁸ Malleus malefic. fol. 77. Corpus mutari potest in diversas ægritudines, ex forti apprehensione.
⁹ Fr. Vales. lib. 5, cont. 6. Nonnunquam etiam morbi diuturnic onsequuntur, quandoque curantur.

PAGE 256

¹ Expedit. in Sinas, lib. 1, cap. 9. Tantum porro multi prædictoribus hisce tribuunt ut ipse metus fidem faciat: nam si prædictum iis fuerit tali die eos morbo corripiendos, ii ubi die advenerit, in morbum incidunt, et vi metus afflicti, cum ægritudine, aliquando etiam cum morte, colluctantur.
² Subtil. 18.
³ Lib. 3 de anima, cap. de mel.   ⁴ Lib. de peste.
⁵ Lib. 1, cap. 63. Ex alto despicientes aliqui præ timore contremiscunt, caligant, infirmantur; sic singultus, febres, morbi comitiales quandoque sequuntur, quandoque recedunt.
⁶ Lib. de incantatione. Imaginatio subitum humorum et spirituum motum infert, under vario affectu rapitur sanguis, ac una morbificas causas partibus affectis eripit.

PAGE 257

¹ Lib. 3, cap. 18, de præstig. Ut impia credulitate quis læditur, sic et levari eundem credibile est, usuque observatum.
² Ægri persuasio et fiducia omni arti et consilio et medicinæ præferenda.—Avicen.
³ Plures sanat in quem plures confidunt.—Lib. de sapientia.
⁴ Marsilius Ficinus, lib. 13, cap. 18, de theologia Platonica. Imaginatio est tanquam Proteus vel chamæleon, corpus proprium et alienum nonnunquam afficiens.
⁵ Cur oscitantes oscitent?—Wierus.

PAGE 258

¹ T[homas] W[right], Jesuit.   ² 3 de anima.
³ Ser. 35. Hæ quatuor passiones sunt tanquam rotæ in curru, quibus vehimur hoc mundo.
⁴ Harum quippe immoderatione spiritus marcescunt.—Fernel. lib. 1 Path. cap. 18.
⁵ Mala consuetudine depravatur ingenium ne bene faciat.—Prosper Calenus, lib. de atra bile. Plura faciunt homines e consuetudine, quam e ratione. A teneris assuescere multum est. Video meliora proboque, deteriora sequor.—Ovid.

Page 259

[1] Nemo læditur nisi a seipso.

[2] Multi se in inquietudinem præcipitant ambitione et cupiditatibus excæcati, non intelligunt se illud a diis petere, quod sibi ipsis si velint præstare possint, si curis et perturbationibus, quibus assidue se macerant, imperare vellent.

[3] Tanto studio miseriarum causas, et alimenta dolorum quærimus, vitamque secus felicissimam, tristem et miserabilem efficimus.—Petrarch. præfat. de Remediis, etc.

[4] Timor et mœstitia, si diu perseverent, causa et soboles atri humoris sunt, et in circulum se procreant.—Hip. Aphoris. 23, lib. 6. Idem Montaltus, cap. 19, Victorius Faventinus, Pract. imag.

[5] Multi ex mærore et metu huc delapsi sunt.—Lemn. lib. 1, cap. 16.

[6] Multa cura et tristitia facinnt accedere melancholiam (cap. 3 de mentis alien.); si altas radices agat, in veram fixamque degenerat melancholiam et in desperationem desinit.

[7] Ille luctus, ejus vero soror desperatio simul ponitur.

[8] Animarum crudele tormentum, dolor inexplicabilis, tinea, non solum ossa, sed corda pertingens, perpetuus carnifex, vires animæ consumens, jugis nox, et tenebræ profundæ, tempestas et turbo et febris non apparens, omni igne validius incendens; longior, et pugnæ finem non habens. . . . Crucem circumfert dolor, faciemque omni tyranno crudeliorem præ se fert.

[9] Nat. Comes, Mythol. lib. 4, cap. 6.

[10] Tully, 3 Tusc. Omnis perturbatio miseria, et carnificina est dolor.

Page 260

[1] Mr. Drayton, in his Heroical Epistles.

[2] Crato, consil. 21, lib. 2. Mœstitia universum infrigidat corpus, calorem innatum extinguit, appetitum destruit.

[3] Cor refrigerat tristitia, spiritus exsiccat, innatumque calorem obruit, vigilias inducit, concoctionem labefactat, sanguinem incrassat, exaggeratque melancholicum succum.

[4] Spiritus et sanguis hoc contaminatur.—Piso.

[5] Luke xxii, 44.

[6] Mærore maceror, marcesco et consenesco miser, ossa atque pellis sum misera macritudine.—Plaut.

[7] Malum inceptum et actum a tristitia sola.

[8] Hildesheim, Spicil. 2 de melancholia. Mærore animi postea accedente, in priora symptomata incidit.

[9] Vives, 3 de anima, cap. de mærore. Sabin. in Ovid.

[10] Herodian, lib. 3. Mærore magis quam morbo consumptus est.

[11] Bothwellius atrabilarius obiit.—Brizarrus Genuensis, hist., etc.

Page 261

[1] Mœstitia cor quasi percussum constringitur, tremit et languescit cum acri sensu doloris. In tristitia cor fugiens attrahit ex splene lentum humorem melancholicum, qui effusus sub costis in sinistro latere hypochondriacos flatus facit, quod sæpe accidit iis qui diuturna cura et mœstitia conflictantur.—Melancthon.

[2] Lib. 3 Æn.

[3] Et metum ideo deam sacrarunt ut bonam mentem concederet. Varro, Lactantius, Aug.

[4] Lilius Girald. Syntag. 1, de diis miscellaniis.

[5] Calendis Jan. feriæ sunt divæ Angeronæ, cui pontifices in sacello Volupiæ sacra faciunt, quod angores et animi sollicitudines propitiata propellat.

[6] Timor inducit frigus, cordis palpitationem, vocis defectum atque

pallorem.—Agrippa, lib. 1, cap. 63. Timidi semper spiritus habent frigidos —Mont.

⁷ [Jupiter the Tragedian, in the dialogue of that name.]

⁸ Effusas cernens fugientes agmine turmas, Quis mea nunc inflat cornua? Faunus ait.—Alciat.

PAGE 262

¹ Metus non solum memoriam consternat, sed et institutum animi omne et laudabilem conatum impedit.—Thucydides.

² Lib. de fortitudine et virtute Alexandri. Ubi prope res adfuit terribilis.

³ Sect. 2. mem. 3, subs. 2.   ⁴ Sect. 2, memb. 4, subs. 3.

⁵ Subtil. lib. 18. Timor attrahit ad se dæmonas. Timor et error multum in hominibus possunt.

⁶ Lib. 2 de spectris, cap. 3. Fortes raro spectra vident, quia minus timent.

⁷ Vita ejus.   ⁸ Sect. 2, memb. 4, subs. 7.   ⁹ De virt. et vitiis.

¹⁰ Com. in Arist. de anima.

PAGE 263

¹ Qui mentem subjecit timoris dominationi, cupiditatis, doloris, ambitionis, pudoris, felix non est, sed omnino miser, assiduis laboribus torquetur et miseria.

² Multi contemnunt mundi strepitum, reputant pro nihilo gloriam sed timent infamiam, offensionem, epulsam. Voluptatem severissime, contemnunt, in dolore sunt molliores, gloriam negligunt, franguntur infamia.

³ Gravius contumeliam ferimus quam detrimentum, ni abjecto nimis animo simus.—Plut. in Timol.

⁴ Quod piscatoris ænigma solvere non posset.

⁵ Ob tragœdiam explosam, mortem sibi gladio conscivit.

⁶ Cum vidit in triumphum se servari, causa ejus ignominiæ mortem sibi conscivit.—Plut.

⁷ Bello victus, per tres dies sedit in prora navis, abstinens ab omni consortio, etiam Cleòpatræ; postea se interfecit.

⁸ Cum male recitasset Argonautica, ob pudorem exulavit.

⁹ Quidam præ verecundia simul et dolore in insaniam incidunt, eo quod a literatorum gradu in examine excluduntur.

¹⁰ Hostratus cucullatus adeo graviter ob Reuclini librum, qui inscribitur Epistolæ obscurorum virorum, dolore simul et pudore sauciatus, ut seipsum interfecerit.

PAGE 264

¹ Propter ruborem confusus, statim cœpit delirare, etc., ob suspicionem, quod vili illum crimine accusarent.

² Horat.

³ Ps. Impudice. B. Ita est. Ps. Sceleste. B. Dicis vera. Ps. Verbero. B. Quippeni? Ps. Furcifer. B. Factum optime. Ps. Sociofraude. B. Sunt mea istæc. Ps. Parricida. B. Perge tu. Ps. Sacrilege. B. Fateor. Ps. Perjure. B. Vera dicis. Ps. Pernicies adolescentum. B. Acerrime. Ps. Fur. B. Babæ. Ps. Fugitive. B. Bombax. Ps. Fraus populi. B. Planissime. Ps. Impure leno, cœnum. B. Cantores probos.—Pseudolus, Act. 1, sc. 3.

⁴ Persius, Sat. 5.   ⁵ Cent. 7, e Plinio.

⁶ Multos videmus propter invidiam et odium in melancholiam incidisse: et illos potissimum quorum corpora ad hanc apta sunt.

⁷ Invidia affligit homines adeo et corrodit, ut hi melancholici penitus fiant.   ⁸ Hor.

⁹ His vultus minax, torvus aspectus, pallor in facie, in labiis tremor, stridor in dentibus, etc.

Page 265

[1] Ut tinea corrodit vestimentum, sic invidia eum qui zelatur consumit.

[2] Pallor in ore sedet, macies in corpore toto. Nusquam recta acies, livent rubigine dentes.

[3] Diaboli expressa imago, toxicum caritatis, venenum amicitiæ, abyssus mentis, non est eo monstrosius monstrum, damnosius damnum; urit, torret, discruciat macie et squalore conficit.—Austin, Domin. prim. Advent.   [4] Ovid.

[5] Declam. 13. Linivit flores maleficis succis in venenum mella convertens.

[6] Statuis cereis Basilius eos comparat, qui liquefiunt ad præsentiam solis, qua alii gaudent et ornantur. Muscis alii, quæ ulceribus gaudent, amœna prætereunt, sistunt in fœtidis.

[7] Misericordia etiam quæ tristitia quædam est, sæpe miserantis corpus male afficit.—Agrippa, lib. 1, cap. 63.

[8] Insitum mortalibus a natura recentem aliorum felicitatem ægris oculis intueri.—Hist. lib. 2, Tacit.

[9] Legi Chaldæos, Græcos, Hebræos, consului sapientes pro remedio invidiæ; hoc enim inveni, renuntiare felicitati, et perpetuo miser esse.

[10] Omne peccatum aut excusationem secum habet, aut voluptatem, sola invidia utraque caret. Reliqua vitia finem habent, ira defervescit, gula satiatur, odium finem habet, invidia nunquam quiescit.

Page 266

[1] Urebat me æmulatio propter stultos.

[2] Jer. xii, 1.   [3] Hab. i.

[4] Invidit privati nomen supra principis attolli.

[5] Tacit. Hist. lib. 2. part. 6.

[6] Peritura dolore et invidia, si quem viderint ornatiorem se in publicum prodiisse.—Platina, Dial. amorum.

[7] Ant. Guianerius, lib. 2, cap. 8, vit. M. Aurelii. Femina vicinam elegantius se vestitam videns, leænæ instar in virum insurgit, etc.

[8] Quod insigni equo et ostro veheretur, quanquam nullius cum injuria, ornatum illum tanquam læsæ gravabantur.

[9] Quod pulchritudine omnes excelleret, puellæ indignatæ occiderunt.

[10] Late patet invidiæ fecundæ pernicies, et livor radix omnium malorum, fons cladium, inde odium surgit, emulatio.—Cyprian, ser. 2, de livore.

[11] Valerius, lib. 3, cap. 9.

[12] Qualis est animi tinea, quæ tabes pectoris, zelare in altero vel aliorum felicitatem suam facere miseriam, et velut quosdam pectori suo admovere carnifices, cogitationibus et sensibus suis adhibere tortores, qui se intestinis cruciatibus lacerent! Non cibus talibus lætus, non potus potest esse jucundus; suspiratur semper et gemitur, et doletur dies et noctes; pectus sine intermissione laceratur.

Page 267

[1] Quisquis est ille quem æmularis, cui invides is te subterfugere potest, at tu non te; ubicunque fugeris, adversarius tuus tecum est, hostis tuus semper in pectore tuo est, pernicies intus inclusa, ligatus es, victus, zelo dominante captivus: nec solatia tibi ulla subveniunt; hinc diabolus inter initia statim mundi, et periit primus, et perdidit.—Cyprian, ser. 2, de zelo et livore.

[2] Hesiod, Op. et Dies.

[3] Rana, cupida æquandi bovem, se distendebat, etc.

[4] Æmulatio alit ingenia.—Paterculus, poster. vol.

[5] Grotius, Epig. lib. 1.

PAGE 268

[1] Anno 1519, between Ardres and Guisnes.
[2] Spartian.   [3] Plutarch.
[4] Johannes Heraldus, lib. 2, cap. 12 de bello sacro.
[5] [See Catullus, 14, 3. The allusion is to Cicero's vehement denunciation of Publius Vatinius.]
[6] Nulla dies tantum poterit lenire furorem. Æterna bella pace sublata gerunt. Jurat odium, nec ante invisum esse desinit, quam esse desiit.—Paterculus, vol. i.
[7] Carthago æmula Romani imperii funditus interiit.—Sallust. Catil.
[8] Ita sævit hæc Stygia ministra ut urbes subvertat aliquando, deleat populos, provincias alioqui florentes redigat in solitudines, mortales vero miseros in profunda miseriarum valle miserabiliter immergat.

PAGE 269

[1] Paul, Col. iii.   [2] Rom. xii.   [3] Grad. 1, cap. 54.
[4] Ira et mœror et ingens animi consternatio melancholicos facit.—Aretæus. Ira immodica gignit insaniam.
[5] Reg. sanit. parte 2, cap. 8. In apertam insaniam mox ducitur iratus.
[6] Gilberto Cognato interprete. Multis, et præsertim senibus ira; impotens insaniam facit, et importuna calumnia; hæc initio perturbat animum, paulatim vergit ad insaniam. Porro mulierum corpora multa infestant, et in hunc morbum adducunt, præcipue si quæ oderint aut invideant, etc.; hæc paulatim in insaniam tandem evadunt.
[7] Sæva animi tempestas, tantos excitans fluctus ut statim ardescant oculi, os tremat, lingua titubet, dentes concrepant, etc.

PAGE 270

[1] Ovid.   [2] Terence.
[3] Infensus Britanniæ Duci, et in ultionem versus, nec cibum cepit, nec quietem; ad Calendas Julias, 1392, comites occidit. [Britain = Brittany.]
[4] Indignatione nimia furens, animique impotens, exsiliit de lecto, furentem non capiebat aula, etc.
[5] An ira possit hominem interimere.
[6] As Troy: sævæ memorem Junonis ob iram.
[7] Abernethy.
[8] Stultorum regum et populorum continet æstus.

PAGE 271

[1] Lib. 2. Invidia est dolor, et ambitio est dolor, etc.
[2] Insomnes, Claudianus; tristes, Virg.; mordaces, Luc.; edaces, Hor.; mœstæ, amaræ, Ovid.; damnosæ, inquietæ, Mart.; urentes, rodentes, Mant., etc.
[3] Galen, lib. 3, cap. 7, de locis affectis. Homines sunt maxime melancholici, quando vigiliis multis, et sollicitudinibus, et laboribus, et curis fuerint circumventi.
[4] Lucian. Podag.
[5] Omnia imperfecta, confusa, et perturbatione plena.—Cardan.

PAGE 272

[1] Lib. 7 Nat. hist. cap. 1. Hominem nudum, et ad vagitum edit natura. Flens ab initio, devinctus jacet, etc.
[2] Δακρυχέων γενόμην καὶ δακρύσας ἀποθνήσκω, ὦ γένος ἀνθρώπων πολυδάκρυτον, ἀσθενές, οἰκτρόν. Lacrimans natus sum, et lacrimans morior, etc.
[3] Ad Marciam.   [4] Boethius.
[5] Initium cæcitas, progressus labor, exitus dolor, error omnia: quem tranquillum, quæso, quem non laboriosum aut anxium diem egimus?—Petrarch.

NOTES

[1] Ubique periculum, ubique dolor, ubique naufragium, in hoc ambitu quocunque me vertam.—Lipsius.

[2] Hom. 10. Si in forum iveris, ibi rixæ et pugnæ; si in curiam, ibi fraus, adulatio; si in domum privatam, etc.

[3] Homer.

[4] Multis repletur homo miseriis, corporis miseriis, animi miseriis, dum dormit, dum vigilat, quocunque se vertit. Lususque rerum temporumque nascimur.

[5] In blandiente fortuna intolerandi, in calamitatibus lugubres, semper stulti et miseri.—Cardan.

[6] Prospera in adversis desidero, et adversa prosperis timeo, quis inter hæc medius locus, ubi non fit humanæ vitæ tentatio?

[7] Cardan, Consol. Sapientiæ labor annexus, gloriæ invidia, divitiis curæ, oboli sollicitudo, voluptati morbi, quieti paupertas, ut quasi fruendorum celerum causa nasci hominem possis cum Platonistis agnoscere.

[8] Lib. 7, cap. 1. Non satis æstimare, an melior parens natura homini, an tristior noverca fuerit: nulli fragilior vita, pavor, confusio, rabies major; uni animantium ambitio data, luctus, avaritia, uni superstitio.

[9] Euripides.

[10] De consol. lib. 2. Nemo facile cum conditione sua concordat; inest singulis quod imperiti petant, experti horreant.

[11] Esse in honore juvat, mox displicet.   [12] Hor.

PAGE 274

[1] Borrhæus, in 6 Job. Urbes et oppida nihil aliud sunt quam humanarum ærumnarum domicilia, quibus luctus et mœror, et mortalium varii infinitique labores, et omnis generis vitia, quasi septis includuntur.

[2] Nat. Chytræus, de lit. Europæ. Lætus nunc, mox tristis; nunc sperans, paulo post diffidens; patiens hodie, cras ejulans; nunc pallens rubens, currens, sedens, claudicans, tremens, etc.

[3] See. p 347.

[4] Sua cuique calamitas præcipua.   [5] Cn. Græcinus.

[6] Epist. 9, lib. 7. Miser est qui se beatissimum non judicat; licet imperet mundo non est beatus, qui se non putat: quid enim refert qualis status tuus sit, si tibi videtur malus?

[7] Hor. Ep. lib. 1, 14.

PAGE 275

[1] Hor. Ser. 1, sat. 1.

[2] Lib. de curat. Græc. affect. cap. 6, de provident. Multis nihil placet; atque adeo et divitias damnant, et paupertatem; de morbis expostulant, bene valentes graviter ferunt, atque, ut semel dicam, nihil eos delectat, etc.

[3] Vix ullius gentis, ætatis, ordinis, hominem invenies cujus felicitatem fortunæ Metelli compares.—Vol. 1.

[4] P. Crassus Mutianus quinque habuisse dicitur rerum bonarum maxima, quod esset ditissimus, quod esset nobilissimus, eloquentissimus, jurisconsultissimus, pontifex maximus.

[5] Lib. 7. Regis filia, regis uxor, regis mater.

[6] Qui nihil unquam mali aut dixit, aut fecit, aut sensit, qui bene semper fecit, quod aliter facere non potuit.

[7] Solomon, Eccles. i, 14.   [8] Hor. Art. Poet.

PAGE 276

[1] Jovius, vita ejus. [Gonsalvo de Cordova, "The Great Captain" 1453-1515).]

[2] 2 Sam. xii, 31.   [3] Boethius, lib. 1, Met. 1.

I—R 886

⁴ Omnes hic aut captantur, aut captant: aut cadavera quæ lacerantur aut corvi qui lacerant.—Petron.
⁵ Homo omne monstrum est, ille nam superat feras, luposque et ursos pectore obscuro tegit.—Heins.

PAGE 277

¹ Quod Paterculus de populo Romano, durante bello Punico per annos 115, aut bellum inter eos, aut belli præparatio, aut infida pax, idem ego de mundi accolis.
² Theocritus, Idyll. 15.
³ Qui sedet in mensa, non meminit sibi otioso ministrare negotiosos edenti esurientes, bibenti sitientes, etc.
⁴ Quando in adolescentia sua ipsi vixerint lautius, et liberius voluptates suas expleverint, illi gnatis imponunt duriores continentiæ leges.

PAGE 278

¹ Lugubris Ate luctusque ferus Regum tumidas obsidet arces. Res est inquieta felicitas.
² Plus aloes quam mellis habet.—Juv. Non humi jacentem tolleres.— Valer. lib. 7, cap. 3.
³ Non diadema aspicias, sed vitam afflictione refertam, non caterva satellitum, sed curarum multitudinem.
⁴ As Plutarch relateth.
⁵ Sect. 2, memb. 4, subsect. 6.
⁶ Stercus et urina, medicorum fercula prima.
⁷ Nihil lucrantur, nisi admodum mentiendo.—Tull. Offic.
⁸ Hor. lib. 2, Od. 1.

PAGE 279

¹ Rarus felix idemque senex.—Seneca, in Herc. Œtæo.
² Omitto ægros, exsules, mendicos, quos nemo audet felices dicere.— Card. lib. 8, cap. 46, de rer. var.
³ Spretæque injuria formæ.   ⁴ Hor.
⁵ Attenuant vigiles corpus miserabile curæ.   ⁶ Plautus.
⁷ Hæc quæ crines evellit, Ærumna.
⁸ Optimum non nasci, aut cito mori.

PAGE 280

¹ Bonæ si rectam rationem sequuntur, malæ si exorbitant.
² Tho. Buovie. Prob. 18.
³ Molam asinariam.   ⁴ Tract. de Inter. cap. 92.
⁵ Circa quamlibet rem mundi hæc passio fieri potest, quæ superflu diligatur.—Tract. 15, cap. 17.
⁶ Ferventius desiderium.
⁷ Imprimis vero appetitus, etc.—3 de alien. ment.
⁸ Conf. lib. 1, cap. 29.
⁹ Per diversa loca vagor, nullo temporis momento quiesco, talis et tal esse cupio, illud atque illud habere desidero.
¹⁰ Ambros. lib. 3 super Lucam. Ærugo animæ.
¹¹ Nihil animum cruciat, nihil molestius inquietat, secretum viru pestis occulta, etc.—Epist. 126.
¹² Ep. 88.

PAGE 281

¹ Nihil infelicius his; quantus iis timor, quanta dubitatio, quanta conatus, quanta sollicitudo ! nulla illis a molestiis vacua hora.
² Semper attonitus, semper pavidus quid dicat, faciatve: ne displice humilitatem simulat, honestatem mentitur.

³ Cypr. Prolog. ad ser. to. 2. Cunctos honorat, universis inclinat, subsequitur, obsequitur; frequentat curias, visitat optimates, amplexatur, applaudit, adulatur: per fas et nefas e latebris, in omnem gradum ubi aditus pater se ingerit, discurrit.

⁴ Turbæ cogit ambitio regem inservire, ut Homerus Agamemnonem querentem inducit.

⁵ Plutarchus. Quin convivemur, et in otio nos oblectemur, quoniam in promptu id nobis sit, etc.

⁶ Jovius, Hist. lib. 1. Vir singulari prudentia, sed profunda ambitione, ad exitium Italiæ natus.

⁷ Lib. 3, de contemptu rerum fortuitarum. Magno conatu et impetu moventur, super eodem centro rotati, non proficiunt, nec ad finem perveniunt.

⁸ Ut hedera arbori adhæret, sic ambitio, etc. ⁹ Vita Pyrrhi.

Page 282

¹ [Where the bodies of executed criminals were dragged to be thrown into the Tiber.]

² Lib. 5 de rep. cap. 1.

³ Ambitio in insaniam facile delabitur, si excedat.—Patricius, lib. 4, tit. 20, de regis instit.

⁴ Imprimis vero appetitus, seu concupiscentia nimia rei alicujus, honestæ vel inhonestæ, phantasiam lædunt; unde multi ambitiosi, philauti, irati, avari, insani, etc.—Felix Plater, lib. 3 de mentis alien.

⁵ Aulica vita colluvies ambitionis, cupiditatis, simulationis, imposturæ, fraudis, invidiæ, superbiæ Titaniacæ; diversosium aula, et commune conventiculum assentandi artificum, etc.—Budæus de asse. lib. 5.

⁶ In his Aphor. ⁷ Plautus, Curcul. Act. 4, sc. 2.

⁸ Tom. 2. Si examines, omnes miseriæ causas vel a furioso contendendi studio, vel ab injusta cupiditate, originem traxisse scies. Idem fere Chrysostomus, Com. in cap. 6 ad Romanos, ser. 11.

Page 283

¹ Cap. 4, 1. ² Ut sit iniquus in Deum, in proximum, in seipsum.

³ Si vero, Crateva, inter cæteras herbarum radices, acaritiæ radicem ecare posses amaram, ut nullæ reliquiæ essent, probe scito, etc.

⁴ Cap. 6 Dietæ salutis. Avaritia est amor immoderatus pecuniæ vel acquirendæ vel retinendæ.

⁵ Malus est morbus maleque afficit avaritia, siquidem censeo, etc. avaritia difficilius curatur quam insania: quoniam hac omnes fere medici laborant.—Hip. Ep. Abderit.

⁶ Ferum profecto dirumque ulcus animi, remediis non cedens medendo exasperatur.

⁷ Qua re non es lassus? lucrum faciendo: quid maxime delectabile? lucrari.

⁸ Extremos currit mercator ad Indos.—Hor.

Page 284

¹ Hom. 2. Aliud avarus, aliud dives.

² Divitiæ ut spinæ animum hominis timoribus, sollicitudinibus, angoribus, mirifice pungunt, vexant, cruciant.—Greg. in Hom.

³ Epist. ad Donat. cap. 2. ⁴ Lib. 9, ep. 30.

⁵ Lib. 9, cap. 4. Insulæ rex titulo, sed animo pecuniæ miserabile mancipium. ⁶ Hor. 10, lib. 1.

⁷ Danda est hellebori multo pars maxima avaris.

⁸ Luke xii, 20. Stulte, hac nocte eripiam animam tuam.

⁹ Opes quidem mortalibus sunt dementia.—Theognis.

[10] Ed. 2, lib. 2. Exonerare cum se possit et relevare ponderibus, pergit magis fortunis augentibus pertinaciter incubare.

[11] Non amicis, non liberis, non ipsi sibi quidquam impertit; possidet ad hoc tantum, ne possidere alteri liceat, etc. Hieron. ad Paulin. Tam deest quod habet quam quod non habet.

PAGE 285

[1] Epist. 2, lib. 2. Suspirat in convivio, bibat licet gemmis et toro molliore marcidum corpus condiderit, vigilat in pluma.

[2] Angustatur ex abundantia, contristatur ex opulentia, infelix præsentibus bonis, infelicior in futuris.

[3] Illorum cogitatio nunquam cessat qui pecunias supplere diligunt.— Guianer. tract. 15, cap. 17.

[4] Hor. 3 Od. 24. Quo plus sunt potæ, plus sitiuntur aquæ.

[5] Hor. lib. 2, Sat. 6. O si angulus ille Proximus accedat, qui nunc deformat agellum.

[6] Lib. 3 de lib. arbit. Immoritur studiis, et amore senescit habendi.

[7] Avarus vir inferno est similis, etc.; modum non habet, hoc egentior quo plura habet.

PAGE 286

[1] Erasm. Adag. chil. 3, cent. 7, prov. 2. Nulli fidentes omnium formidant opes, ideo pavidum malum vocat Euripides: metuunt tempestates ob frumentum, amicos ne rogent, inimicos ne lædant, fures ne rapiant, bellum timent, pacem timent, summos, medios, infimos.

[2] Hall, Characters.

[3] A. Gellius, lib. 3, cap. 1. Interdum eo sceleris perveniunt ob lucrum, ut vitam propriam commutent.

[4] Lib. 7, cap. 6.

[5] Omnes perpetuo morbo agitantur, suspicatur omnes timidus sibique ob aurum insidiari putat, nunquam quiescens.—Plin. Prooem. lib. 14.

[6] Cap. 18. In lecto jacens interrogat uxorem an arcam probe clausit, an capsula, etc. E lecto surgens nudus et absque calceis, accensa lucerna omnia obiens et lustrans, et vix somno indulgens.

[7] Curis extenuatus, vigilans et secum supputans.

[8] Cave quemquam alienum in ædes intromiseris. Ignem extingui volo, ne causæ quidquam sit quod te quisquam quæritet. Si bona fortuna veniat, ne intromiseris. Occlude sis fores ambobus pessulis. Discrucio animi quia domo abeundum est mihi. Nimis hercule invitus abeo, nec quid agam scio.

[9] Plorat aquam profundere, etc. Periit dum fumus de tigillo exit foras.

PAGE 287

[1] Juv. Sat. 14.

[2] Ventricosus, nudus, pallidus, læva pudorem occultans, dextra seipsum strangulans. Occurrit autem exeunti Pœnitentia, his miserum conficiens, etc.

[3] Luke xv. [4] Boethius.

PAGE 288

[1] In Œconom. Quid si nunc ostendam eos qui magna vi argenti domus inutiles ædificant? inquit Socrates.

[2] Sarisburiensis Polycrat. lib. 1, cap 14. Venatores omnes adhuc institutionem redolent centaurorum. Raro invenitur quisquam eorum modestu et gravis, raro continens, et ut credo sobrius nunquam.

[3] Pancirol. Tit. 23. Avolant opes cum accipitre.

[4] Insignis venatorum stultitia, et supervacanea cura eorum, qui dum nimium venationi insistunt, ipsi abjecta omni humanitate in feras degenerant, ut Actæon, etc.

[5] Sabin. in Ovid. Metamor.

NOTES

[6] Agrippa de vanit. scient. Insanum venandi studium, dum a novalibu arcentur agricolæ, subtrahunt prædia rusticis, agricolonis præcluduntur silvæ et prata pastoribus ut augeantur pascua feris. . . . Majestatis reus agricola si gustarit.

[7] A novalibus suis arcentur agricolæ, dum feræ habeant vagandi libertatem: istis, ut pascua augeantur, prædia subtrahuntur, etc.—Sarisburiensis.

[8] Feris quam hominibus æquiores. — Camden de Guil. Conq. qui 36 ecclesias matrices depopulatus est ad Forestam Novam (Mat. Paris).

Page 289

[1] Tom. 2 de vitis illustrium, lib. 4, de vit. Leon. 10.
[2] Venationibus adeo perdite studebat et aucupiis.
[3] Aut infeliciter venatus tam impatiens inde, ut summos sæpe viro acerbissimis contumeliis oneraret, et incredibile est quali vultus animique habitu dolorem iracundiamque præferret, etc.
[4] Unicuique autem hoc a natura insitum est, ut doleat sicubi erraverit aut deceptus sit.
[5] Juven. Sat. 1. Nec enim loculis comitantibus itur Ad casum tabulæ, positased luditur arca. Lemnius, Instit. cap. 44. Mendaciorum quidem, et perjuriorum, et paupertatis mater est alea, nullam habens patrimonii reverentiam, quum illud effuderit, sensim in furta delabitur et rapinas. Saris. Polycrat. lib. 1, cap. 5.   [6] Damhoderius.
[7] Dan. Souter.   [8] Petrar. dial. 27.

Page 290

[1] Sallust.   [2] Tom. 3, Ser. de alea.
[3] Plutus in Aristoph. calls all such gamesters madmen: Si in insanum hominem contigero. Spontaneum ad se trahunt, furorem, et os, et nares, et oculos rivos faciunt furoris et diversoria.—Chrys. Hom. 17.
[4] Paschasius Justus, lib. 1 de alea.
[5] Seneca.   [6] Hall.
[7] Juv. Sat. 11. Sed deficiente crumena et crescente gula, quis te manet exitus . . . rebus in ventrem mersis?
[8] Spartian. Adriano.
[9] Alex. ab Alex. lib. 6, cap. 10. Idem Gerbelius, lib. 5 Græc. desc.
[10] Fynes Moryson.   [11] Justinian. in Digestis.

Page 291

[1] Persius, Sat. 5.
[2] Poculum quasi sinus in quo sæpe naufragium faciunt, jactura tum pecuniæ tum mentis.—Erasm. in Prov. Calicum remiges, chil. 4, cent. 7, prov. 41.
[3] Ser. 33, ad frat. in Eremo.
[4] [A play on words, "Hilary Term" standing for "season of merriment."]
[5] Liberæ unius horæ insaniam æterno temporis tædio pensant.
[6] Menander.   [7] Prov. vii, 22.

Page 292

[1] Merlin. Cocc.   [2] Hor.
[3] Sagitta quæ animam penetrat, leviter penetrat, sed non leve infligit vulnus.—Sup. Cant.
[4] Qui omnem pecuniarum contemptum habent, et nulli imaginationis totius mundi se immiscuerint, et tyrannicas corporis concupiscentias sustinuerint, hi multoties capti a vana gloria omnia perdiderunt.
[5] Hac correpti non cogitant de medela.
[6] Di talem a terris avertite pestem.
[7] Ep. ad Eustochium, de custod. virgin.   [8] Lips. Ep. ad Bonciarium.

Page 293

[1] Ep. lib. 9. Omnia tua scripta pulcherrima existimo, maxime tamen illa quæ de nobis.

[2] Exprimere non possum quam sit jucundum, etc.

[3] Hierome. Et licet nos indignos dicimus et calidus rubor ora perfundat, attamen ad laudem suam intrinsecus animæ lætantur.

[4] Thesaur. Theo.

[5] Nec enim mihi cornea fibra est.—Pers.

[6] E manibus illis Nascentur violæ.—Pers. Sat. 1.

[7] Omnia enim nostra, supra modum placent.

[8] Fab. lib. 10, cap. 3. Ridentur mala qui componunt carmina, verum Gaudent scribentes, et se venerantur, et ultro, Si taceas laudant, quicquid scripsere beati.—Hor. Ep. 2, lib. 2.

[9] Luke xviii, 10.   [10] De meliore luto finxit præcordia Titan.

Page 294

[1] Auson. Sap.

[2] Chil. 3, cent. 10, prov. 97. Qui se crederet neminem ulla in re præstantiorem.

[3] Tanto fastu scripsit, ut Alexandri gesta inferiora scriptis suis existimaret.—Jo. Voschius, lib. 1, cap. 9, de hist.

[4] Plutarch, vit. Catonis.

[5] Nemo unquam poeta aut orator, qui quemquam se meliorem arbitraretur.

[6] Consol. ad Pammachium. Mundi philosophus, gloriæ animal, et popularis auræ et rumorum venale mancipium.

[7] Epist. 5, Capitoni suo. Diebus ac noctibus hoc solum cogito si qua me possum levare humo. Id voto meo sufficit, etc.

[8] Tullius.

[9] Ut nomen meum scriptis tuis illustretur. Inquies animus studio æternitatis, noctes et dies angebatur.—Heinsius, Orat. funeb. de Scal.

[10] Hor. Art. Poet.   [11] Vade, liber felix!—Palingen. lib. 18.

Page 295

[1] In lib. 8.   [2] De ponte dejicere.

[3] Sueton. lib. de gram.   [4] Nihil libenter audiunt nisi laudes suas.

[5] Epis. 56. Nihil aliud dies noctesque cogitant nisi ut in studiis suis audentur ab hominibus.

[6] Quæ major dementia aut dici, aut excogitari potest, quam sic ob gloriam cruciari? Insaniam istam, Domine, longe fac a me.—Austin, Conf. lib. 10, cap. 37.

[7] Mart. lib. 5, 52.

Page 296

[1] Hor. Sat. lib. 1, 2.   [2] Lib. cont. philos. cap. 1.

Page 297

[1] Macrobius, Som. Scip.   [2] Boethius.

[3] Putean. Cisalp. hist. lib. 1.   [4] Plutarch, Lycurgo.

[5] Epist. 13. Illud te admoneo, ne eorum more facias, qui non proficere, sed conspici cupiunt, quæ in habitu tuo, aut genere vitæ notabilia sunt. Asperum cultum et vitiosum caput, negligentiorem barbam, indictum argento odium, cubile humi positum, et quicquid ad laudem perversa via sequitur, evita.

PAGE 298

[1] Hor.

[2] Quis vero tam bene modulo suo metiri se novit, ut eum assiduæ et immodicæ laudationes non moveant?—Hen. Steph.

[3] Mart.   [4] Stroza.

[5] Antony, Octavian, Lepidus.]   [6] Justin.

PAGE 299

[1] Livius. Gloria tantum elatus, non ira, in medios hostes irruere, quod completis muris conspici se pugnantem, a muro spectantibus, egregium ducebat.

[2] [No whoa, or ho, with him; i.e. there's no stopping him. Proverbial.]

[3] I demens, et sævas curre per Alpes. Aude aliquid, etc., Ut pueris placeas, et declamatio fias.—Juv. Sat. 10.

[4] In Moriæ Encom.   [5] Juvenal. Sat. 4.

[6] Sueton. cap. 12, in Domitiano.   [7] Brisonius.

[8] Antonius ab assentatoribus evectus Liberum se patrem appellari jussit, et pro deo se venditavit. Redimitus hedera, et corona velatus aurea, et thyrsum tenens, cothurnisque succinctus, curru velut Liber pater vectus est Alexandriæ.—Pater. vol. post.

[9] Minervæ nuptias ambit, tanto furore percitus, ut satellites mitteret ad videndum num dea in thalamis venisset, etc.

[10] Ælian, lib. 12.   [11] De mentis alienat. cap. 3.

PAGE 300

[1] Sequiturque superbia formam. Livius, lib. 11: Oraculum est, vivida sæpe ingenia luxuriare hac et evanescere, multosque sensum penitus amisisse. Homines intuentur, ac si ipsi non essent homines.

[2] Galeus de Rubeis, civis noster faber ferrarius, ob inventionem instrumenti, cochleæ olim Archimedis dicti, præ lætitia insanivit.

[3] Insania postmodum correptus, ob nimiam inde arrogantiam. ["One Carius, a soldier" = a Carian soldier.]

[4] Bene ferre magnam disce fortunam.—Hor. Fortunam reverenter habe, quicunque repente Dives ab exili progrediere loco.—Ausonius.

[5] Processit squalidus et submissus, ut hesterni diei gaudium intemperans hodie castigaret.   [6] Uxor Hen. 8.

[7] Neutrius se fortunæ extremum libenter experturam dixit: sed si necessitas alterius subinde imponeretur, optare se difficilem et adversam: quod in hac nulli unquam defuit solatium, in altera multis consilium, etc. —Lod. Vives.

[8] Peculiaris furor, qui ex literis fit.

[9] Nihil magis auget, ac assidua studia, et profundæ cogitationes.

PAGE 301

[1] Study is a continual and earnest meditation, applied to something with great desire.—Tully.

[2] Non desunt, qui ex jugi studio, et intempestiva lucubratione, huc devenerunt, hi præ cæteris enim plerumque melancholia solent infestari.

[3] Et illi qui sunt subtilis ingenii, et multæ præmeditationis, de facili incidunt in melancholiam.

[4] Ob studiorum sollicitudinem, lib. 5, tit. 5.

[5] Gaspar Ens, Thesaur. Polit. Apoteles. 31. Græcis hanc pestem relinquite quæ dubium non est, quin brevi omnem iis vigorem ereptura Martiosque spiritus exhaustura sit, ut ad arma tractanda plane inhabiles futuri sint.

[6] Knolles, Turk. Hist.   [7] Acts xxvi, 24.

[8] Nimiis studiis melancholicus evasit, dicens se Biblium in capite habere.

[9] Cur melancholia assidua, crebrisque deliramentis, vexentur eorum animi ut desipere cogantur.

Page 302

[1] Sollers quilibet artifex instrumenta sua diligentissime curat; penicillos pictor; malleos incudesque faber ferrarius; miles equos, arma; venator, auceps, aves et canes; citharam citharædus, etc.; soli Musarum mystæ tam negligentes sunt, ut instrumentum illud quo mundum universum metiri solent, spiritum scilicet, penitus negligere videantur.

[2] Arcus et arma tibi non sunt imitanda Dianæ. Si nunquam cesses tendere mollis erit.—Ovid.

[3] Ephemer. [4] [Marlowe, Hero and Leander, First Sestiad.]

[5] Contemplatio cerebrum exsiccat et extinguit calorem naturalem, unde cerebrum frigidum et siccum evadit, quod est melancholicum. Accedit ad hoc, quod natura in contemplatione, cerebro prorsus cordique intenta, stomachum heparque destituit, unde ex alimentis male coctis, sanguis crassus et niger efficitur, dum nimio otio membrorum superflui vapores non exhalant.

[6] Cerebrum exsiccatur, corpora sensim gracilescunt.

[7] Studiosi sunt cachectici et nunquam bene colorati; propter debilitatem digestivæ facultatis, multiplicantur in iis superfluitates.—Jo. Voschius, parte 2, cap. 5, de peste.

[8] Nullus mihi per otium dies exit, partem noctis studiis dedico, non vero somno, sed oculos vigilia fatigatos cadentesque, in opere detineo.

Page 303

[1] Johannes Hanuschius Bohemus, nat. 1516, eruditus vir, nimiis studiis in phrenesin incidit. Montanus instances in a Frenchman of Tolosa.

[2] Cardinalis Cæsius; ob laborem, vigiliam, et diuturna studia factus melancholicus.

[3] Ingenium sibi quod vanas desumpsit Athenas, Et septem studiis annos dedit, insenuitque Libris et curis, statua taciturnius exit, Plerumque et risu populum quatit.—Hor. Ep. 1, lib. 2.

[4] Pers. Sat. 3. They cannot fiddle; but, as Themistocles said, he could make a small town become a great city.

[5] Pers. Sat. [6] Translated by Mr. B[arton] Holliday.

Page 304

[1] Thomas rubore confusus dixit se de argumento cogitasse.

[2] Plutarch, vita Marcelli. Nec sensit urbem captam, nec milites in domum irruentes, adeo intentus studiis, etc.

[3] [Lake Leman.]

[4] Sub furiæ larva circumivit urbem, dictitans se exploratorem ab inferis venisse, delaturum dæmonibus mortalium peccata.

[5] Petronius. Ego arbitror in scholis stultissimos fieri, quia nihil eorum quæ in usu habemus aut audiunt aut vident.

[6] Novi meis diebus, plerosque studiis literarum deditos, qui disciplinis admodum abundabant, sed si nihil civilitatis habent, nec rem publ. nec domesticam regere norant. Stupuit Paglarensis et furti villicum accusavit, qui suem fetam undecim porcellos, asinam unum duntaxat pullum enixam retulerat.

[7] Lib. 1, Epist. 3. Adhuc scholasticus tantum est; quo genere hominum, nihil aut est simplicius, aut sincerius, aut melius.

Page 305

[1] Jure privilegiandi, qui ob commune bonum abbreviant sibi vitam.

[2] Virg. 6 Æn.

[3] Plutarch. vita ejus. Certum agricolationis lucrum, etc.

[4] Quotannis fiunt consules et proconsules, rex et poeta quotannis non nascitur.

PAGE 306

[1] Matt. xxi.   [2] Hor. Epist. 20, lib. I.
[3] Lib. I de contem. amor.

PAGE 307

[1] Satyricon.   [2] Juv. Sat. 5.
[3] Ars colit astra.   [4] Aldrovandus de avibus, lib. 12, Gesner, etc.
[5] Literas habent queis sibi et fortunæ suæ maledicant.—Sat. Menip.

PAGE 308

[1] Lib. de libris propriis, fol. 24.
[2] Præfat translat. Plutarch.
[3] Polit. disput. Laudibus extollunt eos ac si virtutibus pollerent quos
ob infinita scelera potius vituperare oporteret.
[4] Or as horses know not their strength, they consider not their own
worth.
[5] Plura ex Simonidis familiaritate Hiero consecutus est, quam ex Hieronis
Simonides.
[6] Hor. lib. 4, od. 9.
[7] Inter inertes et plebeios fere jacet, ultimum locum habens, nisi tot
artis virtutisque insignia, turpiter, obnoxie, supparisitando fascibus
subjecerit protervæ insolentisque potentiæ.—Lib. I de contempt. rerum
fortuitarum.   [8] Buchanan, Eleg. lib.

PAGE 309

[1] In Satyricon. Intrat senex, sed cultu non ita speciosus, ut facile appa-
reret eum hac nota literatum esse, quos divites odisse solent. Ego, inquit,
poeta sum. Quare ergo tam male vestitus es? Propter hoc ipsum; amor
ingenii neminem unquam divitem fecit.
[2] Petronius Arbiter.
[3] Oppressus paupertate animus nihil eximium, aut sublime cogitare
potest, amœnitates literarum, aut elegantiam, quoniam nihil præsidii in
his ad vitæ commodum videt, primo negligere, mox odisse incipit.—Heins.

PAGE 310

[1] Epistol. quæst. lib. 4, ep. 21.   [2] Ciceron. dial.
[3] Epist. lib. 2.   [4] Ja. Dousa, Epodon lib. 2, car. 2.

PAGE 311

[1] Plautus.   [2] Barcl. Argenis, lib. 3.
[3] Joh. Howson, 4 Novembris 1597. The sermon was printed by Arnold
Hartfield.

PAGE 312

[1] Pers. Sat. 3.
[2] E lecto exsilientes, ad subitum tintinnabuli plausum quasi fulmine
territi.
[3] Mart.   [4] Mart.   [5] Sat. Menip.

PAGE 313

[1] Lib. 3 de cons.
[2] I had no money, I wanted impudence, I could not scramble, temporize,
dissemble: non pranderet olus, etc. Vis, dicam? ad palpandum et adu-
landum penitus insulsus, recudi non possum, jam senior ut sim talis, et
fingi nolo, utcunque male cedat in rem meam et obscurus inde delitescam.
[3] Vit. Crassi. Nec facile judicare potest utrum pauperior cum primo ad
Crassum, etc.

Page 314

[1] Deum habent iratum, sibique mortem æternam acquirunt, aliis miserabilem ruinam.—Serrarius in Josuam, 7.

[2] Nicephorus, lib. 10, cap. 5.

[3] Lord Cook, in his Reports, second part, fol. 44.   [4] Euripides.

[5] Sir Henry Spelman, de non temerandis ecclesiis.

Page 315

[1] 1 Tim. iv, 2.   [2] Hor.

[3] Primum locum apud omnes gentes habet patricius deorum cultus, et geniorum, nam hunc diutissime custodiunt, tam Græci quam Barbari, etc.

[4] Tom. 1, de steril. trium annorum sub Elia sermone.

[5] Ovid. Fast.

[6] De male quæsitis vix gaudet tertius hæres. [Ill-gotten goods thrive not to the third heir.]   [7] Strabo, lib. 4 Geog.

Page 316

[1] Nihil facilius opes evertet, quam avaritia et fraude parta. Etsi enim seram addas tali arcæ et exteriore janua et vecte eam communias, intus tamen fraudem et avaritiam, etc.—In 5 Corinth.

[2] Acad. cap. 7.

[3] Ars neminem habet inimicum præter ignorantem.

[4] [Frederick Barbarossa, whose favourite bit of Latin follows.]

[5] Lipsius, Epist. quest. lib. 4, epist. 21.

Page 317

[1] Dr. King, in his last lecture on Jonah, sometime Right Reverend Lord Bishop of London.

[2] Quibus opes et otium, hi barbaro fastu litteras contemnunt.

[3] Lucan. lib. 8.   [4] Spartian. Solliciti de rebus nimis.

[5] Nicet. 1. Anal. Fumis lucubrationum sordebant.

[6] Grammaticis olim et dialectices jurisque professoribus, qui specimen eruditionis dedissent, eadem dignitatis insignia decreverunt Imperatores, quibus ornabant heroas.—Erasm. ep. Jo. Fabio epis. Vien.

Page 318

[1] Probus vir et philosophus magis præstat inter alios homines, quam rex inclytus inter plebeios.   [2] Heinsius, præfat. Poematum.

[3] Servile nomen scholaris jam.   [4] Seneca.

[5] Haud facile emergunt, etc.

[6] Media quod noctis ab hora Sedisti qua nemo faber, qua nemo sedebat, Qui docet obliquo lanam deducere ferro: Rara tamen merces.—Juv. Sat. 7.

[7] Chil. 4, cent. 1, adag. 1.

[8] Had I done as others did, put myself forward, I might have haply been as great a man as many of my equals.

Page 319

[1] Catullus.   [2] Juven.

[3] Nemo est quem non Phœbus hic noster solo intuitu lubentiorem reddat.

Page 320

[1] Panegyr.   [2] Virgil.

[3] Rarus enim ferme sensus communis in illa Fortuna.—Juv. Sat. 8.

[4] Quis enim generosum dixerit hunc qui Indignus genere, et præclaro nomine tantum Insignis.—Juv. Sat. 8.

PAGE 321

[1] I have often met with myself, and conferred with, divers worthy gentlemen in the country, no whit inferior, if not to be preferred for divers kind of learning, to many of our academics.

[2] Ipse licet Musis venias comitatus Homere, Nil tamen attuleris, ibis, Homere, foras.

[3] Et legat historias, auctores noverit omnes Tanquam ungues digitosque suos.—Juv. Sat. 7.   [4] Juvenal.

[5] Tu vero licet Orpheus sis, saxa sono testudinis emolliens, nisi plumbea eorum corda auri vel argenti malleo emollias, etc.—Sarisburiensis, Polycrat. lib. 5, cap. 10.

PAGE 322

[1] Juven. Sat. 7.

[2] Euge! bene! no need. Dousa, Epod. lib. 2. Dos ipsa scientia sibique congiarium est.

[3] Quatuor ad portas Ecclesias itur ad omnes; Sanguinis aut Simonis, præsulis atque Dei.—Holcot.

[4] Lib. contra Gentiles de Babila martyre.

[5] Præscribunt, imperant, in ordinem cogunt, ingenium nostrum prout ipsis videbitur, astringunt et relaxant ut papilionem pueri aut bruchum filo demittunt, aut attrahunt, nos a libidine sua pendere æquum censentes. —Heinsius.

PAGE 323

[1] John v.

[2] Epist. lib. 2. Jam suffectus in locum demortui, protinus exortus est adversarius, etc.; post multos labores, sumptus, etc.

PAGE 324

[1] Jun. Acad. cap. 6.

[2] Accipiamus pecuniam, demittamus asinum ut apud Patavinos, Italos.

[3] Hos non ita pridem perstrinxi, in Philosophastro, Comœdia Latina, in Æde Christi Oxon. publice habita, anno 1617, Feb. 16.

[4] Sat. Menip.

PAGE 325

[1] 2 Cor. ii, 17.   [2] Comment. in Gal.   [3] Heinsius.
[4] Ecclesiast.   [5] Luth. in Gal.
[6] Pers. Sat. 2.   [7] Sallust.

PAGE 326

[1] Sat. Menip.   [2] Budæus, de Asse, lib. 5.
[3] Lib. de rep. Gallorum.   [4] Campian.

PAGE 330

[1] Proem lib. 2. Nulla ars constitui potest.

[2] Lib. 1, cap. 19, de morborum causis. Quas declinare licet aut nulla necessitate utimur.

PAGE 331

[1] Quo semel est imbuta recens servabit odorem Testa diu.—Hor.

[2] Sicut valet ad fingendas corporis atque animi similitudines vis et natura seminis, sic lactis proprietas. Neque id in hominibus solum, sed in pecudibus animadversum. Nam si ovium lacte hædi, aut caprarum agni alerentur, constat fieri in his lanam duriorem, in illis capillum gigni severiorem.

[3] Adulta in ferarum persecutione ad miraculum usque sagax.

[4] Tam animal quodlibet quam homo, ab illa cujus lacte nutritur, naturam contrahit.

[5] Improba, informis, impudica, temulenta nutrix, etc.; quoniam in moribus efformandis magnam sæpe partem ingenium altricis et natura lactis tenet.

[6] H'rcanæque admorunt ubera tigres.—Virg.

[7] Lib. 2 de Cæsaribus.

[8] Beda, cap. 27, lib. 1, Eccles. hist.

[9] Ne insitivo lactis alimento degeneret corpus, et animus corrumpatur.

Page 332

[1] Lib. 3 de civ. convers.   [2] Stephanus.

[3] To. 2.   Nutrices non quasvis, sed maxime probas deligamus.

[4] Nutrix non sit lasciva aut temulenta.—Hier.

[5] Prohibendum ne stolida lactet.   [6] Pers.

[7] Nutrices interdum matribus sunt meliores.

Page 333

[1] Lib. de morbis capitis, cap. de mania. Haud postrema causa supputatur educatio, inter has mentis abalienationis causas.   Injusta noverca.

[2] Lib. 2, cap. 4.

[3] Idem.   Et quod maxime nocet, dum in teneris ita timent nihil conantur.

Page 334

[1] Præfat. ad Testam.

[2] Plus mentis pædagogico supercilio abstulit, quam unquam præceptis suis sapientiæ instillavit.

[3] Ter. Adel. 3, 3.   [4] Idem, Act. 1, sc. 2.

Page 335

[1] Camerarius, Emb. 77, cent. 2, hath elegantly expressed it an emblem: Perdit amando, etc.

[2] Prov. xiii, 24.   He that spareth the rod hates his son.

[3] Lib. 2 de consol.   Tam stulte pueros diligimus ut odisse potius videamur; illos non ad virtutem sed ad injuriam, non ad eruditionem sed ad luxum, non ad virtutem sed voluptatem educantes.

[4] Lib. 1, cap. 3.   Educatio altera natura, alterat animos et voluntatem, atque utinam (inquit) liberorum mores non ipsi perderemus, quum infantiam statim deliciis solvimus: mollior ista educatio, quam indulgentiam vocamus, nervos omnes, et mentis et corporis frangit; fit ex his consuetudo, inde natura.

[5] Perinde agit ac siquis de calceo sit sollicitus, pedem nihil curet.   Juven. Nil patri minus est quam filius.

[6] Lib. 3. de sapientia.   Qui avaris pædagogis pueros alendos dant, vel clausos in cœnobiis jejunare simul et sapere, nihil aliud agunt, nisi ut sint vel non sine stultitia eruditi, vel non integra vita sapientes.

Page 336

[1] Terror et metus, maxime ex improviso accedentes, ita animum commovent, ut spiritus nunquam recuperent, gravioremque melancholiam terror facit, quam quæ ab interna causa fit.   Impressio tam fortis in spiritibus humoribusque cerebri, ut extracta tota sanguinea massa, ægre exprimatur, et hæc horrenda species melancholiæ frequenter oblata mihi, omnes exercens, viros, juvenes, senes.

[2] Tract. de melan. cap. 7 et 8.   Non ab intemperie, sed agitatione, dilatatione, contractione, motu spirituum.

[3] Lib. de fort. et virtut. Alex.   Præsertim ineunte periculo, ubi res prope adsunt terribiles.

[4] Fit a visione horrenda, revera apparente, vel per insomnia.—Platerus.
[5] A painter's wife in Basil, 1600, somniavit filium bello mortuum, inde melancholica consolari noluit.
[6] Senec. Herc. Œt.
[7] Quarta pars comment. de statu religionis in Gallia sub Carolo 9, 1572.
[8] Ex occursu dæmonium aliqui furore corripiuntur, ut experientia notum est.   [9] Lib. 8, in Arcad.   [10] Lucret.

PAGE 337

[1] Puellæ extra urbem in prato concurrentes, etc.; mæsta et melancholica domum rediit per dies aliquot vexata, dum mortua est.—Platerus.
[2] Altera trans-Rhenana ingressa sepulchrum recens apertum, vidit cadaver, et domum subito reversa putavit eam vocare; post paucos dies obiit, proximo sepulchro collocata. Altera patibulum sero præteriens, metuebat ne urbe exclusa illic pernoctaret, unde melancholica facta, per multos annos laboravit.—Platerus.
[3] Subitus occursus, inopinata lectio.
[4] Lib. de auditione.   [5] Theod. Prodromus, lib. 7 Amorum.
[6] Effuso cernens fugientes agmine turmas, Quis mea nunc inflat cornua? Faunus ait.—Alciat. embl. 122.

PAGE 338

[1] Judges vii, 19.   [2] Plutarchus, vita ejus.
[3] In furorem cum sociis versus.   [4] Subitarius terræ motus.
[5] Cœpit inde desipere cum dispendio sanitatis, inde adeo dementans, ut sibi ipsi mortem inferret.
[6] Historica relatio de rebus Japonicis, tract 2, de legat. regis Chinensis, a Lodovico Frois Jesuita. A. 1596. Fuscini derepente tanta acris caligo et terræ motus, ut multi capite dolerent, plurimis cor mœrore et melancholia obrueretur. Tantum fremitum edebat, ut tonitru fragorem imitari videretur, tantamque, etc. In urbe Sacai tam horrificus fuit, ut homines vix sui compotes essent, a sensibus abalienati, mœrore oppressi tam horrendo spectaculo, etc. [Froe's narrative is in Hakluyt (Everyman ed. iv. 195–209).]
[7] Quum subit illius tristissima noctis imago.

PAGE 339

[1] Qui solo aspectu medicinæ movebatur ad purgandum.
[2] Sicut viatores si ad saxum impegerint, aut nautæ, memores sui casus, non ista modo quæ offendunt, sed et similia horrent perpetuo et tremunt.
[3] Leviter volant, graviter vulnerant.—Bernardus.
[4] Ensis sauciat corpus, mentem sermo.
[5] Sciatis eum esse qui a nemine fere ævi sui magnate non illustre stipendium habuit, ne mores ipsorum satiris suis notaret.—Gasp. Barthius, præfat. Pornoboscodid.
[6] [i.e. Pope Adrian VI.]
[7] [The statue popularly called Pasquino or Pasquillo, to which the pasquinades were affixed, and from which they got their name.]
[8] Jovius, in vita ejus. Gravissime tulit famosis libellis nomen suum ad Pasquilli statuam fuisse laceratum, decrevitque ideo statuam demoliri, etc.
[9] Plato, lib. 13 de legibus. Qui existimationem curant, poetas vere-antur, quia magnam vim habent ad laudandum et vituperandum.

PAGE 340

[1] Petulanti splene cachinno.
[2] Curial. lib. 2. Ea quorundam est inscitia, ut quoties loqui, toties mordere licere sibi putent.
[3] Ter. Eunuch.   [4] Hor. Ser. lib. 2, sat. 4.

[5] Lib. 2.   [6] De orat.
[7] Laudando, et mira iis persuadendo.
[8] Et vana inflatus opinione, incredibilia ac ridenda quædam musices præcepta commentaretur, etc.

Page 341

[1] Ut voces, nudis parietibus illisæ, suavius ac acutius resilirent.
[2] Immortalitati et gloriæ suæ prorsus invidentes.
[3] 2, 2dæ quæst. 75.   Irrisio mortale peccatum.   [4] Ps. xv, 3.

Page 342

[1] Balthasar Castilio, lib. 2 de aulico.
[2] De sermone lib. 4, cap. 3.   [3] Fol. 55, Galateus.

Page 343

[1] Tully, Tusc. quæst.   [2] Mart. lib. 1, epig. 41.
[3] Tales joci ab injuriis non possint discerni.—Galateus, fol. 55.
[4] Pybrac, in his Quatrains, 37.
[5] Ego hujus misera fatuitate et dementia conflictor.—Tull. ad Attic. lib. 11.

Page 344

[1] Miserum est aliena vivere quadra.—Juv.
[2] Crambe bis cocta.   Vitæ me redde priori.
[3] Hor.   [4] De tranquil. animæ.

Page 345

[1] Lib. 8.   [2] Tullius Lepido, Fam. 10, 27.
[3] Boterus, lib. 1 Polit. cap. 4.   [4] Laet. descrip. Americæ.
[5] If there be any inhabitants.
[6] In Toxari.   Interdiu quidem collum vinctum est, et manus constricta, noctu vero totum corpus vincitur; ad has miserias accedit corporis fœtor, strepitus ejulantium, somni brevitas; hæc omnia plane molesta et intolerabilia.   [7] In 9 Rhasis.

Page 346

[1] William the Conqueror's eldest son.
[2] Sallust.   Romam triumpho ductus tandemque in carcerem conjectus, animi dolore periit.
[3] Camden, in Wiltsh.   Miserum senem ita fame et calamitatibus in carcere fregit, inter mortis metum et vitæ tormenta, etc.
[4] Vies hodie.   ["The Vize" (Burton's "Vies") is the local name.]
[5] Seneca.   [6] Com. ad Hebræos.
[7] Part. 2, sect. 3, memb. 3.
[8] Quem ut difficilem morbum pueris tradere formidamus.—Plut.
[9] Lucan. lib. 1.
[10] As in the silver mines at Freiburg in Germany.—Fynes Moryson.

Page 347

[1] Euripides.
[2] Tom. 4 dial.   Minore periculo solem quam hunc defixis oculis licet intueri.
[3] Omnis enim res, Virtus, fama, decus, divina humanaque, pulchris Divitiis parent.—Hor. Ser. lib. 2, sat. 3.   Clarus eris, fortis justus, sapiens, etiam rex, Et quicquid volet.—Hor.
[4] Et genus, et formam, regina pecunia donat.   Money adds spirits, courage, etc.   [5] Epist. ad Brutum.
[6] Our young master, a fine towardly gentleman (God bless him!) and

hopeful; why, he is heir apparent to the right worshipful, to the right honourable, etc.

[7] O nummi, nummi! vobis hunc præstat honorem.

[8] Exinde sapere eum omnes dicimus, ac quisque fortunam habet.—Plaut. Pseud.

[9] Aurea fortuna, principum cubiculis reponi solita.—Julius Capitolinus, vita Antonini.   [10] Petronius.

PAGE 348

[1] Theologi opulentis adhærent, jurisperiti pecuniosis, literati nummosis, liberalibus artifices.

[2] Multi illum juvenes, multæ petiere puellæ.

[3] Dummodo sit dives barbarus, ille placet.

[4] Plut. in Lucullo, a rich chamber so called.

[5] Panis pane melior.   [6] Juv. Sat. 5.   [7] Hor. Sat. 5, lib. 2.

[8] Bohemus de Turcis, et Bredenbach.   [9] Euphormio.

[10] Qui pecuniam habent, elati sunt animis, [those who have money are] lofty spirits, brave men at arms; all rich men are generous, courageous, etc.

PAGE 349

[1] Nummus ait, Pro me nubat Cornubia Romæ.

[2] Non fuit apud mortales ullum excellentius certamen, non inter celeres celerrimo, non inter robustos robustissimo, etc.

[3] Quicquid libet licet.   [4] Hor. Sat. 5, lib. 2.

[5] Cum moritur dives concurrunt undique cives: Pauperis ad funus vix est ex millibus unus.

PAGE 350

[1] [See Horace, Sat. 1, 2, 1.]

[2] Et modo quid fuit? Ignoscet mihi genius tuus, noluisses de manu ejus nummos accipere.

[3] He that wears silk, satin, velvet, and gold lace, must needs be a gentleman.

[4] Xenophon, Cyropæd. lib. 8.

[5] [Fastidious Brisk is a character in Jonson's Every Man out of his Humour; Sir Petronel Flash is in Eastward Ho! by Jonson, Chapman, and Marston.]

[6] Euripides.   [7] Est sanguis atque spiritus pecunia mortalibus.

[8] In tenui rare est facundia panno.—Juv.   [9] Hor.

[10] Egere est offendere, et indigere scelestum esse.—Sat. Menip.

[11] Plautus [Curculio], Act. 4.

PAGE 351

[1] Nullum tam barbarum, tam vile munus est, quod non lubentissime obire velit gens vilissima.

[2] Lausius, orat. in Hispaniam.

[3] Laet. descrip. Americæ.   [4] Plautus.

[5] Leo Afer, cap. ult. lib. 1. Edunt non ut bene vivant, sed ut fortiter laborent.—Heinsius.

[6] Munster de rusticis Germaniæ, Cosmog. cap. 27, lib. 3.

[7] Ter. Eunuch.

[8] Pauper paries factus, quem caniculæ commingant.

[9] Lib. 1, cap. ult.

[10] Deos omnes illis infensos diceres: tam pannosi, fame fracti, tot assidue malis afficiuntur, tanquam pecora quibus splendor rationis emortuus.

[11] Peregrin. Hieros.

[12] Nihil omnino meliorem vitam degunt, quam feræ in silvis, jumenta in terris.—Leo Afer.   [13] Bartholomæus à Casa.

Page 352

[1] Ortelius, in Helvetia. Qui habitant in Cæsia valle ut plurimum latomi, in Oscella valle cultrorum fabri fumarii, in Vigetia sordidum genus hominum, quod repurgandis caminis victum parat.

[2] I write not this anyways to upbraid, or scoff at, or misuse poor men, but rather to condole and pity them by expressing, etc.

[3] Chremylus, Act. 4 Plut.

[4] Paupertas durum onus miseris mortalibus.

[5] Vexat censura columbas.

[6] Deux-ace non possunt, et six-cinque solvere nolunt: Omnibus est notum quater-tre solvere totum.

[7] Scandia, Africa, Lithuania.

[8] Montaigne, in his Essays, speaks of certain Indians in France, that being asked how they liked the country, wondered how a few rich men could keep so many poor men in subjection, that they did not cut their throats.

Page 353

[1] Angustas animas animoso in pectore versant.

[2] [?obscenely.]   [3] Donatus, vit. ejus.

[4] Prov. xix, 7: "Though he be instant, yet they will not."

[5] Petronius.

[6] Non est qui doleat vicem; ut Petrus Christum, jurant se hominem non novisse.

[7] Ovid. in Trist.   [8] Horat.   [9] Ter. Eunuchus, Act. 2.

Page 354

[1] Quid quod materiam præbet causamque jocandi: Si toga sordida sit?—Juv. Sat. 3.

[2] Hor.   [3] In Phœniss.   [4] Odyss. 17.   [5] Idem.

[6] Mantuan.   [7] De Africa, lib. 1, cap. ult.

[8] Lib. 5 de legibus. Furacissima paupertas, sacrilega, turpis, flagitiosa, omnium malorum opifex.

Page 355

[1] Theognis.

[2] Deipnosophist, lib. 12. Millies potius moriturum (si quis sibi mente constaret) quam tam vilis et ærumnosi victus communionem habere.

[3] Gasper Vilela Jesuita, Epist. Japon. lib.

[4] Mat. Riccius, Expedit. in Sinas, lib. 1, cap. 3.

[5] Vos Romani procreatos filios feris et canibus exponitis, nunc strangulatis vel in saxum eliditis, etc.

[6] Cosmog. 4 lib. cap. 22. Vendunt liberos victu carentes tanquam pecora, interdum et seipsos; ut apud divites saturentur cibis.

[7] Vel bonorum desperatione vel malorum perpessione fracti et fatigati, plures violentas manus sibi inferunt.

Page 356

[1] Hor.

[2] Ingenio poteram superas volitare per arces: Ut me pluma levat, sic grave mergit onus.

[3] Terent.   [4] Hor. Sat. 3, lib. 1.   [5] Paschalius.   [6] Petronius.

[7] Herodotus, vita ejus. Scaliger in Poet. Potentiorum ædes ostiatim adiens, aliquid accipiebat, canens carmina sua, concomitante eum puerorum choro.

[8] Hegio, Ter. Adelph. Act. 4, sc. 3.

Page 357

[1] Donat. vita ejus.　　　　　[2] Euripides.　　　　　[3] Plutarch, vita ejus.
[4] Vita Ter.　　　　[5] Gomesius, lib. 3, cap. 21, de sale.
[6] Ter. Eunuch. Act. 2, scen. 2.　　　[7] Liv. dec. 5, lib. 2.　　　[8] Comineus.
[9] He that hath £5 per annum coming in more than others, scorns him that hath less, and is a better man.　　　[10] Prov. xxx, 8.

Page 358

[1] De anima, cap. de mœrore.　　　　[2] Lib. 12 Epist.　　　[3] Virg. Æn. 4.
[4] Patres mortuos coram astantes et filios, etc.—Marcellus Donatus.
[5] Epist. lib. 2.　Virginium video, audio defunctum, cogito, alloquor.

Page 359

[1] Calpurnius Græcus.　　　　[2] Chaucer.　　　　[3] Præfat. lib. 6.
[4] Lib. de obitu Satyri fratis.

Page 360

[1] Ovid. Met.　　　　[2] Plut. vita ejus.
[3] Nobilis matrona melancholica ob mortem mariti.
[4] Ex matris obitu in desperationem incidit.
[5] Matthias à Michou.　Boter. Amphitheat.
[6] Lo. Vertoman. M. Polus Venetus, lib. 1, cap. 54. Perimunt eos quos in via obvios habent, dicentes, Ite, et domino nostro regi servite in alia vita. Nec tam in homines insaniunt, sed in equos, etc.
[7] Vita ejus.
[8] Lib. 4 vitæ ejus. Auream ætatem condiderat ad humani generis salutem, quum nos, statim ab optimi principis excessu, vere ferream pateremur, famem, pestem, etc.

Page 361

[1] Lib. de asse.　　　　[2] Maph.
[3] Ortelius, Itinerario.　Ob annum integrum a cantu, tripudiis, et saltationibus tota civitas abstinere jubetur.
[4] Virg.　　　[5] See Barletius, de vita et ob. Scanderbeg. lib. 13 Hist.
[6] Matt. Paris.　　　[7] Juvenalis.

Page 362

[1] Multi qui res amatas perdiderant, ut filios, opes, non sperantes recuperare, propter assiduam talium considerationem melancholici fiunt, ut ipse vidi.
[2] Stanihurstus, Hib. hist.
[3] Cap. 3.　Melancholia semper venit ob jacturam pecuniæ, victoriæ repulsam, mortem liberorum, quibus longo post tempore animus torquetur, et a dispositione sit habitus.
[4] Consil. 26.　　　　[5] Nubrigensis.　　　　[6] Epig. 22.

Page 363

[1] Lib. 8 Venet. hist.　　　　[2] [Charles, the Constable de Bourbon.]
[3] Templa ornamentis nudata, spoliata, in stabula equorum et asinorum versa, etc.　Infulæ humi conculcatæ pedibus, etc.
[4] In oculis maritorum dilectissimæ conjuges ab Hispanorum lixis constupratæ sunt.　Filiæ magnatum toris destinatæ, etc.
[5] Ita fastu ante unum mensem turgida civitas, et cacuminibus cœlum pulsare visa, ad inferos usque paucis diebus dejecta.
[6] Sect. 2, memb. 4, subs. 3.

PAGE 364

[1] Accersunt sibi malum.
[2] Si non observemus, nihil valent.—Polydore.
[3] Consil. 26, lib. 2.   [4] Harm watch, harm catch.
[5] Geor. Buchanan.
[6] Juvenis, sollicitus de futuris frustra, factus melancholicus.
[7] Pausanias in Achaicis, lib. 7.   Ubi omnium eventus dignoscuntur. Speculum tenui suspensum funiculo demittunt: et ad Cyaneas petras ad Lyciæ fontes, etc.

PAGE 365

[1] Expedit. in Sinas, lib. 1, cap. 3.
[2] Timendo præoccupat quod vitat ultro, provocatque quod fugit, gaudetque mærens et lubens miser fuit.—Heinsius Austriaco.
[3] Tom. 4, dial. 8, Cataplous.   Auri puri mille talenta, me hodie tibi daturum promitto, etc.
[4] Ibidem.   Hei mihi! quæ relinquenda prædia! quam fertiles agri! etc.
[5] Hadrian.   [6] Industria superflua circa res inutiles.

PAGE 366

[1] Flavæ secreta Minervæ ut viderat Aglauros.—Ov. Met. 2.
[2] Contra Philos. cap. 61.   [3] Matt. Paris.

PAGE 367

[1] Seneca.   [2] [Roman busybodies referred to by Phædrus and Martial.]

PAGE 368

[1] Jos. Scaliger, in Gnomis.
[2] "A virtuous woman is the crown of her husband" (Prov. xii, 4): "but she," etc.
[3] Lib. 17, epist. 105.   [4] Titionatur, candelabratur, etc.
[5] Daniel, in Rosamund.   [6] Chalonerus, lib. 9 de repub.Angl.
[7] Elegans virgo invita cuidam e nostratibus nupsit, etc.

PAGE 369

[1] Prov. x, 1.
[2] De increm. urb. lib. 3, cap. 3.   Tanquam diro mucrone confossis, his nulla requies, nulla delectatio, sollicitudine, gemitu, furore, desperatione, timore, tanquam ad perpetuam ærumnam infeliciter rapti.
[3] Humfredus Lluyd, epist. ad Abrahamum Ortelium.   Mr. Vaughan in his Golden Fleece.   Litibus et controversiis usque ad omnium bonorum consumptionem contendunt.
[4] Quæque repulsa gravis.   [5] Lib. 36, cap. 5.
[6] Nihil æque amarum, quam diu pendere: quidam æquiore animo ferunt præcidi spem suam suam quam trahi. Seneca, cap. 3, lib. 2, de ben. Virg. Plater. Observat. lib. 1.

PAGE 370

[1] Spretæque injuria formæ.   [2] Turpe relinqui est.—Hor.
[3] Scimus enim generosas naturas nulla re citius moveri aut gravius affici quam contemptu ac despicientia.
[4] Ad Atticum epist. lib. 12.   [5] Epist. ad Brutum.

PAGE 371

[1] In Phœniss.   [2] In laudem calvit.   [3] Ovid.
[4] E Cret.   [5] Hor. Car. lib. 3, ode 27.

Page 372

[1] Hist. lib. 3.
[2] Non mihi si centum linguæ sint, oraque centum, Omnia causarum percurrere nomina possem.
[3] Cælius, lib. 17, cap. 2.
[4] Ita mente exagitati sunt, ut in triremi se constitutos putarent, marique vagabundo tempestate jactatos, proinde naufragium veriti, egestis undique rebus, vasa omnia in viam e fenestris, ceu in mare, præcipitarunt: postridie, etc.

Page 373

[1] Aram vobis servatoribus diis erigemus.
[2] Lib. de gemmis.
[3] Quæ gestatæ infelicem et tristem reddunt, curas augent, corpus siccant, somnum minuunt.
[4] Ad unum die mente alienatus.
[5] Part 1, sect. 2, subsect. 3.   [6] Juven. Sat. 3.
[7] Intus bestiæ minutæ multæ necant. Numquid minutissima sunt grana arenæ? sed si arena amplius in navem mittatur, mergit illam. Quam minutæ guttæ pluviæ! et tamen implent flumina, domus ejiciunt, timenda ergo ruina multitudinis, si non magnitudinis.

Page 374

[1] Mores sequuntur temperaturam corporis.
[2] Scintillæ latent in corporibus.   [3] Gal. v.
[4] Sicut ex animi affectionibus corpus languescit: sic ex corporis vitiis, et morborum plerisque cruciatibus animum videmus hebetari.—Galenus.
[5] Lib. 1, cap. 16.

Page 375

[1] Corporis itidem morbi animam per consensum, a lege consortii afficiunt, et quanquam objecta multos motus turbulentos in homine concitent, præcipua tamen causa in corde et humoribus spiritibusque consistit, etc.
[2] Hor.   [3] Humores pravi mentiem obnubilant.
[4] Hic humor vel a partis intemperie generatur, vel relinquitur post inflammationes, vel crassior in venis conclusus vel torpidus malignam qualitatem contrahit.
[5] Sæpe constat in febre hominem melancholicum vel post febrem reddi, aut alium morbum. Calida intemperies innata, vel a febre contracta.

Page 376

[1] Raro quis diuturno morbo laborat, qui non sit melancholicus.—Mercurialis, de affect. capitis, lib. 1, cap. 10, de melanc.
[2] Ad nonum lib. Rhasis ad Almansor. cap. 16. Universaliter a quacunque parte potest fieri melancholicus, vel quia aduritur, vel quia non expellit superfluitatem excrementi.
[3] A liene, jecinore, utero, et aliis partibus oritur.
[4] Materia melancholiæ aliquando in corde, in stomacho, hepate, ab hypochondriis, myrache, splene, cum ibi remanet humor melancholicus.
[5] Ex sanguine adusto, intra vel extra caput.
[6] Qui calidum cor habent, cerebrum humidum, facile melancholici.
[7] Sequitur melancholia malam intemperiem frigidam et siccam ipsius cerebri.
[8] Sæpe fit ex calidiore cerebro, aut corpore colligente melancholiam.—Piso.

PAGE 377

[1] Vel per propriam affectionem, vel per consensum, cum vapores exhalant in cerebrum.—Montalt. cap. 14.

[2] Aut ibi gignitur melancholicus fumus, aut aliunde vehitur, alterando animales facultates.

[3] Ab intemperie cordis, modo calidiore, modo frigidiore.

[4] Epist. 209 Scoltzii.

[5] Officina humorum hepar concurrit, etc.

[6] Ventriculus et venæ meseraicae concurrunt, quod hæ partes obstructæ sunt, etc.

[7] Per se sanguinem adurentes.

[8] Lien frigidus et siccus, cap. 13.

[9] Splen obstructus.   [10] De arte med. lib. 3, cap. 24.

[11] A sanguinis putredine in vasis seminariis et utero, et quandoque a spermate diu retento, vel sanguine menstruo in melancholiam verso per putrefactionem, vel adustionem.

[12] Maginus.

PAGE 378

[1] Ergo efficiens causa melancholiæ est calida et sicca intemperies, non frigida et sicca, quod multi opinati sunt; oritur enim a calore cerebri assante sanguinem, etc., tum quod aromata sanguinem incendunt, solitudo, vigilæ, febris præcedens, meditatio, studium, et hæc omnia calefaciunt, ergo ratum sit, etc.

[2] Lib. 1, cap. 13, de melanch.

[3] Lib. 3 Tract. posthum. de melan.

[4] A fatuitate inseparabilis cerebri frigiditas.

[5] Ab interno calore assatur.

[6] Intemperies innata exurens, flavam bilem ac sanguinem in melancholiam convertens.

[7] Si cerebrum sit calidius, fiet spiritus animalis calidior, et delirium maniacum; si frigidior, fiet fatuitas.

PAGE 379

[1] Melancholia capitis accedit post phrenesim aut longam moram moram sub sole, aut persussionem in capite.—Cap. 13, lib. 1.

[2] Qui bibunt vina potentia, et sæpe sunt sub sole.

[3] Curæ validæ, largiores vini et aromatum usus.

[4] A cauterio aut ulcere exsiccato.

[5] Ab ulcere curato incidit in insaniam, aperto vulnere curatur.

[6] A galea nimis calefacta.

[7] Exuritur sanguis aut venæ obstruuntur, quibus obstructis prohibetur transitus chyli ad jecur, corrumpitur et in rugitus et flatus vertitur.

PAGE 380

[1] Stomacho læso robur corporis imminuitur, et reliqua membra alimento orbata, etc.   [2] Hildesheim.

PAGE 381

[1] Habuit sæva animi symptomata quæ impediunt concoctionem, etc.

[2] Usitatissimus morbus cum sit, utile est hujus visceris accidentia considerare, nec leve periculum hujus causas morbi ignorantibus.

[3] Jecur aptum ad generandum talem humorem, splen natura imbecillior. Piso, Altomarus, Guianerius.

[4] Melancholiam, quæ fit a redundantia humoris in toto corpore, victus imprimis generat qui eum humorem parit.

Page 382

[1] Ausonius.   [2] Seneca, Cont. lib. 10, cont. 5.
[3] Quædam universalia, particularia, quædam manifesta, quædam in
orpore, quædam in cogitatione et animo; quædam a stellis, quædam ab
umoribus, quæ ut vinum corpus varie disponit, etc. Diversa phantas-
.ata pro varietate causæ externae, internæ.
[4] Lib. 1 de risu, fol. 17.   Ad ejus esum alii sudant, alii vomunt, stent,
.bunt, saltant, alii rident, tremunt, dormiunt, etc.

Page 383

[1] T. Bright, cap. 20.
[2] Nigrescit hic humor aliquando supercalefactus, aliquando super-
igefactus.—Melanel. e Gal.
[3] Interprete F. Calvo.
[4] Oculi his excavantur, venti gignuntur circum præcordia et acidi
uctus, sicci fere ventres, vertigo, tinnitus aurium, somni pusilli, somnia
rribilia et interrupta.   [5] Virg. Æn.
[6] Assiduæ eæque acidæ ructationes quæ cibum virulentum pisculen-
umque nidorem, etsi nil tale ingestum sit, referant ob cruditatem.
.entres hisce aridi, somnus plerumque parcus et interruptus, somnia
.surdissima, turbulenta, corporis tremor, capitis gravedo, strepitus
.rca aures et visiones ante oculos, ad venerem prodigi.
[7] Altomarus, Bruel, Piso, Montaltus.
[8] Frequentes habent oculorum nictationes, aliqui tamen fixis oculis
.erumque sunt.
[9] Cent. lib. 1, tract. 9.   Signa hujus morbi sunt plurimus saltus, sonitus
.urium, capitis gravedo; lingua titubat, oculi excavantur, etc.

Page 384

[1] In Pantheon, cap. de Melancholia.
[2] Alvus arida nihil dejiciens, cibi capaces, nihilominus tamen extenuati
.nt.
[3] Nic. Piso. Inflatio carotidum, etc.
[4] Andreas Dudith, Rahamo ep. lib. 3 Crat. epist.   Multa in pulsibus
.perstitio, ausim etiam dicere, tot differentias quæ describuntur a Galeno,
.eque intelligi a quoquam nec observari posse.
[5] T. Bright, cap. 20.
[6] Post 40 ætat. annum, saith Jacchinus in 15, 9 Rhasis. Idem Mer-
.rialis, consil. 86; Trincavellius, tom. 2, cons. 17.
[7] Gordonius. Modo rident, modo flent, silent, etc.
[8] Fernelius, consil. 43 et 45. Montanus, consil. 230. Galen de locis
.fectis, lib. 3, cap. 6.

Page 385

[1] Aphorism. et lib. de melan.
[2] Lib. 2, cap. 6, de locis affect.   Timor et mœstitia, si diutius perseverent,
.c.
[3] Tract. posthumo de melan. edit. Venetiis 1620, per Bolzettam bibliop.
.hi diligentius hanc rem consideranti, patet quosdam esse, qui non
.borant mœrore et timore.
[4] Prob. lib. 3.
[5] Physiog. lib. 1, cap. 8. Quibus multa frigida bilis atra, stolidi et
.midi, at qui calidi, ingeniosi, amasii, divinosi, spiritu instigati, etc.
[6] Omnes exercent metus et tristitia, et sine causa.
[7] Omnes timent, licent non omnibus idem timendi modus.—Aetius,
.etrab. lib. 2, sect. 2, cap. 9.
[8] Ingenti pavore trepidant.
[9] Multi mortem timent, et tamen sibi ipsis mortem consciscunt, alii
.eli ruinam timent.

Page 386

[1] Affligit eos plena scrupulis conscientia, divinæ misericordiæ diffidente Orco se destinant, fœda lamentatione deplorantes.

[2] Non ausus egredi domo, ne deficeret.

[3] Multi dæmones timent, latrones, insidias.—Avicenna.

[4] Alii comburi, alii de rege.—Rhasis.

[5] Ne terra absorbeantur.—Forestus.

[6] Ne terra dehiscat.—Gordon.

[7] Alii timore mortis timentur et mala gratia principum putant se aliqu commisisse, et ad supplicium requiri.

Page 387

[1] Alius domesticos timet, alius omnes.—Aetius.

[2] Alii timent insidias.—Aurel. lib. 1 de morb. chron. cap. 6.

[3] Ille carissimos, hic omnes homines citra discrimen timet.

[4] Virgil.

[5] Hic in lucem prodire timet, tenebrasque quærit; contra, ille caligino fugit.

[6] Quidam larvas, et malos spiritus ab inimicis veneficiis et incantationib sibi putant objectari. Hippocrates. Potionem se veneficam sumpsis putat, et de hac ructare sibi crebro videtur. Idem Montaltus, cap. 2 Aetius, lib. 2, et alii. Trallianus, lib. 1, cap. 16.

Page 388

[1] Observat. lib. 1. Quando iis nil nocet, nisi quod mulieribus mela cholicis.

[2] Timeo tamen metusque causæ nescius, causa est metus.—Heinsi Austriaco.

[3] Cap. 15 in 9 Rhasis. In multis vidi, præter rationem semper aliqu timent, in cæteris tamen optime se gerunt, neque aliquid præter dignitate committunt.

Page 389

[1] Altomarus, cap. 7. Aretæus. Tristes sunt.

[2] Mant. Egl. 1.

[3] Ovid. Met. 4.

[4] Inquies animus.

[5] Hor. lib. 3, od. 1.

[6] Virg.

[7] Menedemus, Heautont. Act. 1, sc. 1.

Page 390

[1] Altomarus.

[2] Seneca.

[3] Cap. 31. Quo stomachi dolore correptum se etiam de consciscend morte cogitasse dixit.

Page 391

[1] Luget et semper tristatur, solitudinem amat, mortem sibi precatu vitam propriam odio habet.

[2] Facile in iram incidunt.—Aret.

[3] Ira sine causa, velocitas iræ.—Savonarola, Pract. major. Velocit iræ signum.—Avicenna, lib. 3, fen. 1, tract. 4, cap. 18.

[4] Suspicio, diffidentia, symptomata.—Crato, Ep. Julio Alexandrin cons. 185 Scoltzii.

Page 392

[1] Hor.

[2] Pers. Sat. 3.

[3] In his Dutch-work picture.

[4] Howard, cap. 7 Differ.

NOTES

Page 393

[1] Tract. de mel. cap. 2.   Noctu ambulant per silvas, et loca periculosa; eminem timent.

[2] Facile amant.—Altom.   [3] Bodine.

[4] Jo. Major, vitis patrum, fol. 202.   Paulus Abbas eremita tanta solidine perseverat, ut nec vestem, nec vultum mulieris ferre possit, etc.

[5] Consult. lib. 1, cons. 17.

[6] Generally as they are pleased or displeased, so are their continual ogitations pleasing or displeasing.

Page 394

[1] Omnes exercent vanæ intensæque animi cogitationes (N. Piso, Bruel) t assiduæ.

[2] Curiosi de rebus minimis.—Aretæus.

[3] Lib. 2 de intell.

[4] Hoc melancholicis omnibus proprium, ut quas semel imaginationes alde receperint, non facile rejiciant, sed hæ etiam vel invitis semper ccurrant.

[5] Tullius, de Sen.

Page 395

[1] Consil. med. pro hypochondriaco.   [2] Consil. 43.

[3] Cap. 5.   [4] Lib. 2 de intell.

[5] Consult. 15 et 16, lib. 1.   [6] Virg. Æn. 6.

Page 396

[1] Iliad 6.

[2] Si malum exasperetur, homines odio habent et solitaria petunt.

[3] Democritus solet noctes et dies apud se degere, plerumque autem in peluncis, sub amœnis arborum umbris vel in tenebris, et mollibus herbis, el ad aquarum crebra et quieta fluenta, etc.

[4] Gaudet tenebris, aliturque dolor.   Ps. cii.   Vigilavi, et factus sum velut nycticorax in domicilio, passer solitarius in templo.

[5] Et quæ vix audet fabula, monstra parit.

[6] In cap. 18, lib. 10, de Civ. Dei.   Lunam ab asino epotam videns.

Page 397

[1] Velc. lib. 4, cap. 5.   [2] Sect. 2, memb. 1, subs. 4.

[3] De reb. cœlest. lib. 10, cap. 13.

Page 398

[1] J. de Indagine, Goclenius.   [2] Hor. de art. poet.

[3] Tract. 7, de Melan.   [4] Humidum, calidum, frigidum, siccum.

[5] Com. in 1 cap. Johannis de Sacrobosco.

Page 399

[1] Si residet melancholia naturalis, tales plumbei coloris aut nigri, tupidi, solitarii.

[2] Non una melancholiæ causa est, nec unus humor vitii parens, sed plures, et alius aliter mutatus, unde non omnes eadem sentiunt symptomata.

[3] Humor frigidus delirii causa, humor calidus furoris.

[4] Multum refert qua quisque melancholia teneatur, hunc fervens et accensa agitat, illum tristis et frigens occupat: hi timidi, illi inverecundi, ntrepidi, etc.

[5] Cap. 7 et 8, Tract. de Mel.

[6] Signa melancholiæ ex intemperie et agitatione spirituum sine materia.

[7] T. Bright, cap. 16, Treat. Mel.

PAGE 400

[1] Cap. 16, in 9 Rhasis.   [2] Bright, cap. 16.
[3] Pract. major. Somnians, piger, frigidus.
[4] De anima, cap. de humor.   Si a phlegmate, semper in aquis fere sunt et circa fluvios plorant multum, etc.
[5] Pigra nascitur ex colore pallido et albo.—Her. de Saxon.
[6] Savonarola.
[7] Muros cadere in se, aut submergi timent, cum torpore et segnitie, et fluvios amant tales.—Alexand. cap. 16, lib. 7.
[8] Semper fere dormit somnolenta, cap. 16, lib. 7.
[9] Laurentius.
[10] Cap. 6 de mel.   Si a sanguine, venit rubedo oculorum et faciei, plurimu risus.
[11] Venæ oculorum sunt rubræ, vide an præcesserit vini et aromatum usus, et frequens balneum, Trallian. lib. 1, 16, an præcesserit mora sub sole
[12] Ridet patiens si a sanguine, putat se videre choreas, musicam audire ludos, etc.
[13] Cap. 2, tract. de melan.
[14] Hor. Ep. lib. 2.   Quidam haud ignobilis Argis, etc.
[15] Lib. de reb. mir.

PAGE 401

[1] Cum inter concionandum mulier dormiens e subsellio caderet, et omne reliqui qui id viderent, riderent, tribus post diebus, etc.
[2] Juvenis et non vulgaris eruditionis.
[3] Si a cholera, furibundi interficiunt se et alios, putant se videre pugnas
[4] Urina subtilis et ignea, parum dormiunt.
[5] Tract. 15, cap. 4.

PAGE 402

[1] Ad hæc perpetranda furore rapti ducuntur, cruciatus quosvis tolerant, et mortem, et furore exacerbato audent et ad supplicia plus irritantur mirum est quantum habeant in tormentis patientiam.
[2] Tales plus cæteris timent, et continue tristantur, valde suspiciosi solitudinem diligunt, corruptissimas habent imaginationes, etc.
[3] Si a melancholia adusta, tristes, de sepulchris somniant, timent ne fascinentur, putant se mortuos, aspici nolunt.
[4] Videntur sibi videre monachos nigros et dæmones, et suspensos et mortuos.
[5] Quavis nocte se cum dæmone coire putavit.
[6] Semper fere vidisse militem nigrum præsentem.
[7] Anthony de Verdeur.
[8] Quidam mugitus boum æmulantur, et pecora se putant, ut Prœti filiæ.
[9] Baro quidam mugitus boum, et rugitus asinorum, et aliorum animalium voces effingit.

PAGE 403

[1] Omnia magna putabat, uxorem magnam, grandes equos; abhorruit omnia parva; magna pocula, et calceamenta pedibus majora.
[2] Lib. 1, cap. 16.   Putavit se uno digito posse totum mundum conterere.
[3] Sustinet humeris cœlum cum Atlante. Alii cœli ruinam timent.
[4] Cap. 1, tract. 15. Alius se gallum putat, alius lusciniam.
[5] Trallianus.   [6] Cap. 7 de mel.
[7] Anthony de Verdeur.   [8] Cap. 7 de mel.

PAGE 404

[1] Laurentius, cap. 6.
[2] Lib. 3, cap. 14. Qui se regem putavit regno expulsum.
[3] Deipnosophist. lib. Thrasylaus putavit omnes naves in Piræum portum appellantes suas esse.

[4] De hist. med. mirab. lib. 2, cap. 1.
[5] Genibus flexis loqui cum illo voluit, et adstare jam tum putavit, etc.
[6] Gordonius. Quod sit propheta, et inflatus a Spiritu Sancto.

PAGE 405

[1] Qui forensibus causis insudat, nil nisi arresta cogitat, et supplices bellos; alius non nisi versus facit.—P. Forestus.
[2] Gordonius.
[3] Verbo non exprimunt, nec opere, sed alta mente recondunt, et sunt viri prudentissimi, quos ego sæpe novi; cum multi sint sine timore, ut qui se reges et mortuos putant, plura signa quidam habent, pauciora, majora, minora.
[4] [In the ratio of three to two, four to three, five to three, seven to five of melancholy.]
[5] Trallianus, lib. 1, 16. Alii intervalla quædam habent, ut etiam onsueta administrent, alii in continuo delirio sunt, etc.
[6] Prac. mag. Vere tantum et autumno.
[7] Lib. de humoribus. [8] Guianerius.
[9] De mentis alienat. cap. 3.

PAGE 406

[1] Levinus Lemnius, Jason Pratensis. Blanda ab initio. [2] Hor.
[3] Facilis descensus Averni. [4] Virg.

PAGE 407

[1] Corpus cadaverosum. Ps. lxvii: Cariosa est facies mea præ ægritudine animæ.
[2] Lib. 9, ad Almansorem. [3] Practica majore.
[4] Quum ore loquitur quæ corde concepit, quum subito de una re ad aliud transit, neque rationem de aliquo reddit, tunc est in medio, at quum incipit operari quæ loquitur, in summo gradu est.
[5] Cap. 19, partic. 2. Loquitur secum et ad alios, ac si vere præsentes. Aug. cap. 11, lib. de cura pro mortuis gerenda. Rhasis.
[6] Quum res ad hoc devenit, ut ea quæ cogitare cœperit, ore promat, atque acta permisceat, tum perfecta melancholia est.
[7] Melancholicus se videre et audire putat dæmones.—Lavater, de spectris, part. 3, cap. 2.
[8] Wierus, lib. 3, cap. 31. [9] Michael, a musician.

PAGE 408

[1] Malleo malef. [2] Lib. de atra bile.
[3] Part. 1, subs. 2, memb. 2. [4] De delirio, melancholia et mania.

PAGE 409

[1] Nicholas Piso. Si signa circa ventriculum non apparent, nec sanguis male affectus, et adsunt timor et mœstitia, cerebrum ipsum existimandum est, etc.
[2] Tract. de mel. cap. 13, etc. Ex intemperie spirituum, et cerebri motu, tenebrositate.
[3] Facie sunt rubente et livescente, quibus etiam aliquando adsunt pustulæ.
[4] Jo. Pantheon. cap. de mel. Si cerebrum primario afficiatur, adsunt capitis gravitas, fixi oculi, etc.
[5] Laurent. cap. 5. Si a cerebro ex siccitate, tum capitis erit levitas, sitis, vigilia, paucitas superfluitatum in oculis et naribus.

[1] Si nulla digna læsio ventriculo, quoniam in hac melancholia capit exigua nonnunquam ventriculi pathemata coeunt, duo enim hæc memb᙮ sibi invicem affectionem transmittunt.

[2] Postrema magis flatuosa.

[3] Si minus molestiæ circa ventriculum aut ventrem, in iis cerebru᙮ primario afficitur, et curare oportet hunc affectum, per cibos flatus exsorte᙮ et bonæ concoctionis, etc.; raro cerebrum afficitur sine ventriculo.

[4] Sanguinem adurit caput calidius, et inde fumi melancholici adus᙮ animum exagitant.

[5] Lib. de loc. affect. cap. 6.   [6] Cap. 6.

[7] Hildesheim, Spicil. 1 de mel. In hypochondriaca melancholia ad᙮ ambigua sunt symptomata, ut etiam exercitatissimi medici de loco affec᙮ statuere non possint.

[1] Medici de loco affecto nequeunt statuere.

[2] Tract. posthumo de mel., Patavii edit. 1620 per Bolzettam bibliop cap. 2.

[3] Acidi ructus, cruditates, æstus in præcordiis, flatus, interdum ventricu᙮ dolores vehementes, sumptoque cibo concoctu difficili, sputum humidu᙮ idque multum sequetur, etc. Hip. lib. de mel., Galenus, Melanelius e Ruf᙮ et Aetio, Altomarus, Piso, Montaltus, Bruel, Wecker, etc.

[4] Circa præcordia de assidua inflatione queruntur, et cum sudore toti᙮ corporis importuno, frigidos articulos sæpe patiuntur, indigestione laboran᙮ ructus suos insuaves perhorrescunt, viscerum dolores habent.

[1] Montaltus, cap. 13, Wecker, Fuchsius, cap. 13, Altomarus, cap. ᙮ Laurentius, cap. 73, Bruel, Gordon.

[2] Pract. major. Dolor in eo et ventositas, nausea.

[3] Ut atra densaque nubes soli effusa, radios et lumen ejus intercipit ᙮ offuscat; sic, etc.

[4] Ut fumus e camino.

[1] Hypochondriaci maxime affectant coire, et multiplicatur coitus ᙮ ipsis, eo quod ventositates multiplicantur in hypochondriis, et coitus sæp᙮ allevat has ventositates.

[2] Cont. lib. 1, tract. 9.

[3] Wecker. Melancholicus succus toto corpore redundans.

[4] Splen natura imbecillior.—Montaltus, cap. 22.

[5] Lib. 1, cap. 16. Interrogare convenit, an aliqua evacuationis retenti᙮ obvenerit, viri in hæmorrhoid., mulierum menstruis, et vide faciem similite᙮ an sit rubicunda.

[6] Naturales nigri acquisiti a toto corpore, sæpe rubicundi.

[7] Montaltus, cap. 22. Piso. Ex colore sanguinis si minuas venam᙮ si fluat niger, etc.

[1] Apul. lib. 1. Semper obviæ species mortuorum; quicquid umbrarum᙮ est uspiam, quicquid lemurum et larvarum oculis suis aggerunt; sib᙮ fingunt omnia noctium occursacula, omnia bustorum formidamina, omni᙮ sepulchrorum terriculamenta.

[2] Differt enim ab ea quæ viris et reliquis feminis communiter contingi᙮ propriam habens causam.

[3] Ex menstrui sanguinis tetra ad cor et cerebrum exhalatione, vitiatur᙮

men mentem perturbat, etc., non per essentiam, sed per consensum
nimus mœrens et anxius inde malum trahit, et spiritus cerebrum obfus-
ntur, quæ cuncta augentur, etc.

PAGE 415

[1] Cum tacito delirio ac dolore alicujus partis internæ, dorsi, hypochon-
ii, cordis regionem et universam mammam interdum occupantis, etc.
[2] Cutis aliquando squalida, aspera, rugosa, præcipue cubitis, genibus, et
gitorum articulis; præcordia ingenti sæpe terrore æstuant et pulsant,
mque vapor excitatus sursum evolat, cor palpitat aut premitur, animus
ficit, etc.
[3] Animi dejectio, perversa rerum existimatio, præposterum judicium.
astidiosæ, languentes, tædiosæ, consilii inopes, lacrimosæ, timentes,
œstæ, cum summa rerum meliorum desperatione, nulla re delectantur,
litudinem amant, etc.

PAGE 416

[1] Nolunt aperire molestiam quam patiuntur, sed conqueruntur tamen de
pite, corde, mammis, etc. In puteos fere maniaci prosilire, ac strangulari
piunt, nulla orationis suavitate ad spem salutis recuperandam erigi, etc.
amiliares non curant, non loquuntur, non respondent, etc., et hæc
aviora, si, etc.

PAGE 417

[1] Clysteres et helleborismum Matthioli summe laudat.

PAGE 419

[1] Examen Conc. Trident. de cælibatu sacerd.
[2] Cap. de satyr. et priapis.   [3] Part. 3, sect. 2, memb. 5, subs. 5.
[4] Vapores crassi et nigri, a ventriculo in cerebrum exhalant.—Fel.
laterus.

PAGE 420

[1] Calidi hilares, frigidi indispositi ad lætitiam et ideo solitarii, taciturni,
on ob tenebras internas, ut medici volunt, sed ob frigus: multi melan-
holici nocte ambulant intrepidi. Vapores melancholici, spiritibus misti,
nebrarum causæ sunt (cap. 1).
[2] Intemperies facit succum nigrum, nigrities obscurat spiritum, obscu-
atio spiritus facit metum et tristitiam.
[3] Ut nubecula solem offuscat. Constantinus, lib. de melanch.
[4] Altomarus, cap. 7. Causam timoris circumfert ater humor passionis
ateria, et atri spiritus perpetuam animæ domicilio offundunt noctem.

PAGE 421

[1] Pone exemplum, quod quis potest ambulare super trabem quæ est
via: sed si sit super aquam profundam, loco pontis, non ambulabit super
am, eo quod imaginatur in animo et timet vehementer, forma cadendi
npressa, cui obediunt membra omnia, et facultates reliquæ.
[2] Lib. 2 de intellectione.   Suspiciosi ob timorem et obliquum discursum,
t semper inde putant sibi fieri insidias. Lauren. 5.
[3] Tract. de mel., cap. 7.   Ex dilatione, contractione, confusione,
nebrositate spirituum, calida, frigida intemperie, etc.
[4] Illud inquisitione dignum, cur tam falsa recipiant, habere se cornua,
sse mortuos, nasutos, esse aves, etc.
[5] 1. Dispositio corporis. 2. Occasio imaginationis.

Page 422

[1] In pro. lib. de cœlo. Vehemens et assidua cogitatio rei erga qua afficitur, spiritus in cerebrum evocat.

[2] Melancholici ingeniosi omnes, summi viri in artibus et disciplin sive circum imperatoriam aut reip. disciplinam omnes fere melancholici. Aristoteles.

[3] Adeo miscentur, ut sit duplum sanguinis ad reliqua duo.

[4] Lib. 2 de intellectione. Pingui sunt Minerva phlegmatici: sanguin amabiles, grati, hilares, at non ingeniosi; cholerici celeres motu, et ob contemplationis impatientes: melancholici solum excellentes, etc.

Page 423

[1] Trepidantium vox tremula, quia cor quatitur.

[2] Ob ariditatem quæ reddit nervos linguæ torpidos.

[3] Incontinentia linguæ ex copia flatuum, et velocitate imaginationis.

[4] Calvities ob siccitatis excessum.   [5] Aetius.

[6] Lauren. cap. 13.   [7] Tetrab. 2, ser. 2, cap. 10.

[8] Ant. Lodovicus, Prob. lib. 1, sect. 5, de atrabilariis.

[9] Subrusticus pudor, vitiosus pudor.

[10] Ob ignominiam aut turpitudinem facti, etc.

[11] De symp. et antip. cap. 12. Laborat facies ob præsentiam ejus q defectum nostrum videt, et natura quasi opem latura calorem illuc mitti calor sanguinem trahit, unde rubor. Audaces non rubent, etc.

Page 424

[1] Ob gaudium et voluptatem foras exit sanguis, aut ob melioris rev rentiam, aut ob subitum occursum, aut si quid incautius exciderit.

[2] Com. in Arist. de anima. Cæci ut plurimum impudentes, nox fac impudentes.

[3] Alexander Aphrodisiensis makes all bashfulness a virtue, eamque s refert in seipso experiri solitum, etsi esset admodum senex.

[4] Com. in Arist. de anima. Tam a vi et inexperientia quam a vitio.

[5] Sæpe post cibum apti ad ruborem, ex potu vini, ex timore sæpe et a hepate calido, cerebro calido, etc.

[6] 2 De oratore. Quid ipse risus, quo pacto concitetur, ubi sit, etc.

[7] Diaphragma titillant, quia transversum et nervosum, quia titillation moto sensu atque arteriis distentis, spiritus inde latera, venas, os, oculo occupant.

[8] Ex calefactione humidi cerebri: nam ex sicco lacrimæ non fluunt.

[9] Res mirandas imaginantur: et putant se videre quæ nec vident, ne audiunt.

Page 425

[1] Laet. lib. 13, cap. 2, descript. Indiæ Occident.

[2] Lib. 1, cap. 17, cap. de mel.

[3] Insani, et qui morti vicini sunt, res quas extra se videre putant, intr oculos habent.

[4] Cap. 10, de spirit. apparitione.   [5] De occult. nat. mirac.

Page 426

[1] Seneca. Quod metuunt nimis, nunquam amoveri posse, nec tol putant.

Page 427

[1] Sanguis upupæ cum melle compositus et centaurea, etc.—Albertus.

[2] Lib. 1, Occult. philos. Imperiti homines dæmonum et umbrarur imagines videre se putant, quum nihil sint aliud quam simulacra anim expertia.

³ Pythonissæ, vocum varietatem in ventre et gutture fingentes, formant voces humanas a longe vel prope, prout volunt, ac si spiritus cum homine loqueretur, et sonos brutorum fingunt, etc.
⁴ [Gloucester Cathedral].

PAGE 428

¹ Tam clare et articulate audies repetitum, ut perfectior sit echo quam ipse dixeris.
² Blowing of bellows, and knocking of hammers, if they apply their ear to the cliff.
³ Memb. 1, subs. 3, of this partition.   ⁴ Cap. 16 in 9 Rhasis.
⁵ Signa dæmonis nulla sunt nisi quod loquantur ea quæ ante nesciebant, ut Teutonicum aut aliud idioma, etc.
⁶ Cap. 12, tract. de mel.
⁷ Tract. 15, cap. 4.   ⁸ Cap. 9.
⁹ Mira vis concitat humores, ardorque vehemens mentem exagitat, quum, etc.

PAGE 429

¹ Præfat. Iamblichi mysteriis.
² Si melancholicis hæmorroides supervenerint, varices, vel ut quibusdam placet, aqua inter cutem, solvitur malum.
³ Cap. 10, de quartana.

PAGE 430

¹ Cum sanguis exit per superficiem et residet melancholia per scabiem, morpheam nigram, vel expurgatur per inferiores partes, vel urinam, etc., non erit, etc., splen magnificatur et varices apparent.
² Quia jam conversa in naturam.
³ In quocunque sit, a quacunque causa, hypocon. præsertim, semper est longa, morosa, nec facile curari potest.
⁴ Regina morborum et inexorabilis.
⁵ Omne delirium quod oritur a paucitate cerebri incurabile.—Hildesheim, Spicil. 2 de mania.
⁶ Si sola imaginatio lædatur, et non ratio.
⁷ Mala a sanguine fervente, deterior a bile assata, pessima ab atra bile putrefacta.
⁸ Difficilior cura ejus quæ fit vitio corporis totius et cerebri.
⁹ Difficilis curatu in viris, multo difficilior in feminis.
¹⁰ Ad interitum plerumque homines comitatur; licet medici levent plerumque, tamen non tollunt unquam, sed recidet acerbior quam antea minima occasione aut errore.
¹¹ Periculum est ne degeneret in epilepsiam, apoplexiam, convulsionem, cæcitatem.
¹² Montal. cap. 25; Laurentius; Nic. Piso.

PAGE 431

¹ Herc. de Saxonia, Aristotle, Capivaccius.
² Favent. Humor frigidus sola delirii causa, furoris vero humor calidus.
³ Heurnius calls madness sobolem melancholiæ [the offspring of melancholy].   ⁴ Alexander, lib. 1, cap. 18.
⁵ Lib. 1, part. 2, cap. 11.
⁶ Montalt. cap. 15.   Raro mors aut nunquam, nisi sibi ipsis inferant.
⁷ Lib. de Insan. Fabio Calico interprete.
⁸ Nonnulli violentas manus sibi inferunt.
⁹ Lucret. lib. 3.

[10] Lib. 2 de intell.   Sæpe mortem sibi consciscunt ob timorem et tristitiam, tædio vitæ affecti ob furorem et desperationem.   Est enim infera, etc. Ergo sic perpetuo afflictati vitam oderunt, se præcipitant, his malis carituri, aut interficiunt se, aut tale quid committunt.

PAGE 432

[1] Psal. cvii, 10.   [2] Job, iii.   [3] Job vi, 8.
[4] Vi doloris et tristitiæ ad insaniam pene redactus.
[5] Seneca.
[6] In salutis suæ desperatione proponunt sibi mortis desiderium.—Oct. Horat. lib. 2, cap. 5.
[7] Lib. de insania.   Sic, sic juvat ire per umbras.
[8] Cap. 3 de mentis alienat.   Mœsti degunt, dum tandem mortem quam timent, suspendio aut submersione, aut aliqua alia vi, præcipitant, ut multa tristia exempla vidimus.
[9] Arculanus in 9 Rhasis, cap. 16.   Cavendum ne ex alto se præcipitant aut alias lædent.

PAGE 433

[1] O omnium opinionibus incogitabile malum!—Lucian.   Mortesque mille, mille dum vivit neces gerit, peritque.—Heinsius Austriaco.
[2] Regina morborum cui famulantur omnes et obediunt.—Cardan.
[3] Eheu, quis intus scorpio, etc.—Seneca, Herc. Œt. Act. 4.
[4] Silius Italicus.

PAGE 434

[1] Lib. 29.
[2] Hic omnis imbonitas et insuavitas consistit, ut Tertulliani verbis utar. Orat. ad Martyr.   [3] Plautus.
[4] Vit. Herculis.   [5] Persius.   [Juv. 10, 188.]
[6] Quid est miserius in vita, quam velle mori?—Seneca.
[7] Tom. 2, Libello, an graviores passiones, etc.   [8] Ter.

PAGE 435

[1] Patet exitus: si pugnare non vultis, licet fugere; quis vos tenet invitos? —De provid. cap. 8.
[2] Agamus Deo gratias, quod nemo invitus in vita teneri potest.
[3] Seneca, epist. 26, et de sacra. 2, cap. 15, et epist. 70, et 12.
[4] Lib. 2, cap. 83.   Terra mater nostri miserta.
[5] Epist. 24, 71, 82.

PAGE 436

[1] 2 Macc. xiv, 42.   [2] Vindicatio Apoc. lib.

PAGE 437

[1] As amongst Turks and others.
[2] Bohemus, de moribus gent.
[3] Ælian, lib. 4, cap. 1.   Omnes 70 annum egressos interficiunt.
[4] Lib. 2.   Præsertim quum tormentum ei vita sit, bona spe fretus, acerba vita velut a carcere se eximat, vel ab aliis eximi sua voluntate patiatur.
[5] Nam quis amphoram exsiccans fæcem exsorberet? (Seneca, epist. 58). Quis in pœnas et risum viveret?   Stulti est manere in vita cum sit miser.
[6] Expedit. ad Sinas, lib. 1, cap. 9.   Vel bonorum desperatione vel malorum perpessione fracti et fatigati, vel manus violentas sibi inferunt vel ut inimicis suis ægre faciant, etc.

PAGE 438

[1] So did Anthony, Galba, Vitellius, Otho, Aristotle himself, etc.; Ajax in despair; Cleopatra to save her honour.

[2] Inertius deligitur diu vivere quam in timore tot morborum semel moriendo, nullum deinceps formidare.

[3] Curtius, lib. 8.

[4] Laqueus præcisus, contr. 1, lib. 5. Quidam naufragio facto, amissis tribus liberis et uxore, suspendit se; præcidit illi quidam ex prætereuntibus laqueum; a liberato reus fit maleficii.—Seneca.

[5] See Lipsius, Manuduc. ad Stoicam philosophiam, lib. 3, dissert. 22; Dr. King's 14th Lect. on Jonas; Dr. Abbot's 6th Lect. on the same prophet.

[6] Plautus.   [7] Martial.

PAGE 439

[1] As to be buried out of Christian burial with a stake. Idem Plato, 9 de legibus, vult separatim sepeliri, qui sibi ipsis mortem consciscunt, etc., lose their goods, etc.

[2] Navis destituta nauclero in terribilem aliquem scopulum impingit.

[3] Observat.

[4] Seneca, tract. 1, lib. 8, cap. 4. Lex, Homicida in se insepultus abjiciatur, contradicitur. Eo quod afferre sibi manus coactus sit assiduis malis; summam infelicitatem suam in hoc removit, quod existimabat licere misero mori.

[5] Buchanan, Eleg. lib.

END OF VOLUME ONE

DATE DUE
